ANNALS OF
THE NEW YORK ACADEMY
OF SCIENCES

Volume 411

EDITORIAL STAFF

Executive Editor
BILL BOLAND

Managing Editor
JOYCE HITCHCOCK

Associate Editor
MARY KATHERINE BRENNAN

The New York Academy of Sciences
2 East 63rd Street
New York, New York 10021

BIOLOGICAL ACTIONS AND MEDICAL APPLICATIONS OF DIMETHYL SULFOXIDE

ANNALS OF THE NEW YORK ACADEMY OF SCIENCES
VOLUME 411

BIOLOGICAL ACTIONS AND MEDICAL APPLICATIONS OF DIMETHYL SULFOXIDE

Edited by J. C. de la Torre

The New York Academy of Sciences
New York, New York
1983

Library of Congress Cataloging in Publication Data

Main entry under title:

Biological actions and medical applications of dimethyl
    sulfoxide.

    (Annals of the New York Academy of Sciences; v. 411)
    Bibliography: p.
    Includes index.
    1. Dimethyl sulfoxide—Physiological effect—
Congresses.   2. Dimethyl sulfoxide—Testing—Congresses.
I. De la Torre, Jack C., 1937-   . II. Series:
[DNLM: 1. Dimethyl sulfoxide—Therapeutic use—Congresses.
2. Dimethyl sulfoxide—Pharmacodynamics—Congresses.
W1 AN626YL v. 411 / QV 60 B615 L982]
Q11.N5   vol. 411   [QP535.S1]   500s   [615.7]   83-13058

ISBN 0-89766-215-6
ISBN 0-89766-216-4- (pbk.)

SP
Printed in the United States of America
ISBN 0-89766-215-6 (cloth)
ISBN 0-89766-216-4 (paper)

ANNALS OF THE NEW YORK ACADEMY OF SCIENCES
VOLUME 411
June 30, 1983
BIOLOGICAL ACTIONS AND MEDICAL APPLICATIONS
OF DIMETHYL SULFOXIDE*

Editor and Conference Chairman
J. C. DE LA TORRE

CONTENTS

*This volume is a result of a conference entitled Conference on Biological Actions and Medical Applications of Dimethyl Sulfoxide, held on September 15–17, 1982 by the New York Academy of Sciences.

Part VII. Central Nervous System

Brief Communications

Late Paper from Part II

Financial assistance was received from:
- DMSO FOUNDATION, INC.
- U.S. ARMY MEDICAL RESEARCH AND DEVELOPMENT
- ANONYMOUS GIFT

DIMETHYL SULFOXIDE:
THE GOLDEN MAZE DILEMMA

The English poet and dramatist John Dryden once wrote: "I think and think of things impossible, yet love to wander in that golden maze."

Dimethyl sulfoxide (DMSO) is a compound that has been in a type of "golden maze" for some time. Twenty years have passed since DMSO was reported to have a number of unusual biological activities. During this period of time, there has been a steady outpouring of scientific papers as well as half a dozen international conferences that have examined the biochemical and pharmacological properties of DMSO on multiplex organic systems. Less work has been done on the clinical applications of DMSO for use in patients despite its apparent relative safety and its potential ability to reverse some life-threatening crises. For example, it's powerful diuretic effect, reported to be greater than furosemide, could be of immediate clinical relevance either as an adjuvant or primary therapy in such potentially fatal conditions as congestive heart failure, pulmonary edema, nephrotic syndrome, cerebral edema, acute renal failure, hepatic cirrhosis, and others. A number of papers in this volume do in fact present other new and exciting applications for DMSO using well-designed experimental protocols.

One of the arguments in the past has been that only double-blind studies can provide proof of drug efficacy by eliminating experimental bias. While this may be true for some drugs in certain clinical disorders, it is not compelling in many cases where DMSO is used since there are now a number of sophisticated bedside and laboratory tests that readily provide measurable end-point values that can be quantitated for statistical analyses or cause and effect relationships.

As researchers, we rely on scientific objectivity to test the validity of a hypothesis, such as whether a drug is effective on a disease process. For example, if research studies consistently show that tissue ischemia is reversed after using drug X, it seems safe to advance the notion that such a drug has potential in modifying ischemic disorders. If in addition, drug X is also shown to reduce subjective painful sensation in humans after its administration, and this phenomenon is supported by animal data under more rigidly controlled conditions, it is again not unreasonable to conclude that drug X could be useful in reducing pain as well. If drug X also happens to be relatively safe, that is, relative to similar drugs on the market, it would be well-advised for all concerned to plan and quickly initiate clinical trials, since pain or ischemia are highly undesirable.

This is the present status of DMSO, even when only two examples of its biological activities are cited among the many presented at this symposium and elsewhere. Dr. Arthur Scherbel, in his summary statement of the 1975 and the present conference, reviewed some of the factors that have stalled clinical testing of DMSO in this country. He recommended a halt to rhetoric and the implementation of carefully designed, rigidly controlled clinical trials to evaluate the efficacy of DMSO in selected disorders.

It is hoped that the new Food and Drug Administration officials will also review these scientific studies and others now in progress, from a perspective that will effectively reduce unnecessary delays in all phases of testing. The advantages of such action, would still uphold the rigorous scientific requirements that guide Food and Drug Administration decisions in approving a drug for the consumer market, but it would also emphasize a humanistic concern for those with pain and illness that in my judgement is a truer reflection of the degree of our civilized behavior.

J. C. de la Torre

INTRODUCTORY REMARKS:
DIMETHYL SULFOXIDE AFTER TWENTY YEARS

Stanley W. Jacob and Robert Herschler

Department of Surgery
Oregon Health Sciences University
Portland, Oregon 97201

We have entered the third decade of research on DMSO as a biological agent. Unfortunately, medical science is still confronting political barriers blocking availability of DMSO as a safe and effective prescription drug. Fortunately the non-medical biological uses for DMSO steadily unfold, demonstrating an amazing diversity of applications.

Should we be satisfied with this status? Perhaps our humanitarian instincts must be sequestered. Whatever the regulatory position in the United States through the 1980s and beyond, mankind has forever lost the optimum economic benefits of a substance with a drum-lot price that could and should not be over a half dollar a pound. At present, a 50% aqueous solution, 50-ml size, for bladder instillation retails in the range of $13.00 while an eight-ounce bottle of nearly anhydrous DMSO for platelet preservation is priced in the range of $100.00.

As one reviews the literature of the past several years, it is apparent that while severe regulatory constraints have suffocated clinical developments with DMSO, other scientific studies, not subject to regulatory overkill, are flourishing to man's benefit.

A status review of the diversity of scientific studies is beyond the scope of this discussion. Only a few areas of special interest have been selected for brief mention here.

The profound effects of DMSO on the growth and morphology of human and lower animal tumor cells have challenged the investigative talents of workers throughout the world. These studies provide a clearer understanding of the processes of malignancy and may lead to better therapy.

Neutralization of trauma-induced pathology to the brain and spinal cord is dramatic and exciting.

Immunological implications from various studies concerned with cell-mediated immunity, competition for receptor sites, or modified pheresic applications that reduce the body titer of disease-inducing immunoglobins via the renal pathway, capitalize on the basic pharmacology and chemistry of DMSO.

Studies defining mutagens and carcinogens utilize DMSO as the safe solvent and carrier. The ability of DMSO to move freely in the humoral fluid and to cross membranes without irreversible damage first attracted our attention. Because various membranes do not act as barriers to DMSO, exciting new findings have been described, as with biological free radicals.

Thus far, studies with DMSO in combination with antineoplastic agents, autoimmune potentiating agents, radiation, or hyperthermic therapy have not progressed as we projected 20 years ago. Philosophically one may speculate as to where the fault lies. Is it possible that the current regulatory fad against combination drug therapy is hindering research? Everyone recognizes that treating one disease with a single therapeutic method is both neat and precise. It is likely, however, that cancer requires a multivalent attack since it is hardly a single neat and precise disease.

Cryobiology as a discipline could hardly exist without DMSO. Biological safety, tissue and cytoplasm mobility, together with an exceptional association with water, which alters freezing properties, are characteristics of DMSO that contribute to the successful preservation of biologicals from subcellular units to the intact embryo.

The cell, the basic unit of eukaryotic life, depends on many structures. The literature teaches that DMSO can strongly influence the development of cellular structures. The effect of actin- and tubulin-production stimulation by DMSO, as demonstrated by several investigations, is at present unclear. It does seem that such findings may lead to modes of therapy with DMSO where cell normalcy is restored after disease alteration.

We now know that mitochondria and other components of cells are protected against lethal challenges, such as hypoxia, by DMSO. It is important to recognize that once DMSO enters a biologic system it becomes a ubiquitous molecule able to scavenge intracellular [OH$^-$] free radicals, a primary trigger of the inflammation process. One must be impressed with the ability of DMSO to not only protect but repair cells damaged by hyperosmotic challenge. Recent studies associated with the use of DMSO with brain trauma demonstrate that the body can tolerate elevated hyperosmotic pressure, perhaps a doubling of normal. This acceptable stress, like radiation, hyperthermia, and chemotherapy (possibly together with these entities), should be studied with malignancy, infections, and other disease categories.

Detoxification by DMSO of diverse chemical toxicants that induce cytotoxicity or mutagenicity were not predictable in the early 1960s. Yet one of the earliest findings with DMSO demonstrated protection against potentially lethal radiation. We have been particularly impressed with the demonstration that DMSO protects the glial cells from damage by otherwise lethal ultrasonic waves. Since each system we consider is a stress system (generally antagonistic to life) and DMSO is a protectant of life under such stress, therefore is not protection against stress a unique, new pharmacologic parameter of usefulness to DMSO's credit? Why isn't this pharmacologic parameter used more generally to improve the practice of medicine?

The physical barrier (generally termed blood-brain barrier) limiting movement into the brain makes it difficult to carry out effective drug therapy. While DMSO moves freely across this barrier, early results as a vehicle/carrier were disappointing. Newer techniques demonstrate improved carrier action. Predictably in the next decade, refinements will be described that could benefit the health and welfare of mankind.

One can hardly await the findings of the next ten years concerning the role of DMSO and metabolites, particularly methylsulfonylmethane, as preferred substrates attracted to receptor sites. Seemingly, DMSO has a role to play in the field of immunology. What factor or technique is yet to be discovered that will complete the building of a medically useful system?

Workers in Europe and Asia have further contributed to our knowledge of the potential of DMSO with infective diseases. Basic and clinical findings teach the usefulness of combinations. Both DMSO and antibiotics are membrane active. In our view a yet unrecognized factor limits optimizing the medical usefulness of such combinations. Great benefits can be reaped if we learn how to better use the extensive list of developed antibiotics rather than continuing to spend irreplaceable resources developing new products to overcome antibiotic resistance.

Having reflected on the past 20 years, a few predictions seem appropriate concerning the future of DMSO in the biological sciences.

It is unlikely that the Food and Drug Administration (FDA) will continue to be successful in blocking DMSO in medicine. Nevertheless, irrespective of the field of research and not limited to DMSO, scientists everywhere face an ever increasing threat of confrontation directly or indirectly with the FDA. Regrettably one cannot exclude the likelihood that with this ever increasing conflict the health of the patient will be compromised.

It seems a certainty that for economic, humanitarian, and scientific reasons, state governments will increasingly intervene in the case of DMSO to protect and improve the health and welfare of the citizenry, and for the legal protection of physicians.

If the Congress of the United States passes legislation excluding the FDA from all regulatory concern with DMSO, we hope that one major reason is the desire of Congress to establish a testing of the efficacy of today's law, which appears to have been written and implemented by the FDA to satisfy a vocal but radical minority. It would be reasonable, two decades after enacting (with some haste) the 1962 drug law revisions, to ascertain whether the present food and drug laws, as implemented by the FDA, are a service or disservice to our people. Both the Congress and the executive branch of our government must feel concern for the millions who now are unable to seek benefit from new drug therapies solely for economic reasons. These reasons are traceable to the cost of the new drug approval process. It now costs more to secure a drug approval then it did to wage war in the last century. If DMSO is made exempt from FDA control, the price of medical DMSO will drop sharply from about $10.00/ounce (DMSO content basis) to roughly forty cents per ounce—allowing in this price for special implementation and research support taxes. Beyond the obvious benefit to the consumer of the approximate $9.60/ounce drop in price, superior formulas with lessened side effects can be provided. Two such formulas now used at the DMSO clinic at the Oregon Health Sciences University are suggested product candidates with intrastate regulated DMSO. Each is an excellent topical product with demonstrated safety and efficacy.

Urea-modified DMSO moderates nuisance-type side effects. The sulfurish breath, skin irritation, and occasional itching as well as skin dryness are lessened. A typical formulation (by weight) is: 60 parts DMSO, 20 parts urea, and 20 parts water. This formulation can be gelled or administered as a liquid for disorders of the musculoskeletal system.

The addition of the potassium salt of para-aminobenzoic acid (KPABA) provides a useful topical agent with various collagen disorders such as scleroderma, Peyronie's disease, Dupuytren's contracture, and hypertrophic scar. One useful formula (by weight) is: 70 parts DMSO, 15 parts urea, 7.5 parts water, and 7.5 parts KPABA.

One product of DMSO appears to have a bright scientific and commercial future. This is the stable metabolite of DMSO referred to as methylsulfonylmethane or MSM. We now refer to it as Factor N, with the intended implication that this biochemical helps maintain our bodies within normal or good health parameters. We predict this will receive international attention as a dietary supplement, interestingly found in particularly high concentration in what has been referred to as the nearly perfect food. The precursors of Factor N, the various salts of dimethyl sulfide, and even DMSO, are found in most of the foods that vertebrates use. Precursor conversion to MSM is accomplished enzymatically. Unfortunately unless our diet is almost solely milk, it appears that our bodies have a possible deficiency.

MSM, an odorless, essentially tasteless, white crystalline chemical demonstrates usefulness as a dietary supplement in man and lower animals. Our research suggests that a minimum concentration in the body may be critical to both normal function and structure.

Limited studies suggest that the systemic concentration of MSM drops in mammals with increasing age. This may be due to dietary habits where one ingests foods with lower MSM potential with maturity or possibly there is a change in the renal threshold. Healthy juvenile rabbits maintain a level at or above 1 ppm body weight, with milk being the dominant food and source. Cow's milk normally contains between 2 and 6 ppm MSM dependent on source and freshness. In an adult man, the circulating concentration varies but may average about 0.2–0.25 ppm. We have no estimate of total body concentration as yet but suspect that MSM is banked in some of the organs, other than the adrenals. Based on radiolabel (^{35}S) studies, the residence time of a single challenge in mammals may be several weeks with gradual dumping via the renal system. Daily output of urine contains several milligrams of MSM. This possibly is not the dominant excretory route.

The following abnormal conditions seen in the clinic have responded to oral MSM generally administered at dosage levels of 250–750 mg/day.

(1) Response to allergy. Oral MSM moderates diverse allergic responses as to pollen and foods. Antiallergy medication and desensitization methods may be sharply reduced.

(2) Control of hyperacidity. Subjects seen to be chronic users of various antacids and histamine H_2 receptor antagonists prefer MSM by reason of relief obtained coupled with freedom from serious, untoward effects.

(3) Hypersensitivity to drugs. Subjects demonstrating drug hypersensitivity as to aspirin, several nonsteroid antiarthritic agents (Naprosyn, Indocin, Motrin), and oral antibiotics, were drug tolerant when MSM was given within an hour before or concurrent with the sensitizing drug.

(4) Control of constipation. Particularly in the older population seen in our clinic, chronic constipation can be a medical problem of concern. To date, over 50 subjects presenting chronic constipation have gained prompt and continuing relief by supplementing the diet with 100 to 500 mg of MSM per day.

(5) We have seen some individuals with severely restricted lung function. Of these, only a few cooperated in vital function assessments. All cooperated in endurance measurements, however. Limited objective and strong subjective evidence suggests the MSM is a useful dietary supplement to reduce lung dysfunction.

(6) Antiparasitic action. In vitro and in vivo tests suggest MSM has activity against a variety of medically important parasitic problems. Thus far work has concentrated on parasitic problems of the intestinal and urogenital tracts. MSM, for example, is active against Giardia, Trichomonads, and round worms. MSM may effect such infections by competing for binding or receptor sites at the mucous membrane surface presenting a blocking interface between host and parasite. We are at present evaluating the action of MSM with a variety of abnormal or medical problems to determine whether any are responsive to a diet supplemented by MSM. One facinating aspect of this work is the observation that with presented function and structure normalcy, MSM appears to be inactive pharmacologically. Only where abnormality occurs have we seen MSM influence a return towards normalcy, defined as being within measurable parameters of good health.

We are intrigued by the fact that MSM is a constant factor in all normal diets of vertebrates and somewhat mystified by the seeming need of the body of adults for a concentration level above that available from a diet presumed as "normal." We hope soon to have data defining any specific interacting role that MSM may have with the water-soluble vitamins, particularly vitamin C, which like MSM is reportedly banked in the adrenals.

It is not possible to directly compare DMSO and derivative MSM, though of the same chemical family. Each is unique unto itself. MSM is a dietary factor derivable from most natural foods. It is conveniently taken alone, or in foods. Taken by mouth, there is no afterbreath. DMSO has certain unpleasant attributes not possessed by MSM.

While MSM is a dietary factor, DMSO is not. DMSO readily penetrates the dermis and less complicated membrane systems while MSM does not. Each contributes to the well-being of mankind, but in differing ways. Both have important implications.

When Dr. Chauncey Leake summarized the first New York Academy of Sciences Symposium on DMSO he said that the well-known legal phrase of res ipsa loquitur applied to the DMSO controversy, stating that "rarely had a new drug came to the attention of the scientific community with so much verifiable information from so many parts of the world." Those remarks were true in 1965. They remain true today.

THE STATUS OF DIMETHYL SULFOXIDE FROM THE PERSPECTIVE OF THE FOOD AND DRUG ADMINISTRATION

John G. Harter

Anti-inflammatory Drug Products
National Center for Drugs and Biologics (17B45)
Food and Drug Administration
Rockville, Maryland 20857

I'm pleased to represent the Food and Drug Administration (FDA) in this volume. I will review the history of DMSO as recorded at the FDA, comment on its current status, and finally, from my prospective as a reviewer, offer some of my own observations and comments.

Since 1963, when Dr. Stanley W. Jacob reported that DMSO penetrates skin rapidly, aids the transport of other drugs across biological membranes, has local analgesic activity, and decreases swelling and promotes healing of injured tissue; DMSO has attracted continuing pubic attention as a potential therapeutic agent in a variety of diseases.

The first investigational new drug exemption (IND) for the study of DMSO in humans was filed with the FDA in 1963. Enormous interest in the drug developed rapidly and it began to be used widely, especially for the treatment of sprains, bruises, and minor burns. By late 1965, an estimated 100,000 patients had received the drug. However, no well-controlled studies were conducted to document clearly that the observed effects were actually caused by the drug. This widespread, uncontrolled use of DMSO was curtailed sharply in November 1965, when the FDA terminated all clinical studies of DMSO because of toxicological studies showing that the drug changed the refractive index of the lens of the eye in experimental animals. The agency's concern at the time was that visual damage might occur in humans exposed to the drug.

A year later this policy was relaxed to permit clinical evaluation of DMSO "... in serious conditions, such as scleroderma, persistent *herpes zoster*, and severe rheumatoid arthritis, for which no satisfactory therapy is now available."

In September 1968, the FDA published a further revision of its DMSO policy permitting topical application to the skin for no more than 14 days for treatment of less serious disabilities, such as acute musculoskeletal conditions (e.g., sprains, bursitis, and tendonitis). This was based on a toxicological study in humans that provided a reassuring result; that is, no evidence of eye toxicity associated with the short-term application of large doses to human volunteers.

In light of the continued lack of evidence of eye damage in humans since that time, the FDA concluded that the regulation establishing specific requirements for clinical testing of DMSO in humans was no longer necessary, so it was revoked in May 1980. Since that time the regulations governing DMSO have been essentially the same as those regulating other investigational drug substances. However, in response to attempts by distributors to sell "not for medical use" DMSO to obvious medical users, the FDA has monitored DMSO distribution and shipments somewhat more closely than other IND drugs.

Similarly, some INDs submitted by individual investigators have been thinly

1

0077-8923/83/0411-0001 $01.75/0 © 1983, NYAS

veiled attempts to get "legal" DMSO to use, not to study. FDA has insisted that DMSO studies under INDs be well-controlled and we have spent considerable time helping less experienced but well-motivated investigators and sponsors design trials that would be adequate to serve as a basis for new drug approval. We will return to what the FDA considers appropriate clinical study design later.

Because of continuing controversy over the FDA's position on DMSO, Dr. Charles C. Edwards, then Commissioner of the FDA, asked the National Academy of Sciences in 1972 to review all available information on the safety and effectiveness of DMSO and provide the FDA and the Congress with an independent judgement on these matters. The National Academy of Sciences appointed a distinguished primary committee with six subcommittees to conduct this review. They screened and reviewed the literature consisting of some 1,200 papers on DMSO, including the proceedings of the first New York Academy of Sciences Symposium on DMSO held in 1966.* In addition they reviewed 193 volumes of reports submitted to the FDA. To this day, the National Academy of Sciences' review stands as the most comprehensive independent evaluation of DMSO by the medical and scientific community.

The Academy concluded that there was inadequate scientific evidence of effectiveness of DMSO for the treatment of any disease; that the toxicity potential of DMSO was sufficiently great that the drug should remain investigational; and that controlled clinical trials were necessary to demonstrate the effectiveness of DMSO. A further conclusion of the Subcommittee on Connective Tissue Diseases was "... that most of the studies reviewed were of such poor quality as to be useless for its purposes...." We will return to this last conclusion when we consider what constitutes appropriate clinical trials.

Prior to 1972, there were 69 INDs filed for DMSO uses ranging from cryopreservation of cells and treatment of frostbite, to treatment of herpes zoster and phantom limb pain. However, the majority of the INDs were for use of the drug in inflammatory conditions, including acute trauma, and chronic conditions, like arthritis and scleroderma. Seventy additional INDs were filed from 1972 through the end of August 1982. These for the most part have been for the same indications with the addition of studies of the effect of DMSO on mental retardation, amyloidosis, retinitis pigmentosa, spinal cord injury, cerebral edema, and bone pain secondary to malignancies. There have been studies of the use of DMSO to enhance transdermal absorption of other drugs but so far no product has emerged from these studies. Currently there are about 35 active INDs for studying DMSO.

Prior to 1972, there were three New Drug Applications (NDAs) submitted for anti-inflammatory indications for DMSO. None were approvable. Since 1972, there have been two additional NDA submissions. One was approved for intravesicular use of 50% DMSO for interstitial cystitis. The other NDA for use of DMSO in the treatment of scleroderma was judged to be non-approvable after re-review at three levels within the FDA. This latter usage is currently being studied under a National Institutes of Health contract for the Cooperative Systematic Studies of Rheumatic Diseases. The study is expected to be completed in six months.

Irregularities were discovered during an audit of the data of one of the interstitial cystitis investigators. Further investigation led to the disqualification of one clinical investigator and part way through the disqualification procedure two other investigators agreed not to do any further clinical studies under INDs. This

*Ann. N.Y. Acad. Sci. 1967. Volume 141.

agreement halted the disqualification procedure. More than half of the data in the interstitial cystitis NDA were supplied by these investigators. The FDA has requested additional studies of interstitial cystitis which the sponsor of the NDA has agreed to conduct. Currently there are no pending NDAs for DMSO.

Dr. J. Richard Crout, who personally reviewed both recent DMSO NDAs, summarized the FDA's position on DMSO when he testified before the Select Committee on Aging of the House of Representatives on March 24, 1980† and I'd like to quote him:

> DMSO is a solvent that crosses body membranes with ease and appears to have analgesic effects when applied locally. There is much testimonial evidence to suggest that DMSO relieves pain after local application to injured or inflamed tissues.
> This is an effect similar to that we usually associate with liniments. Properly controlled studies to prove this point are not available but are technically possible to perform.
> There is no evidence that DMSO alters the course of any disease, or is, in any sense, a miracle drug. To suggest on the basis of the evidence available to date, controlled or uncontrolled, that DMSO is a major medical advance for any serious disease, let alone a variety of such diseases, is misleading. . .
> This is not to deny, or be unsympathetic to, the potential of DMSO to provide symptomatic relief for patients with certain painful disorders or the possibility that a new important use may yet lie undiscovered.
> The FDA is willing, indeed anxious, to approve DMSO for such uses whenever controlled trials meeting the statutory standard are available. We have worked in the past, and stand ready to work in the future, with any party in developing protocols for such trials and in expediting their review.

I think this is a fair statement of the FDA's current position on DMSO. Dr. Vincent V. Karusaitis and I, as the two physicians at the FDA with primary responsibility for the initial reviews and recommendations on DMSO studies in humans, are eager to hear what is new and promising with DMSO. We hope that those of you working on *in vitro* or animal models will find ways to translate your leads into clinically significant treatment benefits.

I'd like to take the rest of my time to talk about our expectations in controlled clinical trials in general and with DMSO in particular. Most indications for which DMSO is a candidate do not involve diseases with end points so objective, stable, and unaffected by other treatments that one can reasonably expect to use either patients as their own controls or historical controls. This forces one into cross-over or parallel-group designs. Again, most of the indications under consideration are in diseases that wax and wane spontaneously to an extent that makes cross-over designs impractical. This leaves us for all practical purposes with parallel-group studies. In studying those conditions for which there currently is no treatment or where effective treatment could be delayed without serious harm to the patient, one would usually employ a placebo control group. Where there is effective treatment available or where even a temporary delay in treatment could jeopardize the outcome, one needs to use a positive control group.

The problem of concealing the presence of DMSO, i.e. masking, is critical. I believe it was this aspect of the studies they reviewed that caused the National Academy of Sciences Subcommittee on Connective Tissue Diseases to comment on the quality of the studies. Some investigators attempted to make placebos by using substances like histamine and garlic to mimic the local and systemic side

---

†Crout, R.J. Hearing before The Select Committee on Age (H.R.). 96th Congress, 2nd Session, 24 March 1980. Comm. Pub. No. 96-232. pp 57–81.

effects of DMSO. They were unsuccessful in masking the trials for observers or patients who had had previous experience with DMSO. Their results have not been accepted by their peers as "proving efficacy."

Others took the position that masking was impossible and they tried to make it "unnecessary" by patient selection or grading schemes that were designed to take bias and subjectivity out of the experiment. The data from such studies have not convinced the FDA or the investigators' peers that these attempts were successful largely because the demonstrated effects have been marginal.

Incidently, because of DMSO's distinctive properties, in the case of positively controlled trials one needs to use two control drugs for masking: one for the positive control as well as one for DMSO.

The solution that I favor for masking DMSO trials is using different doses of DMSO. This is a special case of the placebo control, which defines the lowest level of improvement that one can expect to observe in a masked trial; and of the positive control, which defines the upper or at least standard, level of efficacy seen with standard treatment. With a dose-response approach one needs to find two doses far enough apart on the efficacy-response scale to be distinguishable from one another statistically and yet close enough to each other on the side-effect scale to provide reasonable (convincing) masking (in the case of DMSO this means local effects and effect on breath and/or taste).

So far the dose-response approach has been successful in masking an experiment involving mental retardation but not in establishing efficacy. In my opinion this is because DMSO is probably not effective for the indication studied, although we need a second study to be certain. Critics of the approach are not anxious to repeat the experiment. They claim that DMSO is not like other drugs in that it is effective over a wide range of concentrations and differences in doses can't be demonstrated.

This assertion brings us to another problem area for DMSO. I believe that the concept that DMSO works through mysterious ways, defying ordinary scientific principles, precludes those that believe this concept from doing the kinds of experiments that are necessary to gain approval by the FDA or the medical and scientific communities for DMSO for any indication. It leads to poor experimental design, half-hearted execution of studies and, in my opinion, probably contributes to attempts to "beat the system" by submitting "false information."

This volume provides reassuring evidence that there are scientists who believe not only in the therapeutic potential of DMSO but also that good science is the key to unraveling whatever mysteries and benefits DMSO holds for us. In my opinion, those of you with these dual beliefs will determine the fate of DMSO.

Almost as counterproductive as a mystical belief in DMSO is the notion that there is a conspiracy against DMSO. The idea of an active conspiracy against DMSO is ludicrous to anyone knowledgeable about the FDA, the medical and scientific communities, and the pharmaceutical industry, even when it is cast in its most sinister role with profit as its mainspring. In my view, the results of such accusations are to give false hope to the thousands of sufferers of those diseases for which we have no cure and to make larger profits for those that would prey on those sufferers by selling them "solvent" DMSO for "non-medical uses."

Dr. Crout, in the remarks that I quoted, suggested that DMSO was more akin to a liniment than a miracle drug. I share that belief based on impressions gained from study results I've seen with DMSO and with a variety of anti-inflammatory and analgesic drugs from other studies of similar traumatic and inflammatory conditions. A study, such as we recently received, to investigate DMSO in rheumatoid arthritis resistant to all other therapies is too severe a test for DMSO or any other drug currently being studied in the IND/NDA process. As an adjunct to therapy that is only partially successful would seem to me to be a more appropriate niche for DMSO and one that would still help fill the needs of those sufferers we discussed above. Certainly to expect too much in the way of efficacy from DMSO creates the possibility, or more likely the probability, of designing experiments that will fail to show it to be efficacious.

The last point I'd like to touch on is the potential ocular toxicity of DMSO. Our toxicologists have reviewed studies on DMSO in seven species all of which, after some dose for some duration, show incompletely reversible changes in the lens. It would be a biological quirk for human lenses not to behave similarly. This means that at some dose for some duration we should expect similar results in man. This does not mean that DMSO should not be studied or approved for use in humans. It does mean that we are obligated to define the dose and duration at the earliest possible time so that physicians and patients can make reasoned risk/benefit judgements in deciding whether or not to use DMSO. We can not ethically study the risk of a permanent decrease in vision in normal volunteers or patients taking DMSO chronically for indications that have not been proven to be effective. Therefore we must wait for such studies to be set up in Phase IV, post-approval studies, in populations of patients taking DMSO chronically. My current thinking is that a commitment to do such studies should be a Phase IV requirement for approval for some indications. We will have to wait to evaluate each individual situation, however, and I can postulate circumstances where it would not be feasible and/or reasonable to require such studies.

We look forward to reviewing your data from adequate and well-controlled studies in support of New Drug Applications establishing the safety and efficacy of DMSO for new indications and we hope that we will see that data soon.

TOXICOLOGIC UPDATE OF DIMETHYL SULFOXIDE

Lionel F. Rubin

School of Veterinary Medicine
University of Pennsylvania
Philadelphia, Pennsylvania 19104

The search for novel medical applications of dimethyl sulfoxide (DMSO) has been both wide and continuous, as evidenced by the scope of reports in this volume. Many applications appear to hold great promise, but one must be cognizant of the possibility of untoward effects. The purpose of this paper is to review and update the knowledge of the toxicity of DMSO.

SYSTEMIC TOXICITY OF DMSO

Addition of DMSO to blood produces effects that vary with concentration and method of administration. At concentrations of 50% or more, there is instant hemolysis, white cell sticking, and fibrinogen precipitation.[1] Intravenous injections of DMSO may cause local irritation and necrosis, depending on concentration and frequency.[2,3] The damage occurs rapidly, especially in concentrations of 80% or more. There are perivascular inflammatory reactions and intravascular thrombi. Intraarterial injection of 100% DMSO produced marked injury to endothelium and large turgid masses of agglutinated red blood cells.[1] Intravenous DMSO injections in rhesus monkeys of 3 g/kg in a 40% solution once daily for nine days produced a transient increase in respiratory rate (similar to that in rabbits[5]) and a fourfold increase in diuresis. As expected, there was some erythrocytic hemolysis. The partial thromboplastin time in the treated monkeys decreased temporarily[6] and Freeman and coworkers[7] reported intravenous doses of 0.4 to 4.0 g/kg to rhesus monkeys for five days produced reversible dose-related hemodilution and fluctuations in SGPT, platelet, and leukocyte counts.

In four species in which they have been estimated, the LD_{50}s are between 2.5 and 8.9 g/kg intravenously (mice, rats, cats, dogs) and the symptoms at near lethal doses were similar (spontaneous motor activity, tremors, myasthenia, prostration, transient convulsion, dyspnea, pulmonary edema, and hemorrhaging). Single oral doses have LD_{50}s between 12.8 and 28.3 g/kg (mouse, cat, chicken) and single subcutaneous doses to mice and rats were between 12.5 and 20.5 g/kg.[2,3,7]

Oral administration to mice of 2.5 g/kg per day for six weeks revealed some degeneration of liver and indications of nephritis[5] and in rats oral doses of 1 to 5 g/kg per day for six weeks produced degenerative liver changes and signs of nephritis.[5] In other studies[3,7] at similar doses, no such changes were observed. Dogs given very high doses orally had liver damage (fatty degeneration, cloudy swelling, and granularity of parenchymal cytoplasm[4]) and a marked hemorrhagic gastroenteropathy. Investigation of liver biopsies from rats administered 0.4 ml of DMSO (about 2 g/kg) minutes before showed hepatic sinusoids filled with hemolyzed red blood cells as well as fragmentation of the cytoplasm of Kupffer cells. The hepatocytes had prominent organelles, poor cytoplasmic projections, enlarged mitochondria, and free ribosomes.[8]

Kidney damage generally consists of mild tubular nephrosis, generally related to breakdown products of hemolysis. There was no significant short term

6

0077–8923/83/0411–0006 $01.75/0 © 1983, NYAS

nephrotoxicity observed in human patients administered intravenous DMSO in therapeutic concentrations (1 g/kg as a 10 to 40% solution).[9] The DMSO was infused for 30 minutes to 24 hours for three days. There was evidence of intravascular hemolysis and hemoglobinuria, but there was no effect on tubular excretion of beta-2-microglobulin, a sensitive index of nephrotoxic tubular damage. There were no changes in blood urea nitrogen, creatinine, in mean creatinine clearance time, or in kidney function. Hemoglobinuria was dose related.[10]

TOXICITY IN HUMANS

Yellowlees et al.[11] and Greenfield[12] reported a toxic reaction in two elderly people receiving DMSO intravenously for treatment of arthritis (three daily doses of 100 g of 20% DMSO). In one patient there was serious illness including oliguria, hemolysis, tremor, and loss of consciousness. The second patient did not become ill. Both patients had changes in blood aspartate transaminase, hydroxybutyrate dehydrogenase, and creatine kinase, and elevation of blood creatinine and urea nitrogen. Prothrombin and partial thromboplastin times were significantly shorter.

Knott[13] and van Rijswijk,[14] who had treated patients similarly to Yellowlees et al. but without toxic effect, suggest that the toxic reactions seen in the latter's patients were caused by the action of DMSO as a drug potentiator, and that the reaction may have been due to an enhancement of the toxicity of quinine sulfate, indomethacin, or phenothiazine, which patients were receiving at the time.

Another patient receiving intravenously cryopreserved autologous marrow blood (to which DMSO was added) for treatment of myeloblastic leukemia suffered a reaction to the administration. In addition to a drop in hemoglobin, the patient became agitated, pyrexic, hypotensive, and developed tachycardia. Recovery occurred but the patient died ten days later. O'Donnell et al.[15] believed the mixture was toxic (the patient received 35 g of DMSO as a 10% solution), and suggested that DMSO interactions may be significant and potentially dangerous.

EFFECTS ON SKIN

High concentrations of DMSO solutions applied to skin exaggerate the hygroscopic effects of DMSO, depriving the tissues of water. This exothermic reaction damages tissues. Such damage and skin irritation can be significant, as was shown by the repeated application of 10 ml 100% DMSO to the backs of rabbits.[16]

Skin erythema, edema, and pruritus are frequent occurrences in humans, when concentrations of DMSO greater than 70% are used, but such side reactions also occur at concentrations of 10%. In studies of human subjects, some investigators report incidences of skin irritation troublesome enought to warrant cessation of therapy in 50 to 80% of patients.[17] In one experimental study[18] in humans using 1 g/kg 80% DMSO cutaneously, the incidence of dermatologic reaction (wheal and erythema, scaling and drying) was significant and more than 20% of the subjects dropped out early in the experimental program because of the skin reactions. In this study, there was a significant incidence of eosinophilia attributed to the cutaneous histamine-releasing effect of DMSO.

EFFECTS ON THE EYE

The chronic administration of DMSO results in a unique change in the eyes of laboratory animals. No other compound, to my knowledge, has been reported to produce anything similar. Administration of DMSO causes the cortical fibers of the lens of young, rapidly growing animals to become less relucent than normal;[19,20] in contrast, lenticular fibers in the deeper cortex and the lens nucleus remain unchanged. The change in relucency causes the creation of a major new retracting surface more posteriorly within the lens, as contrasted to the usual major retracting surface of the anterior lens capsule. The alteration in refracting surface results in the production of a refractive error and myopia in affected laboratory animals. The severity of the myopic change increases directly with increasing length of administration of DMSO, or with exposure to higher concentrations. Clinically, severely affected animals appear to have a pearl-like opalescence in the center of the lens, though the lens remains optically clear.

The change in relucency of the lens can be produced either by oral or dermal administration of DMSO. The lenticular changes can be produced by application of DMSO to the skin of rabbits for 11 weeks at a dosage of 1 g/kg per day,[21] in dogs at a dosage of 2.5 g/kg per day for nine weeks, and in swine at a dosage of 1.5 g/kg per day for 16 weeks.[20,21] Administration of higher dosages produces lenticular changes in a shorter time.[21,22] Lenticular changes in rats were reported[17] to occur after dosage of 9 g/kg for 24 weeks, but there has been no clear confirmation of this. In horses administered DMSO cutaneously at about 0.6 g/kg for about two months, there appeared to be a slight change in static refraction toward myopia. Lenticular changes have been reported to occur in rhesus monkeys administered 9 g/kg per day within 14 weeks, and lenticular changes were suspected in those receiving 3 g/kg per day for the same period.[23] Another study[24] failed to detect lenticular changes in rhesus monkeys administered doses up to 9 g/kg orally or cutaneously for 18 months.

In the rabbit, a species highly sensitive to the development of the lenticular change, no effect was observed in animals administered 0.5 g/kg per day cutaneously for 30 days.[21]

The nature of the lenticular change caused by DMSO is still not known. Histologic examination is unrewarding. DMSO does not accumulate in the lens,[25] although DMSO concentrations can be found in cornea, aqueous humor, and vitreous body after acute administration, and concentrations in the sclera and vitreous body are high after chronic administration.[26] The major biochemical changes reported in DMSO-affected lenses are decreased concentration of urea, uric acid, glutathione, and amino acids, with an increase in albuminoids. The lens change is not caused by either hydration or dehydration, nor does DMSO bind to lens protein.[27]

The unique lenticular changes occurring in animals have not been reported to occur in humans.[17,18] The experimental evidence suggests, however, that the possible beneficial effects of DMSO must be weighed against the possible negative effects of administration of DMSO in doses of over 0.5 g/kg per day for more than 90 days.

Other ocular changes have been reported to occur in some animal studies. One study[20] indicated that cataracts occurred in some rabbits administered DMSO, but cataracts did not occur in other studies at similar doses. A peculiar transient cataract was seen in one study utilizing dogs,[20] but this finding has not been confirmed in other studies. Cataracts occurred in guinea pigs administered DMSO cutaneously or subcutaneously.[28]

TERATOGENIC EFFECTS

Administration of 5 g/kg per day to male and female rats for four days prior to mating caused no decrease in fertility, nor was any teratologic effect seen.[5] However, administration of multiple, high doses of DMSO to gravid mice or rats has produced some teratogenic effects.[29] In hamsters, DMSO administered in high doses is teratogenic.[30] In avian embryos, the teratogenic activity of DMSO is definite.[29]

MUTAGENIC EFFECTS

In several tests DMSO is reported to be non-mutagenic. Negative results for mutagenicity were reported for DMSO in the Salmonella/microsome assay[31] and in Drosphila melanogaster[32,33] but DMSO does exhibit genetic activity (DNA damage) in yeast (Saccharomyces cerevisiae).[34] These tests, according to Kapp and Eventoff,[35] do not directly measure the effects of DMSO on chromosome structure. They injected DMSO in various concentrations (1 to 100%, 5 ml/kg) intraperitoneally in rats, and showed that the incidence of aberrant femoral bone marrow cells increased from 10% at the 1% DMSO level to about 70% at the 100% DMSO level, and the incidence of aberrant cells in all treated groups was significantly elevated when compared to controls. They suggest that DMSO effectively disrupts the integrity of rat chromosome structure.

REFERENCES

1. JOHNSON, J. H., R. R. BAKER & S. WOOD, JR. 1966. Effects of DMSO on blood and vascular endothelium. In Fourth European Conference on Microcirculation. H. Hardens, Ed. Karger. Basel.
2. ROSENCRANTZ, H., Z. HADIDIAN, H. SEAY & M. M. MASON. 1963. Dimethyl sulfoxide. Its steroid solubility and endocrinologic and pharmacologic—toxicologic characteristics. Cancer Chemother. Rep. **31**: 7-24.
3. SOMMER, S. & G. TAUBERGER. 1964. Toxicologic investigations of dimethyl sulfoxide. Arzneim. Forsch. **14**: 1050-1053.
4. WILLSON, J. E., D. E. BROWN & E. K. TIMMONS. 1965. A toxicologic study on dimethyl sulfoxide. Toxicol. Appl. Pharmacol. **7**: 104-112.
5. CAUJOLLE, F., D. CAUJOLLE, H. BOUYSSON & M. M. CALVET. 1964. Toxicite et aptitudes pharmacologiques du dimethyl sulfoxyde. C.R. Acad. Sci. Paris **258**: 2224-2226.
6. DE LA TORRE, J. C., J. W. SURGEON, T. ERNEST & R. WOLLMAN. 1981. Subacute toxicity of intravenous dimethyl sulfoxide in rhesus monkeys. J. Toxicol. Environ. Health **7**: 49-57.
7. SMITH, E. R., Z. HADIDIAN & M. M. MASON. 1967. The single- and repeated-dose toxicity of dimethyl sulfoxide. Ann. N.Y. Acad. Sci. **141**: 96-109.
8. SHILKIN, K. B., J. M. PAPADIMITRIOU & M. N. WALTERS. 1966. The effect of dimethyl sulfoxide on hepatic cells of rats. Austr. J. Exp. Biol. Med. Sci. **44**: 581.
9. BENNETT, N. M. & R. S. MUTHER. 1981. Lack of nephrotoxicity of intravenous dimethylsulfoxide. Clin. Toxicol. **18**: 615-618.
10. MUTHER, R. S. & N. M. BENNETT. 1980. Effects of dimethyl sulfoxide on renal function in man. J. Am. Med. Assoc. **244**: 2081-2083.
11. YELLOWLEES, P., C. GREENFIELD & N. McINTYRE. 1980. Dimethylsulphoxide induced toxicity. Lancet **2**(8202): 1044-1046.
12. GREENFIELD, C. 1981. Dimethylsulphoxide toxicity. Lancet **1**(8214): 276-277.
13. KNOTT, L. J. 1980. Safety of intravenous dimethylsulphoxide. Lancet **2**(8207): 1299.

14. VAN RIJSWIJK, M. H. 1981. Dimethylsulphoxide. Lancet 1(8210): 41.
15. O'DONNELL, J. R., A. K. BURNETT, T. SHEEHAN, P. TANSEY & G. A. McDONALD. 1981. Safety of dimethylsulphoxide. Lancet 1(8218): 498.
16. BROWN, V. K., J. ROBINSON & D. E. STEVENSON. 1963. A note on the toxicity and solvent properties of dimethyl sulfoxide. J. Pharm. Pharmacol. 15: 688–692.
17. National Academy of Sciences—National Research Council 1973. Dimethyl sulfoxide as a therapeutic agent. Report on the ad hoc committee on dimethyl sulfoxide.
18. BROBYN, R. D. 1975. The human toxicology of dimethyl sulfoxide. Ann. N.Y. Acad. Sci. 243: 500–509.
19. RUBIN, L. F. & P. A. MATTIS. 1966. Dimethyl sulfoxide: Lens changes in dogs during oral administration. Science 153: 83–84.
20. RUBIN, L. F. & K. C. BARNETT. 1967. Ocular effects of oral and dermal application of dimethyl sulfoxide in animals. Ann. N.Y. Acad. Sci. 141: 333–345.
21. WOOD, D. C., F. S. WEBER & M. A. PALMQUIST. 1971. Continued studies in the toxicology of dimethyl sulfoxide (DMSO). J. Pharmacol. Exp. Therap. 177: 520–527.
22. KLEBERGER, K. E. 1967. An ophthalmological evaluation of DMSO. Ann. N.Y. Acad. Sci. 141: 381.
23. BARNETT, K. C. & P. R. NOEL. 1967. Dimethyl sulfoxide and lens changes in primates. Nature 214: 115–116.
24. VOGIN, E. E., S. CARSON, G. CANNON, C. R. LINEGAR & L. F. RUBIN. 1970. Chronic toxicity of DMSO in primates. Toxicol. Appl. Pharmacol. 16: 606–612.
25. DENKO, C. W., R. M. GOODMAN, R. MILLER & T. DONOVAN. 1967. Distribution of dimethyl sulfoxide—^{35}S in the rat. Ann. N.Y. Acad. Sci. 141: 77–84.
26. HUSKER, M. B., P. M. AHMAD & E. A. MILLER. 1966. Absorption, distribution and metabolism of dimethyl-sulfoxide in the rat, rabbit, and guinea pig. J. Pharmacol. Exp. Therap. 154: 176–184.
27. WOOD, D. C., N. V. WORTH, F. S. WEBER & M. A. PALMQUIST. 1971. Mechanism considerations of dimethyl sulfoxide (DMSO). Lenticular changes in rabbits. J. Pharmacol. Exp. Therap. 177: 528–535.
28. RENGSTORFF, R. H., J. P. PETROLI & V. M. SIM. 1972. Cataracts induced in guinea pigs by acetone, cyclohexanone and dimethyl sulfoxide. Am. J. Optometry 49: 308–319.
29. CAUJOLLE, F. M. E., D. H. CAUJOLLE, S. B. CROS & M. M. J. CALVET. 1967. Limits of toxic and teratogenic tolerance of dimethyl sulfoxide. Ann. N.Y. Acad. Sci. 141: 110–125.
30. FERM, V. H. 1966. Teratogenic effect of DMSO. Lancet 1(7430): 208.
31. McCANN, J., E. CHOI, E. YAMASAKI & B. N. AMES. 1975. Detection of carcinogens as mutagens in the Salmonella/microsome test: Assay of 300 chemicals. Proc. Natl. Acad. Sci. USA 72: 5135–5139.
32. MOLLET, P. 1974. Toxicity and mutagenicity of DMSO in 2 strains of Drosophila melanogaster. Arch. Genet. 47: 184–190.
33. MOLLET. P. 1976. Lack of proof of induction of somatic recombination and mutation in Drosophila by methyl-2-benzimidazole carbonate, dimethylsulfoxide and acetic acid. Mutation Res. 40: 383–388.
34. YEE, B., S. TSUYUMA & B. G. ADAMS. 1972. Biological effects of dimethylsulfoxide on yeast. Biochem. Biophys. Res. Commun. 49: 1336–1342.
35. KAPP, R. W. JR. & B. E. EVENTOFF. 1980. Mutagenicity of dimethylsulfoxide (DMSO). Teratogenesis, Carcinogenesis and Mutagenesis 1: 141–145.

EFFECT OF DIMETHYL SULFOXIDE ON THE BACTERICIDAL FUNCTION OF POLYMORPHONUCLEAR LEUKOCYTES*

John E. Repine, Richard B. Fox, and Elaine M. Berger

Webb-Waring Lung Institute
Departments of Medicine and Pediatrics
University of Colorado Health Sciences Center
Denver, Colorado 80262

Dimethyl sulfoxide (DMSO) is now being widely used to treat various rheumatic, musculoskeletal, and inflammatory conditions, but the therapeutic and detrimental consequences of treating individuals with DMSO remain unclear. We have examined the possibility that DMSO might inhibit the bactericidal function of polymorphonuclear leukocytes (PMN) by scavenging hydroxyl radical ($\cdot$OH), one of the key bactericidal components of PMN. Our results suggest that DMSO can decrease the ability of PMN to kill Staphylococcus aureus in vitro and that this inhibition may occur because DMSO scavenges $\cdot$OH. These observations suggest that DMSO might impair PMN-mediated host defense.

Briefly, we have found that reactions producing $\cdot$OH (xanthine/xanthine oxidase or $Fe^{2+}/EDTA/H_2O_2$) generate methane (CH_4) from DMSO, whereas reactions yielding primarily superoxide anion ($O_2 \cdot^-$) or hydrogen peroxide (H_2O_2) fail to produce CH_4 from DMSO. Mass spectroscopy using d_6-DMSO showed formation of d_3-CH_4 indicating that the CH_4 was derived from DMSO. In addition, CH_4 generation by normal PMN, but not O_2 radical-deficient chronic granulomatous disease (CGD) PMN or heat-killed PMN, increases after stimulation with opsonized zymosan particles or the chemical, phorbol myristate acetate (PMA). Methane production from DMSO also increases as the number of stimulated PMN is increased. The kinetics of CH_4 production approximate other oxidative metabolic activities of stimulated PMN. In contrast, methane production from stimulated phagocytes and DMSO are markedly decreased by purportedly potent $\cdot$OH scavengers (thiourea or tryptophan) and diminished to lesser degrees by weaker $\cdot$OH scavengers (mannitol, ethanol, or sodium benzoate). Superoxide dismutase (SOD), a scavenger of $O_2 \cdot^-$, or catalase, a scavenger of H_2O_2, also decreases CH_4 production but urea, albumin, heat-inactivated SOD, and boiled catalase have no appreciable effect. The results suggest that production of CH_4 from DMSO may reflect release of $\cdot$OH from both chemical systems and PMN.[1,2]

Increasing concentrations of the highly permeable, $\cdot$OH scavenger DMSO progressively decreases killing of Staphylococcus aureus 502A by human PMN in vitro. CH_4, a product of the reaction of the $\cdot$OH with DMSO, is generated in the

*Supported in part by grants from the Council for Tobacco Research, Kroc, Hill, Swan, and Kleberg Foundations, National Institutes of Health, National Institutes of Health Training Grants, Colorado and American Heart Associations, and Colorado and American Lung Associations. J.E.R. is an Established Investigator of the American Heart Association. R.B.F. is the recipient of a Clinical Investigator award from the National Institutes of Health.

11

process. Inhibitions caused by DMSO in the killing of *S. aureus* by PMN exceed inhibitions caused by addition of SOD and/or catalase (see TABLE 1). The specificity of the inhibitory action of DMSO on ·OH formation is further suggested when additional studies showed that DMSO did not decrease O_2·$^-$ production by mixtures of PMN and opsonized *S. aureus*, did not damage PMN as adjudged by electron microscopy or release of LDH, and did not decrease uptake or phagocytosis of *S. aureus* by PMN.[3]

Finally, DMSO also decreases killing of *S. aureus* by H_2O_2. Indeed, two lines of investigation supported the possibility that killing of *Staphylococcus aureus* 502A by H_2O_2 involves formation of the more toxic ·OH by the well-known Fenton reaction. First, growing *S. aureus* overnight in broth media with increasing concentrations of iron increases their content of iron and dramatically enhances their subsequent susceptibility to killing by H_2O_2. Second, in direct relation to their effectiveness as ·OH scavengers, thiourea, dimethyl thiourea, sodium benzoate, and DMSO inhibit H_2O_2-mediated killing of *S. aureus*. CH_4 is produced

TABLE 1

EFFECT OF DMSO ON THE KILLING OF *S. aureus* BY NORMAL PMN

Test Conditions* PMN, *S. aureus*, and Serum	Inhibition (% of Control with No Inhibitor)
+DMSO (140 mM)	16%
+DMSO (210 mM)	27%
+DMSO (280 mM)	37%
+SOD (200 μg/ml)	0%
+Catalase (1 mg/ml)	0%
+SOD (200 mg/ml) plus Catalase (1 mg/ml)	0%

SOD = superoxide dismutase.
*See Reference 3 for details and control values.

from mixtures of DMSO and *S. aureus* with H_2O_2 but not *S. aureus* or H_2O_2 alone.[4,5]

The aforementioned suggests that DMSO could react under certain circumstances to scavenge ·OH and decrease the bactericidal function of PMN. Relatively high concentrations of DMSO, approximately 1-2%, are needed to achieve this inhibition *in vitro*. Whether these levels are realized *in vivo*, as well as whether exposure to lower concentrations of DMSO for longer durations *in vivo* could cause the same effect, is unknown. Furthermore, since the mechanisms by which PMN kill bacteria may be the same as the ones by which they damage tissue, one might speculate that DMSO might also protect against ·OH-mediated tissue injury.[6,7]

ACKNOWLEDGMENTS

We are indebted to Ms. Jill Potts and Ms. Kari Murphy for excellent technical assistance.

REFERENCES

1. REPINE, J. E., J. W. EATON, M. W. ANDERS, J. R. HOIDAL & R. B. FOX. 1979. Generation of hydroxyl radical by enzymes, chemicals, and human phagocytes *in vitro*: Detection using the anti-inflammatory agent—Dimethyl sulfoxide. J. Clin. Invest. **64:** 1642–1651.
2. REPINE, J. E., J. G. WHITE, C. C. CLAWSON & B. M. HOLMES. 1974. Effects of phorbol myristate acetate on the metabolism and ultrastructure of neutrophils in chronic granulomatous disease. J. Clin. Invest. **54:** 83–90.
3. REPINE, J. E., R. B. FOX & E. M. BERGER. 1981. Dimethyl sulfoxide inhibits killing of *Staphylococcus aureus* by polymorphonuclear leukocytes. Infect. Immun. **31:** 510–513.
4. REPINE, J. E., R. B. FOX, E. M. BERGER & R. N. HARADA. 1981. Effect of staphylococcal iron content on the killing of *Staphylococcus aureus* by polymorphonuclear leukocytes. Infect. Immun. **32:** 407–410.
5. REPINE, J. E., R. B. FOX & E. M. BERGER. 1981. Hydrogen peroxide kills *Staphylococcus aureus* by reacting with staphylococcal iron to form hydroxyl radical. J. Biol. Chem. **256:** 7094–7097.
6. REPINE, J. E., O. W. PFENNINGER, D. W. TALMAGE, E. M. BERGER & D. E. PETTIJOHN. 1981. Dimethyl sulfoxide prevents DNA nicking mediated by ionizing radiation or iron/hydrogen peroxide-generated hydroxyl radical. Proc. Natl. Acad. Sci. USA **78:** 1001–1003.
7. TATE, R. M., K. M. VANBENTHUYSEN, D. M. SHASBY, I. F. MCMURTRY & J. E. REPINE. 1982. Oxygen radical mediated permeability edema and vasoconstriction in isolated perfused rabbit lungs. Amer. Rev. Respir. Dis. **126:** 802–806.

DIMETHYL SULFOXIDE PREVENTS HYDROXYL RADICAL-MEDIATED DEPOLYMERIZATION OF HYALURONIC ACID*

Richard B. Fox† and Wendy K. Fox

Webb-Waring Lung Institute
Department of Pediatrics
University of Colorado Medical School
Denver, Colorado 80262

Division of Cell Biology
Department of Medicine
Children's Hospital Medical Center
Department of Pediatrics
Harvard Medical School
Boston, Massachusetts 02115

INTRODUCTION

Dimethyl sulfoxide (DMSO) is an effective scavenger of hydroxyl radicals ($\cdot$OH)[1] that may be useful for detecting and preventing the effects of $\cdot$OH in biological systems. DMSO has the particular advantage of great permeability,[2] which allows it to penetrate cell membranes impenetrable to other antioxidants, particularly enzymatic antioxidants.

To demonstrate DMSO protection of a biological molecule against $\cdot$OH attack, we measured the ability of DMSO to protect hyaluronic acid against depolymerization by $\cdot$OH. Hyaluronic acid has been used previously to study effects of $\cdot$OH, since it is known to be susceptible to depolymerization by $\cdot$OH.[3] Specifically, it was found that the antioxidant enzymes, superoxide dismutase and catalase, prevented depolymerization of hyaluronic acid solutions incubated with xanthine and xanthine oxidase. The xanthine/xanthine oxidase system specifically generates superoxide (O_2^-), which can decompose to hydrogen peroxide (H_2O_2).[4] The O_2^- and H_2O_2 are postulated to interact via the Haber-Weiss mechanism to yield $\cdot$OH.[5] Therefore, the ability of either superoxide dismutase or catalase to prevent xanthine/xanthine oxidase-mediated depolymerization of hyaluronic acid was interpreted to imply that depolymerization resulted from $\cdot$OH, rather than either O_2^- or H_2O_2.[3]

Subsequently, it was reported that depolymerization of hyaluronic acid by the xanthine/xanthine oxidase system was also prevented by DMSO,[6] further supporting involvement of $\cdot$OH in this process. Since the xanthine/xanthine oxidase system generates $\cdot$OH only secondarily to the production of other radicals, we felt it would be useful to test DMSO in a system that more directly and specifically generates $\cdot$OH. Therefore, we produced $\cdot$OH by gamma irradiation of aqueous solutions. We found that DMSO was also effective in preventing radiation-

*Supported by a research grant from the American Lung Association. R.B.F. is the recipient of a Clinical Investigator Award (7 K08 HL 01131-03) from the Division of Lung Diseases of the National Institutes of Health.

†Address: Children's Hospital Medical Center, 300 Longwood Ave., Boston, Mass. 02115.

14

induced depolymerization of hyaluronic acid. We also found that DMSO was effective in yet another ·OH-producing system: DMSO prevented depolymerization of hyaluronic acid by activated polymorphonuclear leukocytes (PMN), an important biological source of ·OH.[7]

METHODS

Hyaluronic acid from human umbilical cord (Grade I, Sigma Chemical Co., St. Louis, Mo.) was dissolved in 100 mM sodium phosphate buffer, pH 7.4, (1.67 mg/ml). Solutions were placed in rubber-stoppered glass tubes (Vacutainer, Becton-Dickenson Co., Rutherford, N.J.). In some tubes, the headspace air was replaced with either oxygen (O_2), nitrous oxide (N_2O), or argon (Ar), and the tubes tumbled for 15 minutes to equilibrate solutions with the headspace gas. Solutions were then exposed to gamma irradiation (^{60}Co, approximately 1.6 krad/min). Since depolymerization of hyaluronic acid is reflected by loss of viscosity in the hyaluronic acid solution, viscosities were determined by measuring the time required for 0.6 ml of solution to flow by gravity from a 1-ml plastic syringe via a 20 gauge injection needle.[3] Since the flows of these solutions through the needle were always laminar (Reynold's number $\leq$ 189, $\leq\leq$ 2100), the viscosities were calculated from the ratios of the flow times for the hyaluronic acid solution divided by the flow time for a reference liquid, water, times the viscosity of the reference liquid (viscosity$_{water}$ = 1.002 centipoise, Hagen-Poiseuille Law). DMSO, superoxide dismutase, and catalase (all from Sigma Chemical Co.) were also added to some solutions.

In additional studies, irradiation was omitted and hyaluronic acid solutions were exposed instead to activated polymorphonuclear leukocytes (PMN). Human PMN were isolated from peripheral blood by standard Ficoll-Hypaque sedimentation[7] and resuspended in Hank's Balanced Salt Solution (HBSS, Gibco, Grand Island, N.Y.) containing Ca^{2+} and Mg^{2+}. In this group of studies, hyaluronic acid was also dissolved in HBSS. Phorbol myristate acetate (Consolidated Midland Corp., Brewster, N.Y.) was added to solutions to activate PMN release of ·OH.[7] DMSO in various concentrations was added to some solutions. Solutions were prepared on ice, incubated at 37°C for 30 minutes, returned briefly to ice to halt reactions and then centrifuged (500 × g) at 4°C for 10 minutes. Viscosities of supernatants were determined as above.

RESULTS

To determine whether DMSO was effective in preventing ·OH-mediated depolymerization of hyaluronic acid, we exposed solutions of hyaluronic acid to gamma radiation (^{60}Co), a potent generator of ·OH in aqueous solutions, in the presence and absence of DMSO. In the absence of DMSO, irradiation decreased viscosities of hyaluronic acid solutions in a dose-dependent manner (FIGURE 1). Addition of DMSO in increasing concentrations increasingly prevented viscosity loss. DMSO did not affect the viscosities of non-irradiated hyaluronic acid solutions or previously irradiated solutions (data not shown).

Radiation of aqueous solutions generates not only ·OH, but also the hydrated electron, e_{aq}^- (a strong reducing agent),[1] which can also depolymerize hyaluronic acid.[8] To improve the specificity of this test system, we equilibrated the HA solutions with either of two gases that scavenge e_{aq}^-, nitrous oxide and oxygen.

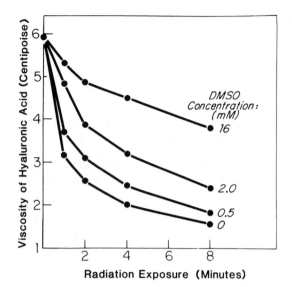

Radiation Exposure (Minutes)

FIGURE 1. Decreases in viscosities of hyaluronic acid solutions due to increasing gamma radiation exposure and prevention of decreases by increasing concentrations of dimethyl sulfoxide.

Nitrous oxide converts e_{aq}^- to $\cdot OH$, while oxygen converts e_{aq}^- to O_2^-.[1] Radiation in the presence of argon served as a negative control. Decrease in viscosity due to radiation was slightly greater in the presence of N_2O (30% of non-irradiated control), compared to Ar (33%, TABLE 1), while decrease in viscosity was less in the presence of O_2 (43%), compared to Ar. To determine whether the protective effect of O_2 was due to generation of O_2^-, rather than scavenging of e_{aq}^-, superoxide dismutase, an enzymatic scavenger of O_2^-, was added prior to irradiation. Addition of superoxide dismutase did not change the degree of

TABLE 1

EFFECTS OF OXYGEN, NITROUS OXIDE, AND DIMETHYL SULFOXIDE ON LOSS OF VISCOSITY IN IRRADIATED HYALURONIC ACID SOLUTIONS

Test Conditions	Viscosity (Centipoise)	% Control	% Protection
HA*	4.6	100	—
HA + RAD† + Ar	1.5	33	0
HA + RAD + N₂O	1.4	30	−4
HA + RAD + O₂	2.3	50	25
HA + RAD + O₂‡	2.3	50	25
HA + RAD + O₂§	2.3	50	25
HA + RAD + Ar + DMSO¶	1.8	39	9
HA + RAD + N₂O + DMSO	1.8	39	9
HA + RAD + O₂ + DMSO	3.1	67	51

*Hyaluronic acid, 1.67 mg/ml in 100 mM sodium phosphate, pH = 7.4.
†Radiation from ^{60}Co, approximately 3.2 krad.
‡Superoxide dismutase (10 µg/ml).
§Catalase (10 µg/ml).
¶Dimethylsulfoxide (2 mM).

viscosity loss in the presence of O_2, nor did catalase, which scavenges H_2O_2 (a degradation product of O_2^-). It appeared from these data that O_2 was effective and specific in blocking the effects of e_{aq}^- in the hyaluronic acid irradiation system.

Next we irradiated hyaluronic acid equilibrated with O_2 in the presence and absence of DMSO (FIGURE 2). DMSO protected against radiation-induced viscosity losses in the presence of both Ar (9% protection) and O_2, but protection was much greater in the presence of O_2 (51%). This suggested that DMSO effectively blocked the ·OH-mediated component of viscosity loss, but not the e_{aq}^- component.

Finally, we also measured the ability of DMSO to prevent depolymerization of hyaluronic acid due to activated polymorphonuclear leukocytes, a potentially important biological source of ·OH. DMSO also prevented PMN-mediated viscosity decreases in a dose-dependent manner (FIGURE 1). Viscosities were linearly related to the logarithm of the DMSO concentration over the range from 2

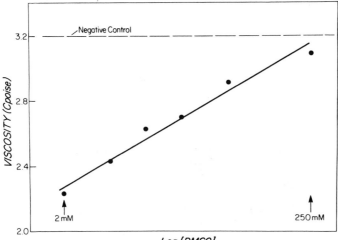

FIGURE 2. Prevention of polymorphonuclear leukocyte-induced viscosity decreases in hyaluronic acid solutions by increasing concentrations of dimethyl sulfoxide.

mM to 250 mM. We have previously reported that DMSO concentrations up to 280 mM were not toxic to PMN metabolism or structure.[9]

DISCUSSION

We found that DMSO protected hyaluronic acid against depolymerization due to either of two sources of ·OH, gamma irradiation or activated PMN. These findings are consistent with previous studies in which DMSO blocked the effects of ·OH in other test systems. Specifically, DMSO prevented depolymerization of hyaluronic acid by enzymatically generated oxygen radicals, presumably including ·OH.[6] Furthermore, DMSO inhibited the bactericidal activities of ·OH generated either by the Fenton reaction:

$$Fe^{2+} + H_2O_2 \rightarrow \cdot OH + OH^- + Fe^{3+},$$

or by activated PMN.[9-11] Also, DMSO protects against radiation *in vivo*,[12] presumably by scavenging ·OH, as in the present *in vitro* studies. Finally, in yet another *in vitro* system, DMSO protected plasmid DNA against nicking by ·OH generated by radiation.[13]

Protection of hyaluronic acid by DMSO against PMN-mediated depolymerization may have some clinical relevance. PMN, which release ·OH,[7] may contribute to breakdown of hyaluronic acid in connective tissues in some inflammatory conditions where influx of PMN is prominent, such as in arthritis.[14] DMSO, or other antioxidants, might then decrease the injurious effects of PMN-released oxidants.

ACKNOWLEDGMENT

We thank John E. Repine for helpful suggestions and encouragement in these studies.

REFERENCES

1. DORFMAN, L. M. & G. E. ADAMS. 1973. Reactivity of the hydroxyl radical in aqueous solutions. U.S. Department of Commerce, National Bureau of Standards. NSRDS-NBS no. 46.
2. RAMMLER, D. H. & A. ZAFFARONI. 1967. Biological implications of DMSO based on a review of its chemical properties. Ann. N.Y. Acad. Sci. 141: 13–23.
3. McCORD, J. M. 1974. Free radicals and inflammation: Protection of synovial fluid by superoxide dismutase. Science 185: 529–531.
4. McCORD, J. M. & I. FRIDOVICH. 1969. Superoxide dismutase: An enzymic function for erythrocuprein (hemocuprein). J. Biol. Chem. 244: 6049–6055.
5. HABER, F. & J. WEISS. 1934. The catalytic decomposition of hydrogen peroxide by iron salts. Proc. R. Soc. Lond. Ser. A1 47: 332–351.
6. DELMAESTRO, R. F., K. E. ARFORS & R. LINDBLOM. 1978. Free radical depolymerization of hyaluronic acid: Influence of scavenger substances. Bibl. Anat. 18(Suppl): 132–135.
7. REPINE, J. E., J. W. EATON, M. W. ANDERS, J. R. HOIDAL & R. B. FOX. 1979. Generation of hydroxyl radical by enzymes, chemicals and human phagocytes *in vitro*: detection with the anti-inflammatory agent, dimethylsulfoxide. J. Clin. Invest. 64: 1642–1651.
8. MOORE, J. S., G. O. PHILLIPS, J. V. DAVIES & K. S. DODSON. 1970. Reactions of connective tissue and related polyanions with hydrated electrons and hydroxyl radicals. Carbohydr. Res. 12: 253–260.
9. REPINE, J. E., R. B. FOX & E. M. BERGER. 1981. Hydrogen peroxide kills *Staphyloccocus aureus* by reacting with staphyloccocal iron to form hydroxyl radical. J. Biol. Chem. 256: 7094–7096.
10. REPINE, J. E., R. B. FOX, E. M. BERGER & R. N. HARADA. 1981. Effect of staphyloccocal iron content on the killing of *Staphyloccocus aureus* by polymorphonuclear leukocytes. Infect. Immun. 32: 407–410.
11. REPINE, J. E., R. B. FOX & E. M. BERGER. 1983. Ann. N.Y. Acad. Sci. (This volume.)
12. ASHWOOD, M. J. 1967. Radioprotective and cryoprotective properties of dimethylsulfoxide in cellular systems. Ann. N.Y. Acad. Sci. 141: 45–62.
13. REPINE, J. E., O. W. PFENNINGER, E. M. BERGER, D. W. TALMAGE & D. E. PETTIJOHN. 1981. Dimethylsulfoxide prevents DNA nicking mediated by ionizing radiation or iron-hydrogen peroxide generated hydroxyl radical. Proc. Natl. Acad. Sci. USA 78: 1001–1003.
14. ZVAIFLER, N. J. 1979. Etiology and pathogenesis of rheumatoid arthritis. *In* Arthritis and Allied Conditions. 9th Edit. D. J. McCarty, Ed.: 417–428. Lea and Febiger. Philadelphia, Pa.

COMPARISON OF THE ANALGESIC EFFECTS OF DIMETHYL SULFOXIDE AND MORPHINE*

Henry J. Haigler†

Department of Pharmacology
Emory University School of Medicine
Atlanta, Georgia 30322

Denise D. Spring

School of Pharmacy
Mercer University
Atlanta, Georgia 30345

The purpose of these experiments was to answer two questions: Does DMSO (dimethyl sulfoxide) have an analgesic effect? If DMSO has an analgesic effect, is this effect related to opiate (i.e. morphine-like) receptors?

DMSO is an analgesic drug.[1-4] It is readily absorbed through the skin and some of which enters the brain. DMSO may act on the central nervous system, peripheral nervous system, or both to produce its analgesic effect. DMSO has a local anti-inflammatory effect when administered topically.[5] Although one report indicated that DMSO had a local anesthetic effect,[6] a more precise test failed to demonstrate any local anesthetic activity.[7]

In order to act on the central nervous system (CNS; the brain and spinal cord) DMSO must cross the blood-brain barrier and enter the CNS. When DMSO is administered either topically or intraperitoneally, the levels achieved in the brain were among the highest of all body tissues.[3] After i.v. administration (in rhesus monkeys), DMSO reaches its highest concentration in the pons, medulla, and spinal cord.[8] Therefore DMSO may produce analgesia by acting on both the peripheral nervous system and the CNS.

If DMSO acts on the CNS, it may act, either directly or indirectly, on opiate (i.e., morphine-like) receptors. For instance, DMSO could act indirectly by enhancing the release of endogenous enkephalins or endorphins from nerve terminals, thereby producing analgesia. Two criteria that a drug should meet if it acts via the same mechanism as morphine are: (1) the drug should produce analgesia on two tests (the tail-flick and hot-plate tests) that are effective in detecting the effects of potent analgesic drugs[9,10] and (2) the analgesic effect of the drug should be blocked by naloxone, a specific narcotic antagonist. Therefore, if DMSO produces analgesia via an action on opiate receptors, it should produce analgesia on both the hot-plate and tail-flick test and these analgesic effects should be blocked by naloxone.

There are two general observations concerning the results in this study. First, DMSO produces an analgesic effect comparable to morphine that is not reversed by naloxone. Secondly, it was difficult to find a route of administration by which a

*Supported in part by National Institute of Drug Abuse Grant 1-RO1-DA-01344-05 and a grant from the Women's Auxiliary of the Veterans of Foreign Wars.

†Present Address, Section Head, CNS Pharmacology, Department of Biological Research, Searle Research and Development, Division of G.D. Searle and Co., 4901 Searle Parkway, Skokie, IL 60077.

known dose of DMSO could be given without producing some toxic effects. Therefore, the results are presented in two sections: the first describes the analgesic effect of DMSO and the second describes the limitations of the rat model associated with this study.

MATERIALS AND METHODS

A total of 67 male Sprague Dawley derived, albino rats, weighing between 250–400 g, were treated with DMSO or morphine and then tested with two analgesic tests, the hot-plate and tail-flick test. In most rats in which there was an analgesic effect apparent after the i.p. administration of DMSO, naloxone (2 mg/kg) was also administered. In most experiments, the observer was "blind" with respect to the experimental treatment. In the naloxone-reversal tests the observer did not know which rats had received naloxone and which rats had received saline.

Analgesia Testing

Tail-Flick

The tail-flick test consists of shining a focused, incandescent light beam on the rat's tail and measuring how long it takes the rat to "flick" his tail.[11] A maximum stimulus duration of 6.0 sec was used to avoid damaging the rat's tail. An increase of 2.3 sec above control (mean tail-flick latency 2.9 ± 0.44 sec) in this study indicated that there was a significant (p < .0001) analgesic effect present. A detailed explanation of the statistical methods used to determine significance has been presented previously.[12]

Hot-Plate

Rats were placed on a heated surface (56°C) of a commercially available hot-plate. The end point was when the rat licked any of its paws.[9,10] If the rat did not lick its paw within 30 sec, the rat was removed; the mean hot-plate latency in untreated rats was 11.2 ± 3.6 sec. Analgesia on this test was considered to exist only if the rat reached the 30 sec cutoff. For both of the above tests, the duration of analgesia was recorded by measuring the latencies on both tests until the latencies were not in the significant range (>2.3 sec above control for tail-flick, or reaching to 30 sec cutoff on the hot-plate) on two successive tests.

Drug Administration

Systemic Administration

DMSO (0.55, 2.75, and 5.5 g/kg) was administered intraperitoneally (i.p.) to 47 rats. In a pilot study, when 100% DMSO (5.5 g/kg) was injected rapidly, it apparently produced pain because the rats writhed and squealed. To minimize this effect in ten rats, the DMSO was diluted to 50% and the same overall dose of

DMSO was administered. The analgesic effect was less with this diluted solution even though the same overall dose was administered. Therefore, in the majority of the studies using i.p. injections, 100% DMSO (Sigma Chemical Co., St. Louis, Mo.) was administered in two divided injections 10 minutes apart. The first measurements of tail-flick and hot-plate latency were made 10 min after the last injection, the subsequent measurement at 30 minutes, 60 minutes, and then at hourly intervals for 6 hours, and another measurement 24 hours later.

In pilot experiments three doses of morphine (2, 4, 10 mg/kg) were injected i.p. to determine which dose produced significant analgesia in the above tests. Based on these experiments, a dose of 10 mg/kg was selected. This dose of morphine was tested in most of the rats (N=30) that had also received i.p. injections of DMSO; nine of these rats were tested for naloxone reversal of the morphine effect. A separate group of naive rats (N=10) were tested with morphine alone to determine duration of its analgesic effects.

Topical Administration

Rats (N=5) were placed in a tube-shaped restraining cage after their backs had been shaved. DMSO was dripped onto their backs and rubbed in for 2–3 minutes. Two other methods (Bath 1 and Bath 2) of topical administration were used. In both Bath 1 and Bath 2 rats were placed in a container with DMSO such that their feet and ventral portion of their body were immersed in 100% DMSO but their tails were kept out of the DMSO. Therefore, if DMSO has a local effect, there should only be an elevation of the latency of the paw lick on the hot-plate test. If, however, the DMSO is absorbed into the systemic circulation and acts at some other site (presumably the CNS) to produce analgesia, there should also be an increase in the tail-flick latency.

In one treatment (Bath 1) rats were held in a container (20 × 10.5 × 6.8 cm) containing 100, 200, or 300 ml of DMSO. In a second treatment (Bath 2), rats were placed on a tubular restraining cage (10.5 × 8.3 × 4.7 cm) and placed in a pan (27.9 × 17.8 × 2.8 cm) filled with 100, 200, or 300 ml of DMSO. The three different volumes were used in order to approximate a dose-response relationship because as the volume increased a greater surface area of the rat's body was exposed to the DMSO. At the lower volume, only the feet were in contact with the solution; at 300 ml the entire ventral portion of the animals was soaked by the DMSO.

Intravenous Administration

In order to determine which dose produced local effects and which dose produced systemic effects, DMSO (2.75 and 5.5 g/kg) was given i.v. via a tail vein while the rats were in a restraining cage. Because the LD_{50} of DMSO given i.v. is 5.2–8.1 g/kg[13] higher doses were not tested intravenously.

Oral Administration

DMSO was administered orally by using an animal feeding needle so that the DMSO (1.5 ml–2 ml) was injected directly into the stomach.

Naloxone Administration

Naloxone (2 mg/kg) was administered i.p. to some rats ($N=40$) that became analgesic on the tail-flick test within 30 min after the topical or i.p. administration of DMSO or the i.p. administration of morphine; other rats that were analgesic received either injections of 0.9% saline ($N=10$) or no treatment ($N=10$). Analgesia testing was continued for at least two hours after each of these treatments.

RESULTS

Analgesia

DMSO administered i.v. and i.p. at high doses (5.5 g/kg), and administered topically (Baths 1 and 2) produced a profound analgesia on both the hot-plate and

TABLE 1

COMPARISON OF ANALGESIC EFFECTS OF DMSO AND MORPHINE
USING TWO ANALGESIC TESTS

Treatment	Dose	N	Percent of Rats Analgesic Within 120 Minutes After Administration	
			Tail Flick	Hot Plate
DMSO				
Intraperitoneal injection	0.55 g/kg	39	13	5
	2.75 g/kg	40	5	5
	5.55 g/kg	30	50	66
Baths 1 and 2	100 ml-1 min	10	0	70
	100 ml-2 min	2	0	100
	200 ml-2 min	12	66	66
	300 ml-2 min	5	80	100
Intravenous injection	2.75 g/kg	4	100	25
	5.55 g/kg	4	50	50
Subcutaneous injection	5.55 g/kg	4	0	0
Orally	5.55 g/kg	4	0	25
Morphine				
Intraperitoneal injection	10 mg/kg	10	90	50

tail-flick tests (TABLE 1; FIGURE 1). This analgesia was apparently not due to a general anesthetic effect because the rats were not ataxic and did not lose their righting reflex.

In both types of bath procedures used, the results followed the same pattern; therefore the data are pooled for succinctness (TABLE 1). At low volumes (100 ml) in which only the rat's feet came into contact with DMSO, the rats were only analgesic on the hot-plate suggesting an analgesic effect due to a direct effect on the feet. However, at greater volumes (200 and 300 ml) analgesia was apparent both on the hot-plate and tail-flick test, although the onset for the analgesia measured by the tail-flick was slower than with the hot-plate (TABLE 1; FIGURE 1).

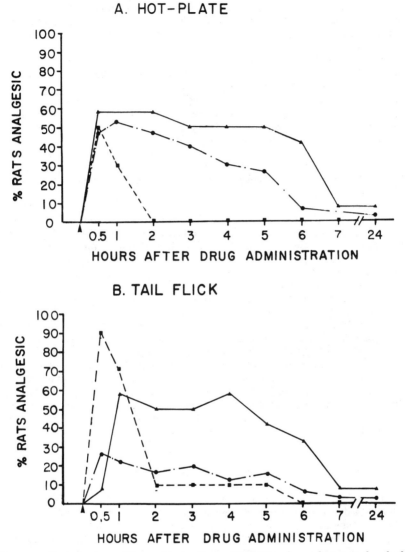

FIGURE 1. A comparison of the analgesic effects of DMSO and morphine tested on both the hot-plate (A) and tail-flick (B) tests. DMSO administered either topically (200 ml, Bath 1, $N=12$; ▲———▲) or intraperitoneally (5.5. g/kg, $N=30$; ●— · —●) produced an analgesic effect that lasted for 6-7 hours but morphine (10 mg/kg, $N=10$; ■———■) produced a shorter term analgesic effect. Note that some rats treated with DMSO were still analgesic 24 hours after treatment. Also note that only the percentages of rats analgesic at any particular time point are given. Therefore, the percentages in this figure are slightly lower than those in TABLE 1 because the table includes all rats that were analgesic within two hours after the administration of DMSO. (From Haigler, H. J. & D. D. Spring. 1981. *Life Sciences* **29:** 1545–1553. With permission from Pergamon Press Ltd.)

Although DMSO under the above conditions produced a graded analgesia, with one component apparently due to a local action and a second component due to a systemic action, it was not clear what the effective dose was for producing analgesia.

An approximation of the dose achieved by Baths 1 and 2 can be derived from the i.p. studies in which 5.5 g/kg produced an effect similar to that produced by the bath (TABLE 1; FIGURE 1). However, to get a better approximation of the effective systemic dose DMSO was administered i.v. via a tail vein to determine what dose would produce the same degree of analgesia as the bath procedure. In general, after an i.v. administration via a tail vein, more rats were analgesic on the tail-flick test than on the hot-plate test supporting the possibility of a local action of DMSO. At 2.75 g/kg, four of four rats tested were analgesic only on the tail-flick but only one on the hot-plate, suggesting a local effect from the i.v. injection into the tail. At a higher dose (5.5 g/kg) two of four were analgesic on both the hot-plate and tail-flick.

Morphine (10 mg/kg) produced an analgesic effect as frequently as DMSO on the hot-plate (FIGURE 1A). However, the duration of morphine analgesia was typically less than 2 h both on the hot-plate and tail-flick (FIGURE 1). In contrast, the time course of DMSO is longer than the time course of morphine (10 mg/kg) (FIGURE 1). Most rats were still analgesic ($N=17$ for tail-flick; $N=30$ for hot-plate) two hours after DMSO was administered, regardless of the route of administration; in two rats the analgesia persisted for 24 h (FIGURE 1).

Naloxone reversed the analgesic effect of morphine in nine of nine rats. In contrast, naloxone treatment was associated with a disappearance of analgesia in only 5 of 31 rats treated with DMSO. Our interpretation is that the analgesia disappeared in these five rats not because it was antagonized by naloxone but because the effect of DMSO had disappeared. Supporting this possibility, there were five rats not treated with naloxone, in which the analgesia after DMSO disappeared over the same time course as the five rats treated with naloxone. In any case, naloxone did not consistently block the effects of DMSO. The difference between the frequency with which naloxone reversed the analgesia produced by DMSO was significantly lower than the frequency with which it reversed the analgesic effects of morphine (Chi square test; $p < .000002$).

Limitations of the Rat Model

It was extremely difficult to find a method by which DMSO could be administered to obtain a reliable effect in most rats without producing a toxic effect in some rats. There were also anomalous results in that a topical administration of DMSO via a bath typically produced analgesia but DMSO administered by either of two other routes, either topical administration by applying the DMSO to the back ($N=5$) or oral administration ($N=4$) did not produce analgesia.

When DMSO was administered i.p., it produced writhing, teeth chatter, and squealing in 35 rats. Because this procedure produced stress and because the rats frequently passed bloody urine after i.p. injection (23% of the rats after 5.5 g/kg; 5% after 2.75 g/kg), we diluted the DMSO with distilled water to obtain a 50% solution and the same overall dose of DMSO was administered. When a given volume of DMSO is added to an equal volume of water there is an increase in temperature (27°C) from the heat of hydration. This increase in temperature may have caused the DMSO to break down so that the total dose of DMSO injected was reduced. For whatever reason, the analgesic effect was apparently less with this diluted solution.

Six of the eight rats that received DMSO i.v. also passed bloody urine but this effect was not apparent in those rats that received topical (bath) DMSO. Rats that passed bloody urine apparently suffered no additional ill effects because none of these rats died. It is possible that there were subtle toxic effects that were not detected. When a dose (2.75 g/kg) of DMSO was injected too rapidly i.v. (in less than 30 sec) four rats (not included in the above data) had tonic-clonic seizures; two of these rats died.

When DMSO was given by partially immersing the rat in DMSO (Bath 1 and Bath 2), the best method found, there were still difficulties. For instance, the only three rats treated with DMSO obtained from Mallinckrodt died for unknown reasons. Therefore, only DMSO obtained from Sigma was used in all succeeding experiments. There were no apparent differences in the DMSO obtained from these two sources based on an NMR analysis (Goldstein and Haigler, unpublished observation). Deaths occurred in only 2 of 31 rats treated with DMSO obtained from Sigma. These deaths occurred after they rolled beneath the surface in escape attempts and covered their head, eyes, and nares with DMSO. All five of the above rats developed ataxia and died within 6–8 hours. Data from the rats that died were deleted from subsequent analysis.

DISCUSSION

DMSO produces analgesia in rats on tests that typically only detect the analgesic effects of potent narcotic analgesic drugs (i.e. the hot-plate and tail-flick tests).[11,12] There seem to be two components of this analgesic effect; one component related to a local effect and the other component related to a systemic effect. If only the feet are exposed to DMSO, the rat becomes analgesic on the hot-plate but not on the tail-flick. If a greater surface of the body is exposed, the rat becomes analgesic on both the hot-plate and tail-flick indicating a central action, because the tail did not come into contact with the DMSO. In one study on patients the authors conclude that the analgesic effect of DMSO arises from a central, not local, analgesic effect.[14] The analgesic effects of DMSO are not consistently blocked by naloxone indicating that these analgesic effects of DMSO do not have the same mechanism of action as morphine.

Based on the i.v. and i.p. data, the systemic dose of the DMSO necessary to achieve analgesia is 5.5 g/kg or greater. Although this dose apparently produces intravascular hemolysis (as indicated by the bloody urine) similar analgesic effects could be achieved if the drug was absorbed more slowly after topical administration. Bloody urine was not observed in the rats treated with DMSO administered topically (i.e., baths).

One attractive feature about DMSO is the long duration of analgesia that it produces. DMSO persists in the blood stream at significant levels for 1.5 to 3 days (human); the half-life in stomach, lung, and brain (rat) is 10–12 h.[2,3] Therefore, it is possible to produce a long-term analgesia via a mechanism other than one related to opiate receptors. However, a comparable duration of actions was apparent after the i.p. administration of DMSO.

It is difficult to explain why DMSO administered i.p. was more effective in producing analgesia as measured on the hot-plate than on the tail-flick test. A similar difference was not apparent when it was administered by Baths 1 and 2.

The hot-plate test is apparently more sensitive in detecting the analgesic effects of DMSO; however, there may be more appropriate tests. These two tests were selected because they allowed a comparison of the analgesic effects of DMSO with those of morphine. It is possible that more appropriate tests would detect analgesia after DMSO was administered either orally or by rubbing it on the rat's back. If DMSO was administered by a particular route and did not produce any effect on these two tests, this route was not used in subsequent experiments. Therefore, it would be premature to conclude that DMSO does not produce analgesia when administered by either the oral route or rubbing it on the rat's back.

Three observations from this study indicated that DMSO should be used with caution if it is used clinically. First, DMSO releases histamine.[15] In one instance a death "possibly related to an acute allergic reaction" to DMSO has been reported.[16] We noted that in two laboratory personnel with a history of allergic rhinitis (hay fever), exposure to DMSO vapors produced itching in the eyes of one and repeated sneezing in another. Therefore, DMSO should be used with caution in allergic individuals.

In our study, the rats passed bloody urine in situations where the concentration of DMSO in the blood increased rapidly (i.p. and i.v.). The bloody urine may be related to intravascular hemolysis. However, in 4,258 clinical cases,[15,17] there has been no evidence of serious toxicity to the blood, liver, or kidneys using numerous laboratory tests. A third observation is that seizures can be induced if DMSO is given rapidly by i.v. injection. Therefore, this drug should be used with caution in patients with a history of seizures.

A possible explanation for the analgesia observed in this experiment is that the administration of DMSO produced stress that in turn produced analgesia. If this stress-induced analgesia were opioid related, naloxone should have blocked the response.[18] Naloxone rarely had an effect on the analgesia associated with DMSO. If the stress-induced analgesia related to DMSO administration was non-opioid related, then naloxone would not block it.[18] However, stress-induced analgesia that is non-opioid related lasts for 11-15 minutes when measured on the tail-flick when continuous electric foot shock is used as the stressor.[18] When restraint was used as the stressor, animals were never analgesic on the hot plate (i.e. they never reached the 30 sec cutoff) after release; some (5 of 9) were analgesic on the tail-flick during the restraint (Hardy and Haigler, unpublished observation). Therefore, a hallmark of stress-induced analgesia is its short duration. If vocalization is an indication of stress, rats treated with DMSO were not undergoing continuous stress because they did not vocalize for more than two minutes after the administration of DMSO; yet the animals were analgesic for as long as six hours. Other than a slight increase in locomotor activity for 1-2 h in animals exposed to the DMSO bath, the animals treated with DMSO were not distinguishable from controls treated as described above, except for the smell of DMSO. Therefore, unless the presence of DMSO either on the fur and skin or in the abdomen is a stressor comparable to continuous electric foot shock and this intensity is maintained for 3-5 hours, the tentative conclusion is that DMSO produces analgesia by a mechanism other than producing stress or irritation.

In conclusion, DMSO is a drug that produced analgesia by acting both locally and systemically. This analgesia appears to be unrelated to that produced by morphine although the two appear to be of comparable magnitude. DMSO had a longer duration of action than morphine (6 h vs. 2 h, respectively).

In spite of the above data, research with DMSO should proceed with caution until the precise dose that produces analgesia and the therapeutic index can be accurately determined. The demonstration that DMSO produces an analgesic effect via a mechanism that is different from morphine indicates that it is worthwhile to pursue the clinical study of DMSO.

ACKNOWLEDGMENTS

We thank Dr. S. G. Holtzman for valuable suggestions and discussions concerning these experiments. We also thank Ms. Sandra Burson and Mr. P. Suresky for technical assistance.

REFERENCES

1. LEAKS, C. D. 1967. Ann. N.Y. Acad. Sci. 141: 1-2.
2. KOLB, K. H., G. JANICKE, M. KRAMER & P. E. SCHULZE. 1967. Ann. N.Y. Acad. Sci. 141: 85-95.
3. DENKO C. W., R. M. GOODMAN, R. MILLER & T. DONOVAN. 1967. Ann. N.Y. Acad. Sci. 141: 77-85.
4. BROWN, J. H. 1967. Ann. N.Y. Acad. Sci. 141: 496-505.
5. WARD, J. R., M. S. MILLER & L. MARCUS. 1967. Ann. N.Y. Acad. Sci. 141: 280-290.
6. BECKER, D. P., H. F. YOUNG, F. E. NULSEN & J. A. JANE. 1969. Exp. Neurol. 24: 272-276.
7. MORRIS, R. W. 1966. J. Pharm. Sci. 55: 438-440.
8. DE LA TORRE, J. C., H. M. KAWANAGA, D. W. ROWED, C. M. JOHNSON, D. J. GOODE, K. KAJIHARA & S. MULLAN. 1975. Ann. N.Y. Acad. Sci. 243: 362-389.
9. BANZIGER, P. 1964. In Animal and Clinical Pharmacologic Techniques in Drug Evaluation. J. H. Nodine & P. E. Siegler, Eds.: 392-396.
10. EDDY, N. B., C. F. TOUCHBERRY & J. E. LIBERMAN. 1950. J. Pharmacol. Exp. Ther. 98: 121-137.
11. D'AMOUR, F. E. & D. L. SMITH. 1941. J. Pharmacol. Exp. Ther 72: 74-79.
12. HAIGLER, H. J. & D. D. SPRING. 1978. Life Sci. 23: 1229-1240.
13. SMITH, E. R., Z. HADIDIAN & M. M. MASON. 1967. Ann. N.Y. Acad. Sci. 141: 96-109.
14. VON DER HARDT, H., H. J. RUPER & H. SUDOE. 1969. Med. Welt. 20: 606-608.
15. BROBYN, R. D. 1975. Ann. N.Y. Acad. Sci. 243: 497-506.
16. Medical Letter. 1965. 7 (#20): p. 80, September 24.
17. JOHN, H. & G. LAUDAHN. 1967. Ann. N.Y. Sci. 141: 506-516.
18. LEWIS, J. W., J. T. CANNON & J. C. LIEBESKIND. 1980. Science 208: 623-625.

DIMETHYL SULFOXIDE AS A VEHICLE FOR TOPICAL ANTIVIRAL CHEMOTHERAPY*

S. L. Spruance,† M. B. McKeough, and J. R. Cardinal

Department of Medicine
Center for Infectious Diseases
Diagnostic Microbiology and Immunology
School of Medicine and
Department of Pharmaceutics
College of Pharmacy
University of Utah
Salt Lake City, Utah 84132

INTRODUCTION

Numerous studies of topical antiviral chemotherapy for recurrent herpes simplex labialis and genitalis have failed to show that treatment alters the clinical course of the disease.[1] Investigators have used large numbers of study subjects, meticulous patient follow-up to document the course of lesions, potent antivirals,[2] and early-treatment study design[3]—still without success. We are concerned that delivery of antivirals through the stratum corneum to infected epidermal cells has been inadequate in most of the published trials.

To evaluate the importance of drug delivery experimentally, we have measured the penetration of acyclovir (ACV) through guinea pig skin in vitro from different drug vehicles and compared these findings with the efficacy of two topical formulations of the drug in the treatment of an experimental cutaneous herpes simplex virus infection.[4] ACV is a potent new compound with striking in vitro activity against herpes simplex virus, a wide toxic/therapeutic ratio, and established clinical activity against cutaneous human HSV infection other than recurrent disease.[2,5-9]

MATERIAL AND METHODS

Experimental Animals and Virus

Hartley, outbred, female albino guinea pigs, 200–250 grams each, were obtained from Charles River Breeding Labs (Wilmington, Mass.). The virus used in these studies was the laboratory strain HSV-1 E115. Virus stock used for inoculation of guinea pigs contained 10^7 PFU/ml.

*Supported in part by Contract NO1-AI-52532 with the National Institute of Allergy and Infectious Diseases and the National Institute of Dental Research.
†Address requests for reprints to: S. L. Spruance, M.D., Department of Medicine, University of Utah School of Medicine, 50 North Medical Drive, Salt Lake City, Utah 84132.

0077–8923/83/0411–0028 $01.75/0 © 1983, NYAS

Penetration of ACV Through Guinea Pig Skin

Guinea pigs were sacrificed and then close-shaved with electric clippers. Clipped, full-thickness skin was removed from the back and sides by dissection and stored in air-tight containers at $-20°C$ until use.

Single-chambered glass diffusion cells were used to measure the flux of ACV from DMSO solution and polyethylene glycol (PEG) ointment. The receiver chamber had a volume of 5.7 ml and was filled with 0.15 M NaCl. Skin was clamped across a 1.6 cm diameter opening at the top of the cell with the stratum corneum facing upwards. There was a single port for withdrawal of samples and stirring was achieved with a magnetic stir bar. The exposed skin surface was enclosed by a short cylinder having a glass stopper for access and a side-arm containing 1 ml of 44% H_2SO_4 in water (w/w) to maintain a constant 50% relative humidity. Samples were withdrawn from the chamber and analyzed by high performance liquid chromatography. The volume withdrawn was replaced with an equal volume of 0.15 M NaCl. Drug flux ($\mu g/cm^2 \cdot h$) was calculated from the steady-state slope of plots of drug concentration ($\mu g/ml$) versus time (h).

Animal Inoculation

Guinea pigs were anesthetized with 30 mg/kg intraperitoneal sodium pentabarbital. Hair on the dorsum was completely removed with electric clippers and chemical depilatory (Nair®). Undiluted virus stock (0.02 ml) was applied to six different areas and the skin was inoculated at each site by ten activations of a six-pronged spring-loaded vaccination instrument (Sterneedle, Pan Ray Division, Ormont Drug, Englewood, N.J.).

Treatment Regimens

Five percent of ACV in PEG and ACV powder was obtained from Burroughs-Wellcome Co. DMSO was obtained from Sigma Chemical Co. The day of inoculation was designated as Day 0. Treatment was begun 24 hours after inoculation and continued for a total of three days (Days 1–3). Regimens designated as 2×/day were given at 9 AM and 9 PM and 4×/day at 9 AM, 1 PM, 5 PM, and 9 PM. A drug and it's corresponding vehicle were always tested opposite each other at the same rostal/caudal level.

Measures of Drug Efficacy and Statistical Procedures

Regrown hair was removed with depilatory and the number and size of lesions in each treatment site on Day 4 tallied. Lesions enumerated ranged from pinpoint erythema to 2.5 mm diameter vesicles. Results of paired data (drug/drug vehicle) were analyzed by the Wilcoxon signed rank test (10) or a paired *t*-test and other unpaired data by a *t*-test. All probability determinations were two-tailed and p ≤ 0.05 was considered significant.

TABLE 1

PENETRATION OF ACV THROUGH GUINEA PIG SKIN *IN VITRO*

Exp. No.	Drug/Vehicle	Lag Time (h)*	Flux ($\mu g/cm^2 \cdot h$)†
1	5% ACV/PEG	65	.182
2	5% ACV/PEG	77	.165
3	5% ACV/PEG	37	.069
4	0.5% ACV/DMSO	14	.676
5	0.5% ACV/DMSO	–	.438
6	0.5% ACV/DMSO	–	.284
7	0.5% ACV/DMSO	12	.432

*Time between beginning of the experiment and the intercept of the slope on the x-axis in a plot of drug concentration in the receiver chamber (y) vs. time (x).

†Flux was calculated from the steady-state slope of plots of drug concentration vs. time, the area of the skin surface exposed to drug and the volume of the receiver chamber.

RESULTS

Penetration of ACV Through Guinea Pig Skin

Comparison of the permeation of topical ACV through guinea pig skin as ACV/PEG or ACV/DMSO was accomplished with a single-chamber diffusion cell. Single doses of 250 mg of 5% ACV in PEG and 100 μl of 0.5% ACV in DMSO were applied to the exposed skin surface of the diffusion apparatus. The volume of the dose corresponded to the amount used for treatment of experimental HSV infection but the concentration of ACV/DMSO was one-tenth that used in the *in vivo* studies. The results are shown in TABLE 1. The mean flux of 5% ACV from PEG in three experiments was 0.14 ± 0.06 and for four experiments with 0.5% ACV in DMSO, 0.46 ± 0.16 ($\mu g/cm^2 \cdot h$, mean ± SD, p = 0.02). A higher concentration of ACV in DMSO would have a proportionately higher flux. In addition, the onset of detectable ACV in the receiver chamber (lag time) occurred more quickly when DMSO was the vehicle (TABLE 1).

TABLE 2

EFFICACY OF ANTIVIRAL NUCLEOSIDES AGAINST EXPERIMENTAL CUTANEOUS HSV INFECTION ON THE DORSUM OF THE GUINEA PIG

Treatment*	Median Number of Lesions on Day 4 at One of the Treatment Sites (range)
Untreated[s]	29 (17–34)
PEG[mb]	28 (16–44)
DMSO[r]	25 (12–36)
5% ACV/PEG[mb]	23 (6–37)
5% ACV/DMSO[r]	5 (1–23)

*Sixteen animals were infected at multiple discrete sites on the dorsum and different sites were untreated or received vehicle or antiviral/vehicle treatment as described in the table. Treatments were given for three days beginning 24 hours after inoculation. Formulations containing PEG were applied 4×/day and those containing DMSO 2×/day. A drug and its corresponding vehicle were always tested opposite each other at the same rostral/caudal level. S = shoulder, mb = midback, r = rump.

*Comparison of Antiviral/Vehicle Combinations for the Prevention
of Experimental HSV-1 Lesions*

Sixteen guinea pigs were infected on the dorsum on Day 0 and 24 hours later on Day 1 different sites on the back of each animal were treated with PEG 4×/day for three days, DMSO 2×/day for three days, 5% ACV/PEG 4×/day for three days, or 5% ACV/DMSO 2×/day for three days as explained in Table 2. The number of lesions present in each treatment site were then tallied on Day 4. Analysis of the number of lesions (TABLE 2) showed that ACV/DMSO reduced the lesion count by 80% compared to the contralateral DMSO control areas (median of 5 vs. 25 lesions, p = 0.001). Treatment with ACV/PEG was also beneficial but to a far lesser degree, effecting an 18% reduction in the number of lesions compared to PEG alone (median of 23 vs. 28 lesions, p = 0.002).

Lesions treated with DMSO were significantly smaller than untreated lesions (TABLE 3, p < 0.05). Lesions treated with ACV/PEG were significantly smaller than those treated with PEG (p < 0.005) but not meaningfully different from the untreated control (p > 0.25).

TABLE 3

THE INFLUENCE OF TREATMENT REGIMENS ON LESION SIZE

Treatment Regimen*	Mean Lesion Diameter ± SEM† (inches)
Untreated	.042 ± .0013
PEG	.046 ± .0016
DMSO	.036 ± .0018
5% ACV/PEG	.040 ± .0012
5% ACV/DMSO	.035 ± .0021

*Animals were treated at different locations on the dorsum with each of the four regimens shown. See TABLE 2 for details.
†Standard error of the mean.

DISCUSSION

The penetration of acyclovir through guinea pig skin *in vitro* was markedly greater with DMSO than when PEG was the vehicle. When 5% ACV in DMSO was compared with 5% ACV in PEG in the treatment of experimental herpes infection in the guinea pig, ACV/DMSO was more effective. The effectiveness of antivirals in DMSO in the guinea pig is likely related to drug penetration, and development of a means to enhance delivery of antivirals to the target cells would appear to be a potentially fruitful next step to further the effectiveness of topical anti-herpesvirus therapy in humans.

Should DMSO be used as a vehicle for topical antiviral therapy in humans? The idea is not new and has been explored by MacCallum and Juel-Jensen,[11] Parker,[12] and Silvestri et al.[13] and advocated by Herrmann and Herrmann.[14] Patient acceptability of skin irritation and the odor of DMSO are unsettled issues at present but may depend on the volume of the application and the location of lesions. DMSO-treated lesions were significantly smaller than untreated lesions in this study. Since DMSO itself does not have antiviral activity *in vivo*[12,15] but can affect white blood cell function,[16,17] it is likely that our results occurred from an anti-inflammatory effect. DMSO has produced changes in the lens of the eye in a wide variety of species of experimental animals, leading some to conclude that eye changes would likely be a consequence of some dose of DMSO in humans.[18] The potential toxicity of DMSO and the protocol requirements for clinical studies have dampened the enthusiasm and interest of pharmaceutical firms in the U.S.A. for commercial development of this agent. However, DMSO has major potential advantages for enhancing the penetration of topically administered antivirals, which could possibly lead to a clinically beneficial treatment for recurrent human HSV infections. Further experimental and clinical studies are indicated and the feasibility of developing DMSO for topical vehicle use in this country should be reconsidered.

REFERENCES

1. OVERALL, J. C., JR. 1979. Dermatologic Diseases. *In* Antiviral Agents and Viral Diseases of Man. G. J. Galasso, *et al.,* Eds. Ch. 7: 305–384. Raven Press. New York.
2. SCHAEFFER, H. J., L. BEAUCHAMP, P. DEMIRANDA & G. B. ELION. 1978. 9-(2-hydroxyethoxymethyl)guanine activity against viruses of the herpes group. Nature **272:** 583–585.
3. SPRUANCE, S. L., C. S. CRUMPACKER, L. E. SCHNIPPER, E. R. KERN, S. MARLOW, J. MODLIN, K. A. ARNDT & J. C., OVERALL JR. 1982. Topical 10% acyclovir in polyethylene glycol for herpes simplex labialis: Results of treatment begun in the prodrome and erythema stages. Abstracts of the 22nd Interscience Conference on Antimicrobial Agents and Chemotherapy. American Society of Microbiology. No. 187.
4. HUBLER, W. R., JR., T. D. FELBER, D. TROLL & M. JARRATT. 1974. Guinea pig model for cutaneous herpes simplex virus infection. J. Invest. Dermatol. **62:** 92–95.
5. CHOU, S., J. G. GALLAGHER & T. C. MERIGAN. 1981. Controlled clinical trial of intravenous acyclovir in heart-transplant patients with mucocutaneous herpes simplex infections. Lancet **1:** 1392–1394.
6. MITCHELL, C. D., S. R. GENTRY, J. R. BOEN, B. BEAN, K. E. GROWTH & H. H. BALFOUR, JR. 1981. Acyclovir therapy for mucocutaneous herpes simplex infections in immunocompromised patients. Lancet **1:** 1389–1392.
7. WADE, J. C., B. NEWTON, C. MCLAREN, N. FLOURNOY, R. E. KEENEY & J. D. MEYERS. 1982. Intravenous acyclovir to treat mucocutaneous herpes simplex virus infection after marrow transplantation. Ann. Intern. Med. **96:** 265–269.
8. STRAUS, S. E., H. A. SMITH, C. BRICKMAN, P. DEMIRANADA, C. MCLAREN & R. E. KEENEY. 1982. Acyclovir for chronic mucocutaneous herpes simplex virus infection in immunosuppressed patients. Ann. Intern. Med. **96:** 270–277.
9. COREY, L., A. J. NAHMIAS, M. E. GUINAN, J. K. BENEDETTI, C. W. CRITCHLOW & K. K. HOLMES. 1982. A trial of topical acyclovir in genital herpes simplex virus infections. N. Engl. J. Med. **306:** 1313–1319.
10. HOLLANDER, M. & D. A. WOLFE. 1973. Nonparametric statistical methods. pp. 27–33. John Wiley & Sons. New York.
11. MACCALLUM, F. O. & B. E. JUEL-JENSEN. 1966. Herpes simplex virus skin infection in man treated with idoxuridine in dimethyl sulphoxide. Results of double-blind controlled trials. Brit. Med. J. **2:** 805–807.
12. SILVESTRI D. L., L. COREY & K. K. HOLMES. 1982. Ineffectiveness of topical idoxuridine in dimethyl sulfoxide for therapy for genital herpes. J. Am. Med. Assoc. **248:** 953–959.
13. PARKER, J. D. 1977. A double-blind trial of idoxuridine in recurrent genital herpes. J. Antimicro. Chemo. **3** (Supplement A):131–138.
14. HERRMANN, E. C., JR. & J. A. HERRMANN. 1977. A neglected cure for cold sores and shingles? Current Prescribing **7:** 27–32.
15. ALENIUS S., M. BERG, F. BROBERG, K. EKLIND, B. LINDBORG & B. OBERG. 1982.

Therapeutic effects of foscarnet sodium and acyclovir on cutaneous infections due to herpes simplex virus type 1 in guinea pigs. J. Infect. Dis. **145:** 569–573.

16. Biological Actions of Dimethyl Sulfoxide. 1975. S. W. Jacob & R. Herschler, Eds. **243:** 1–508. Ann. N.Y. Acad. Sci.

17. REPINE, J. E., R. B. FOX & E. M. BERGER. 1983. DMSO inhibits neutrophil bacteriocidal function. Ann. N.Y. Acad. Sci. (This volume.)

18. HARTER, J. The status of dimethyl sulfoxide from the Food and Drug Administration's perspective. Ann. N.Y. Acad. Sci. (This volume.)

THE *IN VITRO* AND *IN VIVO* EFFECTS OF DIMETHYL SULFOXIDE ON THE PITUITARY SECRETION OF GROWTH HORMONE AND PROLACTIN IN MICE

Hiroshi Nagasawa

Experimental Animal Research Laboratory
Meiji University
Tama-ku, Kawasaki
Kanagawa 214, Japan

INTRODUCTION

It has been shown that dimethyl sulfoxide (DMSO) induces differentiation and function of leukemic cells of mouse,[1-6] rat,[7] and human.[8-12] DMSO was also found to stimulate albumin production in malignantly transformed hepatocytes of mouse and rat[13] and to affect the membrane-associated antigen, enzymes, and glycoproteins in human rectal adenocarcinoma cells.[14] Hydrocortisone-induced keratinization of chick embryo cells[15] and adriamycin-induced necrosis of rat skin[16] were inhibited by DMSO.

Furthermore, modification by DMSO of the function of normal cells has been reported. DMSO stimulates cyclic AMP accumulation and lipolysis and decreases insulin-stimulated glucose oxidation in free white fat cells of rat.[17] It also enhances heme synthesis in quail embryo yolk sac cells.[18]

On the other hand, the information on the role of DMSO in hormone secretion is scanty. Bower and Hadley[19] showed the stimulation by DMSO of melanophore-stimulating hormone secretion by the pituitary of frog and rat. The effects of DMSO on insulin release from Langerhans islets have also been studied.[20,21]

I report here the effects of DMSO on synthesis and release of growth hormone (GH) and prolactin in the anterior pituitary from mice during lactation, in which pituitary is especially active, especially in response to the frequent suckling by pups. Almost all of the studies on the biological action of DMSO have been carried out *in vitro*, despite the general large discrepancy in the results and the significance proposed between the *in vitro* and the *in vivo* studies. Thus, in this paper, the effects of the *in vivo* exposure to DMSO on pituitary hormone secretion were investigated, as well as the effects of the *in vitro* exposure and the resultant mammary gland function of lactating mice given DMSO were studied.

MATERIAL AND METHODS

Animals

A highly inbred strain of C3H/He mice were used at the 145th generation of brother × sister mating. Females were mated with males at two months of age. The number of pups in each litter (litter size) was adjusted to six (three females and three males) on the day of parturition (day 0 of lactation) and normally nursed until day 11 of lactation. On day 12 of lactation, lactating mice were used for studies on the effects of the pituitary exposed to DMSO *in vitro* and *in vivo* on

34

hormone secretion. Throughout the experiments, animals were maintained in an animal room that was air-conditioned ($24 \pm 0.5\,°C$ and 65–70% relative humidity) and artificially illuminated (14 hours light from 5:00 AM to 7:00 PM), and were provided with a commercial diet (CA-1:CLEA Japan Inc., Tokyo, Japan) and tap water *ad libitum.*

Anterior Pituitary Exposure to DMSO

In Vitro Exposure

On day 12 of lactation, the lactating mouse was killed by decapitation. The anterior pituitary was removed and placed three each in a Heraus Petri dish (50 × 12 mm: W.C. Heraus GmbH, Hanau, West Germany) containing 3 ml Waymouth medium (GIBCO Labs., Grand Island, N.Y.) and DMSO (Merck, Darmstadt, West Germany) at the concentration of 0.1%. For the control, phosphate buffer saline (PBS) (pH = 7.4) was added to the medium instead of DMSO at the same concentration. Pituitaries were cultured for 48 hours under sterile conditions and constant gassing with 95% O_2–5% CO_2.

In Vivo Exposure

On day 12 of lactation, the lactating mice were divided into two groups. One group received subcutaneous injection of 0.05 ml DMSO twice daily for two days and once on the morning of day 14. Another group was given PBS and served as the control. Vaginal smears were checked in each mouse every morning throughout the experiment. The weights of the lactating mouse and litter were measured on days 0, 12, and 14 of lactation. The percent change in litter weight was calculated as an index of lactational performance of the lactating mouse. Immediately after the last injection, the mouse was removed from her litter by a wire net for four hours, nursed again for one hour and killed by decapitation. Organs indicated in TABLE 2 were immediately removed and weighed. Inguinal mammary glands were used for the determination of nucleic acid synthetic activity.

Synthesis and Release of GH and Prolactin

Anterior pituitary exposed *in vitro* or *in vivo* to DMSO was placed in a 0.05 ml of Ringer bicarbonate buffer solution (pH = 7.4) containing 270 μg of glucose and 0.75 μCi of [^{14}C]leucine (311 mCi/mmole; The Radiochemical Centre, Amersham, England) and incubated for three hours under constant gassing with 95% O_2–5% CO_2. After incubation, the pituitary was removed, weighed and homogenized in 0.15 ml of distilled water. "Cold" anterior pituitary homogenate was added to each of the pituitary homogenates and the medium as "carrier." GH and prolactin in the pituitary and the medium were fractionated by disc electrophoresis.[22] After electrophoresis, the separating layer was stained with 0.002% amido black. GH and prolactin bands were cut out and prepared for liquid scintillation counting.[23] The value in the medium represented released hormone and the sum of the values in the pituitary and the medium represented the synthesized hormone. The rates of synthesis and release of each hormone were expressed in terms of cpm of incorporated [¹⁴C]leucine into GH and prolactin per mg pituitary. All procedures were the same as detailed by Yamamoto et al.[23] and Yanai and Nagasawa.[24]

Mammary Gland Nucleic Acid Synthesis

Portions of bilateral inguinal mammary glands were cut into 0.5 mm-thick slices. About 50 mg tissue was placed in 2 ml Medium 199 containing 5 μCi [³H]thymidine (5.0 Ci/mmole; The Radiochemical Centre) or 5 μCi [¹⁴C]uridine (60 mCi/mmole; The Radiochemical Centre) and incubated for two hours at 37°C under constant gassing with 95% O_2–5% CO_2. After incubation, nucleic acids in the tissue were extracted and 0.5 ml of extract was mixed with 10 ml Aquasol-2 (New England Nuclear Corp., Boston, Mass.) in a scintillation vial for counting. The procedures were essentially the same as detailed previously.[25]

Statistics

The statistical significance of difference between groups in each parameter was evaluated by Student's t-test.

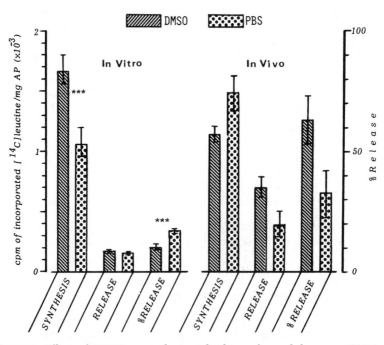

FIGURE 1. Effects of DMSO on synthesis and release of growth hormone (GH) in the anterior pituitary (AP) of C3H/He lactating mouse (Means ± SEM). Numbers of samples are 18 and 5–7 each in the in vitro and the in vivo studies, respectively. ***p < 0.01.

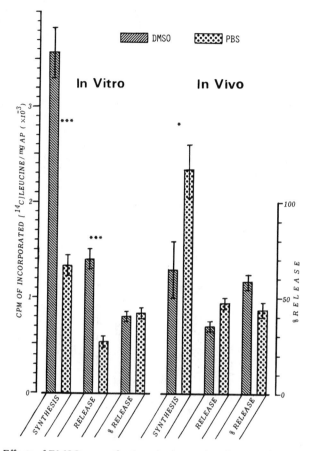

FIGURE 2. Effects of DMSO on synthesis and release of prolactin in the anterior pituitary (AP) of C3H/He lactating mouse (Means ± SEM). Number of samples is the same as in FIGURE 1. *p < 0.05, ***p < 0.01.

RESULTS

Effects of DMSO on Synthesis and Release of Hormones

GH

The results are illustrated in FIGURE 1. Synthesis of GH was significantly higher in the pituitaries cultured in the medium containing DMSO than in those cultured with PBS. Meanwhile, there was little difference between groups in release and, therefore, the percent release of the hormone declined significantly in the pituitary cultured with DMSO than in the control.

The contrast was observed in the *in vivo* study. The anterior pituitary from mice receiving subcutaneous injections of DMSO was lower in synthesis and higher in release of GH than the control. These resulted in the apparently higher percent release in DMSO group. No statistical significance of differences between groups in each parameter would be due partly to the rather large variations in the values.

Prolactin

As shown in FIGURE 2, both synthesis and release of prolactin was significantly higher in the pituitary cultured with DMSO than in the control and no difference was seen between groups in percent release of the hormone.

Prolactin synthesis of the pituitary from mice injected with DMSO was significantly lower than that of the control. The DMSO group was also lower in release and higher in percent release than the control, although not statistically

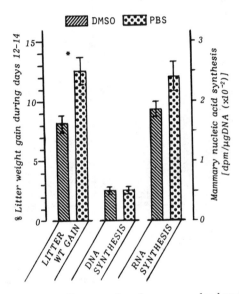

FIGURE 3. Effects of DMSO on litter growth and mammary gland nucleic acid synthesis in C3H/He lactating mouse (Means ± SEM). Number of samples is 5–7 each. *p < 0.05.

significant. These are contrary to the results in the pituitary exposed to DMSO *in vitro.*

Effects of DMSO on Lactational Performance

The results are shown in FIGURE 3. DMSO injection to lactating mice between days 12 and 14 of lactation induced the significant decline in litter weight gain, while there was no difference between groups in litter growth before DMSO injection (between days 0 and 12).

No difference was seen between groups in mammary gland DNA synthesis as an index of mammary gland mitosis; however, RNA synthesis, which is an indicator of the synthesis of milk protein, was decreased by DMSO.

Nagasawa: DMSO on GH and Prolactin 39

TABLE 1

MATERNAL WEIGHT CHANGE IN EACH GROUP*

Group	Number of Mice	Day 0 (g)	Day 12 (g)	% Change (Day 0–12)	Day 14 (g)	% Change (Day 12–14)
DMSO†	7	28.4 ± 0.5	32.2 ± 0.3	13.8 ± 1.3	33.0 ± 0.9	2.3 ± 2.2
PBS	5	28.1 ± 0.6	32.3 ± 0.8	15.8 ± 2.3	32.4 ± 0.8	0.4 ± 1.3

*Means ± SEM.
†Each mouse received subcutaneous injections of 0.05 ml DMSO or PBS twice daily on days 12 and 13 and once on the morning of day 14 of lactation.

Effect of DMSO on Estrous Cycle, Body Weight, and Organ Weight

Anterior pituitary weight was not changed by culture in the medium containing DMSO for 48 hours.

Twice daily subcutaneous injections of DMSO between days 12 and 14 of lactation did not affect estrous cycles substantially; vaginal smears showed continued diestrus throughout the experiment in both experimental and control groups.

There was no difference between mice given DMSO injection and the control in either body weight (TABLE 1) or organ weight (TABLE 2).

DISCUSSION

The previous studies, most of which were performed *in vitro*, have revealed that DMSO induced the differentiation of immature normal and neoplastic cells into functional maturity as well as the modulation of normal cell function. In this study, the synthetic activity of GH and prolactin in the anterior pituitary cells of the lactating mouse was further enhanced by the culture with DMSO. These findings have demonstrated *in vitro* that DMSO can stimulate the function of well-differentiated normal cells which already possess high functional activity. On the other hand, this study also shows that DMSO decreases the pituitary hormone synthesis when administered *in vivo*. In this respect, some discrepancy of DMSO effects was reported on insulin release; McKay and Karow[20] and Smith and Karow[21] found the dose-related inhibition of DMSO of glucose-induced insulin release. However, the latter authors[21] also observed the elicitation by cryoprotectant doses of DMSO of an immediate monophasic release of insulin. It has been proposed that the action of DMSO would largely be dependent upon

TABLE 2

ORGAN WEIGHT OF LACTATING MOUSE IN EACH GROUP*

Group	Number of Mice	Anterior Pituitary (mg)	Adrenal (mg)	Ovary (mg)	Thymus (mg)	Spleen (mg)
DMSO†	7	2.7 ± 0.1	5.8 ± 0.2	11.9 ± 0.2	18.1 ± 1.8	120 ± 10
PBS	5	2.6 ± 0.1	5.7 ± 0.1	11.6 ± 0.7	21.3 ± 1.8	130 ± 5

*Means ± SEM.
†See TABLE 1 for detail of treatment.

concentration, temperature, and duration of exposure, route of administration, etc.[20] This study provides no information on the mechanism of the discrepancy between the in vitro and the in vivo studies in DMSO effects on GH and prolactin secretion. An accumulation of further research is needed.

The decline in lactational performance of the DMSO-injected mice as estimated by decreased litter growth and mammary RNA synthesis would mostly be ascribed to the suppressed pituitary prolactin secretion; prolactin is a primary hormone for maintenance of lactation[26] and the pattern of estrous cycles and body weight and organ weight of the lactating mouse were affected only slightly by DMSO injection.

SUMMARY

Anterior pituitaries from primiparous lactating C3H/He mice cultured in the medium containing 0.1% dimethyl sulfoxide (DMSO) for 48 hours and pituitaries from lactating mice given subcutaneous injections of 0.05 ml DMSO twice daily for two days and once on the morning of the third day were used in the studies of the in vitro and the in vivo effects of DMSO, respectively. Phosphate buffer saline was used in the control. Synthesis and release of growth hormone and prolactin were estimated by the incorporation of [14C]leucine into each hormone during three hours' incubation of the pituitaries pre-exposed to DMSO or PBS. The values in the medium represented released hormone and sum of the values in the medium and the pituitary represented the synthesized hormone. DMSO stimulated synthesis of GH and synthesis and release of prolactin in vitro. Meanwhile, in the in vivo study, synthesis of GH and prolactin were lower in the DMSO-injected mice than in the control. The results suggest that the effects of DMSO on the pituitary secretion of GH and prolactin are adverse in vitro and in vivo. In vivo exposure of pituitary to DMSO resulted in the suppression of lactation.

ACKNOWLEDGMENTS

I thank Prof. Y. Kawazoe, Pharmaceutical Department, Nagoya-City University, Nagoya and Dr. F. Kanzawa, Pharmacology Division, National Cancer Center Research Institute, Tokyo, for their help in preparing the manuscript.

REFERENCES

1. FRIEND, C., W. SCHER, J. G. HOLLAND & T. SATO. 1971. Hemoglobin synthesis in murine virus-induced leukemic cells in vitro: Stimulation of erythroid differentiation by dimethyl sulfoxide. Proc. Natl. Acad. Sci. USA 68: 378–382.
2. LIN, C. S. & M. C. LIN. 1979. Appearance of late-adrenergic response of adenylate cyclase during the induction of differentiation in cell cultures. Exp. Cell Res. 122: 399–402.
3. HANANIA, N., D. SHAOOL, C. PONCY & J. HAREL. 1980. New gene expression in dimethylsulfoxide-treated Friend erythroleukemia cells. Exp. Cell Res. 130: 119–126.
4. ZWIGELSTEIN, G., H. TAPIERO, J. PORTOUKALIAN & A. FOURCADE. 1981. Changes in phospholipid and fatty acid composition in differentiated Friend leukemic cells. Biochem. Biophys. Res. Commun. 98: 349–358.

5. BROWN, A. E., E. L. SCHWARTZ, R. N. DREYER & A. C. SARTORELLI. 1982. Synthesis of sialoglycoconjugates during dimethylsulfoxide-induced erythrodifferentiation of Friend Leukemia cells. Biochim. Biophys. Acta **714**: 217-225.
6. SCHER, B. M., W. SCHER, A. ROBINSON & S. WAXMAN. 1982. DNA ligase and DNase activities in mouse erythroleukemic cells during dimethyl sulfoxide-induced differentiation. Cancer Res. **42**: 1300-1306.
7. KLUGE, N., W. OSTERTAG, D. SUGIYAMA, D. ARNDT-JOVIN, G. STEINHEIDER, M. FURUSAWA & S. DUBE. 1976. Dimethylsulfoxide-induced differentiation and hemoglobin synthesis in tissue culture of rat erythroleukemia cells transformed by 7,12-dimethylbenz(a)anthracene. Proc. Natl. Acad. Sci. USA **73**: 1237-1240.
8. COLLINS, S. J., F. W. RUSCETTI, R. E. GALLAGHER & R. C. GALLO. 1978. Terminal differentiation of human promyelocytic leukemia cells induced by dimethyl sulfoxide and other polar compounds. Proc. Natl. Acad. Sci. USA **75**: 2458-2462.
9. COLLINS, S. J., F. W. RUSCETTI, R. E. GALLAGHER & R. C. GALLO. 1979. Normal functional characteristics of cultured human promyelocytic leukemia cells (HL-60) after induction of differentiation by dimethylsulfoxide. J. Exp. Med. **149**: 969-974.
10. GAHMBERG, C. G., K. NILSSON & L. C. ANDERSON. 1979. Specific changes in the surface glycoprotein pattern of human promyelocytic leukemic cell line HL-60 during morphologic and functional differentiation. Proc. Natl. Acad. Sci. USA **76**: 4087-4091.
11. BONSER, R. W., M. I. SIEGEL, R. T. MCCONNELL & P. CUATRECASAS. 1981. The appearance of phospholipase and cyclo-oxygenase activities in the human promyelocytic leukemia cell line HL60 during dimethyl sulfoxide-induced differentiation. Biochem. Biophys. Res. Commun. **98**: 614-620.
12. TARELLA, C., D. FERRERO, E. GALLO, G. L. PAGLIARDI & F. W. RUSCETTI. 1982. Induction of differentiation of HL-60 cells by dimethyl sulfoxide: Evidence for a stochastic model not linked to the cell division cycle. Cancer Res. **42**: 445-449.
13. HIGGINS, P. J. & E. BORENFREUND. 1980. Enhanced albumin production by malignantly transformed hepatocytes during in vitro exposure to dimethylsulfoxide. Biochim. Biophys. Acta **610**: 174-180.
14. TSAO, D., A. MORITA, A. BELLA, JR., P. LUU & Y. S. KIM. 1982. Differential effects of sodium butylate, dimethyl sulfoxide, and retinoic acid on membrane-associated antigen, enzymes, and glycoproteins of human rectal adenocarcinoma cells. Cancer Res. **42**: 1052-1058.
15. OBINATA, A., K. TAKATA, M. KAWADA, H. HIRANO & H. ENDO. 1982. Reversible inhibition by DMSO of hydrocortisone-induced keratinization of chick embryonic skin. Exp. Cell Res. **138**: 135-145.
16. SVINGEN, B. A., G. POWIS, P. L. APPEL & M. SCOTT. 1981. Protection against Adriamycin-induced skin necrosis in the rat by dimethyl sulfoxide and α-tocopherol. Cancer Res. **41**: 3395-3399.
17. WIESER, P. B., M. A. ZEIGER & J. N. FAIN. 1977. Effects of dimethylsulfoxide on cyclic AMP accumulation, lipolysis and glucose metabolism of fat cells. Biochem. Pharmacol. **26**: 775-778.
18. TERASAWA, T., Y. MIURA & R. MASUDA. 1981. The mechanism of the action of DMSO on the heme synthesis of quail embryo yolk sac cells. Exp. Cell Res. **133**: 31-37.
19. BOWER, S. A. & M. E. HADLEY. 1975. Melanophore stimulating hormone (MSH) release: Inhibition by cytochalasin B and "stimulation" by dimethyl sulfoxide. Endocrinology **96**: 431-439.
20. MCKAY, D. B. & A. M. KAROW, JR. 1980. Glucose-induced insulin release from dimethylsulfoxide-treated rat islets of Langerhans. Res. Commun. Chem. Pathol. Pharmacol. **30**: 15-27.
21. SMITH, J. S. & A. M. KAROW, JR. 1980. The effects of dimethyl sulfoxide on insulin release and phosphate efflux from isolated, perfused islets of Langerhans. Res. Commun. Chem. Pathol. Pharmacol. **30**: 459-468.
22. CHEEVER, E. V., B. K. SEAVEY & U. J. LEWIS. 1969. Prolactin of normal and dwarf mice. Endocrinology **85**: 698-703.
23. YAMAMOTO, K., L. M. TAYLOR & F. E. COLE. 1970. Synthesis and release of GH and

prolactin from the rat anterior pituitary *in vitro* as functions of age and sex. Endocrinology **87:** 21–26.

24. YANAI, R. & H. NAGASAWA. 1972. Synthesis and release of prolactin and GH *in vitro* from the anterior pituitaries of virgin and pregnant mice. Endocrinol. Japon. **19:** 185–190.

25. NAGASAWA, H. & R. YANAI. 1974. Effects of estrogen and/or pituitary graft on nucleic acid synthesis of carcinogen-induced mammary tumors in rats. J. Natl. Cancer Inst. **52:** 1219–1222.

26. MEITES, J. 1966. Control of mammary growth and lactation. *In* Neuroendocrinology. L. Martini & W. P. Ganong, Eds. Vol. 1: 669–707. Academic Press. New York.

LACK OF NEPHROTOXICITY OF DIMETHYL SULFOXIDE IN MAN AND LABORATORY ANIMALS

William M. Bennett, Terry Bristol, William J. Weaver, and
Richard S. Muther

Division of Nephrology
Department of Medicine
Oregon Health Sciences University
Portland, Oregon 97201

INTRODUCTION

Intravenous DMSO has been undergoing extensive clinical testing in the treatment of cerebral edema and other neurological disorders.[1,2] During early therapeutic usage of 1 mg/kg as 10–40% solutions, intravascular hemolysis and hemoglobinuria were noted during the drug infusions. Since these processes have potential adverse effects on renal function, patients receiving this drug had careful observation of renal function before and after such infusions.[3,4] In addition, the effects of similar doses of DMSO on a weight basis were assessed in Sprague-Dawley rats. Finally DMSO was superimposed on a standard model of nephrotoxic acute renal failure in order to assess any additive toxic effects.

MATERIALS AND METHODS

Informed consent was obtained for the use of intravenous DMSO according to a research protocol approved by the Human Research Committee of the Oregon Health Sciences University.

Fourteen patients (12 men and 2 women) with a mean age of 28 years (18–48) were studied. All had chronic stable neurologic deficits related to traumatic spinal cord injury. None had a history of parenchymal renal disease but because of bladder dysfunction, lower urinary tract infections were common. DMSO 1 g/kg body weight in 5% dextrose water was administered intravenously for three successive days. Infusion times of the 10–40% solutions were variable, ranging from 10 minutes to 24 hours. Six patients received two or more separate courses of DMSO infusions. Blood urea nitrogen, serum creatinine, and 12-hour creatinine clearances were measured before and after each DMSO infusion. Urinary sediment examinations were performed by one of the authors (R.S.M.) before and after each infusion. Hematocrit, reticulocyte count, total/indirect bilirubin, lactic acid dehydrogenase, free hemoglobin, and serum haptoglobin were also noted. Urine was qualitatively assayed for hemoglobin and myoglobin and if positive, the pigment was characterized by electrophoresis. Statistical differences in renal function were examined by a paired t test.

Seven additional patients (5 men and 2 women) with a mean age of 24 (17–36) had 24-hour urines collected before DMSO and on each infusion day for creatinine and β-2 microglobulin. The latter was determined by radioimmunoassay (Pharmacia, Piscataway, N.J.). All samples were alkalinized with 1 N sodium hydroxide to prevent β-2 microglobulin degradation prior to assay and were run in duplicate. Differences in excretion were analyzed by a paired t test.

43

0077-8923/83/0411-0043 $01.75/0 © 1983, NYAS

Animal Studies

Four male Fischer rats, weighing 200–300 grams were given 40% DMSO intravenously through the lingual veins at the base of the tongue over 15 minutes under ethyl ether anesthesia daily for three days. Animals were sacrificed 72 hours later for serum creatinine measurements and kidneys were fixed in formalin for light microscopy. Two animals given an equivalent volume of isotonic saline served as controls. The nephropathologist examining the kidneys was unaware of whether or not DMSO had been given.

Further studies were performed on male Fischer 344 rats weighing 200–250 grams. They were fed a standard laboratory chow and were allowed free access to water. Groups of animals received potassium dichromate solution 5, 10, and 20 mg/kg subcutaneously. Half of the rats at each dosage level also received daily injections of 1 g/kg DMSO intraperitoneally as a 67% solution. Control animals received a like volume of physiologic saline with and without DMSO. Animals were sacrificed on days 1, 3, and 5 for serum creatinine determinations. Differences between DMSO-treated animals and their controls receiving $K_2Cr_2O_7$, saline or DMSO alone were analyzed by unpaired t test at each sacrifice time point.

TABLE 1

RENAL FUNCTIONAL PARAMETERS BEFORE AND
AFTER THREE DAYS OF 10–40% DMSO 1 gm/kg

	Before	After	
BUN (mg/dl)	16 ± 2	17 ± 3	p = NS
Serum creatinine (mg/dl)	.7 ± .03	.7 ± .02	p = NS
Creatinine clearance (ml/min)	123 ± 10	128 ± 12	p = NS
N = 14			

RESULTS

No change from baseline in the blood urea nitrogen, serum creatinine, or creatinine clearance was observed after three days of DMSO infusions. This was the case independent of the concentration of DMSO or the duration of infusion. These data are shown in TABLE 1. In the six patients who had additional series of three infusions on separate occasions over 2–6 months, there was no decline in creatinine clearance or elevation of serum creatinine. No patients had urinary sediment abnormalities despite hemoglobinuria. Specifically, there was no increase in qualitative urine protein or glucose and no decrease in first morning specific gravity. Most patients were free of microscopic hematuria and on no occasion did the number of red blood cells per high power field increase over baseline values.

Minutes after each infusion with 20–40% DMSO was begun, reddish discoloration of the urine appeared which persisted for 2–4 hours after the drug was stopped. With 10% infusions the urine was only occasionally pink-tinged. However, qualitative tests for hemoglobinuria were commonly positive even in patients without changes in urine color. Hemoglobin was confirmed by electrophoresis in all cases where the qualitative test was positive. Myoglobin was absent. Indicators of hemolysis after individual infusions are shown in TABLE 2. Total and indirect bilirubin only changed significantly with 20 and 40% infusions and rose 1.6 and 1.2 mg%, respectively.

TABLE 2

HEMOLYSIS AFTER DMSO INFUSIONS

Concentration	Δ Ht%	Δ Free Hb (mg/dl)	Δ Serum Haptoglobin (mg/dl)	Δ LDH (IU/l)
10%	−1.5	+16.6	−40.2	331.2
20%	−4.9	+81	−38	720
40%	−5.0	+102	−62	1210

Urinary β-2 microglobulin excretion did not change significantly over the course of the three infusions. Mean of baseline values was 92.6 µg/l. At 24 hours it was 30.8 µg/l, at 48 hours 79.8 µg/l, and at 72 hours 128.8 µg/l. The normal range in our laboratory is 4–375 µg/l.

No evidence of added nephrotoxicity was noted in rats with dichromate-induced acute renal failure given DMSO versus those with dichromate alone. The time course of development of toxicity with this standard nephrotoxin is shown in FIGURE 1.

In Fischer rats given intravenous DMSO as 40% solutions over three days, simulating the clinical situation, there was no evident histologic damage. Serum creatinine was .58 mg/dl in DMSO animals versus .6 mg/dl in controls. p = NS.

DISCUSSION

Dimethyl sulfoxide is a water-soluble, osmotically active, organic solvent.[5] Used intravenously it has been found to be an effective agent in reducing cerebral edema in patients with head trauma and other neurological insults.[1,2] Because of dose-related hemolysis with subsequent hemoglobinuria, any effects

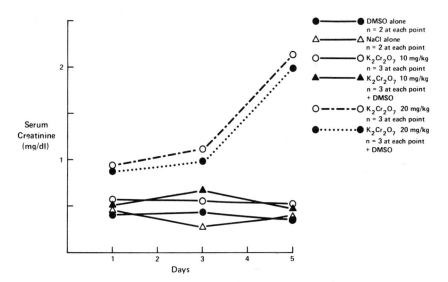

FIGURE 1. Effect of 67% DMSO 1 g/kg i.p. on potassium dichromate-induced acute renal failure.

of DMSO on renal structure and function require close scrutiny. This is of particular importance since massively head-injured patients often serve as organ donors in kidney transplantation.

Our studies show an absence of any decrease in renal function in a group of patients receiving DMSO as experimental therapy for stable spinal cord injuries. Even using the sensitive index of tubular function, β-2 microglobulin, no signs of renal injury appeared. β-2 microglobulin is a protein with a molecular weight of 11,800 that is usually filtered by the glomerulus and reabsorbed by the proximal tubule. Urinary losses are generally quite small amounting to less than 1 mg/day. In various toxic renal insults, such as those due to heavy metals and antibiotics, excretion of β-2 microglobulin increases even without accompanying decreases in glomerular filtration rate.[6]

As further confirmation of the lack of short-term nephrotoxicity of DMSO, Muther et al. reported the successful transplantation of two kidneys harvested from a cadaver donor who had been treated with intravenous DMSO.[7] Despite hemoglobinuria in the donor prior to transplant both recipients regained normal renal function. One kidney was lost to rejection on the 23rd postoperative day. Allograft nephrectomy showed only changes of severe irreversible allograft rejection. The other kidney is still functioning three years after transplant with a serum creatinine of 1.5 mg/dl.

Hemoglobinuria can be associated with acute renal failure in other clinical settings such as hemolytic transfusion reactions and in the experimental model of myohemoglobinuric renal failure produced by intramuscular injection of 50% glycerol.[8] In rats, there was no evidence of renal structural or functional changes following intravenous DMSO in doses similar to those used in patients.

Kedar et al. have reported a protective effect of DMSO on an ischemic model of acute renal failure in rats. This may be mediated by producing an osmotic diuresis or other effects on platelets or blood vessels.[9] It is known that enhanced solute diuresis may ameliorate norepinephrine-induced acute renal failure in the dog.[10] Using dichromate as a standard nephrotoxic model we could show no protective effects of DMSO. It is of interest, however, that nephrotoxicity was not worsened despite frank intravascular hemolysis and hemoglobinuria. The kidney concentrations of gentamicin, a clinically relevant nephrotoxin that causes proximal tubular necrosis, were not affected by ten days of intraperitoneal DMSO given in conjunction with 6 mg/kg of gentamicin.[11]

CONCLUSIONS

No short-term nephrotoxic effects of intravenous DMSO could be discerned in patients or laboratory animals despite hemoglobinuria. Intravenous DMSO is safe to use in patients who are prospective renal transplant donors.

REFERENCES

1. LAHA, R. K., M. DUJOVNY & P. J. BARRIONUEVO. 1978. Protective effects of methylprednisolone and dimethylsulfoxide in experimental middle cerebral artery embolectomy. J. Neurosurg. **49:** 508–516.
2. DE LA TORRE, J. C., H. M. KAWANAGA, D. W. ROWED et al. 1975. Dimethylsulfoxide in central nervous system trauma. Ann. N.Y. Acad. Sci. **243:** 362–389.
3. MUTHER, R. S. & W. M. BENNETT. 1980. Effects of dimethylsulfoxide on renal function in man. J. Am. Med. Assoc. **244:** 2081–2083.

4. BENNETT, W. M. & R. S. MUTHER. 1981. Lack of nephrotoxicity of intravenous dimethylsulfoxide. Clin. Toxicol. **18:** 615–618.
5. JACOB, S. W. & D. C. WOOD. 1967. Dimethylsulfoxide (DMSO): Toxicity, pharmacology and clinical experience. Am. J. Surg **114:** 414–426.
6. WIBELL, L. 1978. The serum level and urinary excretion of beta-2-microglobulin in health and renal disease. Pathol. Biol. **26:** 295–301.
7. MUTHER, R. S., J. M. BARRY & W. M. BENNETT. 1980. Successful cadaveric renal transplantation after donor treatment with dimethylsulfoxide. Transplantation **29:** 507.
8. STEIN, J. H., M. D. LIFSCHITZ & L. D. BARNES. 1978. Current concepts on the pathophysiology of acute renal failure. Am. J. Physiol. **234:** F171–F181.
9. KEDAR, I., J. COHEN, E. JACOB et al. 1981. Alleviation of experimental ischemic acute renal failure by dimethylsulfoxide. Nephron **29:** 55–58.
10. CRONIN, R. E., A. DeTORRENTE, R. E. MILLER et al. 1978. Pathogenetic mechanisms in early norepinephrine-induced acute renal failure: functional and histologic correlates of protection. Kidney Int. **14:** 115–125.
11. RUBINSTEIN, E. & A. LEV-EL. 1980. The effect of dimethylsulfoxide on tissue distribution of gentamicin. Experientia **36:** 92.

OCULAR TOXICOLOGY OF DIMETHYL SULFOXIDE AND EFFECTS ON RETINITIS PIGMENTOSA

Charles A. Garcia*

Department of Ophthalmology
Health Sciences Center
University of Texas
Houston, Texas 77030

INTRODUCTION

Retinitis pigmentosa is a hereditary retinal degeneration that affects the photoreceptor retinal pigment epithelium complex. RP is not one disease but rather a group of diseases that share some common symptoms and some common final characteristics.[1] Clinically, RP patients show varying degrees of night blindness, constricted visual fields, decreased central visual acuity, cataracts, vitreous degeneration, pallor of the optic nerve, attenuation of retinal blood vessels, atrophic and/or cystoid macular changes, pigment epithelial atrophy, and bone spicule or other diffuse pigmentary retinal changes.

Retinitis pigmentosa has three distinct modes of inheritance: autosomal dominant, autosomal recessive, and X-linked. The majority of cases appear to be isolated, i.e., no other cases of retinitis pigmentosa are evident within the family, and there is no evidence of consanguinity. Most isolated cases are presumed to be autosomal recessive, although new mutations and environmental phenocopies cannot be excluded.

The normal retina has ten layers that can be observed by light microscopy, but only four functional cell layers. The retina may be divided into inner and outer sections. The inner cell layers, the ganglion cell layer, and the neurons of the inner nuclear layer are responsible for processing and transmitting back to the brain neural information received from the photoreceptors. The outer section of the retina is also composed of two cell layers. These are the photoreceptors (rods and cones) and the underlying retinal pigment epithelium. The photoreceptors are responsible for light transduction and the pigment epithelium acts as a phagocytic barrier and storage layer.

The inner side of the retina is generally not affected in retinitis pigmentosa until the latest stages of the disease. For the purposes of this paper, we shall focus on the outer segments of the retina.

The retinal photoreceptor is composed of an inner segment and outer segment. The inner segment is composed of four portions: the synaptic region, the nuclear area, the myoid area, and the mitochondrial area (the ellipsoid). This inner segment is joined to the outer segment by a connecting cilium. The outer segment is composed of a series of discs, called lamellae, which trap photons of light incident upon the retina. These discs are produced at the junction of the inner and outer segments and are subject to constant renewal.[2] Each outer segment, composed of about one thousand lamellae, totally renews itself every 8 to 11 days in humans. Shedding of the discs from the end of the outer segment is governed by exposure to light and dark.[3] As discs are shed from the distal end of the photoreceptor outer segments, they are replaced by new lamellae at the

---

*Send correspondence to C.A.G., P.O. Box 34419, Houston, TX 77089.

0077-8923/83/0411-0048 $01.75/0 © 1983, NYAS

junction of the inner and outer segment. The shed photoreceptor outer segments are phagocytized by the retinal pigment epithelium. Once ingested by the pigment epithelium, the discs are recognizable in small intracellular vacuolizations called phagosomes.

HISTOPATHOLOGY OF HEREDITARY RETINAL DEGENERATIONS IN HUMANS AND ANIMALS

In humans, retinitis pigmentosa probably does not represent one specific entity, but rather is a series of distinct biochemical and genetic abnormalities. In animals, we also see a number of different histological and biochemical abnormalities and not just one specific entity.

In humans, the histology of retinitis pigmentosa demonstrates early loss of the rods photoreceptors, and significant abnormalities of the remaining cones and pigment epithelium. In the central retina, the rod outer segments are shortened and thickened. There is vacuolization of the inner segment. The pigment epithelium shows diffuse melanolysosome complex formation. In several areas of the retina, the pigment epithelium becomes bilaminate. In more peripheral retina, the rod outer segments totally disappear, and the inner segments show further thickening. In the peripheral retina, the photoreceptors, both rods and cones, are totally absent. The pigment epithelium abuts the distal end of the Muller cells. No extracellular debris is present.[4]

Two rodent models that manifest hereditary retinal degenerations are the Royal College of Surgeons (RCS) rat and the rd (retinal degeneration) mouse.[5] Because both of these animals demonstrate diffuse, spontaneous panretinal photoreceptor degenerations, as well as non-recordable electroretinograms, which are both observed in the human subject with retinitis pigmentosa, these animals seem to be good models for this disease.

There are, however, marked differences in the histology of these two animal models. The rd mouse shows early development of the retina, and then total, precipitous photoreceptor degeneration between 10 and 20 days of age. The RCS rat, however, shows development of the photoreceptors and buildup of large amounts of extracellular debris, which is of rod origin but is not phagocytized by the retinal pigment epithelium.

CLINICAL TRIAL RESULTS

In 1975, a study was published in the *Annals of the New York Academy of Sciences* that described improvement in or stabilization of visual function, either objectively (visual acuity, visual field, color vision, or dark adaptation) or subjectively, in 48 of 50 patients with either retinitis pigmentosa or macular degeneration who were treated topically with 50 percent aqueous solution of DMSO.[6] This was not a randomized or masked clinical trial. Because of these promising results, we undertook a randomized, masked clinical trial and experimental treatment of human subjects with retinitis pigmentosa and then tested this treatment in the laboratory on the RCS rat.

The earlier study suggested improvement in all genetic types of RP and at all levels of progression of the disease. We patterned the eligibility criteria for our human subjects in much the same way. The route of administration was similar to the early study, that is, topical drops. A dose of 125 mg per eye, per day, in 50% aqueous solution topical drops was used.

Prior to acceptance in the study, each patient underwent a complete eye examination and a genetic history was taken. Visual function was assessed by visual acuity (best refracted). Color vision was evaluated by a Farnsworth-Munsell 100 Hue Test under a Macbeth easel lamp. Visual fields were performed on a Goldmann perimeter with at least two test objects. Dark adaptometry was done on all patients with an 8 degree white test spot centered, ten degrees nasal to the fovea. Objective criteria were obtained with electrophysiological tests consisting of electroretinography, both standard flash electroretinogram and computer-averaged sinusoidal electroretinography.[7] An electrooculogram was also performed on each subject. Fundus photography was done on each patient.

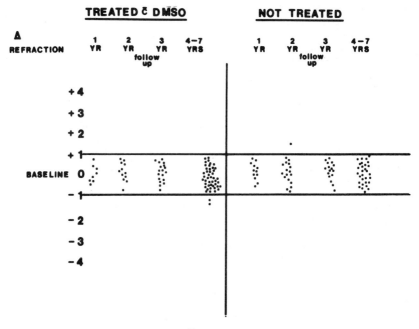

FIGURE 1.

The human subjects were examined at six-month intervals throughout the initial study to determine if any ocular toxicity resulted from prolonged topical administration of DMSO. Later follow-ups were at yearly intervals. Patients were randomly assigned to a treatment or control group. Neither the patient nor the investigator knew whether any particular patient was being treated with DMSO or being given a placebo. On each reexamination, each patient underwent a complete visual function battery as on the initial visit.

Sixty-five patients were treated with DMSO, and fifty-eight served as controls. Data from patient follow-ups at one year, two years, and three years, and four to seven years after the last follow-up were compared (FIGURE 1). No objective, significant improvement was noted for visual acuity, color vision, visual fields, dark adaptation, electroretinography, or electrooculography in treated versus control groups. Over a two-year period, we did find minimal deterioration in visual acuity, but that observation was made both for the treated and non-treated groups. For patients followed over a four-year period or longer, there was a significant deterioration in visual fields, color vision, and visual acuity in both the treated and non-treated groups. Because of our wide range of entering visual acuities, it is impossible to ascertain in this population of patients whether or not a very subtle alteration in the slope of the curve of deterioration might be present. An earlier and more standardized cohort of patients is necessary to determine if any subtle second-order effects are present with DMSO treatment. These findings contradict the earlier study that showed apparent improvement in vision or stabilization of vision in 48 of 50 patients.[6]

No significant ocular toxicity was noted in the study. Approximately 25% of patients reported some brief irritation characterized by a burning or stinging sensation when the drops were applied. Two patients were allergic to the drops and treatment was discontinued because they developed severe conjunctival hyperemia. One patient developed narrow angle glaucoma, apparently unrelated to the treatment, and treatment was discontinued. It is interesting to note that there were no significant refractive changes in the vast majority of these eyes even after four to seven years of administration of the drug.

Since toxicity is generally regarded to be a dose- and time-related function, we see that there appears to be no toxicity at a dose of approximately 125 mg per eye, per day. There is no significant refractive change in the treated versus control group. There are, in the treated group, only two eyes and, in the control group, one eye that show a change in the spherical equivalent of greater than one diopter of refraction.

In summary, in our hands at this dose and treating this population of patients, no significant beneficial effect could be demonstrated over a long term in a randomized, masked clinical study. There is, however, no significant ocular toxicity demonstrable other than allergy in a small number of patients and there is no evidence that prolonged administration of low dose DMSO causes nuclear or cortical cataracts or significant changes in refractive error in a large group of patients who have preexisting lenticular changes.

REFERENCES

1. BLOOME, M. A. & C. A. GARCIA. 1982. Rod and Rod-Cone Dystrophies. In Manual of Retinal and Choroidal Dystrophies. Pp. 39–65. 1st edit. Appleton-Century-Crofts. New York.
2. YOUNG, R. W. 1967. The renewal of photoreceptor cell outer segments. J. Cell Biol. 33: 61.
3. YOUNG, R. W. 1971. The renewal of rod and cone outer segments in the rhesus monkey. J. Cell Biol. 49: 303.
4. KRETZER F. & C. A. GARCIA. Ultrastructure of the retina in a patient with retinitis pigmentosa and progressive dysacusis. (Submitted for publication.)
5. LAVAIL, M. M. 1976. The pigment epithelium in mice and rats with inherited retinal degeneration. In The Retinal Pigment Epithelium. K. M. Zinn & M. F. Marmor, Eds. Harvard University Press. Cambridge, Mass.
6. HILL, R. V. 1975. Dimethyl sulfoxide in the treatment of retinal disease. Ann. N.Y. Acad. Sci. 243: 485–490.
7. ANDERSON, C., A. TROELSTRA, & C. GARCIA. 1979. Quantitative evaluation of photopic ERG waveforms. Invest Ophthalmol. Visual Sci. 18(1): 26–43.

STUDIES ON BIOLOGICAL ACTIONS OF DIMETHYL SULFOXIDE IN FAMILIAL AMYLOIDOSIS*

Shozo Kito, Eiko Itoga, Masae Inokawa, Masatoshi Hironaka,
Takenobu Kishida, and Tomotaka Shinoda†

Third Department of Internal Medicine
Hiroshima University School of Medicine
Hiroshima 734, Japan
†Department of Chemistry
Tokyo Metropolitan University
Tokyo, Japan

Dimethyl sulfoxide (DMSO) had not been regarded as a therapeutic drug against amyloidosis until 1974 when Osserman and Isobe administered it for the first time in six cases of primary amyloidosis.[1] In 1973, we described an outline of the second largest concentration of familial amyloid polyneuropathy (FAP) cases which we discovered. We reported some tentative results of DMSO treatment in 18 cases.[2-5]

In this paper, we are presenting the effects of DMSO administration to patients with primary and familial amyloidosis from both clinical and biochemical viewpoints and *in vitro* effects of DMSO on extracted amyloid fibril proteins.

METHODS

DMSO was therapeutically administered to three cases of primary amyloidosis (PA) and 40 cases of FAP originating from Ogawa Village, Japan. Oral administration of DMSO began with an initial dose of 2–3 ml and was progressively increased to a maintenance level of 10–15 ml. DMSO was also applied to the skin in a dose of 4–6 ml in some patients. Precise clinical and laboratory examinations were performed on these cases.

Twenty-four-hour urines were collected from the four FAP cases and three cases of PA (TABLE 1). Urine samples were prepared in the following two ways. The samples were centrifuged at 3,000 rpm for 20 min and the supernatants were dissolved into 0.1 volume of original samples after lyophilization. In the following descriptions we call these samples lyophilized urinary proteins. Other samples were 100% $(NH_4)_2SO_4$ salting-out urines. Prepared urinary proteins were analyzed by SDS-6M-urea polyacrylamide gel electrophoresis and immunoelectrophoresis.

Three organs from two FAP autopsied cases were used for experiments to study the *in vitro* effects of DMSO on extracted amyloid fibril proteins. Amyloid proteins were extracted from these organs by means of Pras's method.[6] The tissues were cut by scissors into small pieces and homogenized with 0.15 M NaCl by a Polytron (Brinkman). The suspensions were centrifuged at 10,000 rpm for 30 min and water-soluble amyloid proteins (WSAPs) were extracted from the pellets

*Supported in part by grant-in-aids for Scientific Research No. 344041 and No. 437022 from the Ministry of Education (Japan).

TABLE 1

URINARY MATERIALS

Type of Amyloidosis	Case	Age (years)	Sex	Dose of DMSO (ml)	Duration of Illness (years)
FAP	K.S.	65	f	3	6
	Y.M.	59	m	4–6	2
	M.A.	59	f	5	8
	M.I.	41	f	10	7
PA	T.M.	52	f	10	2
	I.O.	49	m	4–10	8
	S.T.	37	m	10	2

Gastrointestinal disturbances

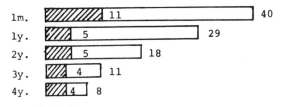

Sensory disturbances

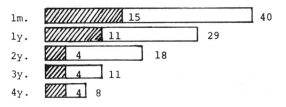

Dysuria

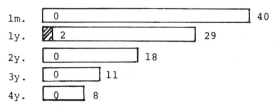

Adverse reactions

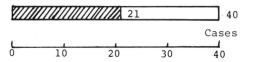

FIGURE 1. Clinical improvement of FAP patients by DMSO administration. Gastrointestinal disturbances include nausea, vomiting, abdominal pain, diarrhea, and constipation. Sensory disturbances include neuralgia, sensory loss, and paresthesia. Dermatitis, diarrhea, and nausea were the main adverse reactions.

by homogenizing with distilled water. WSAPs were then dialyzed and lyophilized. A part of the WSAP was degraded with 0.1 N NaOH and 5 M guanidine-HCl in acetic acid successively. The soluble fraction of this denatured protein will be called GAM in the following descriptions. GAM and WSAP were used for further examinations, namely, SDS-urea polyacrylamide gel electrophoresis (PAGE), and Sephadex G gel filtration.

WSAPs were solubilized in DMSO in water or 0.1 M phosphate buffer in concentrations of 0.1 M, 1 M, 3 M, and 5 M for up to 70 hours at room temperature and solubilizing effects were compared among these solutions. In some experiments, DMSO$_2$ (dimethyl-sulfone: $(CH_3)_2SO_2$) or purified (by distillation) DMSO was used instead of regular DMSO. DMSO was commercially available from Wako Drug Co., Ltd. DMSO$_2$ was a gift from Chelest Chemical Co., Ltd. and purified DMSO was kindly supplied from Hishiyama Co., Ltd.

Urinary proteins and extracted amyloid proteins from the tissues were tested for antigenicity by a double immunodiffusion technique with use of antisera to various plasma proteins, i.e. prealbumin, immunoglobulins, and retinol binding protein.

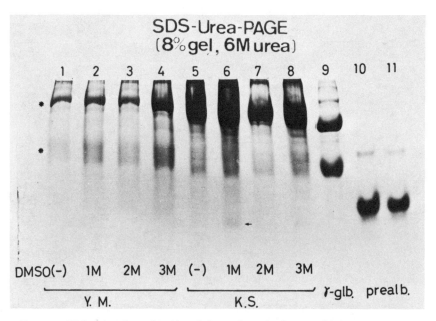

FIGURE 2. SDS-urea polyacrylamide gel electrophoresis of 100% salting-out urines in two FAP cases before and after DMSO administration. Sample No. 1 is an electrophoretic pattern of the pretreatment stage of Y.M. case and samples Nos. 2, 3, and 4 are those of one, two, and three months after DMSO treatment. Sample No. 5, 6, 7, and 8 are SDS-urea-PAGE patterns of urinary proteins from the case K.S. placed in the same order as case Y.M. No. 9 is bovine γ-globulin and Nos. 10 and 11 are prealbumin as marker proteins. In the FAP cases, there are two constant bands (indicated by asterisks) with molecular weights of 50,000 to 70,000 and 30,000. After DMSO administration the 30,000 molecular weight protein was increasingly excreted and the band of the 12,000 molecular weight proteins was visualized (indicated by an arrow).

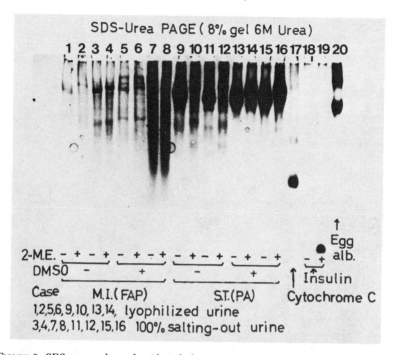

SDS-Urea PAGE (8% gel 6M Urea)

2-M.E. − + − + − + − + − + − + − + − +   − + Egg alb.
DMSO − + − + Insulin
Case M.I.(FAP) S.T.(PA) Cytochrome C
1,2,5,6,9,10, 13,14, lyophilized urine
3,4,7,8,11,12,15,16 100% salting-out urine

FIGURE 3. SDS-urea polyacrylamide gel electrophoresis of 100% salting-out urines and lyophilized urines of a FAP case and a PA case with (+) and without (−) 2-mercaptoethanol before (−) and after (+) DMSO administration.

RESULTS

In about 40% of 40 FAP cases, DMSO induced some clinical improvements in signs and symptoms, such as gastrointestinal disturbances, sensory disturbances, and dysuria (FIGURE 1). Improvement ratios of these symptoms when observed by duration of taking medicine are shown in the figure. For example, one patient showed remarkable reduction of an analgesic area in her anterior chest wall. Some adverse effects were observed in about half of the cases.

As for urinary samples, FIGURES 2 and 3 show SDS-PAGE of 100% salting-out urines before and after DMSO administration. SDS-urea PAGE in seven amyloidosis cases revealed two main bands of molecular weights 50,000 to 70,000 and 30,000. Several bands of lesser molecular weights were also noticed. FIGURE 2 shows SDS gel electrophoretic patterns of two cases of FAP. For the case of Y.M., sample No. 1 is a pattern of the pretreatment stage and samples Nos. 2, 3, and 4 are those of one, two, and three months after DMSO treatment, respectively. In this case, DMSO administration revealed an increase of protein excretion, especially of a protein of molecular weight 30,000. In the case of K.S., a new band of molecular weight 12,000 was visualized after DMSO administration (FIGURE 2). Similar observations were also noticed in another two cases as shown in FIGURE 3. In this figure, one is an FAP case and another is a PA case. SDS-urea PAGE patterns were also compared between pre- and posttreatment stages by DMSO in these cases. The examinations were done using both lyophilized urines and 100%

salting-out urines. No effects were observed by adding 2-mercaptoethanol in these experiments. When we compared sample No. 3 with sample No. 7, there was a very marked increase in protein excretion in 100% salting-out urine. Examination on lyophilized urines showed changes in more discrete bands of molecular weights greater than 70,000 and of 30,000 (FIGURE 3).

Before we proceed to the *in vitro* effects of DMSO on solubilization of amyloid fibril proteins, an outline of our studies on extracted amyloid fibril proteins will be described. FIGURE 4 shows SDS-urea PAGE patterns (17% gel) of WSAPs extracted from various organs. The 14,000 molecular weight band was generally observed. Since there were fewer protein bands in the samples of the

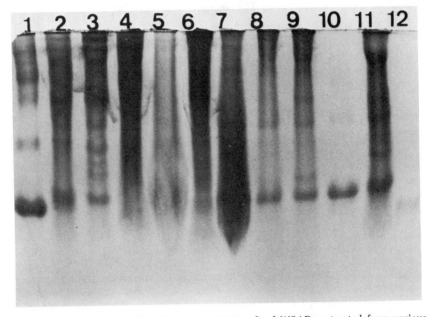

FIGURE 4. The SDS-urea-PAGE patterns (17% gel) of WSAPs extracted from various organs of one FAP patient R.A. Lanes are indicated by numbers in parentheses: (1) Marker proteins (bovine serum albumin, egg albumin, lysozyme and cytochrome c). WSAPs of the (2) uterus, (3) heart, (4) liver, (5) pancreas, (6) tongue, (7) spleen, (8) thyroid, and (11) kidney. (9) The pellets of thyroid tissue homogenized with 0.15 M NaCl. (10) prealbumin. (12) fractionated protein by gel filtration (M.W. 9,000) from a case originating in Israel.

spleen and thyroid, we used these amyloid-laden organs for the following experiments. The 14,000 molecular weight protein band corresponded to prealbumin as a marker protein. This protein was not noticed in the samples from the liver and pancreas. This 14,000 molecular weight protein became more distinct when the WSAPs were pretreated by dithiothreitol (DTT) (FIGURE 5). 2-Mercaptoethanol (2-ME) also showed a similar effect on the amyloid protein. (Data are not shown.) Also, we immunohistochemically confirmed positive prealbumin-like immunoreactivity of the amyloid substance within the tissue. In FIGURE 6, massive deposits of the substance positively reacting with an antiprealbumin

Kito *et al.*: Familial Amyloidosis   57

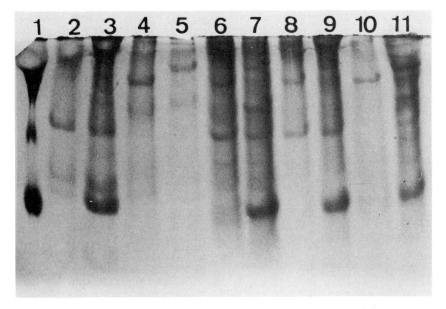

FIGURE 5. The SDS-urea PAGE patterns (17% gel) of WSAPs extracted from various organs with (odd numbers) and without (even numbers) dithiothreitol (DTT). (1) Marker proteins (albumin, egg albumin, lysozyme, and cytochrome c). WSAPs of the (2) and (3) thyroid, (4) and (5) heart, (6) and (7) spleen, (8) and (9) thyroid, and (10) and (11) kidney.

FIGURE 6. Amyloid deposits with prealbumin-like immunoreactivity within the cardiac valve.

serum within the cardiac valve were observed. As the next step, degraded amyloid proteins were examined. In the upper plate of FIGURE 7, a Sephadex G-100 column was equilibrated with 8 M urea in 1 N acetic acid. In this elution profile, fractions 1 and 3 had cross reactions with both prealbumin and retinol binding protein. On the other hand, the only fraction 2 of the lower plate in which the column was equilibrated with 5 M guanidine HCl in 1 N acetic acid had positive immunoreactivity against a prealbumin antiserum (FIGURE 7).

Then we examined *in vitro* effects of DMSO on these amyloid proteins. The relative effectiveness of phosphate buffer, water, 5 M DMSO, 0.1 M DMSO, and 6 M guanidine in solubilizing a suspension of the amyloid fibril protein was shown (FIGURE 8a). The figure represents the increments in O.D. 280 nm of the amyloid fibril proteins with the time course of incubation for 70 hours. It was evident that 6 M guanidine had the most potent amyloid protein-solubilizing effect among these

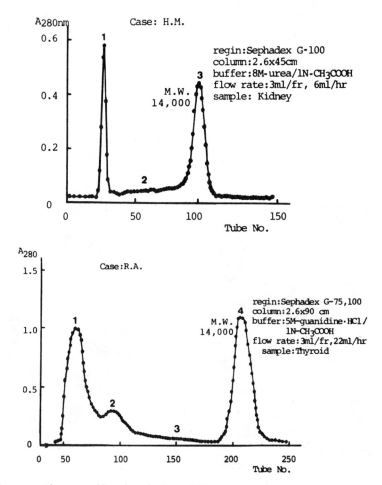

FIGURE 7. Elution profiles of Sephadex gel filtration of GAM of case R.A. In the upper plate, the Sephadex G-100 column was equilibrated with 8 M urea in 1 N acetic acid. In the lower plate, the column was equilibrated with 5 M guanidine HCl in 1 N acetic acid.

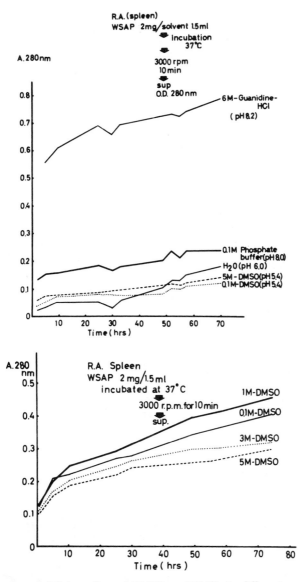

FIGURE 8. The solubilizing effect of DMSO on WSAPs in different conditions. The samples were prepared as shown in the upper part of the plates.

solvents. To exclude effects of pH, we made similar experiments with use of various concentrations of DMSO after adjusting pH to 8.0 by phosphate buffer (FIGURE 8b). This increase in pH remarkably increases the solubilizing effect of DMSO on the amyloid protein two to four times. It was noteworthy that 1 M DMSO showed the most potent solubilizing effect.

Elution profiles of WSAP solubilized in 1 M DMSO for 70 hours through

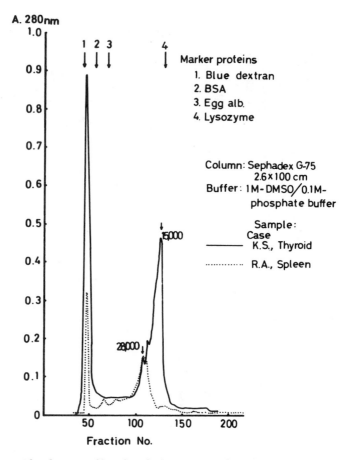

FIGURE 9. The elution profiles of Sephadex G-75 gel filtration of two different organs in FAP cases with use of 1 M DMSO in 0.1 M phosphate buffer (pH 8.0).

Sephadex G-75 column equilibrated with 1 M DMSO in 0.1 M phosphate buffer are shown in FIGURE 9. In addition to the void-volume materials, the spleen of a FAP case (R.A.) and the thyroid of another FAP case (K.S.), revealed different lower molecular weight components (i.e., molecular weights of 28,000 and 15,000). Gel filtration profiles were compared among columns equilibrated with 1 M DMSO commercially available, purified DMSO by distillation, and DMSO$_2$ with 0.1 M phosphate buffer. The experiment was also performed with use of a column with 3 M DMSO in water (FIGURE 10). In all the experiments the same sample of the amyloid fibril protein, the spleen of case R.A., was used. Elution profiles with distilled DMSO and DMSO$_2$ showed similar patterns, which were different from those with DMSO commercially purchased. In FIGURE 11, the elution profiles of the amyloid fibril protein from the spleen of case R.A. were comparatively demonstrated between Sephadex G-75 columns equilibrated with 5 M guanidine in 1 N acetic acid and with 1 M DMSO in phosphate buffer. It was evident that denaturation with 5 M guanidine dissolved the amyloid protein into fewer molecular weight components than denaturation with 1 M DMSO.

Lastly, we present how DMSO and guanidine act on extracted, water-soluble amyloid proteins (FIGURE 12). The upper plate shows that SDS-urea PAGE of WSAP, DMSO-treated WSAP, and the supernatant of the DMSO-treated WSAP and its precipitate. All experiments were performed both with and without 2-ME. In both WSAP and the precipitate of DMSO-treated WSAP with 2-ME, we

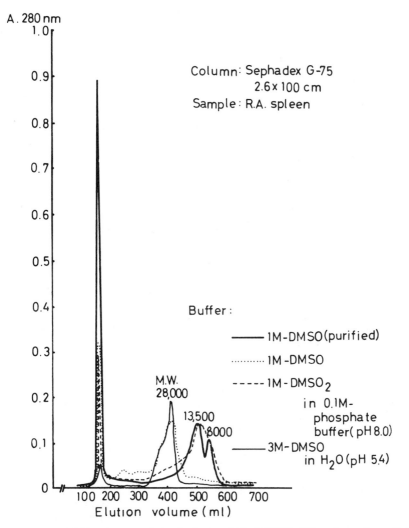

FIGURE 10. Gel filtration patterns by Sephadex G-75 of WSAP of the spleen of case R.A. The elution profiles were compared among columns equilibrated with 1 M DMSO commercially available, purified DMSO by distillation and dimethyl sulfone in phosphate buffer and 3 M DMSO in H_2O.

observed a distinct band corresponding to prealbumin, which was absent in the supernatant of the DMSO-treated WSAP. This means that protein with prealbumin-like immunoreactivity will not be obtained through solubilization of WSAP by DMSO. In the lower plate, we can observe the differences among a guanidine-degraded WSAP and ones treated with different concentrations of DMSO solutions. Treatment with guanidine and 2-ME produced a band corresponding to prealbumin, which was not the case with DMSO.

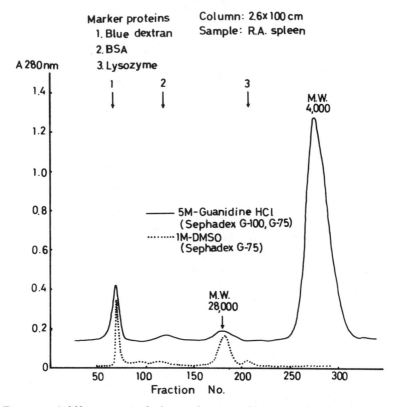

FIGURE 11. Gel filtration on Sephadex G columns equilibrated with 5 M guanidine HCl in 1 N acetic acid and 1 M DMSO in phosphate buffer. The sample was the spleen of case R.A.

DISCUSSION

In 1976, Isobe and Osserman presented evidence that dimethyl sulfoxide can block the precipitation of Bence Jones proteins by heat, affect the solubilization of amyloid fibrils *in vitro*, and diminish the extent of amyloidosis in casein-treated C_3H mice.[7] On the basis of these findings, they administered DMSO to six cases of primary amyloidosis and they judged that there were some improvements in two cases.[1] The detailed mechanism of amyloidgenesis is not yet clarified and there may be considerable differences depending on clinical types.

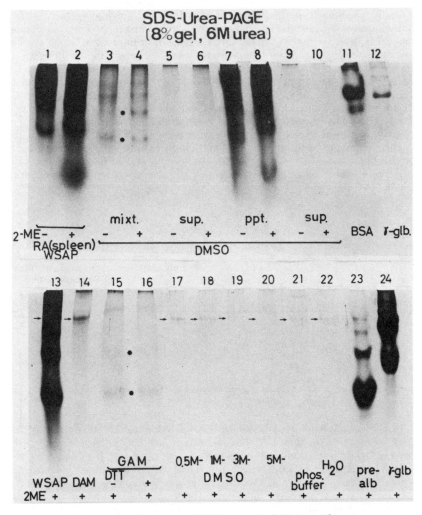

FIGURE 12. SDS-urea PAGE patterns of WSAP, degraded WSAPs with various concentrations of DMSO, with 0.1 N NaOH (alkali-degraded protein: DAM) and GAM. All the samples originated from R.A. case. The samples with cross marks were pretreated with 2-mercaptoethanol. Nos. 15 and 16 are GAM with and without DTT. In the upper plate, asterisks indicate polymers of prealbumin, which are distinctly observed in the suspended mixture of WSAP in 1 M DMSO. Nos. 5, 6, 9, and 10 are patterns of the supernatant after incubation with 1 M DMSO. Precipitates (Nos. 7 and 8) showed similar patterns to WSAP. In the lower plate, Nos. 15 and 16 showed the bands corresponding to prealbumin (asterisks). Supernatants of WSAP treated with various concentrations of DMSO (No. 17, 18, 19, and 20) showed one common band (arrow). This protein was observed also in WSAP, DAM supernatants of WSAPs incubated in phosphate buffer and H_2O.

An amyloid protein is a fibrillar protein with an antiparallel β-pleated structure. Solubility in distilled water is one of characteristics of this protein. It is generally established that gel filtration of a degraded amyloid protein elutes a void-volume material and a low molecular weight component.[8] The void-volume material is heterogeneous by itself and derived from the tissue, while, the low molecular weight component is a more specific protein in amyloidgenesis, originating from the circulating protein, sometimes called a precursor protein. As precursor proteins, an immunoglobulin light chain polypeptide (AL) and/or its amino-terminal variable-region fragments for primary amyloidosis and protein AA, for secondary amyloidosis have been established. As for the familial type, Costa and others suggested that the FAP proteins were closely related to prealbumin subunit.[9] In any case, it is generally accepted that the low molecular weight component is the major fibrillar protein constituent, whereas it is not decided yet whether the void-volume material is an integral part of the amyloid fibril protein or a passive bystander that coprecipitates with the precursor protein.

TABLE 2

DISSOCIATION OF FAP AMYLOID FIBRILS INTO PREALBUMIN-LIKE COMPONENTS

		Immunoreactivity Against Prealbumin Antiserum	Protein of the Corresponding Molecular Weight by SDS-PAGE
Dissociating agents of non-covalent bond	DMSO	–	–
	Urea	+	+
	Guanidine-HCl	+	+
Reducing agents	DTT	+ +	+ +
	2-ME	+ +	+ +

In clinical application of DMSO to FAP patients, we obtained an improvement rate of approximately 40%. On the basis of this fact, we tried to analyze the changes in urinary-excreted proteins and compare between pre- and posttreatment stages. After DMSO treatment, proteins of various molecular weights (such as prealbumin, IgG-, IgA- and kappa-type light chain-like proteins) were increasingly excreted. It is assumed that some of them may be simply a constituent in amyloid fibril formation and some may be playing more important roles in amyloidgenesis as a precursor protein and/or its fragments.

In vitro effects of DMSO on extracted amyloid protein were somewhat different from those of other denaturating or reducing agents. It was quite evident that gel filtration through Sephadex-G column equilibrated with DMSO induced dissociation of noncovalent bond of the amyloid protein. Nevertheless, DMSO was less potent to dissolve it into prealbumin-related substances, which have been advocated as a factor in amyloidgenesis of FAP. In TABLE 2 we compared DMSO with other agents such as urea, guanidine-HCl, DTT, and 2-ME from viewpoints of immunochemistry expecting the appearance of prealbumin-like immunoreactivity and SDS-PAGE. Only DMSO failed to dissolve an amyloid protein to prealbumin-related substances either immunochemically or electrophoretically. Nevertheless, clinical trial of DMSO for amyloidosis therapy was deemed necessary on the basis of the aforementioned results. The exact mechanism of DMSO actions on amyloidosis must await future investigations.

SUMMARY

DMSO was therapeutically administered to patients with FAP and in about half of the patients there was some clinical improvement.

Urinary proteins were analyzed biochemically and immunochemically before and after DMSO administration in seven cases of amyloidosis. As the results, increased excretion of various proteins of different molecular weights in the urine was observed depending on cases and examined organs.

The *in vitro* effects of DMSO on amyloid proteins were examined. DMSO-degraded amyloid proteins showed void-volume materials and lower molecular weight components on Sephadex G column elution profiles as did guanidine-degraded amyloid protein. Among various denaturing or reducing agents, DMSO is the least potent in dissolving amyloid fibrils into prealbumin-related proteins.

ACKNOWLEDGMENTS

We express gratitude to the coworkers of our department, Drs. Yamamura, Shimoyama, Togo, Tokinobu, and Nakane. We are also thankful to Drs. Mochizuki and Nakano of Nagano Central Hospital for their collaborations. We are much obliged to Professor Pras for his assistance with the experiments and valuable discussions.

REFERENCES

1. OSSERMAN, E., T. ISOBE & M. FARHANGI. 1976. Effect of dimethyl sulfoxide in the treatment of amyloidosis. *In* Amyloidosis. O. Wegelius & A. Pasternack, Eds.: 553–564. Academic Press. London.
2. KITO, S., N. FUJIMORI, M. YAMAMOTO, E. ITOGA, Y. TOYOIZUMI, T. KAKIZAKI, Z. MITSUI, H. ICHIKAWA, T. MORIYAMA, K. WAKATSUKI, S. SATO & I. IWASAKI. 1973. One focus of familial amyloid polyneuropathy. Nihon Rinsho **31**(7): 2326–2338.
3. KITO, S., E. ITOGA, K. KAMIYA, T. KISHIDA & Y. YAMAMURA. 1980. Studies on familial amyloid polyneuropathy in Ogawa village, Japan. Eur. Neurol. **19**(1): 141–151.
4. KITO, S., E. ITOGA, Y. ITO, T. KISHIDA, Y. YAMAMURA, T. SHINODA & Y. YAGUCHI. 1979. Clinical and biochemical studies on the Ogawa Village type hereditary amyloidosis with DMSO therapy. *In* Amyloid and Amyloidosis. G.G. Glenner, P.P. Costa & A.F. de Freitas, Eds.: 153–165. Excerpta Medica. Amsterdam.
5. SHINODA, T., Y. YAGUCHI, S. KITO, E. ITOGA & Y. ITO. 1979. Chemical characterization of amyloid fibril proteins in hereditary amyloidosis. *In* Amyloid and Amyloidosis. G.G. Glenner, P.P. Costa & A.F. de Freitas, Eds.: 166–170. Excerpta Medica. Amsterdam.
6. PRAS, M., M. SCHUBERT, D. ZUCKER-FRANKLIN, A. RIMON & E.C. FRANKLIN. 1968. The characterization of soluble amyloid prepared in water. J. Clin. Invest. **47**(6): 924–933.
7. ISOBE, T. & E.F. OSSERMAN. 1976. Effects of dimethyl sulfoxide (DMSO) on Bence Jones protein, amyloid fibrils and casein-induced amyloidosis. *In* Amyloidosis. O. Wegelius & A. Pasternack, Eds.: 247–257. Academic Press. London.

8. NATVIG, J.B., G. HUSBY, K. SLETTEN & T. MICHAILSEN. 1976. Structural and antigenic classification of amyloid fibril proteins in primary, myeloma-associated and secondary amyloidosis. *In* Amyloidosis. O. Wegelius & Pasternack, Eds.: 259–271. Academic Press. London.

9. COSTA, P.P., A.S. FIGUEIRA & F. R. BRAVO. 1978. Amyloid fibril protein related to the prealbumin in familial amyloidotic polyneuropathy. Proc. Natl. Acad. Sci. USA **75**(9): 4499–4503.

DIMETHYL SULFOXIDE IN THE TREATMENT
OF AA AMYLOIDOSIS*

Martin H. van Rijswijk, L. Ruinen, A. J. M. Donker,
J. J. de Blécourt, and E. Mandema

Department of Medicine
University Hospital
59 Oostersingel
9713 EZ Groningen, the Netherlands

INTRODUCTION

Amyloidosis is a disease characterized by organ function disturbances caused by the extracellular deposition of amyloid fibrils. These fibrils are composed of polypeptide chains arranged in a particular molecular structure, the beta-pleated sheet configuration. This molecular structure is common to all types of amyloid and is held responsible for its characteristic properties: insolubility under physiologic conditions, resistance to proteolysis, and binding affinity for Congo red, resulting in a characteristic green birefringence with polarized light. The first two properties account for the replacement and subsequent destruction of vital tissues by amyloid. Differences in the clinical manifestations of amyloid disease can now be related to differences in the primary structure of amyloid fibril proteins.[1] The characteristics of the main types of systemic non-familial amyloidosis are summarized in TABLE 1. In systemic amyloid protein A (AA) amyloidosis, long-standing elevation of serum amyloid protein A (SAA) levels as part of the acute-phase reaction[2] is considered to be a prerequisite for AA amyloid formation. It should be noticed however, that a second predisposing factor must be present to cause the conversion of SAA into amyloid fibrils. The best treatment in case of systemic AA amyloidosis is the eradication of the associated disease or a sufficient suppression of its inflammatory activity. In systemic amyloid protein (light-chain derived) (AL) amyloidosis, the main aim will obviously be to reduce the production of the monoclonal component. A new therapeutic approach was indicated by Isobe and Osserman,[3] who demonstrated that amyloid fibrils could be partially dissolved in DMSO and that treatment of amyloidotic mice with DMSO resulted in a reduction of the amount of amyloid. Their results of DMSO treatment in six patients with AL amyloidosis remained inconclusive.[4] Supportive evidence was provided by Kedar[5] who while studying the AA amyloid mouse model observed a disappearance of amyloid and a simultaneous appearance of amyloid-like material in the urine. Subsequently Ravid[6] demonstrated a similar appearance of amyloid-like material in the urine of patients with renal amyloidosis, after a single dose of DMSO. These observations prompted us to investigate the value of DMSO in the treatment of human AA amyloidosis. Our experiences with DMSO will be presented in the following way: longitudinal data of four patients presented as case histories; a transversal study on the significance of SAA levels for the prognosis of systemic AA amyloidosis; a study on the significance of SAA as an indicator of inflammatory activity; a study on the effect of DMSO on

*Research on amyloidosis and on parameters of inflammation is granted by the Netherlands League against Rheumatism.

67

the solubility of AA amyloid fibrils *in vitro;* and a study on the effect of DMSO on the function of neutrophils *in vitro.* These sections will be followed by a general discussion.

CASE HISTORIES

Patients and Methods

All patients underwent careful clinical and laboratory examinations including immunoelectrophoresis of serum and concentrated urine, immunofluorescence study of bone marrow, and echo- and phonocardiography. Amyloidosis was diagnosed by appropriate biopsies, which were examined by the potassium permanganate method[7] and by immunofluorescence with anti-AA antibodies. Measurements of the glomerular filtration rate (GFR) and the effective renal plasma flow (ERPF) were performed with radioisotopes according to the method described by Donker.[8] SAA levels were measured by radioimmunoassay as described elsewhere.[9] C-reactive protein (CRP) levels were measured by radial

TABLE 1

CLINICOPATHOLOGICAL CORRELATIONS IN SYSTEMIC NON-FAMILIAL AMYLOIDOSIS

	Associated Disease	Amyloid Fibril Protein	Precursor Protein	Major Clinical Manifestation
AL amyloidosis	monoclonal gammopathy	AL	immunoglobulin light chain	nephropathy cardiomyopathy neuropathy
AA amyloidosis	chronic inflammation	AA	SAA	nephropathy

immunodiffusion (LC-Partigen, Behringwerke, Germany). Measurements of serum amyloid P-component (SAP) levels were kindly performed by Dr. M. B. Pepys.[10] DMSO was obtained from E. Merck, Darmstadt, Germany (product No. 2931), and prescribed in the following way: for oral administration: DMSO 200 grams, distilled water ad 1000 ml, three times daily 25 ml; for intravenous administration: DMSO 100 grams, physiologic saline or glucose ad 1000 ml, three times daily 50 ml.

Patient 1

Seropositive rheumatoid arthritis (RA) since 1955, treated with gold and chloroquine (FIGURE 1). Rectal biopsy (February 1977), renal biopsy (September 1977), and liver biopsy revealed extensive amyloid deposition of the AA type. Treatment with DMSO was instituted in September 1977 (GFR 5, ERPF 24 ml/min) and resulted in a remarkable improvement in renal function. In addition there was a decrease of pain, an increase of joint mobility, and a decrease of SAA and CRP levels. After five weeks the dosage of DMSO was reduced from 15 to 10 grams/day, without any particular problems. A renal biopsy was repeated in May 1978 and did not show any evidence of amyloid dissolution. In October 1978 an

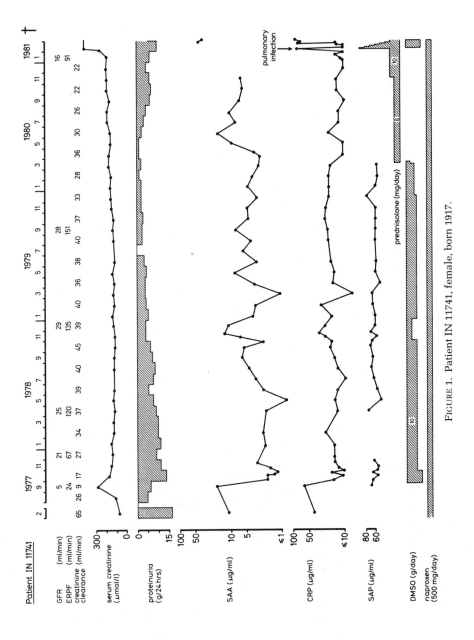

FIGURE 1. Patient IN 11741, female, born 1917.

attempt was made to further reduce the DMSO dosage to 5 grams/daily. This resulted in an increase of SAA and CRP levels and an increase of joint symptoms. In March 1980 therapy was changed from DMSO to prednisolone (3 × 2 mg/day). This change was followed by an increase of SAA levels, a gradual decline of renal function and an increase of proteinuria. Because of this unsatisfactory development, the patient was hospitalized in January 1981 to make a reappraisal of the treatment. At the time of admission GFR and ERPF values had dropped to 16 and

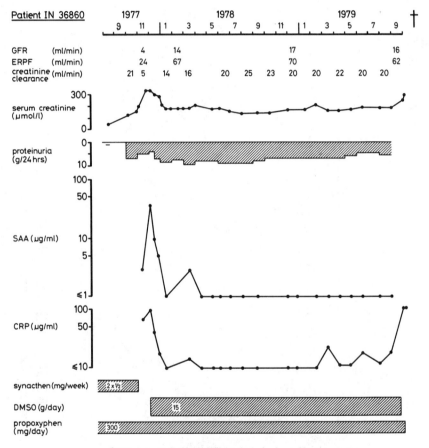

FIGURE 2. Patient IN 36860, female, born 1924.

91 ml/min respectively, and proteinuria had increased to 6 grams/24 hours. Her stay in the hospital was then complicated by a pulmonary infection, which was treated with antibiotics, bronchodilators, and a short course of high-dose prednisolone. Consequently, renal function rapidly deteriorated. The idea of further treatment with chronic intermittent hemodialysis was relinquished. Resumption of DMSO treatment could not alter the course in that stage and the patient succumbed.

At autopsy, severe generalized amyloidosis was found, particularly in the kidneys. There were no signs of thrombo-embolic processes, in particular no renal vein thrombosis. Retrospective evaluation of SAA and CRP levels indicated that the short high-dose prednisolone course given in February 1981, may have initiated the rapid progression of amyloidosis by means of a rebound phenomenon, evoked by too fast a lowering of the prednisolone dosage. The course of the serum amyloid P component (SAP) levels is inconclusive.

Patient 2

Seropositive RA since 1953, treated with chloroquine, gold, D-penicillamine, and synthetic adrenocorticotropic hormone (Synacthen). A decline of renal function was noted in October 1977 (FIGURE 2). Shortly after discontinuation of the Synacthen treatment renal function rapidly deteriorated to GFR 4, ERPF 67 ml/min. Both renal and rectal biopsy revealed AA amyloid deposition. DMSO treatment resulted in remarkable improvement of renal function, SAA and CRP levels dropped significantly, and the patient experienced a decrease of joint complaints. DMSO treatment was uneventful until at the end of September 1979 an acute "flu-like" illness with nausea and vomiting prevented her from taking DMSO. In the first instance she was treated by her general physician at home with antibiotics and bronchodilators because of suspected pneumonia. After two weeks however, she had to be admitted to the hospital, suffering from progressive shortness of breath. At admission there was a prominent right- and left-sided cardiac failure and a renal insufficiency. It was at that moment unclear whether the cardiac failure was due to primary myocardial disease (e.g. viral myocarditis or myocardial infarction) or due to overhydration secondary to renal failure. Supportive treatment was instituted but the patient succumbed within 24 hours. Unfortunately our request for autopsy was not granted. It remains unclear which type of intercurrent disease had prevented her from taking DMSO, but the abrupt discontinuation of DMSO treatment may well be the cause of the rapid development of renal failure.

Patient 3

Seropositive RA since 1974, treated with gold until proteinuria developed in 1975. A renal biopsy revealed membranous glomerulopathy without signs of amyloidosis. Treatment was then continued with prednisolone 10 to 5 mg/day and azathioprine 100 to 50 mg/day (FIGURE 3). In March 1978 she was hospitalized because of persistently active polyarthritis, declining renal function, and hepatomegaly. A rectal biopsy was negative for amyloid, but both renal and liver biopsy showed extensive deposition of AA amyloid. Prednisolone and azathioprine were discontinued and DMSO treatment was instituted. Note (FIGURE 3) the rebound phenomenon of SAA and CRP levels upon discontinuation of the prednisolone. In February 1980 renal function had slightly improved and proteinuria had disappeared. Although a repeated liver biopsy revealed only a slight reduction of amyloid deposition, liver size had returned to normal by both clinical and scintigraphic examination. At that moment it was decided to perform a total hip arthroplasty and DMSO was gradually replaced by prednisolone in order to avoid possible interactions between DMSO and anesthetic drugs. Note the temporary elevation of SAA and CRP levels as a result of major surgery. In the

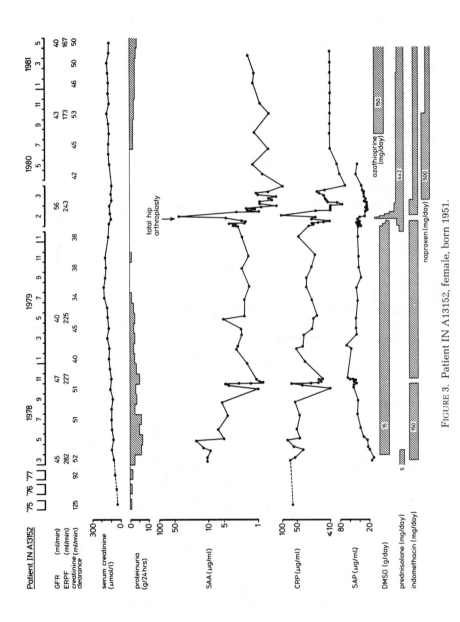

FIGURE 3. Patient IN A13152, female, born 1951.

postoperative period azathioprine was added to the treatment. Under this regimen however, renal function showed a gradual decline and proteinuria again appeared. Renal biopsy was repeated in December 1981 and did not reveal an increase of amyloid, but did reveal the development of nephrosclerosis. This may be related to an insufficient control of her blood pressure. By now this patient has again been started on DMSO treatment. It should be noted, that GFR and ERPF

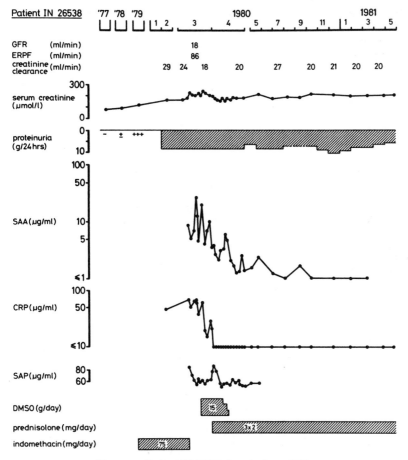

FIGURE 4. Patient IN 26538, female, born 1908.

values were all measured without indomethacin. Creatinine clearance values however, may be negatively influenced by indomethacin treatment, depending on the degree of sodium depletion (sodium excretion ranged from 40 to 100 mmol/24 hours). In this patient, SAP levels tended to show a negative correlation with SAA levels, which would fit in with the idea of SAP consumption during the process of amyloid fibril formation. Such a correlation could not be demonstrated in the other patients.

Patient 4

Seropositive RA since 1953, treated with gold and chloroquine. In December 1979 a decline of renal function and the development of proteinuria were noted. Renal biopsy was performed in March 1980 and revealed the deposition of AA amyloid. Although renal histology already showed extensive interstitial fibrosis and atrophy of tubules, it was decided to start with DMSO, to see whether there was still a reversible component (FIGURE 4). When renal function appeared to be stable during two weeks of treatment, DMSO was gradually replaced by prednisolone (3 × 2 mg/day). In the following year renal function remained stable, but by now is gradually declining. Social circumstances however, do not permit resumption of DMSO treatment. The course of SAP levels is inconclusive.

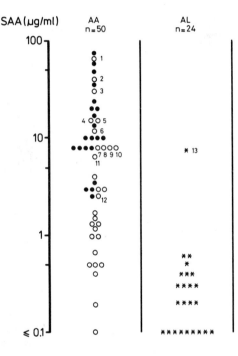

FIGURE 5. The prognostic significance of SAA levels in systemic amyloidosis. (●) AA amyloidosis with progression to renal failure, (O) AA amyloidosis with stable renal function for more then one year after the time of diagnosis, and (★) AL amyloidosis. (For explanation of the indices see text).

THE SIGNIFICANCE OF SAA LEVELS FOR THE PROGNOSIS IN SYSTEMIC
AA AMYLOIDOSIS

SAA levels were measured in serum samples from 74 patients with systemic non-familial amyloidosis. As a pathophysiologic relationship between SAA levels and amyloidosis can only reasonably be expected in patients with AA amyloidosis, the patients were divided into a group with AA amyloidosis, (N = 50) and a group with AL amyloidosis (N = 24). From each patient one representative SAA value was included nearest to the time of diagnosis. The results are shown in FIGURE 5.

Explanation of the indices in FIGURE 5: (1) Patient with systemic AA amyloidosis associated with hypernephroma. Following curative resection of the hypernephroma, SAA levels returned to normal. Follow-up: four years. (2) Patient with systemic AA amyloidosis associated with RA. During DMSO treatment SAA levels decreased and renal function stabilized. Follow-up: two years. (3) Patient with systemic AA amyloidosis associated with RA. Treatment with prednisolone and azathioprine resulted in a decrease of SAA levels and a stabilization of renal function. Follow-up: two years. (4) Patient with idiopathic systemic AA amyloidosis. During hospitalization SAA levels gradually normalized without any specific treatment and renal function stabilized. Follow-up: two years. (5) Patient with systemic AA amyloidosis associated with RA. Treatment with prednisolone resulted in decrease of SAA levels and a stabilization of renal function. Follow-up: one year. (6) Patient with systemic AA amyloidosis associated with RA. Treatment with DMSO resulted in a decrease of SAA levels and a stabilization of renal function (See also FIGURE 3). (7) Patient with systemic AA amyloidosis associated with RA, who had been treated with a low dosage of prednisolone for several years. After an increase of the prednisolone dosage SAA levels decreased and renal function stabilized. Follow-up: two years. (8) Patient with idiopathic systemic AA amyloidosis. During treatment with DMSO SAA levels decreased and renal function stabilized. Follow-up: two years. (9) Patient with systemic AA amyloidosis associated with RA. Treatment with prednisolone resulted in a decrease of SAA levels and a stabilization of renal function. Follow-up: two years. (10) See FIGURE 4. (11) Patient with systemic AA amyloidosis associated with RA. DMSO treatment was badly tolerated and resulted in irregular use (six months). Consequently this patient was treated with prednisolone, which he also used irregularly and finally discontinued at his own responsibility. During a follow-up of two years his renal function is now gradually declining. (12) Patient with systemic AA amyloidosis associated with RA. Treatment with prednisolone resulted in a decrease of SAA levels and a stabilization of renal function. Follow-up: 1.5 year. (13) Patient with systemic AL amyloidosis associated with multiple myeloma. The serum sample was taken during an acute-phase reaction caused by bronchopneumia.

N.B. the patients described in FIGURES 1 and 2 are represented by closed circles in this figure.

The results shown in FIGURE 5 illustrate the role of SAA as the substrate for AA amyloid fibril formation. Highly elevated SAA levels in patients with AA amyloidosis are related to progression to renal failure, with the exception of those patients in whom SAA levels could be reduced by some form of treatment. In patients with AA amyloidosis showing only moderately elevated SAA levels, renal function remained stationary. In patients with AL amyloidosis SAA levels are not related to the progression of their amyloid disease.

SAA AS AN INDICATOR OF INFLAMMATORY ACTIVITY

Patients and Methods

Patients were randomly chosen from the out-patient department of the Division of Rheumatology. The majority of them met with American Rheumatism Association (ARA) criteria[11] for probable, definite, or classical rheumatoid arthritis (N = 297). The remaining patients suffered from miscellaneous seronegative polyarthritides (N = 139). Inflammatory activity was assessed using clinical and laboratory variables, which are empirically known to be associated with active polyarthritis. The score system for inflammatory activity is shown below: patient complaints (morning stiffness/pain on motion) 0–2; physical examination (grip strength/synovial swelling) 0–2; ESR (0–15 mm/16–50 mm > 50 mm in the first hour) 0–2; serum iron level ($\geqslant$ 10 μmol/L < 10 μmol/L) 0–1; serum alkaline phosphatase ($\leqslant$ 120 U/L > 120 U/L) 0–1; and thrombocyte count ($\leqslant$ 250 × 10^9/L > 250 × 10^9/L) 0–1. The correlation coefficient was calculated by linear regression analysis.

Results

SAA levels in patients with polyarthritis show a striking correlation with the inflammatory activity as assessed by the score system described above (FIGURE 6,

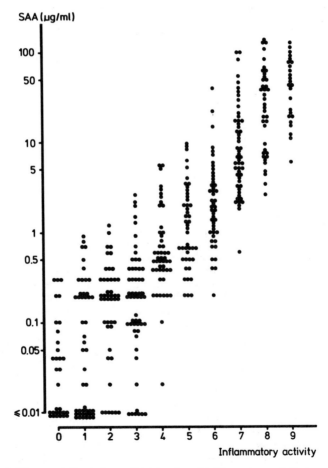

FIGURE 6. The correlation between SAA levels and inflammatory activity in patients with polyarthritis (N = 436).

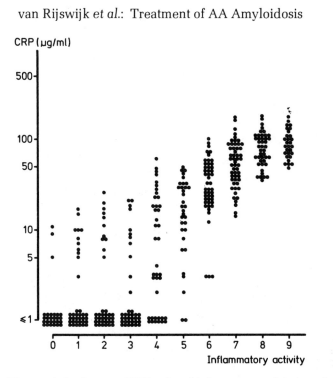

FIGURE 7. The correlation between CRP levels and inflammatory activity in patients with polyarthritis (N = 394).

correlation coefficient: 0.873). A similar correlation could be demonstrated for CRP levels (FIGURE 7, correlation coefficient: 0.827). Furthermore the course of SAA levels closely parallelled the effect of antirheumatic drug treatment in patients with RA (FIGURE 8).

THE EFFECT OF DMSO ON THE SOLUBILITY OF AMYLOID FIBRILS *In Vitro*

Methods

AA amyloid fibrils were isolated from the thyroid of a patient with systemic AA amyloidosis.[12] In short, amyloid fibrils were extracted from a homogenized, saline-washed tissue preparation, by repeated washing with distilled water according to the method described by Pras.[13] The protein content of the supernatants was estimated by measurement of the optical density at 280 nm (OD 280 nm). Supernatants with an OD 280 nm of 0.3 and more were separately pooled and lyophilized. After the OD 280 nm of the supernatants of the water washings had dropped below 0.3, two additional washings were performed with 50% (vol/vol) DMSO in distilled water. Supernatants with an OD 280 nm of 0.3 or more were pooled and lyophilized. The presence of amyloid fibrils in these preparations was established by electron microscopy. Samples of water- and DMSO-extractable fibrils were denatured with guanidine-HCl and applied to a Sepharose Cl-6B

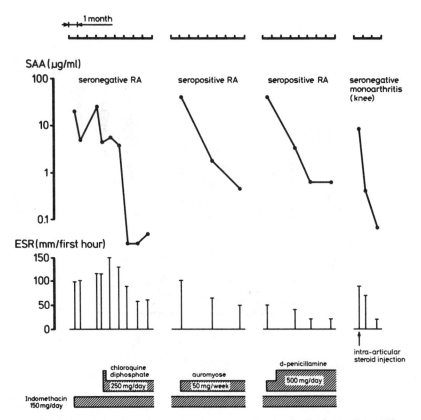

FIGURE 8. The effect of antirheumatic therapy on the level of SAA in four different patients. A comparison is made with the concomitant ESR values.

column. The amyloid fibril protein was recovered from peak 4 (A schematic representation of the procedure so far is given in FIGURE 9). The amyloid protein preparations were analyzed for purity and molecular weight by sodium dodecyl-sulfate polyacrylamide gel electrophoresis (SDS-PAGE), and subsequently identified as AA protein by N-terminal amino acid sequence analysis.[12]

Results

It will be clear from FIGURE 9, that even after exhaustive washings with distilled water, a significant additional amount of amyloid fibrils could be obtained with DMSO. Although both water-soluble and DMSO-soluble fibril preparations showed perfectly clear solutions, amyloid fibrils appeared to be intact on electron microscopy. This is unlike the situation after denaturation with guanidine-HCl, when the fibrillar structure has totally disappeared. Elution profiles after guanidine-HCl denaturation, SDS-PAGE patterns, and amino acid sequences were identical for water- and DMSO-soluble fibril preparations.

THE EFFECT OF DMSO ON INFLAMMATORY CELLS *In Vitro* AND *In Vivo*

Introduction

Several possibilities have been indicated by which DMSO could exert an anti-inflammatory action. Weissmann[14] described a potentiation of the membrane-stabilizing effect of chloroquine and cortisone *in vitro*. Such an effect may be of importance *in vivo*. A second anti-inflammatory mechanism of DMSO was indicated by Repine,[15] who demonstrated the conversion of hydroxyl radicals into methane in the presence of DMSO. This should imply that DMSO acts as a hydroxyl radical scavenger. A third observation of importance was presented by Ambruso,[16] who showed that iron when bound to lactoferrin, a specific granule constituent of polymorphonuclear leukocytes, greatly enhances the generation of highly reactive oxygen radicals. In the study reported here, DMSO was shown to exert an inhibitory effect on the release of specific granule constituents by polymorphonuclear leukocytes.

Materials and Methods

Neutrophils were isolated by Percoll centrifugation. The dextran sedimentation step was omitted in order to avoid inappropriate stimulation of the cells. The

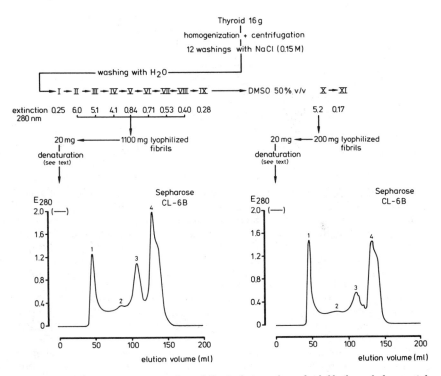

FIGURE 9. Schematic representation of the isolation of amyloid fibrils and the partial purification of protein AA.

experiments were performed in sealed plastic tubes, part of them coated with aggregated human IgG. Lactoferrin levels in the cell-free supernatants were measured by an enzyme-linked immunosorbent assay, using microtiter plates coated with rabbit anti-human lactoferrin. After addition of the antigen in appropriate dilutions followed by thorough washing, a rabbit anti-human lactoferrin-horseradish peroxidase conjugate was added to the wells. After thorough washings ortho-phenylene-diamine-di-HCl was added as a substrate. The reaction product was quantified measuring the OD 492 nm. The dilution curves and the ultimate concentrations were calculated using a computerized Log-Logit transformation.[17] Methane (CH_4) concentrations in samples of the head space gas were measured by gas chromatography.

Results

Aggregated human IgG coated to the wall of the reaction tubes causes a significant release of lactoferrin from human neutrophils as shown in FIGURE 10.

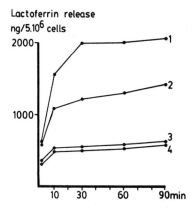

Lactoferrin release
ng/5.10^6 cells

FIGURE 10. The influence of DMSO on the release of lactoferrin by polymorphonuclear leukocytes (number of cells: 5×10^6/ml). (1) Aggregated IgG-coated tubes, (2) Aggregated IgG-coated tubes + 1% DMSO (w/vol), (3) Uncoated tubes, and (4) Uncoated tubes + 1% DMSO (w/vol).

In the uncoated tubes no release of lactoferrin could be demonstrated. In the presence of 1% DMSO (w/vol) the release of lactoferrin is markedly inhibited. In the uncoated tubes no effect of DMSO on the lactoferrin levels could be demonstrated. In this system no methane production occurred in the presence of DMSO within the duration of the experiment, in contrast to experiments where zymosan was used as the stimulating agent. Regarding the observations of Repine et al.,[15] this should imply that no hydroxyl radicals are generated in this system. Consequently the inhibition by DMSO of the lactoferrin release can not be attributed to its function as a scavenger of cytotoxic hydroxyl radicals. It is conceivable, that the inhibition of lactoferrin release by DMSO relies on its membrane-stabilizing properties. In such a concept DMSO may exhibit its anti-inflammatory action in two different ways: by scavenging hydroxyl radicals; and by inhibition of the lactoferrin release, which in turn will lead to a reduction of the hydroxyl radical generation. It remains to be investigated whether the inhibition of the release of other mediators of inflammation adds to this anti-inflammatory action. An example of the effect of DMSO on the lactoferrin release in vivo is shown in FIGURE 11. This patient attended our department very

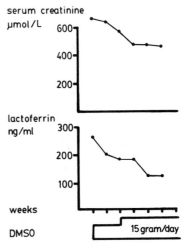

FIGURE 11. The effect of DMSO on plasma lactoferrin levels and serum creatinine in a patient with ankylosing spondylitis and systemic AA amyloidosis.

recently with renal failure due to systemic AA amyloidosis (renal and rectal biopsy) associated with ankylosing spondylitis. Plasma lactoferrin levels dropped significantly during DMSO treatment.

GENERAL DISCUSSION

Although the idea that DMSO might be able to dissolve amyloid prompted us in 1977 to investigate the value of this drug in the treatment of human amyloidosis, we did not obtain evidence for such a process *in vivo*, by repeated biopsies, or by a search for the appearance of amyloid-like material in the urine. The latter procedure does not seem to be of clinical value as has been discussed by several groups.[18-21] We did find several indications for an anti-inflammatory effect of DMSO: the decrease of joint complaints in RA patients treated with DMSO; the decrease of CRP and SAA levels indicating a decrease of inflammatory activity; and the inhibition of neutrophil degranulation by DMSO *in vitro* and *in vivo*. The mechanisms by which DMSO might favorably alter the course of systemic AA amyloidosis are summarized in TABLE 2.

As has been discussed before, an important effect of DMSO might be a reduction of the amount of hydroxyl radicals. Such a reduction may be achieved

TABLE 2

MECHANISMS BY WHICH DMSO MAY FAVORABLY ALTER THE COURSE
OF AA AMYLOIDOSIS

1. DMSO is a scavenger of hydroxyl radicals.[15]
2. DMSO inhibits the release of lactoferrin, which is necessary for the generation of hydroxyl radicals.[16]
3. DMSO may potentiate the membrane-stabilizing action of other compounds (e.g. cortisol and chloroquine).[14]
4. DMSO may increase the susceptibility of amyloid fibrils for amyloid-degrading enzymes.

on the one hand by direct conversion of hydroxyl radicals into methane, and on the other hand indirectly by an inhibition of the release of lactoferrin, necessary for the generation of these hydroxyl radicals. Furthermore the inhibition of neutrophil degranulation will also reduce the effects of other mediators of inflammation, among which are many potentially destructive proteolytic enzymes. In addition, the potentiation by DMSO of the membrane-stabilizing effect of cortisone, as described by Weissman,[14] may be of relevance for the *in vivo* situation.

A second point that merits discussion is the remarkably rapid improvement of renal function observed in some of the patients during DMSO treatment. Such an improvement could not be explained by a reduction of the amount of amyloid in the kidney. Recently attention has been drawn to the fact, that renal function in amyloidosis is mainly related to the development of interstitial fibrosis and to the presence or abscence of an interstitial inflammatory reaction preceding fibrosis.

Careful examination of renal biopsies indeed supported such a relationship. Particularly in those patients biopsied in the early phase of development of renal failure, we found an interstial tissue reaction with an increased cellularity and a separation of tubules. It is conceivable that such a histologic picture precedes the development of fibrosis. It may well be that the action of DMSO on such an interstitial inflammatory reaction accounts for the rapid improvement of renal function in these patients. Such a mechanism would imply that an improvement of renal function during DMSO treatment can only be expected in those patients with rapidly declining renal function, i.e. when there is still a reversible component in the interstitial tissue reaction. In patients with a slowly declining renal function, fibrosis will run parallel to the development of renal insufficiency and one may only expect to maintain renal function on the pretreatment level. The observation that DMSO is capable of inhibiting fibroblast proliferation[22] fits in with such a hypothesis. Supportive arguments for an interstitial inflammatory reaction in the kidney in response to amyloid deposition may be derived from the observation of ^{67}Ga-citrate accumulation in the kidneys of patients with renal amyloidosis.[12,23] As gallium accumulation is due to its binding to lactoferrin,[24-26] an additional anti-inflammatory effect of DMSO exerted locally in the kidneys is conceivable.

A third point of discussion may be the degradation of AA amyloid and its precursor SAA. Kedar reported the existence of an amyloid degrading serum factor.[27] Whether the increased *in vitro* solubility of amyloid fibrils in DMSO could also make them more liable to the supposed degrading factor *in vivo* remains to be established. The degradation of SAA has been shown to occur by membrane-bound enzymes of monocytes and neutrophils.[28,29] It is unclear whether DMSO has any influence on such a process. The last point of discussion must be the safety of DMSO. With the administration schedules used, no serious side effects were encountered, with the only exception of the potentiation of drugs with a receptor-mediated action as previously reported.[30] We have the same experience of safety in the cases of autologous bone marrow transplantation, where DMSO is used as a cryopreservative.

CONCLUSIONS

In our experience DMSO is a non-toxic drug. DMSO may be of value in the treatment of human AA amyloidosis. The effect of DMSO in AA amyloidosis is probably due to its anti-inflammatory properties. Abrupt discontinuation of DMSO treatment in AA amyloidosis should be avoided.

REFERENCES

1. GLENNER, G. G. 1980. N. Engl. J. Med. **30:** 1283–1292, 1333–1343.
2. KUSHNER, I., J. E. VOLANAKIS & H. GEWURZ, Eds. 1982. Ann. N.Y. Acad. Sci. **389.**
3. ISOBE, T. & E. F. OSSERMAN. 1976. In Amyloidosis. O. Wegelius & A. Pasternack, Eds.: 247–257. Academic Press. London.
4. OSSERMAN, E. F., T. ISOBE & M. FARHANGI. 1976. In Amyloidosis. O. Wegelius & A. Pasternack, Eds.: 553–564. Academic Press. London.
5. KEDAR, I., M. GREENWALD & M. RAVID. 1977. Eur. J. Clin. Invest. **7:** 149–150.
6. RAVID M., I. KEDAR & E. SOHAR. 1977. Lancet **1:** 730–731.
7. VAN RIJSWIJK, M. H. & C. W. G. J. VAN HEUSDEN. 1979. Am. J. Pathol. **97:** 43–58.
8. DONKER, A. J. M., G. K. VAN DER HEM, W. J. SLUITER & H. BEEKHUIS. 1977. Neth. J. Med. **20:** 97–103.
9. LIMBURG, P. C., M. H. VAN RIJSWIJK, L. RUINEN, H. J. DE JONG, J. MARRINK, J. J. DE BLECOURT & E. MANDEMA. 1982. In Proc. Amyloid Res. Symp. Reed Books. Chertsey, England. (In press.)
10. PEPYS, M. B. 1981. Clinics Immunol. Allergy **1:** 77–101.
11. ROPES, M. W., G. A. BENNETT, S. COBB, R. JACOX & R. A. JESSAR. 1958. Ann. Rheum. Dis. **18:** 49–53.
12. VAN RIJSWIJK, M. H. 1981. Amyloidosis. University Microfilms Intern. 82–70037. London.
13. PRAS, M., M. SCHUBERT, D. ZUCKER-FRANKLIN, A. RIMON & E. C. FRANKLIN. 1968. J. Clin. Invest. **47:** 924–933.
14. WEISSMANN, G., G. SESSA & V. BEVANS. 1967. Ann. N.Y. Acad. Sci. **141:** 326–332.
15. REPINE, J.E., J. W. EATON, M. W. ANDERS, J. R. HOIDAL & R. B. FOX. 1979. J. Clin. Invest. **64:** 1642–1651.
16. AMBRUSO, D. R. & R. B. JOHNSON. 1981. J. Clin. Invest. **67:** 352–360.
17. RODBARD, D., W. BRIDSON & P. L. RAYFORD. 1969. J. Lab. Clin. Med. **74:** 770–781.
18. SHIRAHAMA, T., M. SKINNER, A. S. COHEN & M. D. BENSON. 1977. N. Engl. J. Med. **297:** 821–823.
19. ORFILA, C., P. DE GRAEVE, A. GUILHEM & J. M. SUC. 1978. Virchows Arch. A. **379:** 113–118.
20. LINDER, L. & M. H. HABER. 1979. Am. J. Clin. Pathol. **71:** 40–42.
21. WINER, R. L., R. B. WUERKER, J. O. ERICKSON & W. L. COOPER. 1979. Am. J. Clin. Pathol. **71:** 36–39.
22. BERLINER, D. L. & A. G. RUHMAN. 1967. Ann. N.Y. Acad. Sci. **141:** 159–164.
23. BEKERMAN, C. & M. I. VYAS. 1976. J. Nucl. Med. **17:** 899–901.
24. HOFFER, P. B., J. HUBERTY & H. KHAYAM-BASHI. 1977. J. Nucl. Med. **18:** 713–717.
25. TZEN, K., Z. H. OSTER, H. N. WAGNER & M. TSAN, 1980. J. Nucl. Med. **21:** 31–35.
26. WEINER, R., P. B. HOFFER & M. L. THAKUR. 1981. J. Nucl. Med. **22:** 32–37.
27. KEDAR, I., E. SOHAR & M. RAVID. 1982. J. Lab. Clin. Med. **99:** 693–700.
28. LAVIE, G., D. ZUCKER-FRANKLIN & E. C. FRANKLIN. 1978. J. Exp. Med. **148:** 1020–1031.
29. SILVERMAN, S. L., E. S. CATHCART, M. SKINNER, A. S. COHEN & L. BURNETT. 1980. In Amyloid and Amyloidosis. G. G. Glenner, P. P. Costa & A. F. Freitas, Eds.: 420–425. Excerpta Medica. Amsterdam.
30. VAN RIJSWIJK, M. H. 1981. Lancet **1:** 41.

EFFECTS OF DIMETHYL SULFOXIDE AND ACUPUNCTURE ON THE CARDIOVASCULAR SYSTEM OF DOGS*

Donald H. Clifford,† Do Chil Lee,‡ and Myung O. Lee‡

†Division of Laboratory Animal Medicine
Department of Anatomy
Medical College of Ohio
Toledo, Ohio 43699
‡Scientific Acupuncture Research Institute of California
11100 Warner Ave., Suite 304
Fountain Valley, California 92708

INTRODUCTION

Dimethyl sulfoxide (DMSO) has been a controversial drug since clinical trials in man were terminated because of the recognition of adverse effects in the eyes of animals.[1] Numerous studies have established that this drug (1) has analgesic properties,[2-4] (2) produces an anti-inflammatory effect,[2-4] (3) penetrates the skin and enhances the penetration of other drugs,[1,4,5] (4) protects tissues against thermal and radiation injury,[2,5] (5) alters cardiac function,[6-9] (6) lowers blood pressure presumably due to vasodilation following cholinesterase inhibition or enhanced binding of calcium,[5,10-13] (7) reduces amyloid deposits in mice,[14] (8) exhibits a bacteriostatic and mycostatic effect,[2,4] (9) is associated with lenticular changes in animals,[1,15,16] (10) causes teratologic effects,[5,17] (11) preferentially destroys abnormal cells in tissue cultures derived from tumors without harming normal cells, induces regression in certain tumors, or causes differentiation of neoplastic cells,[18,19] and (12) produces diuresis,[20] as well as producing other effects in man and animals.[5] Since both DMSO and acupuncture are analgesic and alter function, it was decided to compare their effects on the cardiovascular system in dogs. This model has been used in a continuing comparative study of the effect of analgesic drugs and acupuncture on the cardiovascular system.

Acupuncture produces analgesia as well as autonomic effects on the cardiovascular system.[21-23] Acupuncture by electrocautery at Jen Chung (Go-26) results in a sympathomimetic-like effect on the cardiovascular system in man and animals.[24-27] This form of acupuncture with electrocautery has produced a stronger response than simple needling, twirling, acupressure, needling with electrical stimulation or transcutaneous electrical stimulation in dogs.[28]

MATERIALS AND METHODS

The procedures used in this study have been previously reported.[23,29-31] Following implantation of electromagnetic flowmeters (Zepeda), random source

*This study was partially supported by Biomedical Research Support Grant 5-SO1-RR-05700-10 (NIH) and the Northwest Ohio Chapter of the American Heart Association, and was conducted in conformity with the Guiding Principles in the Care and Use of Animals as approved by the Council of the American Physiological Society.

84

conditioned dogs were observed for ten days to insure that they were healthy and that the flowmeters were well tolerated.

The dogs were subsequently anesthetized with sodium thiopental and maintained on 0.75% halothane in 100% oxygen. Apnea was maintained by an intravenous drip of succinylcholine chloride with the respiratory volume adjusted to maintain $PaCO_2$ at 40 ± 2 torr. The EKG, aortic flow from flowmeter, aortic pressure, exhaled CO_2, stroke volume, $PaCO_2$, PaO_2, and pH were measured or monitored to determine when the dog was in a steady state and during the period of study (FIGURE 1).[27,32]

Dimethyl sulfoxide (DMSO), 100 mg/kg, was administered intravenously by means of a femoral vein. Measurements of the hemodynamic variables (i.e.,

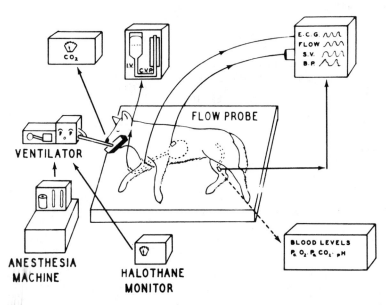

FIGURE 1. Techniques used to measure cardiovascular parameters in dogs under halothane (0.75%) anesthesia. (Courtesy of Lee et al.[32] with permission from the *Canadian Journal of Comparative Medicine*.)

cardiac output, stroke volume, heart rate, mean arterial pressure, pulse pressure, central venous pressure, and total peripheral resistance) were recorded or calculated for five-minute intervals for the first 30 minutes and every 15 minutes for the following 90 minutes. Control values for each animal were determined at 15 and 30 minutes prior to the administration of dimethyl sulfoxide or the application of acupuncture at Jen Chung (Go-26) point and expressed as zero percent.

The acupuncture point, Jen Chung (Go-26), which is located on the philtrum at the midpoint between the upper lip and base of the nose, was located by means of cutaneous impedance equipment, which can be used to measure the resistance through the body at the acupuncture point and adjacent sites.[23,29] Less resistance is recorded at an acupuncture point. Acupuncture was performed by electrocautery. The equipment maintained the 3-mm diameter probe at 80 ± 5°C. The probe was applied for ten minutes.[32]

Changes in hemodynamic variables were determined for the three groups: anesthesia only, intravenous administration of dimethyl sulfoxide (100 mg/kg), and acupuncture by electrocautery at Jen Chung (Go-26) for ten minutes (FIGURES 2-8). The Student's t test (5% level) was used to determine significance for each variable with its initial or control value.

RESULTS

The cardiovascular changes that occurred during the 120 minute period of observation for the three groups (anesthesia only, DMSO, and acupuncture) are

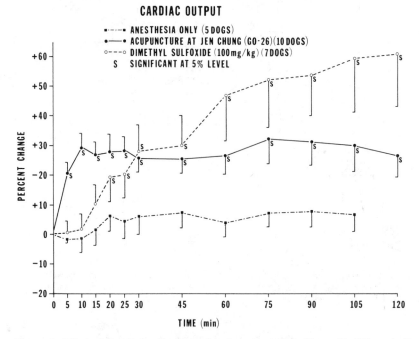

FIGURE 2. Effect of dimethyl sufloxide and acupuncture at Jen Chung (Go-26) on cardiac output of dogs under 0.75% halothane anesthesia. Cardiac output is plotted as percent change from zero, which is the average of two values taken prior to the two-hour period of observation.

graphically summarized in FIGURES 2-8. Values that were significant at the 5% level are indicated. If the function was significantly changed at two or more time intervals it was interpreted as meaningful, significant, for comparative purposes. Values for pH, $PaCO_2$, PaO_2, and base deficit were maintained constant and are not included. Values for acupuncture stimulation at a neutral site were not changed consistently or significantly as previously reported.[32]

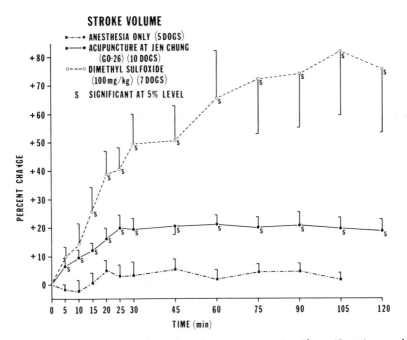

FIGURE 3. Effect of dimethyl sulfoxide and acupuncture at Jen Chung (Go-26) on stroke volume of dogs under 0.75% halothane anesthesia. Stroke volume is plotted as percent change from zero, which is the average of two values taken prior to the two-hour period of observation.

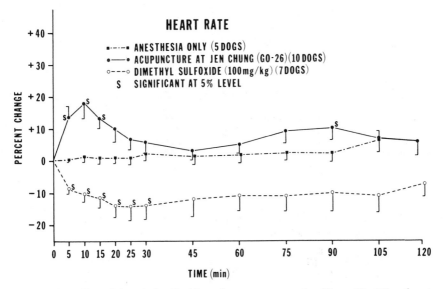

FIGURE 4. Effect of dimethyl sulfoxide and acupuncture at Jen Chung (Go-26) on heart rate of dogs under 0.75% halothane anesthesia. Heart rate is plotted as percent change from zero, which is the average of two values taken prior to the two-hour period of observation.

Annals New York Academy of Sciences

Cardiac Output and Stroke Volume

The cardiac output and stroke volume were significantly increased following the administration of dimethyl sulfoxide (DMSO) and acupuncture (electrocautery) at Jen Chung (Go-26). These functions were not significantly changed at any time interval in animals that were maintained under halothane alone (FIGURES 2 and 3).

Heart Rate

The heart rate decreased significantly following the administration of DMSO and increased significantly after acupuncture at Jen Chung (Go-26) (FIGURE 4).

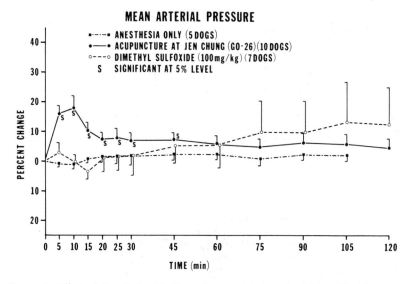

FIGURE 5. Effect of dimethyl sulfoxide and acupuncture at Jen Chung (Go-26) on mean arterial pressure of dogs under 0.75% halothane anesthesia. Mean arterial pressure is plotted as percent change from zero, which is the average of two values taken prior to the two-hour period of observation.

Mean Arterial Pressure and Pulse Pressure

Acupuncture at Jen Chung (Go-26) resulted in a significant increase in mean arterial pressure (FIGURES 5 and 6).

Central Venous Pressure

Central venous pressure was significantly increased following the administration of 100 mg/kg of DMSO (FIGURE 7).

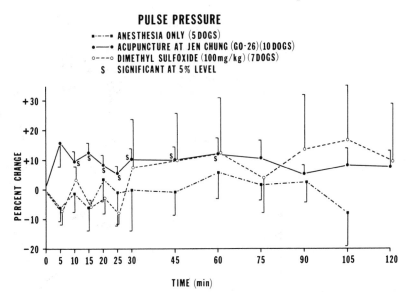

FIGURE 6. Effect of dimethyl sulfoxide and acupuncture at Jen Chung (Go-26) on pulse pressure of dogs under 0.75% halothane anesthesia. Pulse pressure is plotted as percent change from zero, which is the average of two values taken prior to the two-hour period of observation.

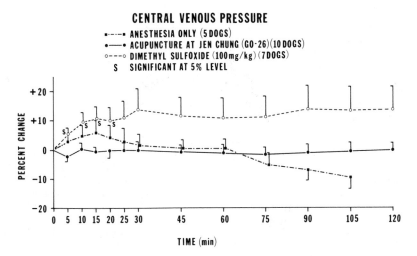

FIGURE 7. Effect of dimethyl sulfoxide and acupuncture at Jen Chung (Go-26) on central venous pressure of dogs under 0.75% halothane anesthesia. Central venous pressure is plotted as percent change from zero, which is the average of two values taken prior to the two-hour period of observation.

Total Peripheral Resistance

Several values were lower following DMSO but not significant due to the larger standard error. Total peripheral resistance was significantly decreased following acupuncture at Jen Chung (Go-26) (FIGURE 8).

DISCUSSION

This study of DMSO and acupuncture is part of a continuing comparison of analgesic drugs and techniques that influence the cardiovascular system. Morphine, sodium salicylate, beta endorphin, and various forms of acupuncture have been the subject to previous studies.[28,33,34] It seems particularly appropriate to

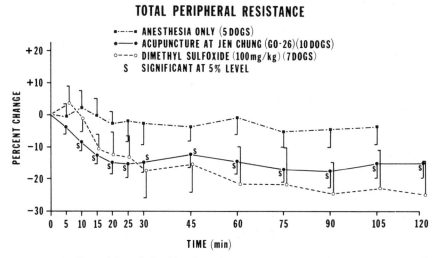

TOTAL PERIPHERAL RESISTANCE

■┄┄┄■ ANESTHESIA ONLY (5 DOGS)
●───● ACUPUNCTURE AT JEN CHUNG (GO-26)(10 DOGS)
○┄┄┄○ DIMETHYL SULFOXIDE (100mg/kg) (7 DOGS)
S   SIGNIFICANT AT 5% LEVEL

FIGURE 8. Effect of dimethyl sulfoxide and acupuncture at Jen Chung (Go-26) on total peripheral resistance of dogs under 0.75% halothane anesthesia. Total peripheral resistance is plotted as percent change from zero, which is the average of two values taken prior to the two-hour period of observation.

compare DMSO and acupuncture since both obtund pain, alter cardiovascular function, and may benefit patients with arthritis and other conditions of the musculoskeletal system. Although DMSO produces changes in the lens of dogs, pigs, and rabbits, ocular changes are not observed in humans and hamsters.[16] Moderate doses of DMSO in man are not associated with other toxic manifestations[20] and there were no toxic or pathologic changes following daily intragastric doses of 1 and 3 ml/kg or daily topical doses of 1, 3, and 9 ml/kg of 90% DMSO for 18 months in Rhesus monkeys.[35]

Acupuncture appears to produce its effects by mediating the release of morphinomimetic substances and/or effecting the autonomic nervous system.[21-23,27,36] Acupuncture at Jen Chung (Go-26) is associated with a prompt and sustained sympathomimetic effect on the cardiovascular system.[27,29]

The administration of DMSO has been associated with vasodilatation and hypotension;[12,37] and positive, negative, or lack of inotropic effects depending on the concentration, species, and other factors.[6,7,38-40] The increase in stroke volume and cardiac output without an increase in blood pressure observed above are consistent with these observations. Similar to the inotropic response an increase, decrease or lack of effect on heart rate (positive or negative chronotropy) may occur following the administration of DMSO.[7,9,11,38-40] Negative chronotropy is dose dependent at 0.14 to 2.82 M concentration of DMSO in rat hearts[38] but after DMSO is washed out, complete recovery from the negative chronotropic effects occurs.[39]

It is difficult to compare the results obtained from dogs under halothane anesthesia used in this study to the effect of DMSO on atrial strips of guinea pigs, rats, and rabbits reported by other investigators. Blockade of atrial adrenoceptors with propranolol or phentolamine prior to the administration of DMSO or catecholamine depletion by pretreatment with resperine does not influence the inotropic effects.[38]

Acupuncture at Jen Chung (Go-26) appears to be mediated by the sympathetic nervous system since it can be blocked by propranolol. The action of DMSO appears to involve more than a simple autonomic effect. Calcium ion binding and the enzymatic changes that have been suggested by other authors as possible mechanisms of action await further study.[11,12,40,41]

Summary

The intravenous administration of dimethyl sulfoxide (100 mg/kg) resulted in a significant increase in cardiac output, stroke volume, central venous pressure, and a significant decrease in heart rate. Acupuncture by electrocautery at Jen Chung (Go-26) produced a significant increase in cardiac output, stroke volume, heart rate, mean arterial pressure, and pulse pressure and a significant decrease in total peripheral resistance in dogs under 0.75% halothane anesthesia. Both DMSO and acupuncture elicit an analgesic effect and enhance cardiovascular function as exemplified by an increase in the cardiac output.

Acknowledgments

The authors wish to thank Miss Carol Perkins and Mr. Jerry Lubinski for aid with the illustrations, and Mrs. Patti Barrett and Mrs. Carolyn Stilwell for aid in preparing the manuscript. The authors are also indebted to Professor Lucien E. Morris for his encouragement and guidance.

References

1. Rubin, L. F. 1975. Toxicity of dimethyl sulfoxide alone and in combination. Ann. N.Y. Acad. Sci. **243** (Part 2): 98–103.
2. Jacob, S. W., R. J. Herschler & E. E. Rosenbaum. 1965. Dimethyl sulfoxide (DMSO): Laboratory and clinical evaluation. J. Am. Vet. Med. Assoc. **147**: 1350–1359.
3. Jones, L. M., N. H. Booth & L. E. McDonald. 1977. Veterinary Pharmacology and Therapeutics. 4th edit. The Iowa State University Press. Ames, Iowa.

4. WOOD, D. C. & J. WOOD. 1975. Pharmacologic and biochemical considerations of dimethyl sulfoxide. Ann. N.Y. Acad. Sci. **243** (Part 1): 7-19.
5. ARONSON, C. E., T. E. POWERS & S. F. SCHEIDY. 1980. Veterinary Pharmaceuticals and Biologicals. pp. 87-95. 1980-1981 Harwal Publishing Company. Media, Penna.
6. SPILKER, B. 1972. Pharmacological studies on dimethyl sulfoxide. Arch. Int. Pharmacodyn. Ther. **200**: 153-167.
7. SHLAFER, M., J. L. MATHENY & A. M. KAROW, JR. 1974. Cardiac inotropism of dimethyl sulfoxide: Osmotic effects and interactions with calcium ion. Eur. J. Pharmacol. **28**: 276-287.
8. MATHENY, J. L., C. M. NORTHUP & A. M. KAROW, JR. 1976. Myocardial function during hypoxia: Effects of dimethyl sulfoxide (DMSO) and different buffers. Cryobiology **13**: 616-624.
9. SHLAFER, M., J. L. MATHENY & A. M. KAROW, JR. 1976. Cardiac chronotropic mechanisms of dimethyl sulphoxide: Inhibition of acetylcholinesterase and antagonism of negative chronotropy. Arch. Int. Pharmacodyn. Ther. **221**: 21-31.
10. SAWADA, M. & M. SATO. 1975. The effect of dimethyl sulfoxide on the neuronal excitability and cholinergic transmission in *Aplysia* ganglion cells. Ann. N.Y. Acad. Sci. **243** (Part 7): 337-357.
11. SAMS, W. M., JR., N. V. CARROLL & P. L. CRANTZ. 1966. Effect of dimethyl-sulfoxide on isolated-innervated skeletal, smooth and cardiac muscle. Proc. Soc. Exp. Biol. Med. **212**: 103-107.
12. JACKSON, C. V., A. M. KAROW & G. O. CARRIER. 1979. Influence of dimethyl sulfoxide (Me$_2$SO) on vascular smooth muscle. Arch. Int. Pharmacodyn. Ther. **237**: 4-15.
13. EVANS, M. H. & P. J. JAGGARD. 1973. Some effects of dimethyl sulphoxide (DMSO) on the frog neuromuscular junction. Br. J. Pharmacol. **49**: 651-657.
14. GLENNER, G. G. 1980. Amyloid deposits and amyloidosis. The B-fibrillosis. N. Engl. J. Med. **302** (Part 2): 1333-1343.
15. RUBIN, L. F. & P. A. MATTIS. 1966. Dimethyl sulfoxide: Lens changes in dogs during oral administration. Science **153**: 83-84.
16. GORDON, D. M. & K. E. KLEBERGER. 1968. The effect of dimethyl sulfoxide (DMSO) on animal and human eyes. Arch. Ophthalmol. **79**: 423-427.
17. CAUJOLLE, F. M. A., D. H. CAUJOLLE, S. B. CROS & M. M. J. CALVERT. 1967. Limits of toxic and teratogenic tolerance of dimethyl sulfoxide. Ann. N.Y. Acad. Sci. **141** (Article 1, Section 3): 110-125.
18. AYRE, J. E. & J. LEGUERRIER. 1967. Some (regressive) effects of DMSO, dexamethasone upon cervical cells in cervical dysplasia and carcinoma *in situ*. Ann. N.Y. Acad. Sci. **141** (Article 1, Section 7): 414-422.
19. DENNIS, A. J. & H. E. WILSON. 1975. Altered mitogenic responses of chronic leukemic lymphocytes and normal human lymphocytes treated with dimethyl sulfoxide. Ann. N.Y. Acad. Sci. **243** (Part 1): 73-80.
20. JACOB, S. W. & D. C. WOOD. 1971. Dimethyl sulfoxide (DMSO)—A status report. Clin. Med. **78**: 21-31.
21. CLIFFORD, D. H. & M. O. LEE. 1978. Trends in acupuncture research. I. Acupuncture in the control of pain. Vet. Med. Small Anim. Clin. **73**: 1513-1516.
22. CLIFFORD, D. H. & M. O. LEE. 1979. Trends in acupuncture research. II. Acupuncture and the autonomic nervous system. Vet. Med. Small Anim. Clin. **74**: 35-40.
23. LEE, M. O., D. C. LEE, S. KIM & D. H. CLIFFORD. 1975. Cardiovascular effects of acupuncture at Tsu San Li (St-36) in dogs. J. Surg. Res. **18**: 51-63.
24. ALTMAN, S. 1979. Acupuncture as an emergency treatment. Calif. Vet. **33**: 6-8.
25. CHOE, Y. T. & S. H. LEE. 1973. Acupuncture and moxibustion, meridians and points. Ko Moon Sa. Seoul, Korea.
26. JANSSENS, L., S. ALTMAN & P. A. M. ROGERS. 1979. Respiratory and cardiac arrest under general anesthesia: Treatment by acupuncture of the nasal philtrum. Vet. Rec. **105**: 273-276.
27. LEE, D. C., M. O. LEE, D. H. CLIFFORD & L. E. MORRIS. 1976. Inhibition of the cardiovascular effects of acupuncture (moxibustion) by propranolol in dogs during halothane anesthesia. Can. Anaesth. Soc. J. **23**: 307-318.

28. LEE, D. C. 1978. Comparison of the cardiovascular effects of acupuncture by various forms of stimulation in dogs during halothane anesthesia. Am. J. Acupuncture **6:** 209–217.
29. LEE, D. C., M. O. LEE & D. H. CLIFFORD. 1975. Cardiovascular effects of moxibustion at Jen Chung (Gov-26) during halothane anesthesia in dogs. Am. J. Chin. Med. **3:** 245–261.
30. LEE, M. O., D. C. LEE & D. H. CLIFFORD. 1978. Cardiovascular effects of acupuncture at Tai Chung (Li-3) point in dogs under halothane anesthesia. Am. J. Acupuncture **6:** 297–304.
31. LEE, M. O., D. H. CLIFFORD, T. TENNEY & D. C. LEE. 1980. Acupuncture at point Gov-1: Cardiovascular effects of needling and twirling in dogs. Am. J. Acupuncture **8:** 31–37.
32. LEE, D. C., D. S. YOON, M. O. LEE & D. H. CLIFFORD. 1977. Some effects of acupuncture at Jen Chung (Gov-26) on cardiovascular dynamics in dogs. Can. J. Comp. Med. **41:** 446–454.
33. LEE, D. C., M. O. LEE & D. H. CLIFFORD. 1980. Comparison of sodium salicylate, morphine sulfate, and acupuncture at Jen Chung (Go-26) on the cardiovascular system of dogs. Am. J. Chin. Med. **8:** 245–253.
34. LEE, D. C., M. O. LEE, K. ICHIYANAGI, D. H. CLIFFORD & L. E. MORRIS. 1980. Interaction of endorphin, naloxone and acupuncture during halothane anesthesia in dogs. 7th World Congress of Anesthesiologists. Hamburg, Germany. Abstract.
35. VOGIN, E. E., S. CARSON, G. CANNON, C. R. LINEGAR & L. F. RUBIN. 1970. Chronic toxicity of DMSO in primates. Toxicol. Appl. Pharmacol. **16:** 606–612.
36. MAYER, D. & D. D. PRICE. 1976. Central nervous system of analgesia. Pain **2:** 379–404.
37. DOMER, F. R., D. M. CHIHAL & H. C. CHARLES. 1977. Cardiovascular and neuromuscular effects of dimethyl sulfoxide in anesthestized rabbits. J. Pharm. Sci. **66:** 269–270.
38. SHLAFER, M. & A. M. KAROW, JR. 1975. Pharmacological effects of dimethyl sulfoxide on the mammalian myocardium. Ann. N.Y. Acad. Sci. **243:** 110–121.
39. SHLAFER, M. & A. M. KAROW, JR. 1971. Ultrastructure function correlative studies for cardiac cryopreservation. I. Hearts perfused with various concentrations of dimethyl sulfoxide (DMSO). Cryobiology **8:** 280–289.
40. KAROW, A. M., JR. 1972. Dimethylsufoxide effect on myocardial β-adrenoceptors. J. Pharm. Pharmacol. **24:** 419–421.
41. ROBINSON, J. D. 1975. Specific modifications of the Na_1K^+-dependent adenosine triphosphatase by dimethyl sulfoxide. Ann. N.Y. Acad. Sci. **243** (Part 1): 60–72.

ACUTE CARDIOVASCULAR EFFECTS
OF DIMETHYL SULFOXIDE

Stuart R. Hameroff, Charles W. Otto, Jeffrey Kanel,
Philip R. Weinstein, and Casey D. Blitt

Departments of Anesthesiology and Surgery
University of Arizona Health Sciences Center
Tucson, Arizona 85724

Dimethyl sulfoxide (DMSO) is a solvent that readily permeates living tissues and membranes. This capability appears related to DMSO's relatively polar nature, acceptance of hydrogen bonds, and compact structure which allow free interactions with water, proteins, carbohydrates, nucleic acids, ionic substances, and other biological constituents.[1] Known for its cutaneous absorption, DMSO has spawned a host of controversial claims regarding its efficacy in various clinical situations. Accepted as a tissue cryoprotectant and radioprotectant,[2] DMSO is reportedly also beneficial in central nervous system trauma and ischemia. Studies in extradural brain compression in rhesus monkeys, respiratory anoxia in rats, and spinal cord trauma in dogs suggest that DMSO may be more protective than steroids or barbiturates without altering neurological or cardiovascular function.[3-5] While adverse cardiovascular effects of barbiturates have required corrective inotropic support in some clinical trials,[6-9] DMSO cardiovascular effects are unclear. In vitro studies on mammalian myocardium[10,11] have shown DMSO-induced depression of conduction and automaticity, but in vivo data on DMSO cardiovascular effects are lacking. In this study, the authors measured acute cardiovascular changes in barbiturate-anesthetized, normovolemic dogs receiving i.v. DMSO in doses of 2 g/kg, which were reported to have protective effects in cerebral ischemia.[3-5]

METHODS

Six mongrel dogs (7-17 kg) anesthetized with pentobarbital (35 mg/kg) had their tracheas intubated, and mechanical ventilation kept $PaCO_2$ at 35-40 torr. In each dog, a femoral artery was cannulated for continuous pressure measurement; a femoral vein was cannulated for fluid and drug administration, and the opposite femoral vein was used to pass a seven French thermodilution pulmonary artery catheter. Pressures were measured with Statham P-23 transducers, lead II of the surface ECG was continuously monitored and all data recorded on a Hewlett Packard 7700 recorder. Thermodilution cardiac outputs were determined with an Edwards Laboratories 9510 A computer.

After stable control values were obtained, 1.86 ml/kg of 0.9% sodium chloride (saline) was infused with a Harvard pump at 5 ml/min and variables measured. When pre-infusion status had returned, 2 g/kg of DMSO (50% aqueous solution, specific gravity, 1.076, 1.86 ml/kg) (Research Industries Corporation, Salt Lake City, Utah) was infused at a rate of 5 ml/min.

In 13 experiments in six dogs, eight variables were measured before, immediately after, and 10 min after each saline and DMSO infusion: cardiac output (L/min), heart rate (beat/min), pulmonary capillary wedge pressure (WP), central

94

TABLE 1

ACUTE CARDIOVASCULAR EFFECTS OF EQUAL VOLUME INFUSION OF DMSO AND SALINE*

	DMSO			Saline		
	Preinfusion	End Infusion	10 min Postinfusion	Preinfusion	End infusion	10 min Postinfusion
Heart rate (min^{-1})	125 ± 11	154 ± 8	150 ± 10	146 ± 25	138 ± 19	147 ± 18
Systemic systolic pressure (mm Hg)	173 ± 11	168 ± 9	183 ± 10	180 ± 18	181 ± 20	190 ± 14
Systemic mean pressure (mm Hg)	130 ± 6	122 ± 6	138 ± 6	135 ± 11	135 ± 11	132 ± 10
Systemic diastolic pressure (mm Hg)	111 ± 5	97 ± 5	114 ± 6**	113 ± 12	113 ± 12	117 ± 5
Systemic vascular resistance (dyne · cm · sec^{-5})	2479 ± 216	1459 ± 121‡	1915 ± 198	2356 ± 214	2174 ± 214	2225 ± 222
Pulmonary systolic pressure (mm Hg)	21 ± 2	30 ± 2‡	27 ± 2	21 ± 3	24 ± 5	23 ± 6
Pulmonary mean pressure (mm Hg)	14 ± 1	21 ± 1¶	18 ± 1†**	14 ± 1	15 ± 1	14 ± 2
Pulmonary diastolic pressure (mm Hg)	11 ± 1	17 ± 1¶	13 ± 1**	11 ± 1	11 ± 0	10 ± 0
Pulmonary vascular resistance (dyne · cm · sec^{-5})	125 ± 15	112 ± 12	129 ± 12	134 ± 20	114 ± 15	109 ± 44
Pulmonary capillary wedge pressure (mm Hg)	7 ± 1	12 ± 1‡	8 ± 1**	6 ± 1	7 ± 1	5 ± 1
Central venous pressure (cm H$_2$O)	0.88 ± 0.4	2.88 ± 0.5	1.38 ± 0.5	0 ± 0	1.33 ± 9	0.50 ± 0.5
Cardiac index (L/min · m^2)	4.56 ± 0.4	6.91 ± 0.5§	6.01 ± 0.5†	4.50 ± 0.5	5.26 ± 0.7	5.83 ± 0.4
Stroke index (ml/beat · m^2)	36 ± 2	45 ± 2‡	40 ± 3	32 ± 4	38 ± 2	39 ± 4

*All values are mean ± SE.
†Different from "preinfusion": p. < 0.05.
‡p < 0.01
§p < 0.005.
¶p < 0.001.
**Different from "end infusion": p. < 0.05, by analysis of variance with a priori contrast.

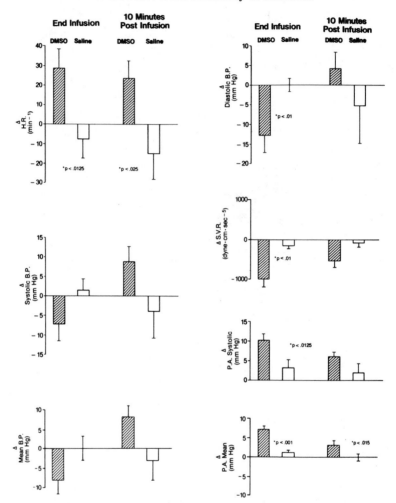

FIGURE 1. Changes in hemodynamic parameters caused by equal volume infusions of dimethylsulfoxide (DMSO) or 0.9% sodium chloride (Saline). Changes from preinfusion values were compared immediately at the end of infusion and ten minutes after infusion by Student's paired *t*-tests. Differences were considered significant (*) if a test showed p < 0.05.

venous pressure (CVP), systemic systolic, mean, and diastolic pressures, pulmonary systolic, mean, and diastolic pressures (mm Hg). Systemic and pulmonary vascular resistances (SVR and PVR), cardiac index,[12] and stroke index were calculated using standard equations. Differences in mean values obtained at the three measurement intervals (preinfusion, immediately after end of infusion, and 10 min after the end of infusion) in the saline and DMSO groups were compared using an analysis of variance with an *a priori* contrast. DMSO-induced changes from control (postinfusion value minus preinfusion) were compared to saline-induced changes using a Student's paired t-test. Differences were considered significant if a test showed p < 0.05.

RESULTS

Values obtained before saline infusion and before DMSO infusion did not significantly differ for any variable studied and there were no significant changes in any variable after saline infusion (TABLE 1, FIGURES 1 and 2). Immediately after DMSO infusion, significant increases were observed in cardiac index, stroke index, and pulmonary systolic, mean, diastolic and WP pressures. SVR significantly decreased. Ten minutes after DMSO infusion, all values had returned toward preinfusion values and only cardiac index remained significantly elevated.

Comparison of the changes caused by infusion of saline and DMSO are shown in FIGURES 1 and 2. Compared immediately after infusion, DMSO caused significant increases in cardiac index, heart rate, WP, pulmonary systolic, mean and diastolic pressures. There were significant decreases in systemic, diastolic pressure, and SVR at end of infusion of DMSO. Ten min after infusion, only the

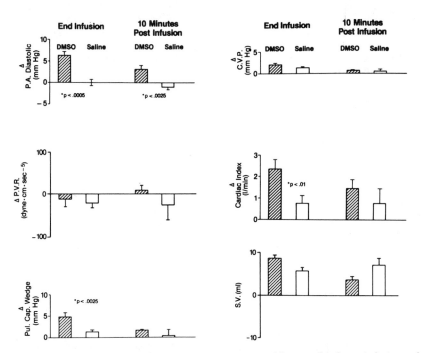

FIGURE 2. Changes in hemodynamic parameters caused by equal volume infusions of dimethylsulfoxide (DMSO) and 0.9% sodium chloride (Saline). Changes from preinfusion values were compared immediately at the end of infusion and ten minutes after infusion by Student's paired t-tests. Differences were considered significant (*) if a test showed p < 0.05.

DMSO-induced heart rate and pulmonary artery diastolic pressure remained significantly increased.

Serum osmolality before and after DMSO infusion measured in one dog rose from 320 to 360 mOsm/L. Several dogs were noted to increase respiratory effort after DMSO infusion.

DISCUSSION

In vitro studies in mammalian myocardium have reported negative chronotropic and varying inotropic responses at DMSO doses of 0.07 to 2.8 mole/L.[10,11] This dose (2 g/kg), if assumed to freely distribute in total body water (0.6 × dog's weight in kg), would result in a maximum concentration of 0.05 mole/L.

These data suggest DMSO cardiovascular effects distinct from those of saline infusion. The data may be interpreted to reflect a transient hyperosmotic expansion of plasma volume resulting in increased cardiac preload and output. The decrease in SVR and relative increase in heart rate may be direct DMSO effects or reflex mechanisms. Other possible explanations of DMSO cardiovascular augmentation include cellular interactions with excitable or contractile membrane and cytoplasmic proteins. Altered solubilities of ions, molecular oxygen, or metabolites in the cellular aqueous phase could also enhance cellular metabolic efficiency.[13] Other possible explanations include altered ventricular compliance, or increased barbiturate solubility in the DMSO aqueous phase, which might reduce receptor binding and barbiturate depression.

Central nervous system (CNS) protective efficacy, intracranial pressure, and blood flow were not evaluated in this study. However, these data indicate that DMSO used for CNS protection may be more acutely acceptable from a cardiovascular standpoint than for example, high dose barbiturates, which are known to depress cardiovascular function and have required vasopressor and inotropic support in experimental and clinical trials.[6-9] This may be particularly relevant in traumatized, hypovolemic patients. Conversely, interpretation of DMSO treatment in experimental or clinical injury or ischemia must be qualified by possible beneficial effects on intracranial pressure and CNS perfusion.

ACKNOWLEDGMENTS

The authors would like to thank Research Industries Corporation, Salt Lake City, Utah (Vickie L. Hunt) for supplying the DMSO for this study.

REFERENCES

1. SZMANT, H. H. 1975. Physical properties of dimethylsulfoxide and its function in biological systems. Ann. N.Y. Acad. Sci. 243: 20.
2. ASHWOOD-SMITH, M. J. 1975. Current concepts concerning radioprotective and cryoprotective properties in cellular systems. Ann. N.Y. Acad. Sci. 243: 246.
3. DE LA TORRE, J. C., H. M. KAWANAGA, D. W. ROWED, et al. 1975. Dimethyl sulfoxide in central nervous system trauma. Ann. N.Y. Acad. Sci. 243: 362.
4. DUJOVNY, M., P. J. BARRIONUEVO, R. D. LAHA, et al. 1977. The role of DMSO and methylprednisolone in canine middle cerebral artery microsurgical embolectomy. Stroke 8: 6.

5. ALBIN, M. S., L. BUNEGIN, P. HELSEL, *et al.* 1980. DMSO protects brain against experimental pressure induced focal ischemia. Crit. Care Med. **8:** 251.
6. SAFAR, P. & E. NEMOTO. 1978. Brain resuscitation. Acta Anaesth. Scan. Suppl. **70:** 60.
7. SIESJO, B. K., C. CARLSSON, M. HAGERDAL, *et al.* 1976. Brain metabolism in the critically ill. Crit. Care Med. **4:** 283.
8. BLEYAERT, A., E. M. NEMOTO, P. SAFAR, *et al.* 1978. Thiopental amelioration of brain damage after global ischemia in monkeys. Anesthesiology **49:** 390.
9. BREIVIK, H., P. SAFAR, D. SANDS, *et al.* 1978. Clinical feasibility trials of barbiturate therapy after cardiac arrest. Crit. Care Med. **6:** 228.
10. SHLAFER, M. & A. M. KAROW. 1975. Pharmacological effects of dimethyl sulfoxide on the mammalian myocardium. Ann. N.Y. Acad. Sci. **243:** 110.
11. SAMS, W. M., N. V. CARROLL, P. L. CRANTZ, *et al.* 1966. Effect of dimethylsulfoxide on isolated innervated skeletal, smooth, and cardiac muscle. Proc. Soc. Exp. Biol. Med. **122:** 103.
12. STAHL, W. R. 1967. Scaling of respiratory variables in mammals. J. Appl. Physiol. **22:** 453.
13. MALININ, T. I. & R. L. NANNALLY. 1976. Proton magnetic resonance (PMR) studies of water in dimethylsulfoxide perfused rat myocardium. Physiol. Chem. Phys. **8:** 71.

THE PROTECTIVE EFFECT OF DIMETHYL SULFOXIDE IN EXPERIMENTAL ISCHEMIA OF THE INTESTINE

M. Ravid, D. Van-Dyk, Joëlle Bernheim, and I. Kedar

Department of Medicine
Sackler School of Medicine
Tel Aviv University
Meir Hospital
Kfar Saba
Heller Institute of Medical Research
The Sheba Medical Center
Ramat Gan, Israel

INTRODUCTION

Mesenteric thrombosis is a catastrophic, often fatal event that invariably necessitates the resection of large segments of irreversibly ischemic or gangrenous bowel.

The oligosymptomatic clinical presentation, the advanced age and the generalized vascular disease of the typical patient, and the lack of safe and rapid diagnostic procedures often result in a delay in surgical intervention beyond the point of no return for the ischemic intestines.

Saline loading,[1] corticosteroids,[2] alpha blockers,[1] and small doses of dopamine[3] were tested and found to have limited or no effect on the impaired mesenteric circulation. Dimethyl sulfoxide (DMSO) was found to afford protection from ischemic damage in experimentally induced cerebral[4,5] and renal ischemia.[6]

In the present investigation we have tested the effect of DMSO on the survival of the small intestine subjected to periods of complete, otherwise irreversible, ischemia.

MATERIAL AND METHODS

Male albino rats, weighing 250–400 g each, were used in the experiments. The animals were fed a standard Purina rat chow and water, ad libitum. They were acclimatized in the laboratory for one week and then starved for 18 hours prior to the experiments. Anesthesia was induced by an intraperitoneal injection of 4 ml · kg^{-1}, 10% chloral hydrate solution, and maintained, when necessary, by ether inhalation.

Segmental ischemia of the intestine was induced by the ligation of the fifth end arcade and the collateral arteries on both sides, near the gut. The ligature on the end arcade was opened after 150 minutes. Only those animals in which the artery resumed its pulsation were included in the experiments.

Towards the end of the ischemic period the femoral vein of 20 rats was cannulated and connected to a Sage constant infusion pump. Following the reestablishment of blood flow to the ischemic segment, DMSO 3 g·kg^{-1} b.w. was infused as a 20% solution at a rate of 0.4 ml·min^{-1}; ten control animals received an equal volume of 0.9% NaCl. In another 13 animals, an intraperitoneal injection of 3 g·kg^{-1} b.w. DMSO was administered as a 100% solution at the

100

0077-8923/83/0411-0100 $01.75/0 © 1983, NYAS

beginning of the ischemic period; to 15 controls of this group an equal volume of 0.9% NaCl was injected intraperitoneally.

Following the termination of ischemia and restoration of blood supply to the gut, the abdomen was closed, to be reopened 24 hours later. Then, the intestine was taken out for macroscopic and microscopic examination and the animals were killed. In a second set of experiments the superior mesenteric artery of 25 male albino rats was clamped for 30 minutes, and of another 25, for 60 minutes. Upon declamping of the artery, DMSO 3 g·kg^{-1} b.w. was administered intravenously to 15 animals in each group as a 20% solution at a rate of 0.4 ml·min^{-1}. The abdomen was closed and reopened 24 hours later for examination of the intestines. Ten control animals in each group received an equal volume of 0.9% NaCl.

TABLE 1

THE EFFECT OF DMSO IN TWO MODELS OF EXPERIMENTAL INTESTINAL ISCHEMIA IN THE RAT

Treatment Group		Number of Animals	Results
Segmental ischemia			
150 min	DMSO i.v.	18/18	Normal intestine
	DMSO i.p.	10/11	Normal intestine
		1/11	Patchy areas of necrosis
	NaCl	18/20	Necrotic intestine
		2/20	Normal intestine
Occlusion of superior mesenteric artery			
30 min	DMSO	15/15	Normal intestine
	NaCl	8/10	Patchy necrosis
		2/10	Normal intestine
60 min	DMSO	15/15	Normal intestine
	NaCl	7/10	Necrosis with perforation
		3/10	Patchy necrosis

RESULTS

Segmental ischemia: four DMSO-treated animals and five controls were excluded because of damaged end arcades, technical problems with cannulation, or burst abdomen. 18 rats received intravenous DMSO, 11 animals received intraperitoneal DMSO. Of the 20 control animals, 7 received intravenous NaCl and 13 intraperitoneal NaCl.

Prior to the reopening of the mesenteric vessel, the ischemic area was well demarcated, bluish-purple colored with signs of organization manifested by encapsulation by small bowel loops. The difference between the DMSO-treated and control animals was evident 24 hours later as outlined in the table.

In all the i.v.-treated rats the bowel segment showed normal appearance with occasional fibrinoid adhesions. A normal bowel segment was also present in 10 of the 11 rats that received an intraperitoneal injection of DMSO during the ischemic period. In the remaining animal there were patchy areas of necrosis without perforation. Microscopic examination revealed mild inflammatory infiltration in the mucosa while the submucosa and serosa were normal (FIGURE 1).

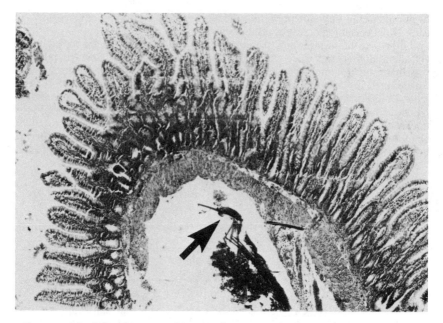

FIGURE 1. Normal architecture of intestinal mucosa and submucosa of a DMSO-treated rat. The arrow points to the suture ligating the artery. H & E, × 40.

In 18 of the 20 control animals the ischemic bowel segment showed diffuse necrosis with perforations and peritonitis. Microscopically all layers were necrotic and heavily inflamed (FIGURE 2). In the two remaining control animals the ischemic segment was edematous but without necrosis.

Superior mesenteric ischemia: Interruption of the blood flow through the superior mesenteric artery for 30 minutes resulted in no deaths. In the control animals the intestines were cyanotic with patchy areas of necrosis without perforation. In the DMSO-treated rats the intestines were normal throughout their entire length. Closure of the superior mesenteric artery for 60 minutes was poorly tolerated by the control animals. Five rats died during the first 24 hours. Their intestines showed large areas of necrosis with perforations and generalized peritonitis. There were no deaths among the DMSO-treated rats. At laparotomy, the gross appearance of the intestines was normal. Careful examination revealed areas of edema and slight color changes. Histopathologic examination revealed only occasional areas of inflammatory infiltrates.

DISCUSSION

In these experiments, the protective effect of DMSO against prolonged, otherwise irreversible ischemia of the small intestine was clearly demonstrated.

There was an unequivocal difference in favor of treated versus control animals in the model of segmental ischemia as well as in the model of total ischemia of the small intestine induced by clamping of the superior mesenteric artery. Segmental ischemia of 150 minutes was chosen because the standard two-hour ischemia used by others[1] resulted, in our hands, in a substantial percentage of spontaneous recovery in control animals. Likewise, failure to interrupt collateral circulation renders the experiment inaccurate by allowing spontaneous recovery. In the model used by us spontaneous recovery is rare, and the protective effect of DMSO is thus clearly apparent.

Intravenous administration of high doses of DMSO resulted in complete recovery of the ischemic lesions in all animals, although the drug was given at the end of the ischemic period. The intraperitoneal route was less effective. Unpublished preliminary experiments failed to show an unequivocal therapeutic effect when DMSO was given after the termination of the ischemic period. However, impregnation of the peritoneum with DMSO at the beginning of the ischemic period allowed the intestine to survive the ischemic episode.

The effect of DMSO when administered after a considerable period of complete ischemia may only be explained by the assumption that without its pharmacologic intervention the ischemia and metabolic acidosis continue, in spite of reinstitution of adequate circulation. Indeed, it was observed by us both in the kidney[6] and in the intestines that the cyanotic grayish color persisted upon reopening of arterial blood supply. However, when DMSO was infused a rapid change of color to normal took place. It is therefore possible that prostacyclin excretion enhanced by DMSO[7] successfully counteracts the anteriolar spasm, thus enabling rapid tissue perfusion. This effect together with the antiaggregant[8] and osmotic influences of DMSO may explain its action.

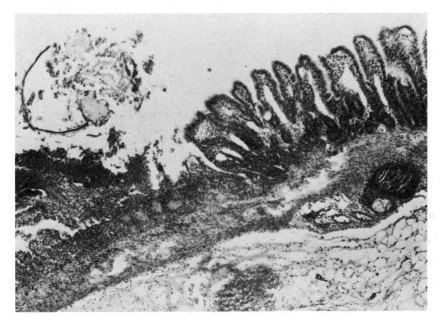

FIGURE 2. Small bowel mucosa and submucosa of a control animal following 150 minutes of ischemia. On the right, normal structure; on the left, the ischemic area with hemorrhagic necrosis. H & E, × 40.

Presently available information leaves little doubt as to the safety of this drug. The favorable results thus far obtained in different animals with diverse models of experimental ischemia may warrant the institution of DMSO treatment of acute, potentially reversible ischemic events in human subjects. The infusion of DMSO may prolong the critical period of ischemia and delay the point of irreversibility.

SUMMARY

Experiments with two models of intestinal ischemia were performed in order to examine the protective effect of dimethyl sulfoxide (DMSO). Segmental ischemia of the small intestine for 150 minutes caused necrosis of the affected bowel in 90% of the animals. Intravenous administration of DMSO or impregnation of the peritoneum with this substance prevented the development of gangrene in 28 of 29 rats. 30 or 60 minutes of complete ischemia of the small intestine, produced by clamping of the superior mesenteric artery, resulted in partial or complete necrosis of bowel segments with a high incidence of perforation and peritonitis and a high mortality rate within the first 24 hours. Intravenous DMSO, given upon declamping of the artery, effectively protected the bowel from the ischemic damage. There were no deaths among DMSO-treated animals and at 24 h there was no evidence of ischemic damage to the intestine.

Though the exact mechanism of action of DMSO is unknown, the results of these and other experiments may warrant clinical trials especially in cases of mesenteric thrombosis.

REFERENCES

1. NORLEN, K., L. RENTZHOG & S. WIKSTROM. 1978. Hemodynamic effects of phenoxybenzamine and volume replacement in segmental ischemia of the rat small intestine. Acta Chir. Scand. **144:** 299–305.
2. NORLEN, K., L. RENTZHOG & S. WIKSTROM. 1978. Hemodynamic effects of methylprednisolone in rats subjected to segmental intestinal ischemia. Acta Chir. Scand. **144:** 307–312.
3. NORLEN, K., L. RENTZHOG & S. WIKSTROM. 1978. The effect of dopamine in segmental ischemia of the small intestine in the rat. Acta Chir. Scand. **124:** 313–320.
4. DE LA TORRE, J. C., J. W. SURGEON, P. R. HILL & T. KHAN. 1977. DMSO in the treatment of brain infarction, basic considerations. In Undersea Medial Society Report. Hallenbeck & Breenbaum, Eds. (11-15-77): 138–161.
5. DE LA TORRE, J. C. & J. W. SURGEON. 1976. Dexamethasone and DMSO in experimental transorbital cerebral infarction. Stroke **7:** 577–583.
6. KEDAR, I., J. COHEN, E. T. JACOB & M. RAVID. 1981. Alleviation of experimental ischemic acute renal failure by dimethyl sulfoxide. Nephron **29:** 55–58.
7. JACKSON, C. V., G. O. CARRIER & A. M. KARROW. 1979. Influence of dimethyl sulfoxide on vascular smooth muscle. Arch. Int. Pharmacodyn. **237:** 4–10.
8. PACE, D. G., J. L. KOVACS & L. R. KLEVANS. 1982. DMSO inhibits platelet aggregation in partially obstructed canine coronary vessels. Fed. Proc. **41(5):** 1530.

THE ROLE OF TOPICAL DIMETHYL SULFOXIDE IN BURN WOUND INFECTION: EVALUATION IN THE RAT*

Douglas J. Raskin, Kathleen H. Sullivan, and
Norman H. Rappaport

Department of Plastic Surgery
Department of Microbiology and Immunology
Baylor College of Medicine
Houston, Texas 77030

INTRODUCTION

The current consensus among surgeons who care for the burn patient is that topical antimicrobial agents are a vital aspect of burn therapy. The ideal topical agent must be of minimal toxicity, penetrate the full thickness of the burn wound, and be amenable to a reasonable regime of application. Among the many agents used as topical antimicrobials, silver sulfadiazine has probably gained the most popularity among clinicians.

Silver sulfadiazine cream (Silvadene) is only 1% silver sulfadiazine by weight; the remainder of this pharmaceutical consists of a hydrophilic base. Although silver sulfadiazine is an effective antimicrobial, its ability to penetrate the burn wound eschar may in some clinical circumstances be less than optimal. The need for a more effective carrier of topical antimicrobials to enhance penetration of drugs through the burn wound motivated this investigation.

Dimethyl sulfoxide, known for its ability to penetrate membranes and skin, has been extensively investigated.[1,2] Furthermore, DMSO has been demonstrated to facilitate transcutaneous penetration of drugs (including antimicrobials for the treatment of skin disorders).[2,3] A relevant investigation demonstrated *in vitro* but not *in vivo* bactericidal activity of this controversial solvent.[4] Studies have shown that DMSO rendered the topical antimicrobial mafenide acetate (Sulfamylon) ineffective *in vivo*.[4] Prior work done with the antimicrobial sodium sulfadiazine indicated that this agent (closely related to silver sulfadiazine) was not destroyed by solution in DMSO.[5] In the latter study, the DMSO potentiated the absorption of sodium sulfadiazine across mucosal membranes *in vivo*.[5]

The past exhaustive investigations of DMSO have shown that this agent is of low toxicity.[6] Since DMSO is applied easily, is of low toxicity, and is able to penetrate tissues, it may be a useful agent in the development of burn wound therapy. The purpose of this preliminary investigation was to evaluate the effectiveness of the antimicrobial silver sulfadiazine when used in combination with DMSO.

*Computational assistance was provided by the CLINFO project, funded by the Division of Research Resources of the National Institutes of Health under Grant RR-00350. K.H.S. acknowledges the training she received under U.S. Public Health Services Training Grant AI 07145 from the National Institute of Allergy and Infectious Diseases. This study was funded by Marion Laboratories (Kansas City, Missouri) through Baylor College of Medicine Grant 630 G09924.

MATERIALS AND METHODS

Materials

Silver sulfadiazine powder and silvadene cream were provided by Marion Laboratories for this investigation. All other chemicals and media components were reagent grade and were obtained from commercial sources.

The isolate of *Pseudomonas aeruginosa* that we used was provided by Dr. Charles Stager of the Ben Taub Hospital Microbiology Laboratory. This isolate was obtained from a patient's blood culture and was sensitive to carbenicillin, tobramycin, gentamicin, and amikacin.

Forty-eight male Sprague-Dawley (300–400 g) white rats were employed in this study.

Burn Method

Using a thermostatically controlled burn generating device developed at this institution,[7] burns, 2 cm in diameter, were made on the depilated dorsum of the anesthetized rats. Twenty-four rats were subjected to second degree burns generated by exposure to 175°F for 15 seconds. Another 24 rats were subjected to third degree burns generated by exposure to 200°F for 15 seconds.

Treatment Regimen

Animals that received second degree burns were divided into four treatment groups of six animals each. The treatment groups were: (a) control (no treatment); (b) silver sulfadiazine cream; (c) DMSO; and (d) silver sulfadiazine in DMSO. The silver sulfadiazine/DMSO (1% w/vol) was prepared twice daily by weighing the dry powder into a glass vial, followed by the addition of DMSO with gentle rotation.

The treatment regimen was begun four hours after the burn and was administered every eight hours thereafter. A sterile swab, saturated with a treatment compound, was rolled over the burn site of each animal. The animals were given rat chow and water *ad libitum*. This format was repeated for rats that received third degree burns. All animals survived.

Microbiological Methods

Cultures of *Pseudomonas aeruginosa* were prepared by inoculation into trypticase soy broth, followed by overnight growth at 37°C with shaking. The culture was diluted 50-fold, and growth was monitored by the measurement of optical density at 430 nm using a Gilford 300-N Spectrophotometer. The culture was harvested during the logarithmic phase of growth at a bacterial concentration of about 1×10^8 colony forming units/ml (cfu/ml). The bacteria were sedimented by centrifugation for five minutes at 10,000 g. The bacterial pellet was resuspended in phosphate-buffered saline (PBS) using a Pasteur pipet and gentle suction. The bacterial suspension was sedimented as before and resuspended in PBS. The optical density of the culture was adjusted to obtain approximately $1 \times$

10^7 cfu/ml. A dilution series in trypticase soy broth was performed to determine an accurate, viable count for the inoculating dose onto the tissue burn site. A sample of 0.2 ml was placed into sterile tubes.

The burn site of each rat was then inoculated, at 24 hours after the burn, using a sterile swab. The volume of bacterial inoculum was 5.8×10^6 cfu for the second degree burn sites and 3.2×10^6 cfu for the third degree burn sites.

Ninety-six hours after the burn, the tissue was excised from each burn site and placed in a preweighed vial containing 2 ml sterile 0.5% Triton X-100/Minimal Essential Media (vol/vol). The vials were again weighed to determine the wet tissue weight. Preliminary experiments indicated that Triton X-100 at this concentration did not alter the viability of *Pseudomonas aeruginosa*, but did enhance ease of homogenization and recovery of organisms.

Tissue samples were homogenized for 2–5 min using a Tissue-Mizer (TEK-Mar) with variable-speed adjustment. The Tissue-Mizer was thoroughly cleaned between specimens, and was rinsed in ethanol prior to each usage. Homogenized samples were centrifuged for 4 min at low speed in a clinical centrifuge in order to sediment large pieces of tissue that were refractory to homogenization.

A portion (0.1 ml) of the supernatant of each sample was diluted in trypticase soy broth in a serial fashion from 10^{-1} to 10^{-8}. Samples (0.1 ml, 0.2 ml) from each dilution tube were plated onto MacConkey agar by spreading. Portions of the undiluted specimen were plated onto sheep blood agar, MacConkey agar, and Sabouraud's agar. The plates were incubated aerobically at 37°C for 24 hours. The number of colonies per plate were determined using a colony counter. At least four plates were counted for each sample. By use of the mean cfu/ml for each sample and the wet tissue weight, the cfu/g of tissue for each sample was calculated. The mean value and standard deviation for each experimental group of animals were determined and an analysis of variance was performed.

Histologic Methods

Tissue was excised from the burn wound at 96 hours for histologic examination. All biopsied burns were sectioned and slides were made for light microscopy. The hemotoxylin and eosin as well as trichrome staining techniques were used to stain the tissue sections.

Results

Control group animals, originally burned to a second or third degree depth, all converted their burns to full thickness injuries by the time of biopsy (at 96 hours). Thrombosed subcutaneous vessels were apparent in all second degree and third degree burns. Bacteria were readily apparent throughout the full thickness of the skin eschar, with invasion of the subcutaneous tissues in both groups (second degree and third degree burns) of control animals.

DMSO-treated second or third degree burns all showed histologic evidence of full thickness skin injury with moderate bacterial infiltration.

Silver sulfadiazine cream (Silvadene) treated thermal burns showed, on light microscopy, moderate integument destruction with subjectively decreased bacterial infiltration. These wounds had thrombosed vessels in the subcutaneous tissues and dermis.

TABLE 1

Pseudomonas aeruginosa COLONY FORMING UNITS PER GRAM OF TISSUE
OBTAINED IN VARIOUS TREATMENT GROUPS

Treatment Group	Burn Type	Mean (cfu/g)*	S.D.†
Control	2°	1.5×10^7	12.95
	3°	1.2×10^8	2.03
Silver sulfadiazine	2°	4.6×10^6	4.26
(cream)	3°	1.1×10^7	12.40
DMSO‡	2°	3.9×10^7	3.41
	3°	9.8×10^7	2.21
Silver sulfadiazine/DMSO	2°	7.9×10^6	3.98
	3°	6.9×10^6	12.90

*Mean (cfu/g) calculated from data transformed to logarithm base 10.
†S.D., Standard deviation, based on data transformed to logarithm base 10.
‡Mean (cfu/g) for 2° burn group based on tissue from five animals (all other groups, six animals each).

Both second and third degree burn wounds treated with 1% silver sulfadiazine in DMSO (w/vol) had become full thickness wounds by the time of biopsy. Bacterial infiltration was present in the dermal tissue of this group of animals.

TABLE 1 illustrates the mean colony forming units per gram of tissue obtained for each experimental group. The mean and standard deviation were obtained by first transforming the data to the logarithm base 10 and then performing the appropriate calculations. As illustrated, the mean values of organisms recovered from burn tissue varied between 10^6 cfu/g tissue and 10^8 cfu/g tissue.

A statistical analysis of the data was performed using the Clinfo computer systems for variance. The results of the statistical analysis are illustrated in TABLE 2. The data showed that the burn tissue of all animals treated with silver

TABLE 2

STATISTICAL ANALYSIS OF DATA: THREE-WAY ANALYSIS OF VARIANCE

Source	df	SS	MS	Computed F	Significance
Treatments	7	11.940	1.707	2.275*	
Main Effects					
Silver sulfadiazine	1	8.376	8.376	11.174*	
DMSO	1	0.078	0.078	0.105	
Burn	1	1.924	1.924	2.567	
Interactions					
Silver Sulfadiazine + DMSO	1	0.065	0.065	0.086	+
Silver Sulfadiazine + Burn	1	0.664	0.664	0.886	+
DMSO + Burn	1	0.630	0.630	0.840	
Silver Sulfadiazine + DMSO + Burn	1	0.001	0.001	0.001	
Error	39	29.234	0.750		
Total	46	41.174			

Abbreviations: df, degrees of freedom; SS, sums of squares; MS, mean square.

sulfadiazine (cream or in combination with DMSO; second degree or third degree burns) contained significantly less organisms per gram of tissue, when compared to all animals not treated with silver sulfadiazine. In contrast, there was no significant main effect of DMSO or of burn type. In addition, when the possibility of an interaction between treatments or between treatments and burn type was examined, no statistically significant differences were found. There was, therefore, no statistically significant enhancement of, or detraction from, silver sulfadiazine efficacy by DMSO.

SUMMARY

The results of this study indicated that there were no statistically significant differences between the effectiveness of 1% silver sulfadiazine in DMSO and 1% silver sulfadiazine in a hydrophilic base (Silvadene), when these formulations were used as antimicrobials applied topically to thermal burn wounds. The antimicrobial efficacy of silver sulfadiazine was not destroyed by mixing this agent with DMSO, since the recovery of *Pseudomonas aeruginosa* was significantly lower in all animals treated with silver sulfadiazine, whatever the formulation, when compared to animals not treated with silver sulfadiazine. Further studies with higher concentrations of silver sulfadiazine in DMSO may be useful. Although the concept of DMSO as a medicinal "carrier" is not novel, with further investigation, it may prove to be germane in the treatment of eschar-covered thermal burns.

ACKNOWLEDGMENTS

We are grateful to George Divine, for his time and expertise in the statistical analysis of our data. We would also like to thank Robert P. Williams, for helpful discussions; and also Cynthia Chappell, and Kathy Gray for technical assistance.

REFERENCES

1. SULZBERGER, M. B., T. A. CORTESE, JR., L. FISHMAN, H. S. WILEY & P. S. PEYAKOVICH. 1967. Some effects of DMSO on human skin *in vivo*. Ann. N.Y. Acad. Sci. **141:** 437–450.
2. WOOD, D. C. & J. WOOD. 1975. Pharmacologic and biochemical considerations of dimethyl sulfoxide. Ann. N.Y. Acad. Sci. **243:** 7–9.
3. KNOWLES, R. P. 1967. Clinical experiences with DMSO in small animal practice. Ann. N.Y. Acad. Sci. **141:** 478–483.
4. KRIZEK, T. J., J. H. DAVIS, J. D. DESPREZ & C. L. KIEHN. 1967. Topical therapy of burns: Experimented evaluation. Plast. Reconstr. Surg. **39:** 248–255.
5. JACOB, S. W., M. BISCHEL & R. J. HERSCHLER. 1964. Dimethyl sulfoxide: Effects on the permeability of biologic membranes (Preliminary report). 1964. Curr. Therapeutic Res. **6:** 193–198.
6. RUBIN, L. F. 1975. Toxicity of dimethyl sulfoxide, alone and in combination. Ann. N.Y. Acad. Sci. **243:** 98–103.
7. RAPPAPORT, N. H., J. B. ASKEW & F. J. GEROW. A new animal model for the controlled depth of burns. Presented: Plastic Surgery Senior Residents Conference. Chapel Hill, North Carolina. April 1980.

DIMETHYL SULFOXIDE EFFECTS ON PLATELET AGGREGATION AND VASCULAR REACTIVITY IN PIAL MICROCIRCULATION*

William Rosenblum

Medical College of Virginia
Virginia Commonwealth University
Richmond, Virginia 23298

The reported effects of dimethyl sulfoxide (DMSO) are many and include the ability to impair platelet aggregation[1,2] and to reduce brain damage after occlusion of cerebral blood vessels.[3,4] In the latter setting the beneficial effect of DMSO has been ascribed to a reduction of cerebral edema.[3,4] Since, in certain situations, a beneficial effect might also accrue from DMSO's ability to impair platelet aggregation, we decided to examine this property of DMSO *in vivo* in a model in which platelet aggregates are produced in response to microvascular injury. Since DMSO is a hydroxyl radical scavenger,[2,5] we decided to compare its action with that of glycerol, another scavenger of hydroxyl radicals,[5] and to compare the action of these scavengers in two microvascular beds injured by identical means in the same species, the mouse.

The comparable effect of the scavengers suggested that the vascular injury in our model, and/or the responses to that injury, were mediated by the hydroxyl radical. In the pial arterioles these responses included not only platelet aggregation but also dilation of the affected arterioles. Free radicals, including perhaps hydroxyl radicals, had already been shown capable of dilating cerebral surface arterioles (pial arterioles) in another species, the cat.[6,7] Therefore we decided to further test both the hypotheses that dilation of the pial arterioles in the mouse can also be produced by hydroxyl radicals and that DMSO can impair such dilation. To do this we utilized a radical-generating system which in aqueous solution can lead to hydroxyl radical formation, and tested the capacity of this system to dilate pial arterioles and the capacity of DMSO and other scavengers to impair this dilation. The results supported both the concept of dilation by radicals and the hypothesis that DMSO protects against such a dilation.

METHODS

Microvascular Injury and Platelet Aggregation

Male mice [International Cancer Research strain (ICR)] were anesthetized with urethan and either the surface vessels of the brain (pial vessels) or the mesenteric vessels were exposed as previously reported.[8,9] The method of injuring the vessels and inducing platelet aggregation has been extensively described in earlier publications.[8-10] Briefly stated, the vessels were observed with a Leitz Ultropak microscope that employs epi-illumination with either a tungsten or a filtered 200 W mercury lamp. The filters include a Leitz BG-12 exciter filter as

*Supported by Hl-18932 from the National Institutes of Health.

well as heat and UV filters. The present studies employed a 10 × ocular and 22 × objective with an immersion attachment. With the mercury lamp the intensity of illumination at the focal plane with all filters in place was 23 × 10^5 μW/cm^2 when measured daily with a silicon diode detector and radiometric filter. The filtered light from the mercury lamp produced no evidence of microvascular damage unless sodium fluorescein was present in the circulation. The latter, like the light, is non-toxic by itself. But when 2% sodium fluorescein, 0.2 ml/25 g body weight, was injected via the tail vein, vascular damage and platelet aggregation rapidly occurred following illumination with the mercury source. The aggregates fluoresced and were readily visible as they adhered to the damaged endothelium. Prior to injecting the fluorescein, observation was performed with the tungsten lamp. Immediately upon injection of fluorescein, which took a second, the illumination was switched to the mercury lamp and this was continued throughout the period of observation. The time required for aggregation to be initiated was measured with a stop watch started the instant the illumination was switched to the mercury source and stopped the instant the first adhering aggregate was recognized. During the brief period of observation, a drop of artificial cerebrospinal fluid (brain) or saline (mesentery) was held between the tip of the immersion attachment and the tissue.

Arterioles are the subject of this presentation. Their internal diameter was measured with an ocular micrometer before induction of aggregation and again after aggregation was complete and the vessel was occluded by platelet thrombi. The fluorescent aggregates often made it easier to determine the internal dimensions of the vessels by providing a clearer boundary between the contents and wall than that provided by tungsten illumination.[10]

In some of the studies, the 2-slit technique of measuring red cell velocity was employed with the aid of a TV microscope, 2-slit velocimeter, and cross correlator (IPM, San Diego, Calif.).[11-14] This gave red blood cell (RBC) velocity at the center of the vessel and from this shear rate at the wall could be calculated. These measurements were taken in the minutes preceding induction of aggregation, using the mercury light for approximately one minute with a green filter replacing the BG-12 filter. This enabled us to determine whether shear rates were systematically altered by the DMSO or glycerol given one hour earlier. We were concerned about this because preliminary studies showed a modest but definite relationship between shear rate and aggregation latency.

The DMSO and glycerol were injected one hour before inducing aggregation. The highest dose was 100% DMSO or glycerol 0.5 ml/100 g body weight. Lower doses were made by diluting the drugs with saline, and injecting the same volume (0.5 ml/100 g). Studies of the pial arterioles employed intraperitoneal injections, while those of the mesentery employed subcutaneous injections. Saline was the control. The mouse's body temperature was maintained at 37°C during the period between drug injection and observation of the vessels, including the period during which aggregation was induced. Drug-treated and control mice were observed in random order.

At the end of each experiment, 100 μl of blood was obtained from the carotid artery and O$_2$, CO$_2$, and pH values determined with an Ultra Micro Blood Gas Analyzer (Radiometer). Mean values ranged between 87 and 104 mm for O$_2$, 25 and 31 mm for CO$_2$, and 7.27–7.38 for pH. No systematic differences were found between treated and control groups and no relationship was found between these values and platelet aggregation latency or changes in vascular diameter; consequently, blood gas and pH values are not referred to later.

TABLE 1

DMSO INHIBITS THE PLATELET AGGREGATION AND REDUCES THE DILATION THAT
ACCOMPANIES INJURY OF PIAL ARTERIOLES BY LIGHT PLUS DYE

	Dose DMSO (ml/kg body weight)			
	5.0 (N = 10)	0.5 (N = 10)	0.05 (N = 10)	Saline (N = 10)
Seconds to				
initiate aggregation	117 ± 49*	71 ± 25	51 ± 13	57 ± 20
Initial diameter (μm)	39 ± 5	39 ± 4	37 ± 8	39 ± 5
Diameter after				
aggregation (% Control)	95 ± 18*	112 ± 11	124 ± 15	122 ± 19

*ANOVA p ≤ .001.
Inhibition of aggregation is manifested by the significant increase in time required for the noxious stimulus to induce aggregation. Analysis of variance (ANOVA) showed a highly significant effect of treatment (DMSO). A similarly significant inhibitory effect of DMSO was also shown with respect to the dilation produced by the injury. In fact, on the average, damaged arterioles constricted rather than dilated in the animals treated with DMSO. All values are mean ± SD.

Free Radical Generation

Mice were prepared as described above but only pial and not mesenteric vessels were studied. The surface of the exposed brain was irrigated with artificial cerebrospinal fluid flowing at 2 ml/min[15,16] at 37°C and pH 7.40 ± 0.03 (mean ± standard deviation) as measured in the fluid passing over the craniotomy site. The pH was maintained constant throughout an experiment. Acetaldehyde plus xanthine oxidase were mixed in artificial cerebrospinal fluid whose pH was adjusted with 95% O_2, 5% CO_2 to give a final pH with the reactants of 7.4 ± 0.05 (mean ± range). The final concentration of reactants was 0.5 mM acetaldehyde and 0.1 units per ml xanthine oxidase. This was delivered as a bolus of 1.0 ml at 37°C delivered in 60 seconds. The mixture of acetaldehyde and xanthine oxidase generates superoxide, which in aqueous solution is known to produce, by several routes, the hydroxyl radical.[17,18]

In some experiments either catalase (36 units/ml) or superoxide dismutase (30 units/ml) were added to the reactants, still maintained at pH 7.4 ± 0.05 (mean ±

TABLE 2

GLYCEROL INHIBITS THE PLATELET AGGREGATION AND REDUCES THE DILATION THAT
ACCOMPANIES INJURY OF PIAL ARTERIOLES BY LIGHT PLUS DYE

	Dose Glycerol (ml/kg body weight)			
	5.0 (N = 10)	2.5 (N = 10)	0.25 (N = 10)	Saline (N = 10)
Seconds to				
initiate aggregation	157 ± 46*	111 ± 37	49 ± 9	46 ± 14
Initial diameter (μm)	36 ± 7	36 ± 5	34 ± 6	35 ± 5
Diameter after				
aggregation (% Control)	98 ± 23†	111 ± 20	118 ± 30	133 ± 19

*ANOVA p < .001, †ANOVA p < .02.
Glycerol inhibited the aggregation and the dilation produced by local injury (see legend to TABLE 1).

range) in the artificial cerebrospinal fluid. Superoxide dismutase, by scavenging superoxide, not only reduces its concentration in the reaction mixture, but also reduces hydroxyl production from superoxide and water.[17,19] Catalase also reduces hydroxyl production by scavenging hydrogen peroxide, which is produced by superoxide and which in turn produces hydroxyl radicals.[17,19] In other studies, DMSO was injected intraperitoneally, 0.5 ml/100 g body weight. The DMSO was diluted with saline, which was used as a vehicle control.

Arteriolar diameter was continuously monitored with the TV microscope and image splitter as described by Baez.[20]

RESULTS

Microvascular Injury with Light Plus Dye

Aggregation in pial arterioles was significantly delayed by both DMSO and glycerol in a dose-dependent fashion. This is shown in TABLES 1 and 2. In the

TABLE 3

DMSO HAS MODEST INHIBITORY EFFECT ON PLATELET AGGREGATION IN MESENTERIC ARTERIOLES INJURED BY LIGHT PLUS DYE

	Dose DMSO (ml/kg body weight)			
	5.0 ($N = 10$)	0.5 ($N = 10$)	.05 ($N = 10$)	Saline ($N = 10$)
Seconds to initiate aggregation	72 ± 37*	50 ± 30	49 ± 24	46 ± 18
Initial diameter (μm)	67 ± 15	68 ± 18	67 ± 13	68 ± 15
Diameter after aggregation (% control)	49 ± 27	61 ± 11	49 ± 20	49 ± 14

*ANOVA p = .2, ANCOVA with shear rate as covariant p = .1. If saline, 0.05 and 0.5 ml/kg are pooled and compared with 5 ml/kg, the effect of the latter is significant at the 0.05 level.

Unlike its effect on the response of the pial microcirculation to damage, the inhibitory effect of DMSO on aggregation in damaged mesenteric arterioles was less readily demonstrable, and manifest statistically only if the low dose groups are pooled.

DMSO study, shear rates for the four treatment groups were 1115 ± 320, 1307 ± 129, 1270 ± 329, and 1117 ± 300 sec^{-1} (M ± SD). These values were not different from each other and were unrelated to the effect of DMSO on aggregation.

Also shown in TABLES 1 and 2 is a significant dose-related reduction in the amount of dilation induced by exposure to light plus dye and accompanying aggregation. At the highest dose of both DMSO and glycerol the dilation was, on the average, totally abolished.

Aggregation in mesenteric arterioles was delayed only by the highest dose of DMSO and analysis of variance showed no effect of treatment over the four treatment groups (TABLE 3). If the two groups given the lowest dose and the control are combined, on the grounds that their values are essentially identical, then the pooled group had a significantly shorter aggregation latency than the group receiving 5 ml/kg (p < .05 Student t test). The shear rates in the four treatment groups varied from 672 ± 271 to 768 ± 180 sec^{-1} (M ± SD). Analysis of covariance showed an effect of shear rate on aggregation latency at the .08 level. Correction

TABLE 4

GLYCEROL INHIBITS PLATELET AGGREGATION IN MESENTERIC ARTERIOLES INJURED BY
LIGHT PLUS DYE

	Dose Glycerol (ml/kg body weight)			
	5.0 (N = 10)	2.5 (N = 10)	0.25 (N = 10)	Saline (N = 10)
Seconds to initiate aggregation	164 ± 30*	110 ± 45	65 ± 30	51 ± 24
Initial diameter (μm)	81 ± 15	86 ± 16	79 ± 10	77 ± 18
Diameter after aggregation (% control)	63 ± 25	64 ± 21	49 ± 27	52 ± 21

*p < .01 ANOVA.
Glycerol inhibited aggregation in mesenteric arterioles. This is manifest by prolongation
of the time required for the noxious stimulus to induce aggregation.

for this effect resulted in a minor adjustment of mean latency values with no
effect whatsoever on the outcome of the comparison between treatment groups.

Unlike DMSO, glycerol was as potent an inhibitor of aggregation in the
mesentery as it was in the pia. TABLE 4 shows a significant-dose dependent
lengthening of aggregation latency by glycerol.

Both TABLES 3 and 4 show that DMSO and glycerol failed to modify the
constriction caused in this microvascular bed by exposure to light plus dye and
accompanying platelet aggregation.

Free Radical Generation with Acetaldehyde Plus Xanthine Oxidase

Acetaldehyde plus xanthine oxidase dilated pial arterioles and this dilation
was inhibited by the presence of either superoxide dismutase or catalase in the
reaction mixture or by injecting the mice one hour earlier with 0.5 ml/100 g

TABLE 5

EFFECT OF DMSO AND OTHER SCAVENGERS ON DILATION OF PIAL ARTERIOLES PRODUCED
BY ACETALDEHYDE PLUS XANTHINE OXIDASE

Exp. No.	Scavenger	Dilation*	
1	DMSO 0.5 ml/100 g	6 ± 5 (N = 10)	p < .01
	Saline	17 ± 4 (N = 10)	
2	SOD 30 units/ml	3 ± 3 (N = 10)	p < .001
	Boiled SOD	20 ± 5 (N = 10)	
3	Catalase 36 units/ml	12 ± 4 (N = 5)	p < .001
	Boiled catalase	22 ± 4 (N = 5)	
	Nothing	24 ± 8 (N = 5)	

$$*\text{Dilation} = \frac{\text{New diam.} - \text{Old diam.}}{\text{Old diam.}} \times 100.$$

DMSO, a hydroxyl radical scavenger; superoxide dismutase (SOD) a superoxide scavenger; and catalase, a scavenger of hydrogen peroxide; each significantly reduced the dilation
produced by acetaldehyde plus xanthine oxidase. SOD or catalase was added to that
radical-generating system prior to its application to the cerebral surface and was present in
the mixture throughout the period of observation. DMSO was given intraperitoneally, one
hour before.

DMSO. These data are shown in TABLE 5. In each study, control and drug-treated mice were prepared and observed in random order.

Test of DMSO Against Dilation Produced by Carbon Dioxide

Since DMSO inhibited both the dilation produced by light plus dye and that produced by acetaldehyde plus xanthine oxidase it was of interest to test its effect against a strong dilator, whose action is not thought to be mediated by hydroxyl radical. Inhalation of carbon dioxide is among the most potent of cerebral vasodilators.[21] The inspired CO_2 was increased by having the animals breathe 10% CO_2 + 90% air, instead of air. The maximal dilation was recorded in animals injected with saline and compared with that of animals injected with DMSO. The control and DMSO-injected animals were randomly alternated and were all injected one hour prior to testing. As shown in TABLE 6, DMSO had no effect on dilation produced by CO_2. In each study the final concentration of arterial CO_2 was the same in both control and DMSO-treated mice.

TABLE 6

DMSO FAILS TO IMPAIR DILATION OF PIAL ARTERIOLES BY CARBON DIOXIDE

	Dilation*	Arterial CO_2
DMSO i.p. 0.5 ml/100 g	19 ± 7 $(N = 10)$	75 ± 6
Saline	20 ± 8 $(N = 10)$	73 ± 6

$$*\text{Dilation} = \frac{\text{New diam.} - \text{Old diam.}}{\text{Old diam.}} \times 100.$$

DMSO had no effect on dilation produced by increased concentrations of inspired CO_2. DMSO was injected one hour before challenge with CO_2.

DISCUSSION

The data clearly show a dose-dependent lengthening effect of DMSO and of glycerol on the latency of platelet aggregation in injured pial arterioles, and a dose-dependent reduction in the dilation that accompanies injury and aggregation. Since both DMSO and glycerol scavenge hydroxyl radicals,[2,5] the similarity of the two drugs' actions in our model of cerebrovascular injury supports the hypothesis that hydroxyl radicals may be important mediators of the cerebral microvascular responses in the model. The similarity of glycerol's effect to that of DMSO would then also support the suggestion[22,28] that hydroxyl radical scavenging accounts for many of DMSO's pharmacologic effects.

It has been proposed[8] that the injury in our model is produced by heat generated as the dye absorbs light, in the manner of a laser whose energy is absorbed by carbon particles or Evan's blue.[23] It is possible that radicals are produced as a result of heat-induced damage. However it seems more likely that the injury is produced by radicals generated at the time the fluorescein is excited, a possibility we had overlooked. There is precedent for radical formation as a cause of cerebrovascular injury with resultant dilation of pial arterioles.[6,7] In either case, that is whether a cause of injury or a result of injury, the hydroxyl radical could cause dilation, and the latter could then be inhibited by radical scavengers.

Platelet aggregation in our model is thought to be stimulated by the microvascular damage, since it does not occur outside the illuminated field. Damaged endothelium is observed with electron microscopy.[8] However, aggregation latency is increased by drugs that impair aggregation in vitro[8] but not by an anti-inflammatory drug with little effect on aggregation in vitro.[24] This suggests that the antiaggregating action of drugs in our model can be the result of a direct action of the drugs on the platelets, rather than the consequence of a protective effect on the vessel wall. We cannot rule out the latter in the present study, because we have not compared the morphologic changes in the vessel wall of control animals with those seen in the DMSO or a glycerol-treated group. In considering the alternative, namely an effect of DMSO and glycerol on platelets themselves, it is pertinent to point out that DMSO has been found to impair aggregation of human platelets in vitro.[2] In vitro studies of DMSO's action on mouse platelets have not been reported. If DMSO inhibits aggregation through an action on the platelet, the question would remain as to whether this effect is mediated by hydroxyl scavenging within the platelet. Since the radical is thought to be destructive, it would be difficult to imagine a facilatory role for the radical in platelet aggregation. However small amounts of some reactive species are thought essential to the activity of cyclooxygenase, an enzyme implicated in platelet aggregation.[25,26]

The effect of DMSO and glycerol on platelet aggregation in mesentery was similar to that seen in brain, except that the inhibitory effect of DMSO was not statistically significant with the sample size used, unless we combined the two lower dose groups with the saline control, and compared this combined group with the group receiving the highest dose of DMSO. Using the same model of microvascular injury, we have previously shown that drugs that impair aggregation in vitro and in cerebral microvessels can actually accelerate aggregation in mesenteric vessels.[9] This difference in drug actions on brain and mesenteric vessels in presumably related to a difference in substance(s) produced by the two tissues or to a differential effect of drugs on these tissues.[9] Alternatively, at least in the present study, we should consider the possibility that the weaker effect of DMSO on platelet aggregation within mesenteric vessels may be related to the route of drug administration. In the studies of cerebral vessels intraperitoneal injection was used, while a subcutaneous route was employed in the studies of mesentery. If lower blood levels were achieved by the latter route, and this accounts for the weaker effect of DMSO, the same phenomenon must not have applied to the study of glycerol, where a powerful antiaggregatory effect was seen in both brain and mesentery, although once again a subcutaneous route was employed for studies of the latter.

A major difference between cerebral and mesenteric vascular beds is reflected in the fact that injury by light plus dye caused dilation of pial arterioles and constriction of mesenteric arterioles.[27] The reason for this difference is unknown but we postulate that in each bed both dilating and constricting agents are released and oppose one another. Some of these factors may come from the aggregating platelets[27] and may be products of the arachidonate cascade.[27]

The hypothesis that free radicals, probably including hydroxyl radical, are generated by light plus dye and are dilating forces in the pial circulation, is supported not only by the blunting effect of the hydroxyl scavengers DMSO and glycerol, but also by the studies with acetaldehyde and xanthine oxidase. This system generates superoxide and from reactions of the latter, hydroxyl radical.[18] In the presence of this radical-generating system, pial arterioles dilated. The fact that both superoxide dismutase and catalase inhibited the dilation supports the assumption that superoxide and hydrogen peroxide contributed to the dilation and is compatible with the postulate that hydroxyl is involved, since the peroxide produced by reactions of water and superoxide rapidly reacts itself to produce hydroxyl.[17,18] Since DMSO also inhibited the dilation we have further evidence of DMSO's ability to impair radical-mediated dilation. Since DMSO is a hydroxyl radical scavenger[2,5] we have additional evidence that hydroxyl radicals do, in fact, mediate the dilation produced by acetaldehyde plus xanthine oxidase.

Before accepting the action of DMSO as one dependent upon its hydroxyl radical scavenging capacity, it was necessary to show that DMSO was incapable of inhibiting dilations produced by mechanisms other than hydroxyl radicals. So far as we know, the dilation caused by CO_2 is such a response.[21] When we tested DMSO against this response, no effect was seen.

In light of our results it may be useful to reevaluate the literature concerning possible beneficial effects of both DMSO and glycerol in cerebrovascular accidents.[3,4] These benefits have been ascribed to reduction of cerebral edema, and this may indeed be the case. However the basis of such a reduction might lie in the hydroxyl scavenging capacity of these agents, which could blunt a cascade of damaging events triggered by radical production. Among these events might be dilation, which by increasing blood flow through damaged vessels could actually increase edema and be detrimental rather than beneficial. In addition, it is possible that platelet aggregation occurs in ischemic regions, and that impairment of aggregation by DMSO or glycerol could account for reports of benefit from these agents. Since improved flow may be either harmful or beneficial, depending on when and where it occurs, it is conceivable that therapy with either DMSO or glycerol may sometimes fail[30] or even prove harmful.

CONCLUSION AND SUMMARY

DMSO is a hydroxyl radical scavenger that inhibits platelet aggregation *in vivo* in injured microvessels, and that also inhibits the dilation displayed by pial arterioles following a local injury. The injurious stimulus is a result of local excitation of circulating sodium fluorescein by an appropriate light source. It is likely that this excitation results in the generation of hydroxyl radicals, which are the immediately injurious agent. This postulate is supported not only by the inhibitory effect of DMSO but also by the inhibitory effect of glycerol, another hydroxyl scavenger. Both the hypothesis that DMSO inhibits hydroxyl-mediated dilation, and the hypothesis that free radicals can dilate pial arterioles, are further supported by direct evidence from studies employing local application of xanthine oxidase plus acetaldehyde. This well established radical-generating system dilated pial arterioles. The dilation was inhibited by the local application of superoxide dismutase and also by local application of catalase, as well as by intraperitoneal administration of DMSO. Since DMSO failed to inhibit the dilation produced by increases of inspired CO_2, we believe that the inhibitory effect of DMSO on the other dilating stimuli in these studies was due to the hydroxyl scavenging properties of this drug, rather than to other nonspecific effects.

REFERENCES

1. GOROG, P. 1975. Antiarthritic and antithrombotic effects of topically applied dimethyl sulfoxide. Ann. N.Y. Acad. Sci. **243:** 91–97.
2. PANGANAMALA R. V., H. M. SHARMA, R. E. HEIKKILA, J. C. GEER & D. G. CORNWELL. 1976.

Role of hydroxyl radical scavengers dimethyl sulfoxide, alcohols and methional in the inhibition of prostaglandin biosynthesis. Prostaglandins **11**: 599–607.

3. DE LA TORRE, J. C. & J. W. SURGEON. 1976. Dexamethasone and DMSO in experimental transorbital cerebral infarction. Stroke **7**: 577–583.

4. LAHA, R. K., M. DUJOVNY, P. J. BARRIONUEVO, S. C. DECASTRO, H. R. HELLSTROM & J. C. MAROON. 1978. Protective effects of methyl prednisolone and dimethyl sulfoxide in experimental middle cerebral artery embolectomy. J. Neurosurg. **49**: 508–516.

5. DORFMAN, L. M. & G. E. ADAMS. 1973. Reactivity of the Hydroxyl Radical in Aqueous Solutions. U.S. Dept. Commerce, Natl. Bureau Standards #46. Washington, D.C.

6. KONTOS, H. A., E. P. WEI, J. T. POVLISHOCK, W. D. DIETRICH, C. J. MAGIERA & E. F. ELLIS. 1980. Cerebral arteriolar damage by arachidonic acid and prostaglandin G_2. Science **209**: 1242–1245.

7. KONTOS, H. A., E. P. WEI, W. D. DIETRICH, R. M. NAVARI, J. T. POVLISHOCK, N. R. GHATAK, E. F. ELLIS & J. L. PATTERSON, JR. 1981. Mechanism of cerebral arteriolar abnormalities after acute hypertension. Am. J. Physiol. **240**: H511–H527.

8. ROSENBLUM, W. I. & F. EL-SABBAN. 1977. Platelet aggregation in the cerebral microcirculation. Effect of aspirin and other agents. Circ. Res. **40**: 320–328.

9. ROSENBLUM, W. I., F. EL-SABBAN & E. F. ELLIS. 1980. Aspirin and indomethacin enhance platelet aggregation in mouse mesenteric arterioles. Am. J. Physiol. **239**: H220–H226.

10. ROSENBLUM, W. I. 1978. Fluorescence induced in platelet aggregates as a guide to luminal contours in the presence of platelet aggregation. Microvasc. Res. **15**: 103–106.

11. WAYLAND, H. & P. C. JOHNSON. 1967. Erythrocyte velocity measurement in microvessels by a two slit photometric method. J. Appl. Physiol. **22**: 333–337.

12. BAKER, M. & H. WAYLAND. 1974. On-line volumetric flow rate and velocity profile measurement for blood in microvessels. Microvasc. Res. **7**: 131–143.

13. TOMPKINS, W. R., R. MONTI & M. INTAGLIETTA. 1974. Velocity measurements by self tracking correlator. Res. Sci. Inst. **45**: 647–649.

14. LIPOWSKY, H. & B. W. ZWEIFACH. 1978. Application of the "two-slit" photometric technique to measurement of microvascular volumetric flow rates. Microvasc. Res. **15**: 93–101.

15. ROSENBLUM, W. I. 1976. Pial arteriolar responses in the mouse brain revisited. Stroke **7**: 283–287.

16. ROSENBLUM, W. I. & B. W. ZWEIFACH. 1963. Cerebral microcirculation in the mouse brain. Arch Neurol. **9**: 414–423.

17. FRIDOVICH, I. 1975. Superoxide dismutase. Ann. Rev. Biochem. **44**: 147–159.

18. KELLOGG, E. W. & I. FRIDOVICH. 1975. Superoxide, hydrogen peroxide, and singlet oxygen in lipid peroxidation by a xanthine oxidase system. J. Biol. Chem. **250**: 8812–8817.

19. FRIDOVICH, I. 1976. Oxygen radicals, hydrogen peroxide and oxygen toxicity. In Free Radicals in Biology. W. A. Pryor, Ed. **1**: 239–277.

20. BAEZ, S. 1966. Recording of microvascular dimensions with an image splitter television microscope. J. Appl. Physiol. **21**: 299–301.

21. KONTOS, H. A., A. J. RAPER & J. L. PATTERSON, JR. 1977. Analysis of vasoactivity on pial vessels of local pH, pCO_2 and bicarbonate. Stroke **8**: 358–359.

22. ROSENBLUM, W. I. & F. EL-SABBAN. 1982. Dimethyl sulfoxide (DMSO) and glycerol, hydroxyl radical scavengers, impair platelet aggregation within and eliminate the accompanying vasodilation of, injured mouse pial arterioles. Stroke **13**: 35–39.

23. KOVACS, I. B., A. TIGYI-SEBES, K. TROMBITAS & P. GOROG. 1975. Evans blue, an ideal energy absorbing material to produce intravascular microinjury by He-Ne gas laser. Microvasc. Res. **10**: 107–124.

24. ROSENBLUM, W. I. & F. EL-SABBAN. 1979. Use of AHR-5850 and 6293 to distinguish the effect of anti-platelet aggregating drug properties from the effect of anti-inflammatory properties, on an in vivo model of platelet aggregation. Microvasc. Res. **17**: 309–313.

25. COOK, H. W. & W. E. M. LANDS. 1976. Mechanism for suppression of cellular biosynthesis of prostaglandins. Nature **260**: 632.

26. COOK, H. W. & W. E. M. LANDS. 1975. Evidence for an activating factor formed during prostaglandin biosynthesis. Biochem. Biophys. Res. Commun. **65**: 464–471.

27. SMITH, J. B. 1980. The prostanoids in hemostasis and thrombosis. A review. Am. J. Path. **99:** 743–804.
28. ASHWOOD-SMITH, M. J. 1975. Current concepts concerning radio-protective and cryo-protective properties of dimethyl sulfoxide in cellular systems. Ann. N.Y. Acad. Sci. **243:** 246–256.
29. ROSENBLUM, W. I., F. EL-SABBAN & E. F. ELLIS. 1980. Aspirin and indomethacin nonsteroidal antiinflammatory agents alter the responses to microvascular injury in brain and mesentery. Microvasc. Res. **20:** 374–378.
30. LARSSON, O., N. MARINOVICH & K. BARBER. 1976. Double blind trial of glycerol therapy in early stroke. Lancet **1:** 832–834.

THE EFFECT OF PERCUTANEOUS DIMETHYL SULFOXIDE ON CUTANEOUS MANIFESTATIONS OF SYSTEMIC SCLEROSIS

Arthur L. Scherbel

Department of Rheumatic and Immunologic Diseases
Cleveland Clinic Foundation
9500 Euclid Avenue
Cleveland, Ohio 44106

SYSTEMIC SCLEROSIS

Systemic sclerosis (diffuse scleroderma) is a generalized disorder of connective tissue characterized by inflammatory, fibrotic, and degenerative changes. It usually affects the skin, subcutaneous tissue, and certain abdominal organs, notably the gastrointestinal tract, heart, lung, and kidney. The disease may remain confined for variable periods of time, but in most cases, there is eventual progression with progressive, visceral involvement that may cause death from myocardial, renal, or pulmonary failure.[1]

While there is general agreement that pathogenic mechanisms may involve collagen, histopathologic changes involving the connective tissue have not been clearly defined and opinions vary regarding the abnormal changes that occur.[2] It has been reported that there are no abnormalities in the collagen or amorphous ground substance.[3,4] It has also been reported that amorphous material is increased[5,6] while others have reported that collagen fibers are increased.[7] Various other studies have suggested that there are biochemical abnormalities within the connective tissue, i.e., depolymerized ground substance[8] and increased cutaneous hexosamine.[9] Measurements of hydroxyproline and hydroxylysine from scleroderma skin are reported to be decreased suggesting either production of an abnormal collagen or a change from one type of collagen to another.[10] In addition, an increase in the ratio of Type III to Type I collagen in the dermis has been reported, although in whole skin this ratio is normal.[11]

Vascular factors may be important in the pathogenesis of the disease.[12] Raynaud's phenomenon occurs in almost 100% of patients and may precede the disease by months or years. The microvasculature, arterioles, and small arteries show distinct abnormalities that result in varying degrees of luminal narrowing. Persistent or recurring cutaneous ulcers, which may be inflammatory, occlusive, or calcific, occur in approximately 70% of patients with systemic sclerosis. Interstitial calcinosis, which is a characteristic feature of the disease, may be associated with calcific ulcers that occur over various areas of the skin. Cutaneous ulcers vary in size from approximately 1 mm to 1 cm or greater in diameter and are usually preceded by Raynaud's phenomenon. They are usually painful and may limit function of the involved digits. Areas of the body most frequently involved include digits of the upper and lower extremities, ankles, dorsum of the feet, lower legs, wrists, elbows, and ears. Analgesic abuse occurs commonly because the pain may be persistent and severe. Spontaneous healing of ulcers varies from a few days to months or even years. Ulcer size and healing time may vary greatly without known cause. Increased activity of the hands or minor trauma to the fingers may increase ulcer size or prolong healing time. Progressive,

120

0077-8923/83/0411-0120 $01.75/0 © 1983, NYAS

vascular occlusion may eventually result in autoamputation of the involved digits. Cutaneous ulcers may re-appear following surgical amputation of one or more digits.

There is increasing evidence that abnormalities of the immune system may also be involved in the pathogenesis of the disease. Other than antibody to centromere, auto-antibody patterns in systemic sclerosis are variable.[13] Increased lymphokine production has been reported[14,15] and it has recently been reported that excess T cell helper function is present in patients with systemic sclerosis. Scleroderma T cells induce more IgM synthesis by normal B cells than do normal T cells and these T cells include increased collagen synthesis by normal fibroblasts.[16,17]

TREATMENT

Numerous therapeutic measures, including corticosteroids, sodium endrate, reserpine, serotonin inhibitors, potassium aminobenzoate, chloroquine, colchicine, cytotoxins, and penicillamine, have been used but none are consistently or highly effective.[18,19] During the past decade, a number of reports have appeared in the literature on the effect of DMSO on healing of cutaneous ulcers in systemic sclerosis.[18,20-24]

Dimethyl Sulfoxide

Dimethyl sulfoxide (DMSO) is a versatile, commercially available solvent possessing many chemical properties that have both industrial and medicinal value. It can reduce the freezing point of water, moisten and disperse particles, and form complexes with many inorganic salts. It is used to preserve red blood cells, white blood cells, bone marrow, bovine spermatozoa, and whole organs before transplantation, by low temperatures or freezing techniques.[25-28] A great volume of literature has appeared during the past two decades on the pharmacologic actions reported to occur with DMSO. While it is not within the scope of this report to discuss pharmacologic actions of the drug, it is likely that analgesic, vasodilatory, and membrane-penetrating actions, as well as pharmacologic effects on collagen metabolism[29] and prostaglandin synthesis[30,31] may be responsible for clinical effectiveness in the treatment of cutaneous manifestations of systemic sclerosis.

METHODS

Patients

Nineteen of 22 patients who participated in the study had systemic sclerosis and 3 had localized scleroderma. Of those patients with systemic sclerosis, 13 were female and 6 were male. The females ranged in age from 30 to 70 years with an average of 50.3 years. Males ranged in age from 40 to 60 years with an average of 50.6 years. The disease duration of females ranged from 1 to 20 years with an average of 6.7 years. In males, the disease duration was 2 to 13 years with an average of 8 years. Three patients were studied with localized (linear) scleroderma. Two were females ranging in age from 8 to 20 years with an average of 14 years. The disease duration was 4 years with an average of 4 years. One male was 36 years with a disease duration of 12 years.

Design of the Study

Patients with systemic sclerosis were studied in two six-month phases. During the first six months, one extremity was treated and compared at three-month intervals with the untreated bilateral counterpart. Variables measured included skin softening, joint motion, grip strength, and ulcer activity. During the second phase of the study, both extremities were treated. A comparison of all ulcers that were present at the beginning of the study was made with those that existed upon completion of the study.

Pre-treatment Evaluation

All patients were given a complete general examination. Laboratory studies included hemoglobin, red cell count, white cell count with differential count, platelet estimate, SMA-12, and routine urinalysis. An ophthalmologic evaluation included retinal and slit lamp examination, as well as refraction. A repeat ophthalmologic evaluation was carried out at six-month intervals during the study. In patients with generalized disease, a 12-hour wet Addis test, esophagram, additional enzymes (CPK, aldolase), serum electrophoresis, serum glycoproteins, creatinine clearance, electrocardiogram, and pulmonary function studies were obtained.

Method of DMSO Administration

The skin tolerance to topical application of DMSO was variable and, therefore, the concentration of the drug was individualized, especially at the onset of treatment. Initially, the extremity to be treated was immersed in 35% DMSO for five minutes three times daily. After approximately two days, the concentration of DMSO was increased to 46% by diluting two parts of 70% DMSO with one part of distilled water. The number of treatments by immersion was increased to four times daily. After one to two more days, the treatment with DMSO was increased to 15 minutes four times daily. If early signs of ulcer healing did not appear after two weeks of treatment, immersion time was temporarily increased to one-half hour four times daily. Immersion time was gradually reduced as ulcer healing appeared. The DMSO solution was changed weekly. Patients with localized scleroderma applied DMSO solution to cutaneous lesions with a cotton applicator. DMSO was allowed to penetrate the cutaneous lesions for approximately one-half hour. The quantity of DMSO applied ranged between 25 ml and 30 ml per application and the frequency and concentration of DMSO was increased depending upon the individual tolerance of the patient.

Follow-Up Evaluation

Patient evaluation at three-month, follow-up visits included an estimation of skin softening, joint motion, grip strength, cutaneous ulcer activity, and the need for analgesic medication. Global evaluation was carried out at each visit and the patients were questioned regarding any adverse effects of DMSO. Laboratory data included complete blood count with differential count, platelet estimate, and SMA-12. Ophthalmologic examinations were obtained at each visit and the patients were questioned regarding any adverse effects of DMSO. Laboratory data included complete blood count with differential count, platelet estimate, and SMA-12. Ophthalmologic examinations were obtained at six-month intervals.

RESULTS

The three- and six-month results were very similar for skin softening and joint motion. Therefore, the results of the comparison analysis at six months are described.

		Treated				
		1	2	3	4	Total
Untreated	1	0	3	2	0	5
	2	0	1	7	1	9
	3	0	0	3	0	3
	4	0	0	0	0	0
	Total	0	4	12	1	17

FIGURE 1. Comparison of treated vs. untreated hands (skin texture).

Skin Softening

Seventeen of 19 patients were evaluated for skin softening over the dorsum of the hands. Two patients were not included in this part of the study because of the interfering location of skin ulcers. A comparison analysis was made at three months and again at six months between an extremity that had been treated and a bilateral counterpart that was untreated. Skin softening was evaluated by the examiner's ability to pinch the skin up and away from the subcutaneous tissue. Skin softening was graded as follows: (1) None–Tightly bound, (2) Mild–Movable, (3) Moderate–Slightly pliable, (4) Marked–Moderately pliable, and (5) Complete–Normal.

Skin Texture

A two-way tabulation was employed to display the results with scores for the untreated hand in the left, vertical margin and scores for the treated hand in the top horizontal margin (FIGURE 1). An entry in a cell above the main diagonal box

		Treated		
		1	2	Total
Untreated	1	1	4	5
	2	0	10	10
	Total	1	14	15

FIGURE 2. Comparison of treated vs. untreated hands (joint motion).

favored the treated hand and an entry below the diagonal favored the untreated hand. Minimal to mild improvement in skin softening occurred in all patients except one who showed moderate improvement with treatment. Complete improvement did not occur in any of the patients. In 13 of 17 patients, the treated hand improved more than the untreated hand. There were 4 patients where improvement was the same (main diagonal boxes). In 12 of 17 patients, improvement was noted in the untreated hand, which suggested a carry-over, systemic effect of the drug. No patients showed greater improvement in the untreated hand as compared to the treated hand.

Joint Motion

Fifteen of 19 patients were evaluated for increase in range of joint motion involving both metacarpophalangeal joints and proximal interphalangeal joints. A comparison analysis was made with treated and untreated extremities at three and six months. Results of the six-month evaluation are described. Four patients were excluded because of auto-amputation of fingers or the location of ulcers that interfered with joint function. Increase in joint motion was graded as follows: (1) No change-ROM (range of motion), (2) Mild-20% increase, (3) Moderate-45% increase, and (4) Complete-normal ROM.

Improvement in joint motion occurred in 14 of 15 patients but it seldom exceeded 20 degrees in these particular joints (FIGURE 2). No patients showed complete return of joint motion. Four patients showed improvement of the treated hand only and no patients showed improvement of the untreated hand only. However, 10 patients showed mild improvement in both hands, which suggested a carry-over, systemic effect of the drug. It was observed during the study that improvement in lateral abduction and adduction of all fingers at the metacarpophalangeal joints occurred almost consistently. This subtle change in finger motion was difficult to measure but it did result in the patient's increased ability to carry out finer movements, which resulted in greater dexterity of the hands for such functions as holding a knife and fork when eating, combing the hair, or holding a toothbrush.

Grip Strength

Grip strength was measured using a shortened blood pressure cuff with the cuff area restricted to a diameter of 9 cm. Grip measurements were obtained when the cuff was inflated to 20 mm Hg and the patient was asked to squeeze the cuff as hard as possible. Sixteen of 19 patients who were capable of squeezing the inflated blood pressure cuff were entered into this study. The analysis was restricted to the treated hand only. Measurements were taken initially and at three-month intervals for 12 months.

The scattered diagram (FIGURE 3) compares the final grip strength with the initial grip strength. For comparison, the line of identity was superimposed on this graph. A point falling on this line would indicate that the initial and terminal grip strengths were the same. The point above the line indicates improvement and the point below indicates a decrease or loss in grip strength. Thus, 12 of 16 (75%) patients showed an increase in grip strength and 3 of 16 (19%) had a decrease in grip strength. There was no change in grip strength in 1 patient during the study. Grip strength for treated hands increased from an initial mean value of 155 mm Hg to a final mean value of 193 mm Hg. The average improvement was 38 mm Hg. Of the 12 patients who improved, the mean improvement was 58 mm Hg. The three patients who did not show improvement decreased an average of 29 mm Hg. These changes were statistically significant at the 5% level.

A comparison was also made between grip strengths obtained in both hands of 11 patients (who were capable of gripping with both hands) to compare results between treated and untreated hands. Grip strengths for treated hands increased significantly from 158 mm Hg to 183 mm Hg, which was statistically significant at the 5% level. Grip strengths for the untreated hand also increased from 170 mm Hg to 184 mm Hg, although the increase was not significant at the 5% level.

The individual changes in grip strength (grip strength of treated hand minus grip strength of untreated hand) are plotted in FIGURE 4. The mean change for treated hands was 41 mm Hg, which was not significantly different from that of the untreated hands at 17 mm Hg. A covariance analysis of the change in grip

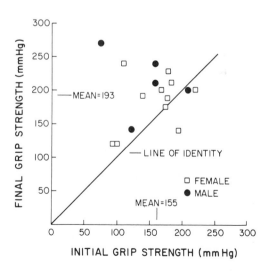

FIGURE 3. Grip strength of treated hand.

strength, with the initial grip strength as the covariate, revealed no significant difference between treated and untreated hands at the 5% level.

Cutaneous Ulcers

Fifteen (79%) of 19 patients with systemic sclerosis presented a total of 61 cutaneous ulcers at the beginning of the study. These included 9 (69%) of 13 females and all 6 males (100%). There was variability in the onset, appearance, number and size, location, healing time, and frequency of recurring ulcers. Single ulcers appeared in 4 patients (26%) while 10 patients (66%) had multiple recurring ulcers. Multiple ulcers appeared initially in 1 patient (7%). The majority of ulcers classified as medium or small (.05 cm in diameter or less) was located over digits but occasionally, a complete digital occlusion with infarction occurred

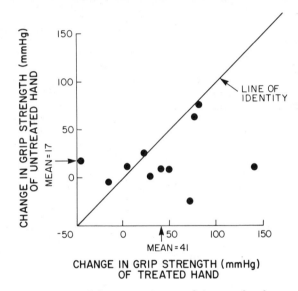

FIGURE 4. Comparison of change in grip strength in treated and untreated hands.

resulting in a large digital ulcer. Ulcers 1 cm in diameter or greater usually appeared over ankles, dorsum of the feet, or lower extremities. Spontaneous healing of ulcers, as well as the recurrence of ulcers, ranged from a few days to 12 months or longer. Seven patients noted ulcers during the first year of illness. In three patients, ulcers appeared during the second year of illness. The remaining patients showed ulcers during the third, fourth, fifth, and eighth year of illness and four patients had ulcers involving both upper and lower extremities. In one out of four patients with ulcers involving upper and lower extremities, comparison studies were carried out in the lower extremities while simultaneously, both upper extremities were treated. In the remaining three patients, comparison studies were carried out in the upper extremities while simultaneously, both lower extremities were treated. It is possible that these patients had a greater carry-over, systemic effect of DMSO which resulted in improved healing of the untreated ulcers.

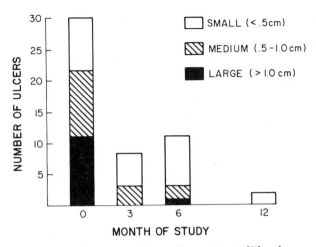

FIGURE 5. Healing of finger ulcers—"treated" hands.

Rate of Ulcer Healing

At the beginning of the study, 61 original ulcers were present in 15 (79%) of 19 patients. After three months of treatment 22 (73%) of 30 ulcers were healed (FIGURE 5). The remaining 8 ulcers were medium or small in size (.05 cm in diameter or less). In contrast, 5 (17%) of 31 ulcers were healed in the untreated extremities (FIGURE 6). In the untreated extremities, 10 ulcers remaining were .05 cm in diameter. At the end of six months, improvement was noted in both treated and untreated extremities. Ten ulcers (30%) were present in the treated extremi-

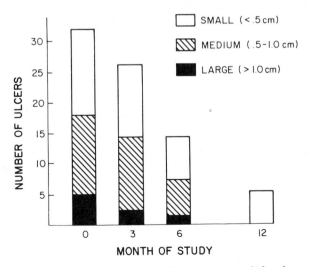

FIGURE 6. Healing of finger ulcers—"untreated" hands.

ties (1 large, 2 medium and 7 small ulcers). Fifteen ulcers (48%) were present in the untreated extremities (1 large, 6 medium and 8 small ulcers). It is apparent that the greatest effect of DMSO on ulcer healing occurred during the first three months of treatment. During the second three months of treatment, there was very little difference between treated and untreated extremities. It is likely that improvement noted in the untreated extremities was due to a carry-over systemic effect of DMSO.

During the last six months of the study, both extremities were treated with DMSO, which resulted in further disappearance of 18 (72%) of 25 ulcers. Seven small, painless ulcers were present at the end of the study. All large or medium ulcers had either healed completely or were significantly smaller in size.

It was also observed during the study that the recurrence rate for re-appearing ulcers diminished as the healing time decreased (FIGURE 7). No ulcers re-

Reappearance Interval	# of Patients	New Ulcers	
		Expected	Observed
< 2 months	3	23	0
2-3 months	4	20	7
> 3 months	3	10	9
Total	10	53	16

FIGURE 7. Effect of DMSO on recurrence of ulcers.

appeared more frequently with treatment than without treatment. In 10 patients with a history of recurring ulcers, it was noted that 16 ulcers re-appeared during the study in contrast to an estimation of 53 ulcers that might have been expected to occur.

Localized Scleroderma

Patients with localized (linear) sclerodermatous lesions without apparent systemic involvement improved more rapidly, consistently, and more completely than those with generalized disease. Improvement was characterized by lessening of skin binding and induration, as well as lessening of fibrotic contractures. A return of original skin pigmentation occurred in two of three Caucasian patients in the study. Improvement was most marked in the eight year old female.

DISCUSSION

It is apparent that the desirable effect of DMSO on skin manifestations of systemic sclerosis is palliative rather than curative. In the majority of patients, continuation of treatment is necessary for prolonged periods of time in order to maintain the improved state. It is important to realize that there is variability in therapeutic response to DMSO in patients with systemic sclerosis. Usually, a high concentration of the drug is necessary to obtain maximum therapeutic effect. On the other hand, a low concentration of the drug will cause less skin irritation. Therefore, a gradual increase in concentration of DMSO should be carried out for the majority of patients receiving treatment. DMSO exerted a desirable, but variable, therapeutic effect on skin softening, joint mobility, and grip strength. It was most effective in relieving ulcer pain and shortening the healing time for ulcers, as well as decreasing the occurrence rate of re-appearing ulcers. During the study, clinical improvement was observed in both treated and untreated extremities. Characteristically, the improvement appeared first in the treated extremity and then was observed some weeks later in the untreated extremity. In no instance did the untreated extremity show greater improvement than the treated extremity. These observations are best explained by rapid membrane-penetrating action of DMSO, which resulted in a systemic, carry-over effect of the drug. This, in turn, resulted in some improvement of the untreated extremity. It is highly unlikely that all untreated extremities improved spontaneously during the time that the bilateral counterpart was treated with DMSO.

SUMMARY

(1) DMSO exerts a palliative, therapeutic effect on healing of cutaneous ulcers in systemic sclerosis.

(2) The therapeutic response was variable and, therefore, the concentration of DMSO, as well as frequency and duration of treatments, should be individualized to obtain maximum healing effect with a minimum of adverse reactions.

(3) There was no evidence of ocular toxicity or other serious toxicity manifestations in this group of patients treated with topical DMSO for one year or longer.

(4) Delayed improvement was observed in the untreated extremity in the majority of patients studied. In no instance did improvement in the untreated extremities exceed improvement in the treated, bilateral counterpart. It is believed this resulted from a systemic, carry-over effect of DMSO rather than spontaneous improvement in the disease course.

(5) DMSO is a worthwhile, supplemental, therapeutic agent providing the limitations of therapy are understood.

REFERENCES

1. RODNAN, G. P. 1963. The natural history of progressive systemic sclerosis (diffuse scleroderma). Bull. Rheum. Dis. **13:** 301–304.
2. SCHERBEL, A. L., L. J. McCORMACK & J. K. LAYLE. 1967. Further observations on the effect of dimethyl sulfoxide in patients with generalized scleroderma (progressive systemic sclerosis). Ann. N. Y. Acad. Sci. **141:** 613–639.
3. O'LEARLY, P. A., H. MONTGOMERY & W. E. RAGSDALE. 1947. Dermatohistopathology of various types of scleroderma. Am. Med. Assoc. Arch. Dermatol. **75:** 78.
4. STROUGHTON, R. & G. WELLS. 1950. A histochemical study on polysaccharides in normal and diseased skin. J. Invest. Derm. **14:** 37.
5. SEVILLE, R. H. 1952. Scleroderma dermatomyositis (with electromicrographics). Brit. J. Derm. **64:** 467.
6. FLEISCHMAJER, R. 1064. The collagen in scleroderma. Arch. Derm. **89:** 437.

7. FISCHER, E. R. & G. P. RODNAN. Pathologic observations concerning the cutaneous lesion of progressive systemic sclerosis: an electron microscopic histochemical and immunohistochemical study. Arthritis Rheum. 3: 536.

8. MUSSO, L. A. 1954. A contribution to the pathogenesis of the changes in the collagen-ground substance equilibrium in morphea (scleroderma). Brit. J. Derm. 66: 377.

9. BOSS, N. F. & J. B. FOLEY. 1954. Effects of growth, fasting and trauma on the concentrations of connective tissue hexosamine and water. Proc. Soc. Exp. Biol. Med. 86: 690.

10. BLUMENKRANTZ, N. & G. ASBOE HANSEN. 1978. Abnormal skin collagen in scleroderma. Acta Derm. Venereol. (Stockh.) 48: 75-76.

11. FLEISCHMAJER, R., W. DESSAU, R. TIMPL, T. KREIG, C. LUDERSCHMIDT & M. WIESTNER. 1980. Immunofluorescence analysis of collagen, fibronectin and basement membrane protein in scleroderma. J. Invest. Dermatol. 75: 270-274.

12. CAMPBELL, P. & E. CARWILLE LEROY. 1975. Pathogenesis of systemic sclerosis: A vascular hypothesis. Semin. Arthritis Rheum. 4 (4): 351-368.

13. TAN, E. M., G. RODNAN, I. GARCIA, Y. MOROI, M. FRITZLER & C. PEEBLES. 1980. Diversity of antinuclear antibodies in progressive systemic sclerosis. Anti-centromere antibody and its relationship to CREST syndrome. Arth Rheum. 24: 617-625.

14. JOHNSON, R. & L. M. ZIFF. 1976. Lymphokine stimulation of all collagen accumulation. J. Clin. Invest. 48: 240-252.

15. HUGHES, P., S. HOLT & N. R. ROWELL. 1974. Leukocyte migration inhibition in progressive ststemic sclerosis. Brit. J. Dermatol. 91: 1-6.

16. KRAKAUER, R. S., J. SUNDEEN, D. N. SAUDER & A. L. SCHERBEL. 1981. Abnormalities of immunoregulation in progressive systemic sclerosis. 117: 80-82.

17. CATHCART, M. & R. S. KRAKAUER. 1981. Brief communications: Immunologic enhancement of collagen accumulation in progressive systemic sclerosis (PSS). Clin. Immunol. Immunopathol. 21: 128-133.

18. SCHERBEL, A. L., L. J. MCCORMACK & J. J. POPPO. 1965. Alteration of collagen in generalized scleroderma (progressive systemic sclerosis) after treatment with dimethyl sulfoxide. Clevel. Clin. Q. 32: 47-56.

19. JASON, M. I. V., C. LOVELL, C. M. BLACK & R. S. WILSON. 1977. Penicillamine therapy in systemic sclerosis. Proc. R. Soc. Med. 70 (Suppl. 3): 82-88.

20. ERLICH, G. E. & R. JOSEPH. 1965. Dimethyl sulfoxide in scleroderma. Penn. Med. J. December: 51-53.

21. ENGEL, M. F. 1972. Dimethyl sulfoxide in the treatment of scleroderma. South. Med. 65: 71-73.

22. TUFFANELLI, D. 1966. A clinical trial with dimethyl sulfoxide in scleroderma. Arch. Dermatol. 93: 724-725.

23. BINNICK, S. A., S. S. SHORE, A. CORMAN & R. FLEISCHMAJER. 1977 Failure of dimethyl sulfoxide in the treatment of scleroderma. Arch. Dermatol. 113: 1398-1402.

24. JABLONSKA, S. 1975. Scleroderma and pseudoscleroderma. Polish Med. Publ., Warsaw: 623-624.

25. LOVELOCK, J. E. & M. W. H. BISHOP. 1959. Prevention of freezing damage to living cells by dimethyl sulfoxide. Nature 183: 1394-1395.

26. ASHWOOD-SMITH, M. J. 1961. Preservation of mouse bone marrow at 79°C with dimethyl sulfoxide. Nature 190: 1204-1205.

27. DESHPANDE, P. J., J. FELLMAN & S. W. JACOB. 1962. Studies on viability of hearts following depression of freezing point. (Abstract). Circulation 26 (part 2): 708.

28. ROWE, A. W. & A. P. RINFRET. 1962. Controlled rate freezing of bone marrow. (Abstract). Blood 20: 636-637.

29. GRIES, G., G. BUBLITZ & J. LINDNER. 1967. The effect of dimethyl sulfoxide on the components of connective tissue (clinical and experimental investigations). Ann. N. Y. Acad. Sci. 141: 630.

30. RAO, C. V. 1977. Differential effects of detergents and dimethyl sulfoxide on membrane prostaglandin E and F_{2a} receptors. Life Sci. 20: 2013-2022.

31. LAHANN, T. R. & A. HORITA. 1975. Effects of dimethyl sulfoxide (DMSO) on prostaglandin synthetase. Proc. West. Pharmacol. Soc. 18: 81-82.

DIMETHYL SULFOXIDE IN ACUTE ISCHEMIA OF THE KIDNEY

I. Kedar,* E. T. Jacob, N. Bar-Natan, and M. Ravid

Departments of Medicine and Surgery
Sackler School of Medicine
Tel-Aviv University
The Heller Institute of Medical Research
Sheba Medical Center
Israel

INTRODUCTION

The reversibility of acute ischemic renal failure depends largely on the promptness of reinstitution of adequate perfusion. Various pharmacological agents were tried but none was effective in alleviating renal and other organ failure once the ischemic period was long enough to produce irreversible damage in control animals.[1-8]

Dimethyl sulfoxide (DMSO) is the only agent found to date with the potential to alleviate an otherwise irreversible ischemic renal failure.[9] We present here further data on experimental ischemic renal failure (IARF) in the rat and dog treated with DMSO.

MATERIAL AND METHODS

The Rat Model

Male albino rats weighing 270–350 g were used. They were fed a standard Purina rat chow and water ad libitum. Anesthesia was induced by 3.6% chloral hydrate 10 ml kg^{-1} i.p. and maintained by ether inhalation. The model of IARF was previously described,[9] in short: a unilateral nephrectomy was performed and the remaining kidney was decapsulated. The animals were allowed to recover. They were operated on again seven days later; the renal vessels were clamped to produce complete ischemia for 60 min. Upon termination of the ischemic period, a 20% solution of DMSO (3 g kg^{-1} b.w.) were administered through a cannula in the femoral vein at a rate of 0.3 ml min^{-1}. Control animals received an equal volume of 0.9% NaCl.

Forty animals received DMSO and 20 received an equivalent dose of NaCl. In 20 additional rats the kidney was perfused with 10% DMSO prior to the clamping of the artery.

Eleven animals died during the operations, leaving 33 DMSO-treated, 18 control, and 17 perfused rats for further investigation. Cardiac blood samples were drawn for the determination of urea and creatinine values. The animals were observed for three weeks. Formalin-fixed paraffin blocks were prepared from the kidneys of five control animals, which died of renal failure, and of five DMSO-treated rats, which were sacrificed on the sixth day.

*Send all correspondence to: I.K., Heller Institute of Medical Research, The Chaim Sheba Medical Center, Tel-Hashomer Hospital 52621, Israel.

0077-8923/83/0411-0131 $01.75/0 © 1983, NYAS

The Dog Model

Thirteen mongrel dogs weighing 12–17 kg were used. Anesthesia was induced and maintained by intravenous pentobarbital. A laparotomy was performed and the left renal artery exposed and clamped for 60 min. Upon declamping a 20% solution of DMSO (3 g kg^{-1} b.w.) was infused intravenously at 10 ml min^{-1} to five dogs. Five control animals received normal saline.

Three dogs died during or shortly after the operation. Of the ten dogs that survived, a second laparotomy with a contralateral nephrectomy was performed at 21 days. The dogs were closely observed, venous blood was drawn at 48 h intervals for urea and creatinine determination.

RESULTS

Of the 33 DMSO-treated rats, one died on the second post-operative day. The remaining 32 fared well. Twenty-four hours after the ischemic episode the mean blood urea was 60 ± 18 mg/100 ml (SD) and the mean plasma creatinine was 1.6 ± 0.3 mg/100 ml (SD). DMSO infusion brought about a rapid change of color from cyanotic blue to normal pink within less than 10 minutes. Urine flow started 5–10 min thereafter.

The 17 animals in which the kidney was perfused with DMSO prior to the induction of ischemia all survived the procedure and showed near normal renal function 24 h later. (Mean blood urea 74 ± 16 mg/100 ml, mean plasma creatinine 1.55 ± 0.4 mg/100 ml). Of the 18 control rats that survived the procedure none lived longer than five days. Death was attributed to a typical uremic syndrome. At 24 h, the mean blood urea of this group was 254 ± 42 mg/100 ml and the mean plasma creatinine was 7.2 ± 0.9 mg/100 ml. These data are summarized in TABLE 1. Histopathological examination of renal tissue from control animals disclosed massive necrosis and hemorrhage. The slides of DMSO-treated rats showed slight swelling of the renal tubules. The cellular elements were well preserved and the glomeruli were normal.

TABLE 2 outlines the results of blood urea and creatinine in the ten dogs that completed the experimental procedure. All DMSO-treated animals survived. There was a very mild and transient decline of renal function with a rapid return to normal within 2–4 days. In the control animals a severe, albeit transient, renal failure developed with peak urea values of 100 mg/100 ml and creatinine values of 2.6–3.3 mg/100 ml. One dog died of uremia.

TABLE 1

THE EFFECT OF DMSO ON ACUTE ISCHEMIA OF THE KIDNEY IN AN ALBINO RAT MODEL

Group	Number of Animals	Blood Urea at 24 h (mg/100 ml) mean ± SD	Plasma Creatinine at 24 h	Survival at 7 days
DMSO after ischemia	33	69 ± 18	1.6 ± 0.3	32/33
DMSO perfusion prior to ischemia	17	74 ± 16	1.55 ± 0.4	17/17
Normal saline	18	254 ± 42	7.2 ± 0.9	0/18

TABLE 2

EFFECT OF DMSO ON ACUTE RENAL ISCHEMIA IN THE DOG

Dog	Treatment	U_o	C_o	U_2	C_2	U_4	C_4	U_7	C_7	Outcome
1	DMSO	17	0.8	36	1.2	29	1.3	20	1.1	alive
2	DMSO	33	0.9	48	1.6	36	1.4	23	0.9	alive
3	DMSO	28	1.1	27	1.0	24	1.1	19	0.8	alive
4	DMSO	19	1.0	49	2.0	56	2.1	28	1.2	alive
5	DMSO	26	0.9	34	1.5	42	1.4	30	1.3	alive
6	NaCl	36	0.8	102	2.3	280	7.3	—	—	dead
7	NaCl	21	0.7	68	2.2	82	2.6	48	1.5	alive
8	NaCl	30	0.8	79	3.1	94	3.2	36	1.3	alive
9	NaCl	12	1.0	114	3.0	136	3.3	43	1.7	alive
10	NaCl	27	1.1	136	3.6	110	2.8	29	1.0	alive

U, urea mg/100 ml; C, creatinine mg/100 ml; $_0$, before nephrectomy; and $_{2,4,7}$, days following nephrectomy.

DISCUSSION

The unequivocal protective effect of DMSO on a kidney subjected to acute ischemia was previously demonstrated in our laboratory.[9] The present experiments lend further support to those observations by broadening the spectrum with another animal model and increasing the number of animals.

The critical period of renal ischemia is no doubt prolonged by the post factum administration of DMSO. Likewise, perfusion of the kidney with DMSO offers protection against ischemia induced thereafter.

The model of renal ischemia in the dog deserves some comment. Laparotomy followed by nephrectomy and induction of renal ischemia of the remaining kidney were poorly tolerated by the dogs. The experimental model finally employed utilized the intact contralateral kidney as a kind of dialysis. The effect of the ischemic trauma on the kidney became apparent only after the contralateral nephrectomy was performed three weeks later. Thus, this model exemplifies a possible clinical course of patients who sustained an episode of hemorrhagic shock with resultant renal failure. DMSO treatment given shortly after the reestablishment of adequate renal blood flow may shorten the period of recovery of the kidney and possibly facilitate recovery of otherwise irreversible renal damage.

The mechanism of action of DMSO is complex and not fully understood. Several known properties of this agent may partially account for it effect on ischemic tissue. Among them are membrane stabilization[10] with minimizing of lysosomal disruption, very effective vasodilatation,[3] and antiaggregant effect.[11]

SUMMARY

Renal ischemia was produced in rats by clamping of the renal artery for 1 h. Upon termination of the ischemic period a 20% solution of DMSO (5 g kg^{-1} b.w.) was given intravenously to 33 rats. Eighteen control animals received normal saline. All DMSO-treated animals survived while all control animals died within the subsequent seven days. At 24 h following the experiment, the mean blood urea of the control rats was 254 mg/100 ml and the mean plasma creatinine 7.2 mg/100 ml. By contrast, the DMSO-treated rats had a mean blood urea of 69 mg/100 ml and plasma creatinine of 1.6 mg/100 ml. In 17 animals the kidney was perfused with DMSO prior to the closure of the renal artery. All these rats survived the procedure and showed near normal kidney function at 24 h.

The renal artery was clamped for 60 min in ten dogs. Five dogs received DMSO (3 g kg^{-1} b.w.) and the other five received an equivalent dose of normal saline. Three weeks later a contralateral nephrectomy was performed. Renal function was normal in the DMSO-treated dogs. One control dog died of uremia, in the remaining four a transient renal failure was observed.

These experiments in two different animals highlight the protective effect of DMSO on the ischemic kidney when the drug is administered after the ischemic period.

REFERENCES

1. ARENDSHORST, W. J., W. F. FINN & C. W. GOTTSCHALK. 1975. Pathogenesis of acute renal failure following temporary renal ischemia. Circ. Res. 37: 558–568.
2. CIOFFI, R. F., J. M. B. O'CONNELL & R. J. SHALHOUB. 1975. Effect of prostaglandin A$_1$ on acute renal failure in the rat. Nephron 15: 29–34.
3. DE LA TORRE, J. C., J. W. SURGEON, P. K. HILL & T. KHAN. 1977. DMSO in the treatment of brain infarction basic considerations. Hallenbeck, Breenbaum, Undersea Medical Soc. Report No. 11-15-77, pp. 138–161.
4. DE LA TORRE, J. C. & J. W. SURGEON. 1976. Dexamethasone and DMSO in experimental transorbital cerebral infarction. Stroke 7: 577–583.
5. ELIAHU, H. E., A. IAINA, S. SOLOMON & S. GAVENDO. 1977. Alleviation of anoxic experimental acute renal failure in rats by beta-adrenergic blockade. Nephron 19: 158–166.
6. FINE, L. G. 1970. Acquired prostaglandin E$_2$ deficiency as the cause of oliguria in acute tubular necrosis. Israel J. Med Sci. 6: 346–350.
7. FINNEY, J. W., H. C. URSHEL, G. A. BALLA, G. J. RACE, B. E. JAY, H. P. PINGREE, H. L. DORMAN & J. T. MALLAMS. 1976. Protection of the ischemic heart with DMSO alone or DMSO with hydrogen peroxide. Ann. N.Y. Acad. Sci. 141: 231–241.
8. FLORES J., D. R. DIBONA, C. H. BECK & A. LEAF. 1975. The rate of cell swelling ischemic renal damage and the protective effect of hypertonic injury. Am. J. Physiol. 228: 1436–1439.
9. KEDAR I., J. COHEN, E. T. JACOB & M. RAVID. 1981. Alleviation of experimental ischemic acute renal failure by dimethyl sulfoxide. Nephron 29: 55–58.
10. JACKSON C. V., D. O. CARRIER & A. M. KARROW. 1979. Influence of dimethyl sulfoxide on vascular smooth muscle. Arch. Int. Pharmacodyn. 237: 4–10.
11. PAGE D. G., J. L. KOVACS & L. R. KLEVANS. 1982. DMSO inhibits platelet aggregation in partially obstructed canine coronary vessels. Fed Proc. 41(5):1530.

DIMETHYL SULFOXIDE EFFECTS ON ISOLATED FAT CELLS

Paul B. Wieser

Division of Science and Mathematics
Biscayne College
Miami, Florida 33054

Dimethyl sulfoxide has been characterized as a dipolar aprotic solvent.[1] It is able to act as a strong hydrogen bond acceptor[2] but possesses no hydrogens suitable to act as hydrogen bond donors. Thus, DMSO is able to compete with water molecules where water is acting as a hydrogen bond acceptor.[2] These factors have been used to explain the ability of DMSO to act as a solvent for many nonpolar molecules and its ability to rapidly penetrate biological membranes in high concentration.[1-3]

DMSO also has been shown to have a wide variety of direct biological effects,[1,3] including stimulation of melanophore-stimulating hormone release,[4] and induction of differentiation in various cell types in culture.[5,6]

The effects of DMSO on glucose metabolism, lipolysis, and cyclic AMP metabolism in isolated fat cells were tested. The two metabolites of DMSO, dimethylsulfone and dimethylsulfide,[7] were also tested to determine if these substances might be responsible in part for the observed effects of DMSO.

MATERIAL AND METHODS

Free white fat cells were obtained from 120 to 160 g female Sprague-Dawley rats (Charles River CD strain) fed laboratory chow ad libitum. White fat cells were isolated by a modification of the procedure of Rodbell[8] from the pooled parametrial adipose tissue of two or more rats. Krebs-Ringer phosphate buffer of the following composition was used in all experiments: NaCl, 128 mM; CaCl$_2$, 1.4 mM; MgSO$_4$, 1.4 mM: KCl, 5.2 mM; and Na$_2$HPO$_4$, 10 mM. The buffer was prepared daily and adjusted to pH 7.4 with NaOH after addition of bovine fraction V albumin powder (No. 10101, Armour). All incubations were done in duplicate for each experiment at 37°C in a shaking incubator in the presence of 0.5 mM glucose.

In the experiments with DMSO, it was necessary to allow the experimental tubes to cool before the addition of hormones or cells because of the large amount of heat generated when DMSO is mixed with aqueous solutions. The pH of the incubation medium was not affected by the addition of DMSO.

Labeled glucose conversion to carbon dioxide and triglyceride content of fat cells were determined as previously described.[9] Samples were also removed at the end of the experiment for glycerol analysis.[10]

Total cyclic AMP (cells plus medium) was measured by a modification of the procedure of Gilman,[11] using rabbit muscle protein kinase: 0.1 ml of 2 N HCl was added to the tubes prior to placing in a boiling water bath for 1 min. The tubes were allowed to cool and were neutralized with 0.05 ml of 4 N NaOH. Duplicate 20 μl aliquots were removed for determination of cyclic AMP.[12] The cyclic AMP standards were made up in incubation medium treated in the same manner as the

135

0077-8923/83/0411-0135 $01.75/0 © 1983, NYAS

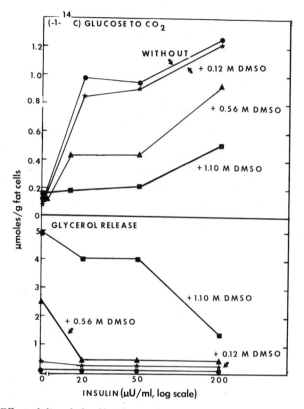

FIGURE 1. Effect of dimethyl sulfoxide on glucose oxidation and lipolysis. Fat cells (33 mg/tube) were incubated for 1 h in the presence of 0.5 mM [1-^{14}C]glucose and the concentration of insulin indicated. Dimethyl sulfoxide (DMSO) (0.12 M, stars; 0.56 M, triangles; or 1.10 M, squares) was present from the start of the incubation. The data are the result of two experiments done in duplicate.

unknowns. The free cyclic AMP was separated from the bound cyclic AMP by charcoal adsorption.[13]

Membrane-bound adenylate cyclase activity was determined on ghosts prepared by hypotonic lysis of fat cells.[14] The ghosts (60 μg protein) were used immediately and incubated for 10 min at 37°C in a total volume of 100 μl containing 40 mM Tris buffer (pH 8.0), 5 mM MgCl$_2$, 30 mM KCl, 8 mM creatine phosphate, 1 mg creatine phosphokinase, 1 mM ATP, and the test substances. Cyclic AMP was determined after the reaction mixture containing the ghosts was boiled for 3 min and then diluted to a final volume of 1 ml. Twenty-microliter aliquots were measured by the protein kinase binding assay for cyclic AMP. However, the cyclic AMP binding protein was that from the 10,000 g supernatant of homogenized bovine adrenal glands. The assay was conducted as described by Brown et al.[15] to eliminate interference by ATP.

Soluble cyclic AMP phosphodiesterase was measured using the 48,000 g supernatant of homogenized fat cells. The precipitate from the 48,000 g centrifugation was washed and resuspended in 2 ml of 40 mM Tris buffer (pH 7.4) and

0.25 M sucrose and was used to assay particulate phosphodiesterase activity. The phosphodiesterase assay was carried out according to the procedure of Thompson and Appleman.[16]

Crystalline bovine insulin was a gift of Eli Lilly Co. and contained less than 0.003% glucagon by weight. The other hormones and DMSO were from Sigma Chemical Co.

RESULTS

FIGURE 1 shows the effect of dimethyl sulfoxide on insulin-stimulated glucose oxidation and lipolysis. The concentrations chosen represent 0.8, 4, and 8% of DMSO in the incubation medium. The low dose of DMSO had no significant effect on basal or insulin-stimulated glucose oxidation. This is an important consideration since DMSO has been used as a solvent for many water-insoluble compounds and the data indicate that higher concentrations of DMSO should not be used in experiments with fat cells. The higher concentrations of DMSO did not alter basal glucose oxidation but did inhibit the stimulation by insulin. This might have been secondary to activation of lipolysis by DMSO (FIGURE 1), since free fatty acids have been shown to inhibit insulin-stimulated glucose oxidation.[17] However, insulin completely blocked the lipolytic effect of 0.56 M DMSO but there was still a decrease in insulin-stimulated glucose oxidation.

TABLE 1 shows that DMSO is able to potentiate the lipolytic effect of 100 ng/ml of glucagon, 0.15 μM norepinephrine, or 50 μM theophylline but does not cause a further increase in lipolysis due to the combination of norepinephrine and theophylline. DMSO was able to potentiate the rise in cyclic AMP elicited by norepinephrine in the presence or absence of theophylline (FIGURE 2). There was a significant increase in cyclic AMP due to norepinephrine at 40 sec in the presence of 1.1 M DMSO, while no increase in cyclic AMP could be detected in the absence of 1.1 M DMSO. DMSO also increased cyclic AMP accumulation in the presence of 0.15 μM norepinephrine, 50 μM theophylline or 100 ng/ml of glucagon after a 10-min incubation (data not shown).

To determine the mechanism of this rise in cyclic AMP, the activity of adenylate cyclase in fat cell ghosts was measured in the presence and absence of dimethyl sulfoxide. DMSO stimulated the rise in adenylate cyclase activity due to norepinephrine, glucagon, and fluoride ion (FIGURE 3). There was a slight

TABLE 1

EFFECT OF DMSO ON LIPOLYSIS

	Glycerol Release (μmoles/g fat cells)	
Additions	Basal	Change Caused by 1.10 M DMSO
None	0.8 ± 0.6	+1.5 ± 1.1
Norepinephrine (0.15 μM)	9.0 ± 3.6	+18.6 ± 6.3
Theophylline (50 μM)	0.6 ± 0.3	+15.7 ± 0.8
Norepinephrine + theophylline	32.0 ± 3.7	−1.5 ± 1.7
Glucagon (100 ng/ml)	6.3 ± 2.2	+25.5 ± 9.6

Fat cells (37 mg/tube) were incubated for 1 h in the presence or absence of 1.10 M DMSO and glucagon, norepinephrine, theophylline, or both agents. The data are the mean ± standard error for four experiments done in duplicate.

increase in basal cyclase activity. However, when the same series of experiments was repeated with the phosphodiesterase inhibitor 1-methyl-3-isobutyl xanthine present at a concentration of 1 mM, DMSO was unable to further stimulate adenylate cyclase activity due to norepinephrine or glucagon.

TABLE 2 shows that DMSO was able to inhibit both soluble and particulate cyclic nucleotide phosphodiesterase activity at the two concentrations of cyclic AMP tested. The inhibition caused by 1.3 M DMSO was comparable to that of 50 μM theophylline.

The possibility that known metabolites of DMSO (i.e. dimethylsulfone or dimethylsulfide[7]) could be responsible for the effects of DMSO on cyclic AMP

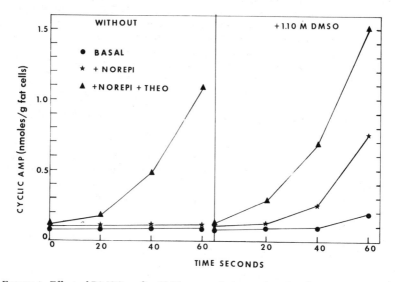

FIGURE 2. Effect of DMSO cyclic AMP accumulation at short incubation times. Fat cells (41 mg/tube) were incubated for the times indicated in the presence of norepinephrine (0.15 mM) or norepinephrine (0.15 μM) and theophylline (50 μM). Dimethyl sulfoxide (1.1 M) was present where indicated. The data are from a representative experiment done in duplicate.

accumulation was examined. These compounds paradoxically decreased cyclic AMP accumulation due to norepinephrine. Dimethylsulfide at a concentration of 100 mM decreased cyclic AMP from 0.38 nmoles/g in the presence of norepinephrine (0.15 μM) to 0.05 nmoles/g; dimethylsulfone (500 mM) also caused cyclic AMP to decrease to 0.05 nmoles/g when norepinephrine and dimethylsulfone were incubated together. At lower concentrations of these agents (i.e., 100 μM), there was no detectable effect on cyclic AMP accumulation.

Other parameters of lipolysis in fat cells were tested with negative results. DMSO (1.1 M) did not affect the binding of [³H]cyclic AMP to protein kinase isolated from rabbit muscle or the activity of cyclic AMP-dependent protein kinase from fat cells either in the presence or absence of cyclic AMP. There was no effect of DMSO (1.1 M) on the activity of hormone-sensitive triglyceride lipase

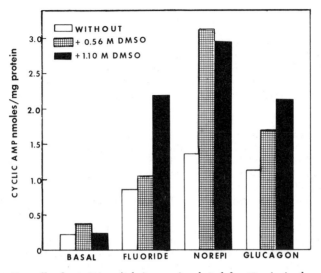

FIGURE 3. Fat cells ghosts (62 μg/tube) were incubated for 10 min in the absence or presence of fluoride, norepinephrine, or glucagon. Adenylate cyclase activity is expressed as pmoles cyclic AMP accumulated over 10 min. The results are the mean of three experiments done in duplicate.

from chicken adipose tissue in the activated (i.e. cyclic AMP present) or in the basal state.

The stimulation of cyclic AMP accumulation by 1.1 M DMSO was reversible, since in fat cells washed three times after prior incubation with DMSO for 10 min, the rise in cyclic AMP accumulation due to norepinephrine and theophylline was actually reduced from a control value of 1.6 to 0.8 nmoles/g. The direct addition of 1.1 M DMSO to these cells increased cyclic AMP by 4.7 nmoles/g in cells previously exposed to DMSO and to 3.5 in control cells. These results indicated that the effects of DMSO are readily reversible and do not result from irreversible inactivation of cyclic AMP phosphodiesterase.

TABLE 2

INHIBITION OF CYCLIC AMP PHOSPHODIESTERASE BY DMSO

Source of Enzyme	Cyclic AMP (μM)	Phosphodiesterase Activity (pmoles/min × mg protein)	% Inhibition by DMSO (1.3 M)
48,000 g supernatant	0.1	30 ± 6	39 ± 3
48,000 g supernatant	1.0	181 ± 34	45 ± 2
48,000 g precipitate	0.1	21 ± 4	35 ± 8
48,000 g precipitate	1.0	99 ± 24	24 ± 11

Fat cells were homogenized and then centrifuged at 48,000 g for 30 min. The phosphodiesterase activity during a 10-min incubation of both the precipitate and supernatant was examined at cyclic AMP concentrations of 0.1 μM and 1.0 μM. Effect of DMSO is expressed as percent inhibition and the data are the mean ± standard error of three experiments.

DISCUSSION

The ability of dimethyl sulfoxide to inhibit insulin-stimulated glucose oxidation is not the result of the increased lipolysis observed in the absence of insulin with DMSO (FIGURE 1). Free fatty acids have been shown to inhibit insulin action on fat cells[17] but DMSO still inhibited insulin-stimulated glucose oxidation under conditions (0.56 M DMSO plus insulin) in which there was no lipolytic action of DMSO.

The lipolytic effect of DMSO and its ability to potentiate lipolysis due to agents such as norepinephrine or glucagon (TABLE 1) may result from DMSO's potentiation of cyclic AMP accumulation due to these agents (TABLE 1 and FIGURE 2). Cyclic AMP accumulation due to DMSO alone was slight, but there was a potentiation of the rise in cyclic AMP due to norepinephrine or norepinephrine plus theophylline (FIGURE 2).

The mechanism by which DMSO increased cyclic AMP accumulation due to catecholamines could result from stimulation of adenylate cyclase activity. However, DMSO did not stimulate adenylate cyclase activity caused by catecholamines in the presence of a phosphodiesterase inhibitor. A much more likely possibility is that DMSO itself inhibits cyclic AMP phosphodiesterase and this effect predominates in intact cells. the activation of lipolysis by DMSO may be secondary to an elevation of cyclic AMP accumulation resulting from inhibition of cyclic AMP phosphodiesterase.

ACKNOWLEDGMENT

The author would like to express his thanks to Ms. Gail Horacek for assistance in the preparation of this manuscript.

REFERENCES

1. DAVID, N. A. 1972. A. Rev. Pharmac. **175:** 353–374.
2. MACGREGOR, W. 1967. Ann. N.Y. Acad. Sci. **141:** 3–12.
3. WOOD, D. C. & J. WOOD. 1975. Ann. N.Y. Acad. Sci. **243:** 7–19.
4. BOWER, A. & M. E. HADLEY. 1975. Endocrinology **96:** 431–439.
5. LEVY, J., M. TERODA, R. A. RIFKIND & P. A. MARKS. 1975. Proc. Natl. Acad. Sci. USA **72:** 28–32.
6. ORKIN, S. H., F. I. HAROSI & P. LEDER. 1975. Proc. Natl. Acad. Sci. USA **72:** 98–102.
7. KOCSIS, J. J., S. HARKAWAY & R. SNYDER. 1975. Ann. N.Y. Acad. Sci. **243:** 104–109.
8. RODBELL, M. 1964. J. Biol. Chem. **239:** 375–380.
9. FAIN, J. N., M. P. CZECH & R. SAPERSTEIN. 1973. In Methods in Investigative and Diagonostic Endocrinology. S. A. Berson, Ed. **2:** 267.
10. FAIN, J. N., N. REED & R. SAPERSTEIN, 1967. J. Biol. Chem. **242:** 1887–1894.
11. GILMAN A. G. 1979. Natl. Proc. Acad Sci. USA **67:** 305–312.
12. FAIN, J. N. & P. B. WIESER. 1975. J. Biol. Chem. **250:** 1027–1034.
13. JOHNSON M. E. M., N. M. DAS, F. R. BUTCHER & J. N. FAIN. 1972. J. Biol. Chem. **247:** 3229–3235.
14. BIRBAUMER, L., S. L. POHL & M. RODBELL. 1969. J. Biol. Chem. **244:** 3468–3476.
15. BROWN, B. L., J. D. M. ALBANO, R. P. EKINS, A. M, SGHERZI & W. TAMPION. 1971. Biochem. J. **121:** 561–562.
16. THOMPSON, W. J. & M. M. APPLEMAN. 1971. Biochemistry **10:** 311–317.
17. FAIN, J. N. & L. ROSENBERG. 1972. Diabetes **21:** 414–425.

INDUCTION OF GLOBIN GENE EXPRESSION DURING ERYTHROID CELL DIFFERENTIATION*

Richard A. Rifkind,† Michael Sheffery,†
Helen R. Profous-Juchelka,‡ Roberta C. Reuben,‡
and Paul A. Marks†

†DeWitt Wallace Research Laboratory
Memorial Sloan-Kettering Cancer Center
New York, New York 10021

‡Department of Biochemical Genetics
Merck Institute for Therapeutic Research
Merck Sharp & Dohme Research Laboratories
Rahway, New Jersey 07065

INTRODUCTION

Murine erythroleukemia cells (MELC) are transformed erythroid cell precursors that may be induced, by a variety of agents, including DMSO, to initiate the program of terminal cell differentiation and cell division characteristic of normal erythropoiesis.[1] Features of this process include the accumulation of α and β globin mRNA;[2,3] α, β^{maj}, and β^{min} globins, and associated hemoglobins;[4,5] accumulation of red cell surface proteins such as spectrin;[6] increased enzyme activities related to the heme synthesis;[7] and commitment to terminal cell division.[8,9] Terminal cell differentiation and division in normal cells is initiated by action of erythropoietin;[1] commitment to terminal differentiation in MELC, a multistep process,[10] is accomplished by exposure to any one of a wide variety of chemical and physical agents.[1,11,12] A short list of inducers of MELC differentiation is provided (TABLE 1). Work in this laboratory has addressed the characterization, at cellular and molecular levels, of features of uninduced and induced MELC that may provide insight into the mechanism of action of differentiation inducers, such as DMSO, and the mechanisms determining gene expression during the process of cell differentiation.

Studies from this and other laboratories, provide data suggesting that differentiation depends, at least in part, upon an effect of inducer during a specific phase of the cell division cycle. McClintock and Papaconstantinou[13] and Levy et al.[14] have shown that chemical inducers must be present during at least one or two S phases of the cell cycle to initiate gene expression characteristic of erythroid cell differentiation. MELC, arrested in cell cycle, do not differentiate,[15,16] while MELC synchronized in the G2 and G1 show accelerated commitment to terminal differentiation compared to S phase or unfractionated MELC cultured under similar conditions.[17] We have shown that inducer-mediated events during early S phase are needed for subsequent expression of the α and β globin genes.[18] During this critical period of early S phase the α and β globin structural genes are replicated.[19] Taken together, these studies suggest that induced gene expression

*The original studies reported in this paper were supported, in part, by the National Cancer Institute (PO 1 CA-31768 and CA-08748), the American Cancer Society (CH-68D), and the Bristol Myers Cancer Grant Program.

0077-8923/83/0411-0141 $01.75/0 © 1983, NYAS

may be associated with changes in chromatin configuration and DNA that occur during gene replication.

CHROMATIN STRUCTURE AND GLOBIN GENE EXPRESSION

During induced erythroid differentiation in MELC there is a greater than tenfold increase in the rate of accumulation of globin mRNA.[20] Work from several laboratories has established that changes in DNA and chromatin structure are associated with potential and actual gene expression in a variety of cell systems.[21-23] These include changes in the pattern of DNA methylation, in binding of high mobility group (HMG) proteins 14 and 17,[26] sensitivity of chromatin to digestion by DNase I,[27,28] and the appearance of sites or regions "hypersensitive" to digestion by DNase I, usually (but not invariably) found upstream of the 5' end of active (or potentially active) genes.[22,38] Sites of S1-nuclease sensitivity have recently been demonstrated to be associated with, but not necessarily identical to, sites of DNase I hypersensitivity.[29] McGhee and Felsenfeld[30] have shown that the DNase I hypersensitive region adjacent to the active chick β globin gene displays the absence of normal nucleosomal structures and the presence of what appears

TABLE 1

A SHORT LIST OF INDUCERS OF GENE EXPRESSION IN MELC

Polar compounds	dimethyl sulfoxide (DMSO); hexamethylene bisacetamide (HMBA)
Fatty acids	butyric acid
DNA intercalators	actinomycins
Modified bases	azacytidine
Phosphodiesterase inhibitors	methylisoxanthine
Ion-flux agents	ouabain
Physical agents	ultraviolet light, x-ray
Post-transcription-acting agent	hemin

to be a stretch of protein-free DNA. In our laboratory, several of these features of DNA and chromatin configuration have been examined in detail with respect to the changes in gene expression at the globin loci during induced MELC differentiation.[31]

DNA METHYLATION

The pattern of DNA methylation has been cited as a molecular characteristic that distinguishes expressed and unexpressed genes.[24,25] Relative hypomethylation is associated with transcription of a gene sequence; however, not all potential methylation sites within a domain need be unmethylated for transcription. In the rabbit β globin domain, demethylation of some, but not all methylated sites correlates with gene activity.[32] A small decrease in overall DNA methylation has been described during induced differentiation of MELC.[33]

We have recently examined the pattern of DNA methylation in the region of the β^{maj} and α globin genes during induced MELC differentiation assayed by use of the methyl-sensitive isoschizomer-pair of restriction enzymes, Msp I and Hpa

II, as well as other restriction enzymes.[31] Compared to the chick globin genes,[34] there are relatively few potentially methylated sites that can be assayed by these restriction enzymes in the mouse globin domains. Of the sites near the β^{maj} globin gene, one site is fully methylated, one is partially methylated, and one is unmethylated, in uninduced cells. Most, but not all, sites near the α globin genes are unmethylated in uninduced cells. No detectable change in the pattern of DNA methylation around either the α or β globin genes is observed during induced differentiation. Within the limits of resolution of the present assay, inducer-mediated globin gene expression in MELC is not accompanied by a change in the pattern of DNA methylation near the α_1 or β^{maj} genes. It is possible that MELC, which are transformed erythroid precursors approximately at the CFUe stage of differentiation, have been blocked in their development at a stage subsequent to the acquisition of the pattern of DNA demethylation critical for transcription of the globin genes.

DNASE I SENSITIVITY OF GLOBIN GENE-ASSOCIATED CHROMATIN

Studies of the sensitivity of MELC DNA to DNase I, assayed by liquid hybridization,[35] suggest that the globin gene chromatin of uninduced MELC is in an "active" configuration, accessible to nuclease action. We have compared, by the method of Southern,[36] the DNase I sensitivity of α and β^{maj} globin genes with that of another gene locus (Igα), which is not expressed in MELC. Both the β^{maj} and α globin genes, are more sensitive to digestion by DNase I than is the Igα gene in uninduced MELC,[31] suggesting that a stably propagated change in chromatin and DNA structure in the vicinity of the globin domains has occurred during development of these erythroid precursors, at a stage prior to that at which they were arrested during virus transformation. Taken together, the observations on methylation pattern and DNase I sensitivity suggest that the globin gene domains of MELC, before induction to the terminal stages of differentiation, already display a differentiation-specific configuration, compatible with and perhaps essential for expression of the globin genes.

DNASE I HYPERSENSITIVITY SITES IN GLOBIN GENE CHROMATIN

We have recently demonstrated the appearance, during induced differentiation, of specific sites displaying a six- to ten-fold increase in DNase I sensitivity in chromatin regions near both the α and β^{maj} globin genes (FIGURE 1).[31] These constitute the first demonstrated change in chromatin configuration associated with induced differentiation. The DNase I hypersensitive site near the β^{maj} globin gene is located within an approximately 200 base pair (bp) region in the 5'-flanking region of the gene and a DNase I hypersensitive site is also generated, 5' to the α_1 globin gene.[31]

Small amounts of globin gene-related subfragments are also generated during DNase I digestion of uninduced MELC nuclei. Several interpretations are possible. Since the MELC population employed in these studies (strain DS19) displays a low level of spontaneous differentiation (less than 1%), the low level of globin gene DNase I hypersensitivity sites detected in uninduced cells may reflect the configuration of globin gene-associated chromatin in these spontaneously differentiating cells. It cannot be ruled out, however (and see below), that the observed low level of spontaneous DNase I hypersensitivity reflects a low level of constitutive globin gene expression in uninduced MELC.[38,39]

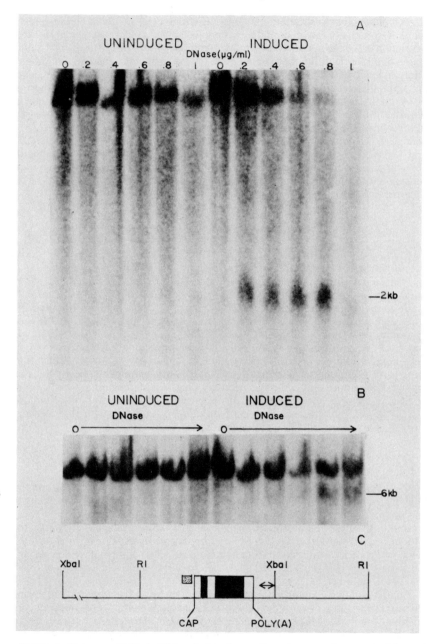

FIGURE 1. Hypersensitivity to DNase I of a chromatin region near the 5' end of the β^{maj} globin gene in induced MELC. (A) Nuclei were prepared from uninduced (left) or induced (right) MELC and digested with the concentration of DNase I in λg/ml indicated above each lane. DNA was purified, digested with Xba I, and analyzed by the method of Southern[36]

GLOBIN GENE EXPRESSION DURING INDUCED DIFFERENTIATION

When MELC are cultured in the presence of DMSO, HMBA (hexamethylene bisacetamide), or butyric acid, commitment to terminal cell division and differentiation is first detected by 12 to 16 h;[8] at this same time accumulation of newly synthesized α globin mRNA can be first detected in the cytoplasm.[38] Cytoplasmic accumulation of newly synthesized β globin mRNA sequences is not detected until about 8 h later, and by 48 h there is achieved an approximately tenfold increase in the globin mRNA content.[38,42] Hemin, another inducer of MELC,[43] unlike the polar compounds (such as DMSO and HMBA) or the fatty acids (such as butyric acid), rapidly (by 6 h) and simultaneously initiates the accumulation of both α and β globin mRNA but fails to induce commitment to terminal cell division (FIGURE 2 and TABLE 2).[38,43,44] Although the principal β-like mRNA induced by the polar inducers and by fatty acids is β^{maj} mRNA, hemin initiates accumulation of β^{min} globin mRNA;[42,45] β^{min} is the principal globin detected in uninduced MELC populations.[38,39,42,45]

It has been demonstrated that the increase in β globin mRNA content induced by DMSO reflects, to a substantial degree, an increase in gene transcription as assayed by the technique of nascent chain elongation.[46] By the same approach, we have shown that HMBA and butyric acid both elicit an increase in the rate of transcription of α and β globin genes; furthermore, by 48 to 72 h of culture with these inducers there is an approximately twofold greater increase in the rate of transcription of α globin genes relative to the β globin gene (TABLE 3).[47] These observations, taken together with the studies on DNA and chromatin configuration described above, suggest that regulation of gene expression, as modulated both by polar inducers and by fatty acid inducers is exerted, to a substantial degree, at the level of gene transcription.

Hemin, as already noted, also induces the accumulation of cytoplasmic α and β globin mRNA. However, although hemin initiates the accumulation of cytoplasmic mRNA to a degree only slightly less than that of the other inducers (FIGURE 2), hemin fails to increase the rate of nuclear chain elongation and, by this criterion, does not stimulate globin gene transcription (TABLE 3). This suggests an effect of hemin at a post-transcriptional step, acting upon a low but constitutive level of globin gene transcription. It should be noted that, while increasing globin mRNA accumulation, hemin maintains the α/β mRNA ratio characteristic of uninduced cells (aproximately one) and the predominant β-like transcript (β^{min} globin mRNA) found in uninduced cells.[42] These studies appear to distinguish two

---

with a β^{maj} globin gene-specific probe (C). A DNase I-generated subfragment of 2 kb is indicated. (B) DNA, purified from another DNase I digestion series, was digested with EcoRI and analyzed with the β^{maj} globin gene probe. Increasing concentrations (from zero) of DNase I are indicated by the arrows above the lanes. A DNase I-generated subfragment of about 6 kb, produced from induced cell nuclei, is indicated. (C) A simplified restriction map around the β^{maj} globin gene showing the location of adjacent EcoRI and Xba I sites. The 5' and 3' ends of the map (based on the direction of transcription) are to the left and right, respectively. The size and location of the β^{maj} globin gene-specific probe sequence[40] are indicated by the double-headed arrow extending from the 3' Xba I site. The probe is located in the 3' flanking sequence of the β^{maj} globin gene and does not cross-react with the β^{min} globin gene. The β^{maj} globin gene is represented by the open (exon) and solid (intron) boxes. The cap and poly (A) addition sites are indicated. The DNase I-hypersensitive region (stippled box) is mapped from data presented in A and C. These data are taken from Sheffery *et al.*[31]

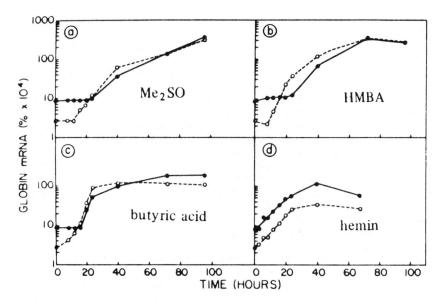

FIGURE 2. Accumulation of α and β mRNAs in MELC. Cells were treated with each inducer (Me$_2$SO, 280mM; HMBA, 5mM; butyric acid, 1.5 mM; and hemin, 0.1 mM), RNA extracted, and analyzed by molecular hybridization for α (O-------O) and β (●———●) globin mRNA sequences. These data are taken from Nudel et al.[38]

mechanisms that contribute to the control of accumulation of globin mRNA during differentiation. DMSO and similar compounds, both of which can initiate both the process of commitment to terminal cell division and the characteristic erythroid cell program of gene expression, act to augment the rate of globin gene transcription. Hemin, on the other hand, which does not cause commitment to terminal cell division, apparently induces globin mRNA accumulation by a

TABLE 2

EFFECT OF HMBA AND HEMIN ON ACCUMULATION OF NEWLY SYNTHESIZED
CYTOPLASMIC α AND β GLOBIN MRNA*

		Globin mRNA†		
Inducer	Commitment (%)‡	α (%)	β (%)	α/β
None	0	.004	.005	0.80
5 mM HMBA	81	.076	.030	2.53
0.1 mM Hemin	2	.018	.024	0.75

*These data are taken from Profous-Juchelka et al.[42]

†[³H]RNA retained on filter, expressed as percent of applied cytoplasmic [³H]RNA extracted from cells exposed to [³H]uridine for two hours.

‡Assayed at 72 hours after initiation of culture and expressed as proportion of cells giving rise to small hemoglobinized colonies.

post-transcriptional mechanism, directed presumably at the processing or stabilization of a constitutive level of globin mRNA found in uninduced MELC. The existence of a low level of globin gene expression in uninduced MELC is consistent with the observed hypomethylation and DNase I sensitivity of the globin genes in chromatin from uninduced MELC and the low, but detectable, DNase I hypersensitivity in the 5' flanking regions of these genes in uninduced cells.

SUMMARY

We can provide increasing insight, albeit still incomplete, into the changes in MELC that accompany globin gene expression induced by polar chemicals, such as DMSO, and other agents. These transformed, CFUe-like erythroid precursor cells exhibit in their uninduced state, a DNA methylation pattern and globin gene

TABLE 3

TRANSCRIPTION OF α AND β GLOBIN GENES DURING INDUCED MELC DIFFERENTIATION*

| | Time In | Globin mRNA† | |
| | Culture | α | β |
Inducer Added	(h)	(%)	(%)
None	48	.005	.004
5 mM HMBA	48	.032	.015
None	48	.002	.001
1.5 mM Butyric acid	48	.010	.004
None	48	.003	.002
0.1 mM Hemin	48	.003	.002

*These data are adapted from Profous-Juchelka *et al.*[47]
†Newly transcribed globin mRNA (nuclear chain elongation) is expressed as the percent of total extracted nuclear [^{32}P]RNA, which hybridizes to specific α and β globin DNA probes, after a 5 min exposure to [^{32}P]UTP.

chromatin configuration (DNase I sensitivity) that is compatible with actual or potential gene transcription. Such features may reflect alterations in chromatin configuration that have occurred at a stage prior to leukemic transformation, during the differentiation of earlier erythroid precursor cells and associated with the restriction in developmental potential characteristic of progression to the CFUe (or MELC) stage of erythropoiesis.

Uninduced MELC display a low level of globin gene transcription, producing globin mRNA or mRNA precursors whose processing or stabilization is the target of action of hemin. The major increase in MELC globin gene transcription that is initiated by DMSO, HMBA, or butyric acid, is accompanied by, and perhaps preceded by,[48] an increase in DNase I hypersensitivity in the regions 5' to the active globin genes. This suggests that reorganization of chromatin structure in the globin gene domains is associated with accelerated globin gene transcription and may be characteristic of a developmental transition during terminal differentiation in the erythroid cell lineage.

REFERENCES

1. MARKS, P. A. & R. A. RIFKIND. 1978. Ann. Rev. Biochem. **47:** 419–448.
2. ROSS, J., Y. IKAWA & P. LEDER. 1972. Proc. Natl. Acad. Sci. USA **69:** 3620–3623.
3. OHTA, Y., M. TANAKA, M. TERADA, O. J. MILLER, A. BANK, P. A. MARKS & R. A. RIFKIND. 1976. Proc. Natl. Acad. Sci. USA **73:** 1232–1236.
4. BOYER, S. H., K. D. WU, A. N. NOYES, R. YOUNG, W. SCHER, C. FRIEND, H. PREISLER & A. BANK. 1972. Blood **40:** 823–835.
5. OSTERTAG, W., H. MELDERIS, G. STEINHEIDER, N. KLUGE & S. DUBE. 1972. Nature (London) New Biol. **239:** 231–234.
6. EISEN, H., S. NASI, C. P. GEORGOPOULOS, D. ARNDT-JOVIN & W. OSTERTAG. 1977. Cell **10:** 689–695.
7. SASSA, S., S. GRANICK, C. CHANG & A. KAPPAS. 1975. In Erythropoiesis. Proc. Fourth Intl. Conf. on Erythropoiesis. K. Nakao, J. W. Fisher & F. Takaku, Eds.: 383–395. University of Tokyo Press. Tokyo.
8. FIBACH, E., R. C. REUBEN, R. A. RIFKIND & P. A. MARKS. 1977. Cancer Res. **37:** 440–444.
9. GUSELLA, J., R. GELLER, B. CLARKE, V. WEEKS & D. HOUSMAN. 1976. Cell **9:** 221–229.
10. CHEN, Z. X., J. BANKS, R. A. RIFKIND & P. A. MARKS. 1982. Proc. Natl. Acad. Sci. USA **79:** 471–475.
11. REUBEN, R. C., R. A. RIFKIND & P. A. MARKS. 1980. Biochim. Biophys. Acta **605:** 325–346.
12. REUBEN, R. C., P. L. KHANNA, Y. GAZITT, R. BRESLOW, R. A. RIFKIND & P. A. MARKS. 1978. J. Biol. Chem. **253:** 4214–4218.
13. McCLINTOCK, P. R. & J. PAPACONSTANTINOU. 1974. Proc. Natl. Acad. Sci. USA **71:** 4551–4555.
14. LEVY, J., M. TERADA, R. A. RIFKIND & P. A. MARKS. 1975. Proc. Natl. Acad. Sci. USA **72:** 28–32.
15. HARRISON, P. R. 1977. In International Review of Biochemistry of Cell Differentiation II. J. Paul, Ed. **15:** 227–267.
16. CONKIE, D., P. R. HARRISON & J. PAUL. 1981. Proc. Natl. Acad. Sci. USA **78:** 3644–3648.
17. GELLER, R., R. LEVENSON & D. HOUSMAN. 1978. J. Cell Physiol. **95:** 213–222.
18. GAMBARI, R., M. TERADA, A. BANK, R. A. RIFKIND & P. A. MARKS. 1978. Proc. Natl. Acad. Sci. USA **75:** 3801–3804.
19. EPNER, E., R. A. RIFKIND & P. A. MARKS. 1981. Proc. Natl. Acad. Sci. USA **78:** 3058–3062.
20. GAMBARI, R., P. A. MARKS & R. A. RIFKIND. 1979. Proc. Natl. Acad. Sci. USA **76:** 4511–4515.
21. WEISBROD, S. 1982. Nature **297:** 289–295.
22. ELGIN, S. C. R. 1981. Cell **27:** 413–415.
23. IGO-KEMENES, T., W. HORZ & H. G. ZACHAU. 1982. Annu. Rev. Biochem. **51:** 89–121.
24. FELSENFELD, G. & J. McGHEE. 1982. Nature **296:** 602–603.
25. DOERFLER, W. 1981. J. Gen. Virol. **57:** 1–20.
26. WEISBROD, S. T. 1982. Nucleic Acids Res. **10:** 2017–2042.
27. WEINTRAUB, H. & M. GROUDINE. 1976. Science **193:** 848–856.
28. GAREL, A. & R. AXEL. 1976. Proc. Natl. Acad. Sci. USA **73:** 3966–3970.
29. LARSEN, A. & H. WEINTRAUB. 1982. Cell **29:** 609–622.
30. McGHEE, J. D., W. I. WOOD, M. DOLAN, J. D. ENGEL & G. FELSENFELD. 1981. Cell **27:** 45–55.
31. SHEFFERY, M., R. A. RIFKIND & P. A. MARKS. 1982. Proc. Natl. Acad. Sci. USA **79:** 1180–1184.
32. SHEN, J. C.-K. & T. MANIATIS. 1980. Proc. Natl. Acad. Sci. USA **77:** 6634–6638.
33. CHRISTMAN, J. K., N. WEICH, B. SCHOENBRUN, N. SCHNEIDERMAN & G. ACS. 1980. J. Cell Biol. **86:** 366–370.
34. WEINTRAUB, H., A. LARSEN & M. GROUDINE. 1981. Cell **24:** 333–344.
35. MILLER, D. M., P. TURNER, A. NIENHUIS, A. W., D. E. AXELROD & T. V. GOPALAKRISHNAN. 1978. Cell **14:** 511–524.
36. SOUTHERN, E. M. 1975. J. Mol. Biol. **98:** 503–517.
37. WU, C. 1980. Nature **286:** 854–860.

38. NUDEL, U., J. SALMON, E. FIBACH, M. TERADA, R. A. RIFKIND, P. A. MARKS & A. BANK. Cell **12:** 463–469.
39. DONALDSON, D. S., A. R. McNAB, G. ROVERA & P. J. CURTIS. 1982. J. Biol. Chem. **257:** 8655–8660.
40. HOFER, E. & J. E. DARNELL, JR. 1981. Cell **23:** 585–593.
41. ROUGEON, F. & B. MACH. 1977. Gene **1:** 229–239.
42. MARKS, P. A., R. A. RIFKIND, A. BANK, M. TERADA, R. GAMBARI, E. FIBACH, G. MANIATIS & R. REUBEN. 1979. *In* Cellular and Molecular Regulation of Hemoglobin Switching. G. Stamatoyannopoulos & A. W. Neinhuis, Eds.:437–455. Grune & Stratton. New York.
43. ROSS, J. & D. SAUTNER. 1976. Cell **8:** 513–520.
44. GUSELLA, J. F., S. C. WEIL, A. S. TSIFTSOGLOU, V. VOLLOCH, J. R. NEUMANN, C. KEYS & D. E. HOUSMAN. 1980. Blood **56:** 481–487.
45. LOWENHAUPT, K. & J. B. LINGREL. 1979. Proc. Natl. Acad. Sci. USA **76:** 5173–5177.
46. HOFER, E., R. HOFER-WARBINEK & J. D. DARNELL, JR. 1982. Cell **29:** 887–893.
47. PROFOUS-JUCHELKA, H. R., R. C. REUBEN, P. A. MARKS & R. A. RIFKIND. 1982. Mol. Cell Biol. (In press.)
48. RIFKIND *et al.* 1983. (Manuscript in preparation.)

MECHANISMS OF THE SYNERGISTIC EFFECT OF ORAL DIMETHYL SULFOXIDE ON ANTINEOPLASTIC THERAPY*

Claire Ann Thuning, Miriam S. Fanshaw, and Joel Warren

The Goodwin Institute for Cancer Research
1850 N.W. 69 Avenue
Plantation, Florida 33313

INTRODUCTION

Penetration of dimethyl sulfoxide (DMSO) into vascular and nonvascular tissues of the body occurs rapidly following administration by peripheral or oral routes.[1] This is probably related to its capacity as a dipolar, aprotic solvent to accelerate certain reactions and to transport substances of low molecular weight across protein membranes.[2]

These properties led us to investigate the ability of DMSO to potentiate antineoplastic activity of the alkylating agent, cyclophosphamide (CPA). Studies reported to this Academy in 1975 demonstrated that the parenteral injection of CPA into tumor-bearing rats ingesting DMSO in their drinking water ad libitum resulted in modest enhancement of antineoplastic effects as gauged by a decrease in the median tumor diameter and the prolongation of survival time. However, when CPA was mixed with 2% DMSO and offered orally ad libitum in drinking water to achieve a sustained level of drug, there was a significant increase in its leuko-depressive and tumor-inhibiting activity.[3,4]

These investigations have been continued, and in this report, we further explore the effects of ingested DMSO on the activity of a group of 12 antitumor drugs, which have diverse modes of actions.

MATERIALS AND METHODS

Animals and Tumor

Fischer 344 rats weighing 68–72 grams, obtained from the Texas Inbred Mouse Co., A. R. Schmidt Sprague-Dawley and our own colony, were randomized into groups of ten with even sex distribution in each cage. They were fed Purina laboratory chow ad libitum. A typical experiment consisted of one control group and 16 treated groups of tumor-bearing animals.

The tumor used, the Nova rat leukemia-1871 (NRL-1871), appeared spontaneously in a germfree Fischer 344 rat and it has been maintained by intraperitoneal (i.p.) transplantation of spleen suspensions every 10–14 days.[5] The histopathology of NRL-1871 has been described by Pearson et al.[6] When 5,000 tumor cells are inoculated subcutaneously (s.c.) into the inguinal region, the resulting neoplasm initially grows as a localized solid tumor palpable by the 10th to 12th day and is uniformly fatal within 18–22 days with spread to the major organs. The

*This work was supported by the National Cancer Institute, National Institutes of Health (Contract #N01-CM-53814).

0077–8923/83/0411–0150 $01.75/0 © 1983, NYAS

intracranial (i.c.) inoculation of 1,000 cells into the temporal cortex is followed by massive invasion of the meninges with or without hydrocephalus. This quickly becomes a generalized leukemia and death ensues in 13-16 days.

Chemotherapeutic Assays

DMSO (Mallinckrodt reagent grade) was freshly prepared in tap water for ingestion. Drugs prepared daily in either distilled water or 0.3% hydroxypropyl cellulose depending upon their solubility, were administered i.p. or per os by intubation or ad libitum. To minimize possible decomposition, water bottles containing DMSO and/or drug were made light-tight with aluminum foil wrapping. The average liquid consumption for a cage of ten rats was measured daily.

The protocols initially adopted for parenteral therapy schedules and drug preparation procedures, were based on those developed by the Drug Evaluation Branch, National Cancer Institute.[7] Four doubling concentrations of each compound were tested simultaneously in the drinking water of rats without DMSO or with 2% DMSO offered ad libitum. Addition of DMSO to the drinking water was begun six days prior to drug therapy and continued for at least 48 hours after removal of the antineoplastic drug. The ingested dose per rat was calculated on the basis of the ingestion rate of the mixture in drinking water (average 16-18 ml/24 h). While the quantity varied somewhat from animal to animal (±3.0 ml), the oral effectiveness or toxicity of a drug could be reproduced in successive experiments. In the first series of assays, when the susceptibility of NRL-1871 to these compounds was unknown, treatment was daily from day 10 through day 18. When it was recognized that the tumor burden at 10 days exceeded the effectiveness of several compounds, we compared their efficacy with treatment initiated 2, 4, and 6 days after implantation.

Experimental Design

Each experiment involved a comparison of drug activity in water or DMSO using groups of 10-15 rodents for each concentration of anticancer drug tested. Surviving animals were killed and autopsied 60 days after tumor implant. The median survival time (MST) and median tumor diameter were calculated as described by Geran et al.[7] A test in which the life span of the treated rats was at least 25% longer than in the controls (i.e., reproduced T/C%, MST Test/Control, of 125 or greater) was regarded as indicative of effectiveness.[7] Death of rats without a palpable tumor or splenomegaly within 10 days after tumor implantation was considered as due to drug toxicity.

We also examined the effect of ingested DMSO on the concentration of CPA in blood plasma, brain, and liver tissues of normal rats. Four of five replicate experiments utilized a pair of male Fischer 344 rats of approximately equal body weight. Each rat was fed 2% (vol/vol) DMSO in the drinking water for 48 h. On the third day, 1.0 ml of 5% DMSO or water was intubated into the test or control animal followed one hour later by intubation of ^{14}C-labeled CPA at a dose of 100 mg/kg.

Tail blood samples, taken at intervals, were centrifuged for determination of hematocrit and collection of plasma. After the last blood sample, the rats were sacrificed and a homogenate of brain and liver was made in distilled water. Methylene chloride extraction of all samples removed unmetabolized CPA from

TABLE 1

EFFECT OF DMSO ON CHEMOTHERAPEUTIC COMPOUNDS IN TUMOR-BEARING RATS

| Test Compounds | Route Administration | | Site of Tumor | DMSO | | |
	Drug	DMSO		MST	60-Day Survival	Tumor Growth
CPA DAG	Oral Combined		Lymphoma Intracranial	Inc. Inc.	Inc. 0	ND ND
CPA DAG	Oral Combined		Subcutaneous	0 0	0 0	Red. Red.
CPA DAG MTX CCNU M-CCNU BCNU	Intubation	Oral Ad Libitum	Intracranial	0	0	0
CPA DAG MTX CCNU M-CCNU 6-MP 5-FU N-Mustard Chlorambucil Adriamycin	i.p.	As drug diluent 2%	Intracranial	0	0	Red. Red. ND ND ND ND ND Red. Red. 0
CCNU	i.v.	As diluent	Intracranial	Inc.	0	ND

Abbreviations: ND, Not Done; Inc., Increased; Red., Reduced; 0, No Effect; MST, Mean Survival Time; i.p., Intraperitoneal; and i.v., Intravenous.

the cytotoxic, metabolized form. The radioactivity of the fractions was quantitated.

RESULTS

Survival of Untreated Tumor-bearing Rats

The baseline for median survival time was determined by observation of a total of 770 tumored, untreated control rats with either a s.c. implant in the inguinal region, or an i.c. implant of tumor into the meninges. These were s.c. = 19.0 ± 1.55 (S.D.) days; i.c. = 15.3 ± 1.5 (S.D.) days. Median tumor diameter from time after implantation was measured for all inguinal growths and was highly consistent between successive groups of untreated rodents.

DMSO Alone Has No Effect on NRL-1871

We have reported earlier that prolonged ad libitum oral ingestion of DMSO in Fischer 344 rats was well tolerated, and that concentrations as high as 8% had been ingested in the drinking water for over 30 days without acute toxicity.[3]

No evidence of antineoplastic activity was observed in over 800 rats bearing the inguinal tumor and ingesting oral DMSO ad libitum at concentrations ranging from 0.25% to 32%. Treatment was begun as early as 6 days before and also initiated at various intervals after tumor implantation.

Effect of Route of Administration on the Interaction of DMSO and Antitumor Drugs as Judged by Survival Time

Subcutaneous Inguinal Tumors

The efficacy of 12 compounds given i.p. was assayed in rats bearing a s.c. implanted lymphoma and drinking water alone or a solution of 2% DMSO. The drugs were: methotrexate, 6-MP, nitrogen mustard, chlorambucil, cyclophosphamide, vinblastine, vincristine, CCNU, daunomycin, M-CCNU, adriamycin, and dianhydrogalactitol (DAG) (TABLE 1). There was no consistent enhancement of the median survival time of these rodents when the drugs were administered daily by this route. The use of DMSO as a vehicle for drug injection was, likewise, investigated with no resulting potentiation of drug antitumor activity.

Because of the cyclic elevations and rapid excretion of drugs when they are administered i.p., we investigated the activity of mixtures of drugs ingested ad libitum in 2% DMSO or in water. Due to drug insolubility or the failure of rats to drink the mixture, these experiments could only be performed with CPA and DAG, which were willingly ingested. In preliminary experiments, using water alone as solvent, both drugs, when given ad libitum in the drinking bottle, were highly and equally effective in the treatment of s.c. inguinal tumors. The prolonged ingestion of 2% DMSO did not decrease the optimal dose of CPA or of DAG, or increase the survival time.

Meningeal Leukemia

In contrast, the most significant evidence of potentiation was obtained when the tumor was implanted into the central nervous system (CNS) and drug was combined with DMSO and ingested ad libitum. TABLE 2 shows the results of a series of experiments in which CPA was tested over a range of four concentrations in rats bearing NRL-1871 implanted in a meningeal site. Not only was

TABLE 2

ENHANCING EFFECT OF ORAL DMSO-CPA MIXTURE AD LIB IN TREATMENT OF MENINGEAL LEUKEMIA IN RATS

Dose*	MST (T/C%)†		Day 60	Survivors
(mg/kg/day)	H₂O	DMSO‡	H₂O	DMSO
6	125 ± 7.8	157 ± 21.3	0/30	4/30
8	136 ± 8.9	155 ± 14.9	0/30	1/30
12	137 ± 3.7	245 ± 61.0	0/30	12/30
16	142 ± 1.9	332 ± 74.5	1/30	15/30

*Drug given for 24 h on day 2.
†Median survival time (% test/control) ± S.E.
‡DMSO given day 2–4.

median survival time increased with DMSO at all four dose levels, but the number of day-60 survivors was significantly increased. If all of the CPA assays are combined, the number of day-60 survivors are 8 of 550 in the CPA + "water" group as compared to 70 of 550 in the CPA + DMSO group.

The effect of DMSO on DAG antitumor activity was difficult to assess, though there was sporadic indication of potentiation. This was because of the marked effectiveness of this compound in the rat meningeal tumor system, leaving little room for demonstration of DMSO enhancement.

Effect of Ingested DMSO on Therapeutic Activity of Anticancer Drugs as Judged by Tumor Growth

The effectiveness of drugs when inoculated into the rat peritoneal cavity was not enhanced by the concurrent ingestion of DMSO if the outcome was based on an increase in survival time. In contrast, this approach did produce a significant alteration in the growth patterns of palpable inguinal tumors and often prolonged the duration of this tumor-free condition. This was observed even with compounds, such as methotrexate and adriamycin, whose effectiveness, as measured by prolongation of survival, was not influenced by DMSO. The suppression or retardation of tumor growth by DMSO-drug combinations was most apparent when treatment with the anticancer drug was started late in the disease, when the reduction in size of the larger tumors could be more pronounced. In FIGURE 1, we have plotted the median tumor diameter response to i.p. treatment with one sub-curative dose level of four different anticancer drugs with and without ingested DMSO. In rats receiving drug plus DMSO, the median tumor diameter was initially, consistently smaller than that seen with the same dose of drug alone. In the case of DAG, tumors failed to appear in either group until day 23 when only the rats ingesting water developed rapidly growing neoplasms. Seven of ten rats in the DMSO-treated group failed to develop grossly detectable tumors for 60 days and were considered as cured. However, in those animals where these remissions terminated, the tumors grew as rapidly as the untreated implants and the rodents receiving DMSO did not survive longer than those given drug alone.

Nitrogen mustard, when administered i.p. relatively late in the course of tumor growth, caused disappearance of tumor within 72 hours in all animals. However, the neoplasms in the water-fed group reappeared three days earlier than those in the DMSO-fed rodents with no survivors in either group.

An example of a compound being ineffective when administered to water-fed rats but showing transient activity when given to DMSO-fed rodents is shown in the case of CCNU. In both assays there was retardation in tumor growth associated with the ingestion of DMSO, but this was short-lived and the tumors grew as rapidly as the controls at the cessation of treatment.

Effect of Oral DMSO on the Toxicity of Antineoplastic Compounds

Of critical importance to any clinical use of DMSO-drug combinations in the treatment of cancer is the possibility of increased drug toxicity associated with the ingestion of DMSO. We have examined toxicity levels when i.p., oral-intubated, or oral-ingested combinations of DMSO drug were used. Data based on 1,260 inguinal tumor-bearing animals ingesting DMSO and treated i.p. or orally are summarized in TABLES 3–5. Only those deaths that occurred within the first 10 days of treatment and prior to the appearance of tumor are tabulated. These results indicate that the toxicity of the effective antitumor drugs was usually not increased in rats ingesting 2% DMSO.

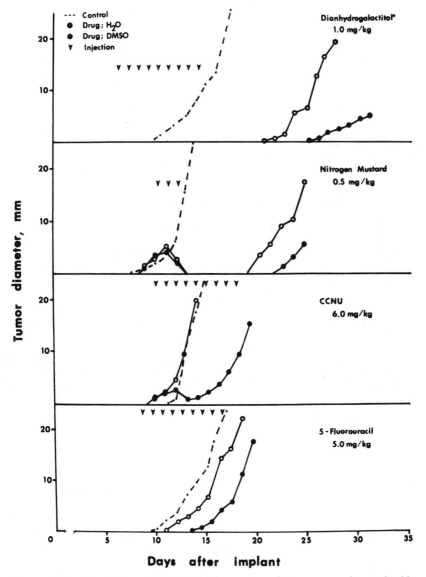

FIGURE 1. The effect of ingested DMSO on four antineoplastic compounds as judged by median tumor diameter. All drugs were administered intraperitoneally on the days indicated by an arrow.

TABLE 3

ORAL DMSO DOES NOT INCREASE THE TOXICITY OF ANTINEOPLASTIC COMPOUNDS
GIVEN TO RATS INTRAPERITONEALLY

Compound	Dose (mg/kg)	Toxic Deaths*	
		H_2O	DMSO
Methotrexate	0.7–5.6	0/40	0/40
6-MP	6.0–200	12/210	6/210
N-Mustard	0.125–2.0	11/130	20/130
Chlorambucil	6.0–24	0/60	0/60
Cyclophosphamide	5.0–70	0/160	2/160
Vinblastine	0.4–0.8	3/30	4/30
Vincristine	0.4	3/20	6/20
CCNU	12	0/20	0/20
Daunomycin	4.8	0/10	0/10
M-CCNU	12	0/10	0/10
Adriamycin	2.8–11.2	10/210	13/209
Dianhydrogalactitol	0.5–4	0/140	0/140

*Death through day 10 and prior to appearance of tumor in controls.

Influence of DMSO on Tissue Levels of CPA in the Rat

In an attempt to understand the possible mechanism of DMSO-drug interaction, we examined the influence of DMSO on tissue distribution of CPA. The results shown in FIGURE 2 indicate a more rapid, two-fold increase in the plasma concentration of total CPA in the DMSO as compared with water-fed rats within one hour of administration. The clearance of the drug in these animals was accelerated so that CPA plasma levels were comparable in both groups within two hours. When both metabolized and unmetabolized fractions of CPA were determined (FIGURE 3), the same degree of drug elevation existed in the DMSO group. It is evident, however, that the unmetabolized drug fractions constituted the major portion of the rapidly excreted CPA seen in FIGURE 2.

A similar increased uptake was observed for both forms of the drug in brain and liver tissue of rodents ingesting DMSO (TABLE 6). For example, at 80 minutes, levels of metabolized CPA were increased 119% in brain and 81% in liver tissue. These differences had become negligible at three hours.

TABLE 4

DMSO DOES NOT INCREASE THE TOXICITY OF ANTINEOPLASTIC COMPOUNDS GIVEN BY
ORAL INTUBATION TO RATS BEARING MENINGEAL TUMOR

Compound	Per Os Dose (mg/kg)	Toxic Deaths*	
		H_2O	DMSO
Cyclophosphamide	6–16	0/40	0/40
CCNU	4–16	0/39	0/39
M-CCNU	12–32	0/39	0/39
Dianhydrogalactitol	0.4–3.2	7/66	11/61
BCNU	2–12	0/40	0/38

*Death through day 10 and prior to appearance of tumor in controls.

TABLE 5

DMSO DOES NOT INCREASE THE TOXICITY OF CYCLOPHOSPHAMIDE OR
DIANHYDROGALACTITOL GIVEN PER OS AD LIB

		Dose	Toxic Deaths*	
Compound	Tumor Site	(mg/kg/day)	H_2O	DMSO
Cyclophosphamide	Inguinal	4–32	4/70	0/70
	Meningeal	9–32	2/200	0/200
Dianhydrogalactitol	Meningeal	0.2–4	1/230	2/230

*Death through day 10 and prior to appearance of tumor in controls.

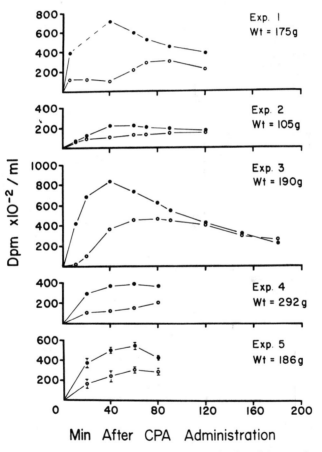

Min After CPA Administration

FIGURE 2. The effect of ingested DMSO on plasma levels of total CPA in the rat. In the first four experiments, each point represents the dpm per ml of plasma of an individual rat ingesting either water (O) or DMSO (●) prior to CPA administration. Experiment 5 consists of mean CPA values (±S.D.) for three water-fed and two DMSO-fed rats.

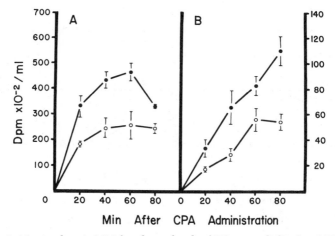

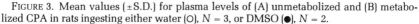

Min   After   CPA   Administration

FIGURE 3. Mean values ($\pm$S.D.) for plasma levels of (A) unmetabolized and (B) metabolized CPA in rats ingesting either water (O), $N = 3$, or DMSO (●), $N = 2$.

DISCUSSION

This report is an amplification of our original observations that DMSO potentiated the effect of CPA when both are ingested as a mixture. It also serves to uncover several factors that may be involved in this DMSO interaction. These are: (1) Ingestion of DMSO at a concentration of 2% for over one year was well tolerated in the Fischer 344 rat. It did not significantly increase the oral toxicity of a series of antitumor drugs when they were combined in the drinking water. (2) When used as a vehicle for drug injection, DMSO failed to alter the potency of this group of diverse antineoplastics. (3) The site of tumor implantation and growth may play a role in the enhancing effect of DMSO. A rat lymphoma growing i.c. was considerably more responsive to oral DMSO and CPA than a s.c. implant of the same neoplasm. (4) The administration of drug and DMSO as a mixture may retard tumor growth better than drug alone. However, this potentiation is transient and may not be accompanied by a prolongation of the survival

TABLE 6

DISTRIBUTION OF CPA AND ITS CONVERSION PRODUCTS AS RELATED TO INGESTION OF
WATER OR DMSO

CPA	Sampling Time	% Increase: DMSO/Water*		
		Plasma	Brain	Liver
Total	80 min	49	52	57
Metabolized	80 min	102	116	54
Unmetabolized	80 min	37	42	59
Total	180 min	−11	17	N.D.†
Metabolized	180 min	0	18	N.D.
Unmetabolized	180 min	−28	17	N.D.

*% Increase based on difference in mean dpm/ml; S.E. <5% for all means.
†N.D. = not done.

time. (5) The higher tissue levels of CPA associated with ingested DMSO may help to explain the therapeutic enhancement of this drug in the rat lymphoma system. Though increased amounts of drug in the plasma appear to account for elevated levels in brain tissue, there is a small additional increase, particularly at 180 minutes. This may be accounted for by alteration of blood-brain barrier permeability. The recent observation of Broadwell et al., that DMSO opens the blood-brain barrier to horseradish peroxidase in mice, suggests a mechanism whereby CPA-DMSO was more effective in treating a cranial tumor than a peritoneal neoplasm.[8]

In summary, we believe that DMSO modifies the pharmacology of CPA in the rat by increasing the systemic availability of CPA and enhancing diffusion of the drug across tissue membranes. It likewise accelerates drug efflux from the plasma, which correlates with the observance of little increase in drug toxicity when it was used together with DMSO in the therapeutic studies described above. The ability of DMSO to increase the effectiveness but not the toxicity of certain antineoplastic compounds is probably the result of a rapid pulse of compound through the tumor tissue.

In two recent studies of human cancer patients, the concomitant administration of large volumes of DMSO failed to augment the chemotherapeutic response ratio. Egorin et al. reported that 5-10% DMSO, when given to brain tumor patients by mouth or i.v., failed to alter the behavior of CPA in the plasma, urine, or cerebrospinal fluid. The clinical course of the ten patients in this study was not significantly affected by the ingestion of DMSO.[9]

Aisner and Wiernik treated 15 renal carcinoma patients with thiotepa combined with 2% oral DMSO. There was no augmentation of the somewhat minimal activity of this compound against this tumor.[10]

The reconciliation of our findings in the Fischer rat to these discouraging human clinical tests is difficult. Two possibilities to be considered are: the NRL-1871 lymphoma in the rat CNS constitutes a tumor-host system that is uniquely responsive to DMSO, or the pharmacokinetics of CPA in the DMSO-treated rat differ from that in the DMSO-treated human. Research thus far on the synergistic effects of DMSO in human cancer has been conducted in patients with advanced tumors whose responsiveness to any antineoplastic regimen is poor. Trials in the early stages of meningeal leukemia and in other neoplasms with a good response rate to alkylating agents might be more meaningful.

SUMMARY

The purpose of this study was to determine whether dimethyl sulfoxide (DMSO) when administered in conjunction with antitumor drugs would potentiate their activity against a rodent tumor. Twelve compounds of diverse modes of action were examined using standard protocols of the National Cancer Institute. Median survival time and median tumor diameter were the parameters used for determining any synergistic effects of DMSO when it was ingested in the drinking water and the drug administered parenterally. The continuous ingestion of DMSO alone mixed in drinking water at concentrations between 0.25-32% was not toxic and had no effect on the tumor. Although the intraperitoneal inoculation of drugs into animals ingesting DMSO did not enhance drug effectiveness, when both DMSO and drug were added to the drinking water, it did increase antineoplastic potency. DMSO ingestion also inhibited the tumor growth rate of several parenterally administered drugs even though these same compounds failed to prolong the survival time of tumor-bearing rats. The toxicity of 12 compounds when combined with DMSO was only moderately increased in four instances.

Orally ingested DMSO was found to cause a twofold increase in the concentration of labeled CPA in plasma, brain, and liver tissues. This elevation persisted for approximately two to three hours but subsequently returned to the same level as that observed in water-fed rodents. The DMSO-enhancement of tissue levels coupled with a more rapid drug rate clearance offers one explanation for the therapeutic benefit noted when oral DMSO was administered concomitantly with CPA.

ACKNOWLEDGMENT

We are deeply indebted to Dr. Ruth Geran of the Drug Evaluation Branch of the National Cancer Institute for providing us with test compounds, guidance in protocol design, and valuable advice. We are also grateful to the Mead Johnson Company for providing a generous supply of cyclophosphamide.

REFERENCES

1. KLIGMAN, A. M. 1965. Topical pharmacology of DMSO. J. Am. Med. Assoc. **193:** 796–809.
2. RAMMLER, D. H. & A. ZAFFARONI. 1967. Biological implantation of DMSO based on a review of its chemical properties. Ann. N.Y. Acad. Sci. **141:** 13–23.
3. WARREN, J., M. R. SACKSTEDER, H. JAROSZ, B. WASSERMAN & P. E. ANDREOTTI. 1975. Potentiation of antineoplastic compounds by oral dimethyl sulfoxide in tumor-bearing rats. Ann. N.Y. Acad. Sci. **243:** 194–208.
4. WARREN, J. & M. R. SACKSTEDER. 1974. Increased effectiveness of antineoplastic compounds in rodents ingesting dimethyl sulfoxide. Proc. IX Intl. Cancer Congress. U. Veronesi et al., Ed. (Oct. 20–26, 1974) Florence, p. 471 (abstract).
5. SACKSTEDER, M. R., L. KASZA, J. L. PALMER & J. WARREN. 1973. Cell transformation in germfree Fischer rats. In Germfree Research. J. B. Heneghan, Ed.: 153–157. Academic Press. New York.
6. PEARSON, J. W., S. D. CHAPARAS, J. A. TORGERSEN, K. PERK, M. A. CHIRIGOS & N. A. SHER. 1974. The effect of drug therapy against a histologically defined rat leukemia. Cancer Res. **34:** 355–361.
7. GERAN, R. I., N. H. GREENBERG, M. M. MACDONALD & B. ABBOTT. 1972. Protocols for screening chemical agents and national products against animal tumors and other biological systems. Cancer Chemotherapy Rep. (part 3) **3**(2): 1–103.
8. BROADWELL, R. D., M. SALCMAN & R. S. KAPLAN. 1982. Morphologic effect of dimethyl sulfoxide on the blood-brain barrier. Science **217:** 164–165.
9. EGORIN, M. J., R. S. KAPLAN, M. SALCMAN, J. AISNER, M. COLVIN & P. H. WIERNIK. 1982. Cyclophosphamide plasma and cerebrospinal fluid kinetics with and without dimethyl sulfoxide. Clin. Pharmacol. Ther. **32:** 122–128.
10. AISNER, J. & P. H. WIERNIK. 1978. Thiotepa (NSC-6396) and dimethyl sulfoxide (NSC-763) in the treatment of renal cell carcinoma. Cancer Clinical Trials Spring: 23–25.

PLATELET CRYOPRESERVATION USING DIMETHYL SULFOXIDE

Charles A. Schiffer, Joseph Aisner, and Janice P. Dutcher

Cell Component Therapy Section
Division of Hematologic Malignancies
University of Maryland Cancer Center
Baltimore, Maryland 21201

As a result of the increased intensity of therapy being administered to patients with leukemia and other types of cancer, there has been an enormous increase in the use of platelet transfusion in the last decade. During this time there was also a great deal of research directed towards the feasibility of long-term platelet preservation. Thus, whereas in the late 1960s, it was possible to store platelets for only 24 hours, new plastic bags have been developed that permit storage of platelets in the liquid state at ambient temperatures for 4 to 5 days.[2,3] Better understanding of platelet physiology, metabolism, and post-transfusion kinetics have developed as a result of some of these advances.

There has also been considerable interest in longer term preservation of platelets in the frozen state. Although initially intended to provide a stored pool of platelets from random donors for use in emergencies, there is now more interest in storing allogeneic and autologous platelets for use in the management of alloimmunized patients. Approximately 40 to 50% of patients with adult acute leukemia become alloimmunized and refractory to random donor platelets following initial induction chemotherapy.[4] Because subsequent, often intensive therapy is administered to such patients in an attempt to prolong or reinduce remission, these patients can require histocompatible platelets on an intermittent basis for months to years. Although many patients can be supported with human leukocyte antigen (HLA)-matched platelets from family members or volunteer donors, the costs of HLA typing, computer processing, donor recruitment, and plateletpheresis are large and donor pools of sufficient size are not available in most blood centers.[5] To address these problems a program of autologous frozen platelet transfusions was initiated at the University of Maryland Cancer Center (then known as the Baltimore Cancer Research Center) approximately 10 years ago. This program has expanded appreciably through the years such that more than 200 autologous transfusions are administered per year, largely to alloimmunized patients.[6-9] This represents about 15% of the total transfusions administered to patients with leukemia at our center (TABLE 1). Dimethyl sulfoxide (DMSO) at a final concentration of 5% was utilized in most of these studies, although other technical changes were made through the years. In this report, we will summarize the overall clinical results of this program, compare the results obtained in other laboratories utilizing similar technology, and comment about future problems requiring investigation.

METHODS

Platelet Collection

In the autologous program, platelets are obtained when patients are in remission with normal blood counts. Frequently, patients develop a thrombocyto-

161

0077-8923/83/0411-0161 $01.75/0 © 1983, NYAS

sis as they recover from marrow aplasia and an attempt is made to plateletpherese patients at this time in order to maximize platelet yields per donation. It is often possible to obtain the equivalent of three transfusions or more from a single donation if the collection is done at a time of a high platelet count. Plateletpheresis is done either by repeated manual bag plateletpheresis[10] or using blood cell separators.[11] In general, the yields obtained using blood cell separators are considerably higher and these machines are used whenever technically possible. The major limitation is usually venous access in patients who have received multiple courses of chemotherapy. Recently, increased use of a permanent right atrial (Hickman) catheter has provided guaranteed venous access for these patients.[12]

Platelet Freezing

The methodology for platelet freezing and thawing have been outlined in detail elsewhere.[8,9] Briefly, platelets obtained by manual bag plateletpheresis are

TABLE 1

AUTOLOGOUS FROZEN PLATELET TRANSFUSION OVERALL RESULTS

Years	Number of Patients	Number of Transfusions	Number of Days Frozen	Freeze-Thaw Loss	1 Hour Posttransfusion CCI
1976–78	40 (23)*	141	139†	13.4†	13,600†
			(13–1237)	(0–55)	(0–30,800)
1979	44 (23)	234	164	14.2	12,000
			(11–824)	(0–62)	(0–30,600)
1980	38 (25)	211	197	15.8	11,800
			(11–1081)	(0–61)	(0–34,900)
1981	33 (23)	122	102	17.2	12,500
(5 months)			(12–740)	(0–59)	(0–36,800)

*Numbers of patients alloimmunized.
†Means with ranges in parentheses.
There was no relationship between the number of days frozen or the freeze-thaw loss and the posttransfusion increments.
CCI = corrected count increment (see text).

pooled and centrifuged slowly (180 g × 3 min) to remove contaminating red cells if gross red cell contamination is obvious. Platelets obtained from cell separators are also centrifuged to remove contaminating red cells if present. After counts are done, the platelets are concentrated by further centrifugation (1400 g × 15 min), resuspended in plasma, and transferred to a 200 ml polyolefin bag. The volume in which the cells are resuspended is adjusted so that 4 to 6 units (3 to 5 × 10^{11} platelets) are frozen in a single bag. This represents an appropriate-sized transfusion for an average adult. Earlier studies suggested, for reasons which are not well understood, that overall results are improved using the thinner polyolefin cryogenic bags rather than standard polyvinyl chloride bags.[6,13] In addition, the polyolefin is less susceptible to breakage at liquid nitrogen temperatures. Ten ml of DMSO plus a sufficient amount of autologous plasma to bring the final volume to 100 ml is then added over 15 min with gentle agitation. The bag is sealed and inserted between two metal plates and placed in the vapor phase of a liquid nitrogen freezer at approximately −120°C. At this temperature a freezing rate of approximately of 8–10°C per minute results.[8]

Platelet Thawing

Platelets are thawed rapidly in a 37°C water bath without agitation. One hundred ml of autologous plasma, which has been collected at the time of the original donation, plus 10 ml of acid citrate dextrose (ACD) are added over 10 to 15 minutes. The ACD is added to decrease platelet clumping. The platelets are then transferred to a standard polyvinylchloride bag and centrifuged at 1400 × g for 15 minutes. The supernatant plasma is removed and the platelets are resuspended in 50–100 ml of autologous plasma. The final preparation, which rarely shows evidence of clumping, is administered through a standard blood filter shortly after thawing. More than 90% of the DMSO is removed during the single centrifugation[14] and there are no untoward side effects following infusion of the small amounts of residual DMSO.

The freezing procedure takes approximately 45 minutes to 1 hour; thawing can be accomplished in 30 to 45 minutes. The procedure is relatively simple and easily learned and frozen platelets are presently available seven days a week at our center.

Posttransfusion Results

In order to standardize results for patients of different size receiving differing numbers of platelets, posttransfusion increments are expressed as corrected count increments (CCI) one hour posttransfusion where:

$$CCI = \frac{\text{absolute increment} \times \text{body surface area } (m^2)}{\text{number of platelets transfused } (\times 10^{11})}.$$

Thus, if a 2 m^2 individual received 4 × 10^{11} platelets and had an increment from 10,000 to 50,000, the CCI = 40,000 × 2/4 = 20,000. As a means of comparison, fresh platelets administered to clinically stable thrombocytopenic patients produce CCI of 18,000 to 22,000 one hour posttransfusion.

As summarized in TABLE 1, the corrected count increments utilizing autologous frozen platelets have been consistent through the years, averaging approximately 60% of what one would predict utilizing fresh platelets. Although isotopic labeling studies have not been done, monitoring of serial posttransfusion counts suggests relatively normal survival of transfused platelets.

Because of the often continued requirement of patients with leukemia for platelet transfusion, storage times have averaged four to six months in most of these studies. Successful transfusions of platelets which have been frozen for at least three years at −120°C have been reported however[15] and there does not appear to be significant deterioration of the results with increased duration of storage at this temperature. There are no data available with storage for more than 6 months at higher temperatures (−80°C) in mechanical freezers.

Although bleeding times have not been done in recent years, earlier studies demonstrated a shortening of bleeding times in patients in whom adequate posttransfusion increments were obtained.[7,8] In addition, numerous patients have received frozen platelets with cessation of clinically obvious bleeding posttransfusion. Invasive diagnostic procedures have been performed without incident in many thrombocytopenic patients solely under cover of frozen platelet transfusions. These observations indicate that previously frozen platelets can function hemostatically. There are no data however to indicate the relative efficacy of frozen compared to fresh platelets in terms of hemostatic effectiveness.

All of the patients receiving autologous patients were adults with acute leukemia. In recent years we have focused attention upon patients who are alloimmunized and now approximately 70% of the patients receiving autologous platelets are patients who would otherwise require histocompatible platelets from HLA-matched donors. In this regard the program is quite cost-effective in that, except for the cost of liquid nitrogen, there is not a substantial difference between the cost per transfusion of frozen platelets or platelets obtained by plateletpheresis from histocompatible donors. This is particularly true because a substantial proportion of platelets from apparently histocompatible donors are not effective. Of note is that for some of our patients, autologous frozen platelets were the only

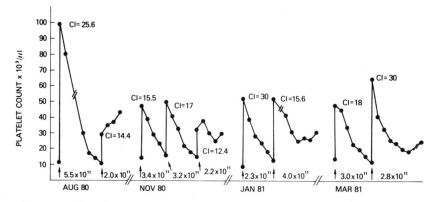

FIGURE 1. This alloimmunized patient received multiple autologous frozen platelet transfusions during sequential courses of intensive maintenance chemotherapy.

source of platelets because of the lack of suitable family or histocompatible allogeneic donors. In these patients it would have been difficult if not impossible to administer maintenance or subsequent reinduction therapy.

An example of such a patient is shown in FIGURE 1. This patient was alloimmunized with high titers of lymphocytotoxic antibody and had only a small number of suitable compatible donors. She received intermittent intensive maintenance chemotherapy and was supported entirely with her own platelets during multiple courses without any clinically significant hemorrhage. Of additional interest is that the levels of lymphocytotoxic antibody decreased in this patient over time, presumably because of an absence of exposure to histoincompatible platelets. This observation has been made in other patients, many of whom could successfully receive random donor platelets for the period of time that antibody levels fell. Usually such patients have an anamenestic antibody rise after random donor transfusions, although in occasional patients this antibody rise is blunted, presumably by the immunosuppressant effect of chemotherapy.

Patient acceptance of the platelet freezing program has been excellent. Our patients are quite knowledgeable about hemorrhagic consequences of thrombocytopenia and the practical difficulties of obtaining donors should they be alloimmunized. Patient appointments are scheduled whenever possible at the time of other clinic visits so as to minimize inconvenience. In addition patients often donate on days that they would be in clinic to begin maintenance chemotherapy, thereby further decreasing extra visits to the hospital. Donors known to be compatible with certain patients also donate at their convenience thereby decreasing the number of occasions where donors are called upon to donate on short notice because of patient emergencies.

DISCUSSION

The consistent results obtained in our laboratory over a number of years demonstrate the feasibility and clinical importance of large-scale programs of platelet cryopreservation. Similar results using DMSO as a cryoprotective agent have been found in smaller studies in other laboratories.[13,14,16,17] The results of the more recent studies are listed in TABLE 2. Similar basic technology was utilized in all of these studies with the major variation being in freezing rate. Recoveries of 40 to 60 percent have been reported using either controlled-rate freezing (1 degree per minute), relatively rapid freezing (such as utilized in our studies), or slower freezing rates of 2 to 3 degrees per minute achieved by placing the platelets in a mechanical freezer. Other variations have included differences in the freezing bag (polyolefin versus polyvinylchloride), DMSO concentration (up to 10%), and collection methodology. It has been demonstrated that results are similar using manual plateletpheresis methods or cell separators. In recent studies at our institution, the corrected count increment following 66 transfusions of frozen platelets collected using the Haemonetics Model 30 processor (Haemonetics Corp., Natick, Mass.) was 12,300 (range 0-36,800) compared to a mean CCI of 11,700 (0-34,900) using manual plateletpheresis technique (N = 211). Similar results have been reported using the IBM 2997 Blood Cell Separator.[23]

It has been difficult however to do systematic comparisons of different techniques because of an absence of *in vitro* assays that correlate with posttransfusion results. Indeed, this has been a problem that has complicated research in all areas of platelet storage. The situation with respect to platelet cryopreservation is perhaps even more complicated because of an incomplete understanding of the mechanism by which cryoprotective agents work. One recent comparative study deserves comment. In this study, platelets from the same histocompatible donor-recipient pairs were either administered fresh or frozen using two rates of freezing.[19] Results in a small number of studies appear to be superior using controlled-rate freezing compared to more rapid rates obtained by placing the platelets in liquid nitrogen. This study differs from our procedure in two important respects. The concentration of DMSO used was 10%. Perhaps more critically, the platelets were administered immediately after thawing without further centrifugation and removal of the DMSO. Although single infusions of large amounts of DMSO are reasonably well tolerated by patients,[19] this would be less practical in the setting where multiple transfusions are administered to a patient during courses of therapy. Nonetheless this is a reasonable, albeit cumbersome experimental design and further studies of this type would be of importance.

TABLE 2

Reference	DMSO %	Freezing Rate (degree/min)	Freeze-Thaw Loss (%)	Collection Method	Recipients	Post-transfusion Recovery	Storage Time	Comments
Beaujean et al.[18]	5	-1	15	Model 30	Thrombocytopenic patients	52% of fresh	12 months	No correlation between in vitro tests and in vivo results
Lazarus et al.[19]	10	-1	13.5	Manual bag	Thrombocytopenic patients	22,900 CCI 7,600	"several days to weeks"	No post-thaw wash
Zaroulis et al.[20]	5	-8 -2-3	35	Manual bag	Thrombocytopenic patients	35% (^{51}Cr)	30 days	6-8 hours storage post-thaw
Vecchione et al.[21,22]	5 5	-2-3 -2-3	20 21	Model 30 Bag CPD A1 CPD A2 CPD A3	Normals (autologous) Normals (autologous)	50% of fresh (^{51}Cr) 41% (^{51}Cr)	1-57 days	- -
Melaragno et al.[23]	5.5-7.5	-2-3	27	IBM 2997	Normals (autologous)	55% (^{51}Cr)	-	Minimal further processing after platelets collected from blood processor
Daly et al.[15]	5	-8	22	Manual bag	Thrombocytopenic patients	12,600 CCI (46% of fresh)	3 years	Long storage duration

Model 30 = Haemonetics Blood Cell Processor, IBM 2997 = IBM 2997 Blood Cell Processor, and CPD = citrate phosphate dextrose anticoagulant.
Posttransfusion recoveries using ^{51}Cr are normally 60-70%.

Other cryoprotective agents have also been used for platelet freezing. Preliminary results with hydroxyethyl starch,[24] dimethyl acetamide,[25] and polyvinylpyrrolidone compounds[26] indicate that some apparently viable platelets can be found postfreezing and thawing and further testing of these compounds may be of interest. More data are available using combinations of glycerol-glucose as cryoprotective agents. Initial reports using these approaches were quite promising based on *in vitro* tests.[27,28] Recently, we have completed a study comparing autologous platelets from the same individual using either DMSO or glycerol-glucose as cryoprotectants.[29] The corrected count increments one hour posttransfusion were considerably better using DMSO (12,700 versus 7,100, p < .025). In addition, the glycerol-glucose method was more difficult and time-consuming requiring considerably more active technologist time. Similar results with glycerol-glucose have been reported by Herve *et al.*[30] Until further improvements in this technique are made, it would seem that blood banks interested in platelet cryopreservation for general clinical use should utilize DMSO as a cryoprotective agent.

A great deal of the progress that has been made in this area has been accomplished because of empiric "tinkering." It is unlikely that significant further advances will be made using DMSO alone as a cryoprotective agent and it is possible that combinations of cryoprotective agents may be more effective. Again, we are hampered by an incomplete understanding of the mechanisms and action of these agents. It is also possible that further significant improvement may not be achievable. It may be, for example, that a certain percentage or group of platelets will not be able to survive the rigors of freezing and thawing. When one collects platelets from patients, one collects a heterogeneous population in terms of platelet age. It is possible that older platelets nearing senescence will never be able to survive platelet freezing. Comparative studies of the ability of large (young?) versus small (older?) platelets to tolerate freezing and thawing have not been done and are quite difficult to perform. We have been unable to demonstrate a correlation between predonation platelet count, modal volume of the collected platelets or the time in the patient's course at which the platelets were obtained with subsequent *in vivo* recovery. These are relatively crude analyses because of the enormous clinical variation in the patients.

Despite these limitations, it is clear that frozen platelets and particularly frozen histocompatible platelets can play a very important role in the management of patients with leukemia and other tumors. There is increased familiarity with cryobiologic techniques in a number of laboratories worldwide because of the increasing use of autologous and allogeneic frozen marrow transplantation. Programs of autologous frozen platelet transfusion should be easily coordinated with these transplant programs and would make eminent clinical sense. These programs are cost-effective and it is likely that in coming years frozen platelets will be available in many large blood centers or university transfusion programs.

REFERENCES

1. McCullough, J., J. Undis & J. W. Allen. 1978. Platelet production and inventory management. *In* Platelet Physiology and Transfusion. C.A. Schiffer, Ed.: 17–38. American Association Blood Banks. Washington, D.C.
2. Murphy, S. & T. Simon. 1981. Characteristics of prolonged platelet storage in a new container. Transfusion 21: 637.
3. Blajcman, M. A., J. G. Kelton, A. F. Senyl & C. Klein. 1981. The maintenance of hemostatic function, survival, platelet membrane glycoproteins and pH of human

platelet concentrates stored for 5 days in new polyvinyl chloride blood bags. Blood **58**(suppl): 178a.//0A

4. DUTCHER, J. P., C. A. SCHIFFER, J. AISNER & P. H. WIERNIK. 1981. Long-term follow-up of patients with leukemia receiving platelet transfusions: Identification of a large group of patients who do not become alloimmunized. Blood **58**: 1007-1011.

5. DUQUESNOY, R. J., J. VIEIRA & R. H. ASTER. 1977. Donor availability for platelet transfusion support of alloimmunized thrombocytopenic patients. Transpl. Proc. **9**: 519-521

6. SCHIFFER, C. A., D. H. BUCHHOLZ, J. AISNER, J. H. WOLFF & P. H. WIERNIK. 1976. Frozen autologous platelets in the supportive care of patients with leukemia. Transfusion **16**: 321-329.

7. SCHIFFER, C. A., J. AISNER & P. H. WIERNIK. 1976. Clinical experience with transfusion of cryopreserved platelets. Brit. J. Haematol. **34**: 377-385.

8. SCHIFFER, C. A., J. AISNER & P. H. WIERNIK. 1978. Frozen autologous platelet transfusion for patients with leukemia. N. Eng. J. Med. **299**: 7-12.

9. SCHIFFER, C. A., J. AISNER, J. P. DUTCHER, P. A. DALY & P. H. WIERNIK. 1982. A clinical program of platelet cryopreservation. In Cytopheresis and Plasma Exchange; Clinical Indications. W. R. Vogler, Ed.: 165-180. Alan R. Liss, Inc. New York.

10. SCHIFFER, C. A., D. H. BUCHHOLZ & P. H. WIERNIK. 1974. Intensive multi-unit plateletpheresis of normal donors. Transfusion **14**: 388-394.

11. AISNER, J., C. A. SCHIFFER, J. H. WOLFF & P. H. WIERNIK. 1976. A standardized technique for efficient platelet and leukocyte collection using the Model 30 Blood Processor. Transfusion **16**: 437-445.

12. WADE, J. C., K. A. NEWMAN, S. C. SCHIMPFF, D. A. VAN ECHO, R. A. GELBER, W. P. REED & P. H. WIERNIK. 1981. Two methods for improved venous access in acute leukemia patients. J. Am. Med. Assoc. **246**: 140-144.

13. KIM, B. K. & M. G. BALDINI. 1973. Preservation of viable platelets by freezing. Effect of plastic containers. Proc. Soc. Exp. Biol. **142**: 345-350.

14. HANDIN, R. I. & C. R. VALERI. 1972. Improved viability of previously frozen platelets. Blood **40**: 509-513.

15. DALY, P. A., C. A. SCHIFFER, J. AISNER & P. H. WIERNIK. 1979. Successful transfusion of platelets cryopreserved for more than 3 years. Blood **54**: 1023-1027.

16. KIM, B. K. & M. G. BALDINI. 1974. Biochemistry, function and hemostatic effectiveness of frozen human platelets. Proc. Soc. Exp. Biol. Med. **145**: 830-835.

17. SPECTOR, J. I., J. A. YARMALA, L. D. MARCHIONNI, C. P. EMERSON & C. R. VALERI. 1977. Viability and function of platelets frozen at 2 to 3°C per minute with 4 to 5 per cent DMSO and stored at −80°C for 8 months. Transfusion **17**: 8-15.

18. BEAUJEAN, Fr., Ch. LEFORESTIER & P. MANNONI. 1979. Clinical and functional studies of platelets frozen in 5% dimethyl sulphoxide. Cryo-Letters **1**: 98-103.

19. LAZARUS, H. M., E. A. KANIECKI-GREEN, S. E. WARM, M. AIKAWA & R. H. HERZIG. 1981. Therapeutic effectiveness of frozen platelet concentrates for transfusion. Blood **57**: 243-249.

20. ZAROULIS, C. G., J. I. SPECTOR, C. P. EMERSON & C. R. VALERI. 1979. Therapeutic transfusions of previously frozen washed human platelets. Transfusion **19**: 371-378.

21. VECCHIONE, J. J., S. M. CHROMICZ, C. P. EMERSON & C. R. VALERI. 1980. Cryopreservation of human platelets isolated by discontinuous-flow centrifugation using the Haemonetics model 30 blood processor. Transfusion **20**: 393-400.

22. VECCHIONE, J. J., A. J. MELARAGNO, A. HOLLANDER, S. DEFINA, C. P. EMERSON & C. R. VALERI. 1982. Circulation and function of human platelet isolated from units of CPDA-1, CPDA-2, and CPDA-3 anticoagulated blood and frozen with DMSO. Transfusion **22**: 206-209.

23. MELARAGNO, A. J., W. A. ABDU, R. J. KATCHIS, J. J. VECCHIONE & C. R. VALERI. Cryopreservation of platelets isolated with the IBM 2997 blood cell separator: A rapid and simplified approach. (In press.)

24. CHOUDHURY, C. & M. J. GUNSTONE. 1979. Freeze preservation of platelets using hydroxyethyul starch (HES); A preliminary report. Cryobiology **15**: 493-501.

25. DJERASSI, I., A. ROY, J. KIM & J. CAVINS. 1971. Dimethylacetamide, a new cryoprotective agent for platelets. Transfusion **11**: 72-76.

26. SMILLIE, J. A., A. C. MUNRO, G. C. WOOD & R. MITCHELL. 1981. Cryopreservation of human platelets and polyvinylpyrrolidone. Transfusion **21:** 552–556.
27. DAYIAN, G. & A. W. ROWE. 1976. Cryopreservation of human platelets for transfusion. A glycerol-glucose, moderate rate cooling procedure. Cryobiology **13:** 1–8.
28. DAYIAN, G. & J. H. PERT. 1978. A simplified method for freezing human blood platelets in glycerol-glucose using a statically controlled cooling rate device. Transfusion **19:** 255–260.
29. KOTELBA-WITKOWSKI, B. & C. A. SCHIFFER. 1982. Cryopreservation of platelet concentrates using glycerol-glucose. Transfusion **22:** 121–124.
30. HERVE, P., G. POTRON, C. DROULE, M. P. BEDUCHAUD, M. MASSE, C. COFFE, J. F. BOSSET & A. PETERS. 1981. Human platelets frozen with glycerol in liquid nitrogen: Biological and clinical aspects. Transfusion **21:** 384–390.

CARDIAC PHARMACOLOGY OF DIMETHYL SULFOXIDE AND ITS POSTULATED RELEVANCE TO ORGAN PRESERVATION IN ISCHEMIC OR HYPOXIC STATES

Marshal Shlafer

Department of Pharmacology
University of Michigan Medical School
Ann Arbor, Michigan 48109

Beginning with the studies published by Sams and colleagues[1] in 1966, there has been a growing list of effects of dimethyl sulfoxide (DMSO) on the myocardium. Many of the studies of cardiac effects of DMSO focused on its use in high (multimolar) concentrations to reduce freeze-thaw–induced injury to the heart, with the ultimate goal being long-term cryopreservation of human hearts for transplantation. Studies aimed at using DMSO for cryopreservation of other organs such as the kidney were also prevalent during the 1970s. Despite the fact that these organ cryopreservation studies invariably involved organ ischemia, albeit under extremely low temperatures, little consideration was given to evaluating the effects of DMSO under more common settings of global cardiac ischemia as occurs intraoperatively during some cardiothoracic surgical procedures, or in the context of regional ischemia that can precipitate infarction. Although there were two studies of the effects of DMSO on myocardial ischemia,[2,3] the relative paucity of studies in more clinically relevant ischemic states may have been due to both an incomplete understanding of the processes contributing to ischemic injury, and a failure at the time to appreciate and apply new facts about the pharmacology of DMSO that had been elucidated in a variety of noncardiac and nonischemic settings, many of which overtly shared no obvious relationships with cardiac pathophysiology.

This paper first briefly summarizes the major pharmacological effects of DMSO on the normal mammalian myocardium, considering their possible implications to human medicine and cardiac ischemic states in particular, but also suggesting that although these effects are intrinsically interesting and demonstrate the diverse actions of this drug, they may be of little utility in currently encountered clinical situations. Evidence will then be presented to support the concept that an important component of ischemic injury to the heart and possibly to other ischemic organs is generation of oxygen radicals, including the hydroxyl radical. A proposal will then be made that the hydroxyl radical-scavenging ability of DMSO, combined with its ability to permeate cells readily, may confer upon the drug a unique and important adjunctive role for preventing this aspect of cell death in some clinical settings of ischemia.

EFFECTS OF DMSO ON THE MYOCARDIUM

Because of the problems associated with interpreting the direct cardiac effects of any drug with peripheral vascular effects, most of the work describing the cardiac effects of DMSO has been conducted on isolated hearts or other

170

0077–8923/83/0411–0170 $01.75/0 © 1983, NYAS

convenient *in vitro* myocardial preparations. The major actions noted below are grouped in terms of actions on cardiac contractile force development, rate and automaticity, and on myocardial structure and biochemistry. It will become apparent that most of these effects are produced by DMSO concentrations in excess of 0.1 M, concentrations exceeding those likely to occur or persist in the blood of intact animals. This singular observation is liable to restrict utilization of DMSO for its cardiac actions in clinical medicine.

DMSO can produce either positive or negative inotropy.[4] Aside from the expected dose-dependency of these responses, the nature of the response depends upon the particular muscle preparation studied (e.g., atrial versus ventricular myocardium), and upon the species of animal from which the tissue was taken. In most preparations studied DMSO concentrations of 70 mM or less increase contractile force, although the positive inotropic responses are rather transient. Above 70 mM or so the responses become particularly species-dependent. For example, guinea pig atrium develops positive inotropic responses to DMSO concentrations as high as 1.4 M, with peak positive inotropic responses occurring with DMSO concentrations around 840 mM. In contrast, negative inotropic responses predominate in feline atrium and papillary muscle and in canine trabecular muscle,[5] even with DMSO concentrations as low as 70 mM. In contrast to the transience of the positive inotropic responses to DMSO, the negative inotropic responses are usually long-lasting, even upon removal of the DMSO, and may reflect frank myocardial damage by the drug.

Osmotic effects,[6] inhibition of Na,K-ATPase,[7-9] and stimulation of adenyl cyclase activity[7] appear to play roles in the positive inotropic responses to DMSO, yet with available data it is impossible to evaluate the relative contributions of each of these possible mechanisms to overall changes of contractility. Although DMSO can release histamine,[10] which is cardiotonic in some preparations, and may also release other cardioactive mediators from mast cells or basophils, it is unlikely that these processes mediate the direct inotropic effects of DMSO seen in isolated cardiac preparations. DMSO concentrations that produce positive inotropy stimulate ATP-dependent Ca uptake by isolated striated muscle sarcoplasmic reticulum,[7,11,12] including cardiac microsomes.[7,11] Stimulation of this subcellular process is typical of some (e.g., catecholamines) but not all (e.g., digitalis glycosides) drugs that produce positive inotropy. None of the contractile effects of DMSO is antagonized specifically by beta-adrenergic blockers,[13] H_1-type antihistamines,[13] or other classical receptor blockers at doses that do not intrinsically alter cardiac contractility. Catecholamine depletion does not affect the positive inotropic responses to DMSO.[6]

In isolated rabbit atria the positive inotropic responses to isoproterenol are potentiated by low DMSO concentrations.[14] It has not been established that DMSO can potentiate the cardiotonic actions of endogenous or exogenous catecholamines or related beta-adrenergic agonists in the intact animal.

Although DMSO concentrations of approximately 140 mM or less can produce slight increases of cardiac spontaneous rate, measured in rabbit right atria not treated with other drugs, the predominant effect of DMSO at higher concentrations is a significant dose-dependent negative chronotropic effect, accompanied as noted above by significant negative inotropy. However, in contrast to the ill-defined mechanisms responsible for the direct inotropic effects of DMSO, it appears that a major mechanism for the negative chronotropic actions in these isolated preparations is inhibition of acetylcholinesterase in vagal neuroeffector junctions of the heart (e.g., nodal tissue), with suppression of intrinsic pacemaker cell rates due to acetylcholine accumulation.[15] Evidence to support the relative specificity of this effect comes from observations that pretreating atria with atropine at concentrations as low as 1 μM can almost completely block the negative chronotropic effects of 1.4 M DMSO, an effect of DMSO that in the absence of atropine decreases spontaneous rate by almost 90%. Moreover, if one depresses spontaneous rate by initial DMSO treatment and then adds atropine while the atria are still exposed to DMSO, atrial rate will promptly return to values not far below those measured before DMSO addition. Unmasking the direct effects of DMSO on spontaneous rate by pretreating atria with atropine shows that DMSO concentrations as high as 840 mM actually produce slight, but statistically significant, increases of spontaneous rate.[15]

In the relatively simple isolated atrial preparations, DMSO decreases contractile rate without appreciably altering rhythm. The situation is different however in the intact heart, in which DMSO concentrations higher than 140 mM or so decrease rate and alter rhythm, presumably by an acetylcholine-related effect to slow conduction through the atrioventricular node. It is likely that the ability of DMSO to enhance or precipitate digitalis glycoside toxicity in the intact animal[16]—toxicity that is manifest primarily as cardiac arrhythmias—is due to synergistic effects to slow atrioventricular nodal conduction (an acetylcholine-related or vagal effect) and to inhibit Na,K-ATPase directly.

The functional effects noted above are generally reversible with short-term (1 h or less) exposure to DMSO concentrations not exceeding approximately 1.4 M, followed by DMSO removal.[17,18] Similarly, based on electron microscopic evidence, the heart undergoes no obvious ultrastructural changes with this treatment.[17,18] The absence of marked changes upon exposure to DMSO-containing solutions with such high osmolality is probably due in part to the drug's ability to permeate membranes quickly, so that osmotic gradients are dissipated quickly. Nevertheless DMSO concentrations over 1.4 M or so can produce irreversible functional and structural disruption, which at least partially may be due to extreme osmotic imbalances. When given to hearts that have been damaged by some pathological process that is likely to impart damage characterized in part by increases of membrane permeability, lower concentrations of DMSO than that noted above may provoke further damage which is not likely due to the drug's osmotic properties, but rather to some other action on membrane function and structure.

Depending upon the concentration of DMSO administered, the drug can produce a variety of metabolic stimulating and suppressing actions in various biological systems.[19] Perhaps of most relevance to myocardial bioenergetics is the potential action of DMSO on myocardial oxidative phosphorylation, which provides the majority of ATP for cardiac contraction. At very high molar concentrations, exceeding those likely to be reached in vivo as the result of systemic DMSO administration, the drug profoundly suppressed a variety of enzymatic indicators of mitochondrial function.[20] Lower concentrations, in the range of 10 to 100 mM, produced no apparent metabolic suppression of isolated perfused brains, and actually appeared to modestly stimulate glycolysis.[21] When added to normally respiring isolated heart mitochondria, DMSO concentrations up to 840 mM had no significant effect on mitochondrial respiratory control or on estimated rates of oxidative ATP synthesis,[22] and DMSO concentrations as high as 1.4 M only moderately slowed ADP-stimulated respiratory rates. The possible implications of these observations to the tolerance of heart and other organs to hypoxia or ischemia are discussed below.

DMSO AND OXYGEN DEPRIVATION

Few if any of the cardiac effects of DMSO summarized above constitute a rational mechanism for why or how the drug might be used as an adjunct to tissue preservation in hypoxic or ischemic states, except of course for the recognized ability of DMSO to act as an effective cryoprotectant. Instead, the utility of the drug may not be due to any specific cardiac contractile or metabolic action, but may involve its ability to (1) permeate cells rapidly and extensively, reaching specific intracellular sites at which damaging metabolites may be generated; (2) aid in the cellular permeation of other known protective drugs, whether they be beta-adrenergic blockers, calcium channel blockers, antioxidants or other compounds; and, perhaps most importantly, (3) to scavenge hydroxyl radicals. This position is taken because evidence from various disciplines strongly suggests that (1) a component of "ischemic" damage to the heart involves paradoxical damage from reperfusion[23] and, specifically, from reoxygenation and the generation of cytotoxic oxygen radicals.[24,25] Similar adverse changes occur with reoxygenation of the oxygen-deprived but nonischemic myocardium. (2) Anoxia- or ischemia-induced central nervous system pathology[26,27] may involve lipid peroxidative changes and other evidence of excessive biological oxidation, some of which reflect oxygen free radical phenomena. Similar changes occur in ischemic gut[28] and they may occur in virtually all other oxygen-deprived organs that are subsequently reoxygenated. (3) In regional myocardial ischemia and infarction, local inflammatory responses involving leukocyte infiltration, thrombosis, and vascular endothelial alterations occur.[29,30] These processes may ultimately be directed at tissue repair, but they may also transiently contribute to tissue damage. Some of these processes involve free radical phenomena. Similar changes may occur during rejection of transplanted hearts.[31]

This plus other circumstantial evidence suggests that in organ ischemia mitochondrial reduction of molecular oxygen, which normally occurs by tetravalent reduction to water, may change such that there is greater formation or accumulation of univalent reduction products, including superoxide anion, hydrogen peroxide, and hydroxyl radical, the latter of which is perhaps most cytotoxic. Inflammatory processes propagated by white blood cells could also serve as an important source of oxygen radicals. Overall, hypoxia with or without ischemia can damage organs by processes including accumulation of reduced electron transport system components that may spontaneously autoxidize during oxygen deprivation;[32] accumulation of reductants during oxygen deprivation that may be innocuous in the relative absence of oxygen, but autoxidize to toxic species upon reoxygenation;[32] release of chemotactic factors from the damaged organ that, when reperfused with blood, attract and possibly activate granulocytes, producing inflammatory reactions involving oxygen free-radical generation;[32] conversion of xanthine dehydrogenase to xanthine oxidase, which in the presence of suitable substrates can generate oxygen radicals;[33] and depletion of cellular oxygen radical-metabolizing enzymes[34] and endogenous antioxidants. Any or all of the above processes may occur during organ hypoxia or ischemia, producing damaging oxygen metabolites.

If the above mechanisms do contribute to ischemic damage, then the most efficient means of dealing with them would involve enzymatically degrading superoxide anion and hydrogen peroxide so that hydroxyl radical formation from these precursors or from reaction of hydrogen peroxide with metal chelates, is reduced. Using both buffer-perfused and blood-perfused isolated heart models of

global ischemia, it has been shown[24,25] that supplementing hypothermic cardioplegia solutions with Cu-Zn superoxide dismutase and catalase significantly prevented many manifestations of ischemic damage, including loss of ventricular
contractility and compliance, marked increases of coronary vascular resistance,
and disrupted mitochondrial oxidative phosphorylation. While this strongly
incriminates oxygen radicals as participants in ischemic damage under some
conditions, many questions arise, including whether oxygen-related damage is
intercepted intracellularly, extracellularly, or at both sites, and which specific
oxygen metabolite(s) is (are) responsible for the damage.

Superoxide dismutase and catalase have high molecular weights (about 32,000
and 250,000, respectively), and so it is conceivable that only under extreme
ischemic conditions during which cell membrane permeability has greatly
increased could they gain access to the intracellular space to act upon their
substrates, which are apt to be generated by the mitochondrion. With the very
high molecular weight of catalase in particular, it is difficult to envisage that
appreciable amounts would enter the cell unless it were so damaged as to be
virtually nonviable. If the endogenous defense mechanisms for hydrogen peroxide are compromised, as suggested by the work of Guarnieri and colleagues,[34]
then hydrogen peroxide could become an important source of hydroxyl radical.
Since superoxide dismutase would act only to generate more hydrogen peroxide
from superoxide anion, that enzyme alone could theoretically exacerbate damage
by forming more precursor for hydroxyl radical. Moreover, if hydroxyl radical
were a damaging species in cardiac ischemia, if it is generated largely by
processes depending on mitochondrial univalent reduction of oxygen, and if the
radical's reactivity is so great that it can only diffuse a few angstroms before acting
upon a target molecule, then a hydroxyl radical scavenger with at least the
following three properties might confer some small but discrete protection: an
ability to scavenge hydroxyl radical well; an ability to reach likely sites of
hydroxyl radical generation, such as the mitochondrion; and a relative lack of
cellular toxicity in general, and a lack of adverse mitochondrial effects in
particular. DMSO appears to fulfill these criteria.

Preliminary data[22] showed that brief preischemic perfusion of isolated hearts
with 70 mM DMSO before a 2-h global ischemic period prevented significant
changes of mitochondrial oxidative phosphorylation measured when the mitochondria were isolated after 1 h of cardiac reperfusion. The preservation of
mitochondrial integrity was identical to that obtained when superoxide dismutase
plus catalase were used as pretreatments.[24] However, unlike the results with the
enzyme supplements, DMSO failed to provide added and needed preservation of
myocardial contractility and coronary vascular resistance, compared to values of
these parameters measured in drug-free nonischemic hearts. The lack of protection of these and other important parameters by DMSO may have been due to a
failure to optimize the dose of DMSO or other aspects of the study design that
affected the way in which DMSO was used. Also, persistent contractile dysfunction in the DMSO-treated hearts could reflect damage due to superoxide anion
and/or hydrogen peroxide, and if this were the case one would expect that
superoxide dismutase, catalase, or the two combined, but not DMSO alone, would
be necessary to confer protection. Nevertheless the discrete mitochondrial effects
of DMSO were consistent and significant, and were not accompanied by
indications that DMSO worsened the ischemically damaged hearts.

Since the data with DMSO noted above were obtained using selected
conditions, it is difficult to make conclusions about mechanisms by which the
drug protected. However, it is tempting to speculate that since DMSO can

scavenge hydroxyl radical directly, and superoxide dismutase and catalase serve indirectly to suppress synthesis of hydroxyl radical precursors, that these three interventions may have protected by virtue of their effects on oxygen metabolism. Of course, the similarities of the mitochondrial protective effects of DMSO with those of the enzyme interventions may be purely coincidental, and at least in the case of DMSO the actual mechanism of protection may still be unknown and unrelated to the proposed effects on hydroxyl radical. However, of the pharmacological effects of DMSO listed so far, none of the direct cardiac effects of the drug can adequately explain its ability to provide limited, discrete, but nevertheless important, mitochondrial protection, and so the drug's hydroxyl radical scavenging ability appears to be a reasonable explanation.

Finney and colleagues[2] showed that DMSO plus hydrogen peroxide reduced ischemic damage of porcine hearts subjected to coronary artery ligation, postulating that DMSO might act by enhancing tissue delivery of oxygen derived from the peroxide. It was felt that the hydrogen peroxide might chemically produce what was tantamount to hyperbaric oxygenation, which many investigators have shown to benefit various ischemic or hypoxic states (and, of course, others have documented the damaging effects of hyperoxia in other conditions, postulating that oxygen radical-mediated cytotoxicity occurs). Finney and colleagues[2] did not measure systemic or myocardial oxygen tensions in their experiments, and this may be important since others have shown that systemic hydrogen peroxide administration produces trivial effects on blood oxygen tensions.[35] Myers and Donovan[36] showed that DMSO plus hydrogen peroxide, but not DMSO alone, increased oxygen partial pressure in devascularized (ischemic) rabbit skin flaps. Although this initially appears to support the concept that DMSO can aid in the cellular delivery of oxygen, they failed to control their experiments by evaluating hydrogen peroxide alone, so from their data it is impossible to determine whether DMSO really affects tissue oxygen tensions. Also, their data were highly species-dependent. Interestingly, Shattock and associates[37] recently showed that hydrogen peroxide concentrations greater than 30 μM are intrinsically toxic to the normal heart, and that concentrations as low as 6 μM kill hearts that are already damaged partially by ischemia. Therefore, since it is questionable whether DMSO actually enhances cellular oxygen delivery in the presence of hydrogen peroxide, and since there is a more fundamental question of whether hydrogen peroxide might damage ischemically injured tissues further, more carefully controlled experiments are needed to determine whether DMSO plus hydrogen peroxide (or hyperbaria) is a rational and effective combination for protecting or salvaging ischemic or hypoxic organs.

Leon and colleagues[3] showed that systemic administration of DMSO reduced myocardial fiber necrosis and ventricular aneurysm development in rats given high doses of isoproterenol. They postulated that DMSO might have protected either by an oxygen delivery-related mechanism, or by anti-inflammatory actions. However, one component of damage in this model of cardiac pathology is excessive stimulation of cardiac contractility and, more importantly, of oxygen demand in excess of oxygen delivery. Mitochondrial oxygen flux is also stimulated greatly. Collectively, the isoproterenol intervention induces what is essentially myocardial ischemia.[38] This excessive metabolic activity could also increase generation of cytotoxic oxygen metabolites, including hydroxyl radical, that could be scavenged by DMSO. The anti-inflammatory actions of DMSO that are also likely to involve hydroxyl radical scavenging may also be operative in the isoproterenol necrosis model.

Although there are many overt functional and morphologic similarities between the paradoxical effects of myocardial reoxygenation and reperfusion after oxygen and flow deprivation, and those effects seen with readministration of calcium after a period of calcium depletion (the so-called oxygen paradox and the calcium paradox[39]), the underlying mechanisms of damage by oxygen and by calcium are likely to be different. Whereas there is evidence that DMSO can reduce myocardial damage due to reoxygenation,[22,40] Ruigrok and colleagues[41] have shown that 1.4 M DMSO does not protect hearts against the effects of calcium repletion after calcium depletion. However, these data[41] should be interpreted cautiously since the DMSO concentration tested was the same as the highest concentration tolerated by normal (nonischemic) myocardium[17] and so it is possible that lower concentrations may have given different and perhaps more positive results.

SUMMARY

There is a wide variety of clinical states in which organ hypoxia and ischemia followed by reoxygenation and reperfusion are unavoidable, and in which organ viability may be compromised by many factors, only one of which may involve oxygen radical-mediated damage. In organ transplantation, for example, although there are many techniques for preserving graft function (some favoring ischemic storage and others favoring continuous perfusion with nonoxygenated solutions that are hypoxic, although not truly anoxic) virtually every technique involves some duration of ischemia, oxygen deprivation, or both.[42,43] Intraoperatively, warm ischemia and reperfusion occur routinely, as in endarterectomy, renal revascularization and nephrolithotomy, streptokinase dissolution of coronary thrombi, balloon dilatation of stenotic coronary vessels, and so on. Open heart surgery relies upon myocardial ischemia, albeit facilitated by varying degrees of hypothermia and, often, cardioplegia. Organ trauma such as that to the central nervous system also involves aberrations of blood flow and oxygen delivery at normothermia, plus many other factors, such as coagulopathy (platelet aggregation, inflammation), that may be modified beneficially by one or more of the recognized properties of DMSO,[44] including its ability to scavenge hydroxyl radical. The role of DMSO in these settings is discussed elsewhere in this volume.

If DMSO is to have more widespread utility in managing organ hypoxia and ischemia, how might its diverse pharmacological properties be used most effectively? It is not likely that it can be used optimally alone as the sole drug intervention, nor at high (multimolar) concentrations, which could be intrinsically damaging. Instead it may be most useful when administered at low (less than 100 mM) concentrations, which are still biologically active, in conjunction with appropriate physical interventions such as hypothermia, and with pharmacological supplements such as membrane-stabilizing or anti-inflammatory drugs, beta-blockers, calcium antagonists, metabolic substrates, and oxygen-metabolizing enzymes, all of which are now receiving considerable attention as clinically useful cytoprotective agents. If the efficacy of these other drugs is limited in part by their relative inability to attain protective concentrations at intracellular sites, then supplemental DMSO might provide two kinds of benefits: an intrinsic ability to protect by the mechanisms noted above, plus a potential and largely untested ability to aid the cellular delivery of other protective drugs, some of which have very high molecular weights which restrict them to the vascular space or at least to the extracellular space. Evidence to support the latter synergistic effect comes from the data of Broadwell and colleagues[45] that show dramatically that systemic administration of DMSO allows substances with molecular weights as high as 70,000 to cross the blood-brain barrier, which is exquisitely selective in its permeability characteristics. Prospective studies emanating from these observations and speculations will hopefully have a positive impact on the use of DMSO for managing organ hypoxia and ischemia.

REFERENCES

1. SAMS, W. M., N. V. CARROLL & P. L. CRANTZ. 1966. Effect of dimethyl sulfoxide on isolated-innervated skeletal, smooth and cardiac muscle. Proc. Soc. Exp. Biol. Med. **122:** 103–107.
2. FINNEY, J. W., H. C. URSCHEL, G. A. BALLA, G. J. RACE, B. E. JAY, H. P. PINGREE, H. L. DORMAN & J. T. MALLAMS. 1967. Protection of the ischemic heart with DMSO alone or DMSO with hydrogen peroxide. Ann. N. Y. Acad. Sci. **141:** 231–241.
3. LEON, A. S., C. M. BLOOR & B. PITT. 1970. The effect of dimethylsulfoxide on the healing of experimental myocardial necrosis. Am. Heart J. **79:** 384–389.
4. SHLAFER, M. & A. M. KAROW, JR. 1975. Pharmacological effects of dimethyl sulfoxide on the mammalian myocardium. Ann. N.Y. Acad. Sci. **243:** 110–121.
5. SPILKER, B. 1970. Inotropic actions of dipolar aprotic solvents. J. Pharmacol. Expt. Therap. **175:** 361–367.
6. SHLAFER, M., J. L. MATHENY & A. M. KAROW, JR. 1974. Cardiac inotropism of dimethyl sulphoxide: Osmotic effects and interactions with calcium ion. Eur. J. Pharmacol. **28:** 276–287.
7. BURGES, R. A., K. J. BLACKBURN & B. SPILKER. 1969. Effects of dimethyl sulfoxide, dimethyl formamide and dimethyl acetamide on myocardial contractility and enzyme activity. Life Sci. **8:** 1325–1335.
8. KANIIKE K., E. ERDMANN & W. SCHONER. 1974. Studies on the differential modes of (Na plus K)-ATPase and its partial reactions by dimethylsulfoxide. Biochim. Biophys. Acta **352:** 275–286.
9. ROBINSON, J. D. 1975. Specific modifications of the Na+,K+-dependent adenosine triphosphatase by dimethyl sulfoxide. Ann. N. Y. Acad. Sci. **243:** 60–72.
10. KLIGMAN, A. M. 1965. Topical pharmacology and toxicology of dimethyl sulfoxide (DMSO). J. Am. Med. Assoc. **193:** 796–803.
11. SHLAFER, M. 1975. Dimethyl sulfoxide effects on calcium uptake and release by isolated cardiac sarcoplasmic reticulum. Fed. Proc. **34:** 793.
12. THE, R. & W. HASSELBACH. 1977. Stimulation and inhibition by dimethyl sulfoxide and ethylene glycol on ATPase activity and calcium transport of sarcoplasmic membranes. Eur. J. Biochem. **74:** 611–621.
13. SPILKER, B. 1972. Pharmacological studies on dimethyl sulfoxide. Arch. Int. Pharmacodyn. Therap. **200:** 153–167.
14. KAROW, A. M., JR. 1972. Dimethylsulphoxide effect on myocardial β-adrenoceptors. J. Pharm. Pharmacol. **24:** 419–423.
15. SHLAFER, M., J. L. MATHENY & A. M. KAROW, JR. 1976. Cardiac chronotropic mechanisms of dimethyl sulfoxide: Inhibition of acetylcholinesterase and antagonism of negative chronotropy by atropine. Arch. Int. Pharmacodyn. Therap. **221:** 21–31.
16. MELVILLE, K. I., B. KLINGNER & H. E. SHISTER. 1968. Effects of dimethyl sulfoxide (DMSO) on cardiovascular responses to ouabain, proscillaridin and digitoxin. Arch. Int. Pharmacodyn. Therap. **174:** 277–293.
17. SHLAFER, M. & A. M. KAROW, JR. 1971. Ultrastructure-function correlative studies for cardiac cryopreservation. I. Hearts perfused with various concentrations of dimethyl sulfoxide. Cryobiology **8:** 280–289.
18. FEUVRAY, D. & J. DELEIRIS. 1973. Effect of short dimethylsulfoxide perfusions on ultrastructure of the isolated rat heart. J. Mol. Cell. Cardiol. **5:** 63–70.
19. SHLAFER, M. 1981. Pharmacological considerations in cryopreservation. *In* Organ

Preservation for Transplantation. 2nd edit. A. M. Karow, Jr & D. E. Pegg, Eds.: 177-212. Marcel Dekker. New York.

20. CONOVER, T. E. 1975. Influence of organic solutes on various reactions of energy conservation and utilization. Ann. N. Y. Acad. Sci. 243: 24-37.
21. GHOSH, A. K., T. ITO, S. GHOSH & H. A. SLOVITER. 1976. Effects of dimethylsulfoxide on metabolism of isolated perfused rat brain. Biochem. Pharmacol. 25: 1115-1117.
22. SHLAFER, M., P. F. KANE & M. M. KIRSH. 1982. Effects of dimethyl sulfoxide on the globally ischemic heart: Possible general relevance to hypothermic organ preservation. Cryobiology 19: 61-69.
23. HEARSE, D. J. 1977. Reperfusion of the ischemic myocardium. J. Mol. Cell. Cardiol. 9: 605-616.
24. SHLAFER, M., P. F. KANE & M. M. KIRSH. 1982. Superoxide dismutase plus catalase enhances the efficacy of hypothermic cardioplegia to protect the globally ischemic, reperfused heart. J. Thorac. Cardiovasc. Surg. 83: 830-839.
25. SHLAFER, M., P. F. KANE, V. Y. WIGGINS & M. M. KIRSH. 1982. Possible role for cytotoxic organ metabolites in the pathogenesis of cardiac ischemic injury. Circulation (Suppl.):I-85-I-92.
26. DEMOPOULOUS, H. P., E. S. FLAMM, D. D. PIETRONIGRO & M. L. SELIGMAN. 1980. Free radical pathology and the microcirculation in the major central nervous system disorders. Acta Physiol. Scand. (Suppl.) 492: 91-119.
27. SIESJÖ, B. K., S. REHNCRONA & D. S. SMITH. 1980. Neuronal cell damage in the brain: Possible involvement of oxidative mechanisms. Acta Physiol. Scand. (Suppl.) 492: 121-127.
28. GRANGER, D. N., G. RUTILI & J. M. MCCORD. 1981. Superoxide radicals in feline intestinal ischemia. Gastroenterology 81: 22-30.
29. EL-MARAGHI, N. & E. GENTON. 1980. The relevance of platelets and fibrin thromboemboli of the coronary microcirculation, with special reference to sudden cardiac death. Circulation 62: 936-944.
30. ROMSON, J. L., B. G. HOOK, V. H. RIGOT, M. A. SCHORK, D. P. SWANSON & B. R. LUCCHESI. 1983. The effect of ibuprofen on accumulation of ^{111}In-labelled platelets and leukocytes in experimental myocardial infarction. Circulation. (In press.)
31. CHRISTMAS, S. E. & G. G. MACPHERSON. 1982. The role of mononuclear phagocytes in cardiac allograft rejection in the rat. I. Ultrastructural and cytological features. Cell. Immunol. 69: 248-270.
32. FRIDOVICH, I. 1979. Hypoxia and oxygen toxicity. In Advances in Neurology. Cerebral Hypoxia and Its Consequences. S. Fahn, J. N. Davis & L. P. Rowland, Eds. 26: 255-259. Raven Press. New York.
33. ROY, R. S. & J. M. MCCORD. 1982. Ischemia-induced conversion of xanthine dehydrogenase to xanthine oxidase. Fed Proc. 41: 767.
34. GUARNIERI, C., F. FLAMIGNI & C. M. CALDARERA. 1980. Role of oxygen in the cellular damage induced by reoxygenation of the hypoxic heart. J. Mol. Cell. Cardiol. 12: 797-808.
35. OLSON, R. D. & R. C. BOERTH. 1978. Hydrogen peroxide: Beneficial effects in rabbits following acute coronary occlusion. Am. J. Physiol. H234: 28-34.
36. MYERS, M. B. & W. DONOVAN. 1975. Effect of dimethyl sulfoxide and hydrogen peroxide on tissue gas tensions. Ann. N. Y. Acad. Sci. 243: 320-324.
37. SHATTOCK, M. J., A. S. MANNING & D. J. HEARSE. 1982. Effects of hydrogen peroxide on cardiac function and postischemic recovery in the isolated "working" rat heart. Pharmacology 24: 118-122.
38. DEL MAESTRO, R. F. 1980. An approach to free radicals in medicine and biology. Acta Physiol. Scand. (Suppl.) 492: 153-168.
39. HEARSE, D. J., S. M. HUMPHREY & G. R. BULLOCK. 1978. The oxygen paradox and the calcium paradox: Two facets of the same problem? J. Mol. Cell. Cardiol. 10: 641-668.
40. MATHENY, J. L., C. WEISMAN, A. M. KAROW, JR. & M. SHLAFER. 1975. Myocardial function during hypoxia: Protective effects of dimethyl sulfoxide. Res. Commun. Chem. Pathol. Pharmacol. 10: 641-668.

41. RUIGROK, T. J. C., P. DeMOES, A. M. SLADE & W. G. NAYLER. 1981. The effect of dimethylsulfoxide on the calcium paradox. Am. J. Pathol. **103:** 390–403.
42. TOLEDO-PEREYRA, L. H. 1981. Organ preservation. I. Kidney and pancreas. J. Surg. Res. **30:** 165–180.
43. TOLEDO-PEREYRA, L. H. 1981. Organ preservation. II. Liver, heart, lung and small intestine. J. Surg. Res. **30:** 181–190.
44. ROSENBLUM, W. I. & F. EL-SABBAN. 1982. Dimethyl sulfoxide (DMSO) and glycerol, hydroxyl radical scavengers, impair platelet aggregation within and eliminate the accompanying vasodilation of injured mouse pial arterioles. Stroke **13:** 35–39.
45. BROADWELL, R. D., M. SALOMAN & R. S. KAPLAN. 1982. Morphologic effect of dimethyl sulfoxide on the blood-brain barrier. Science **217:** 164–166.

EFFECTS OF DEXAMETHASONE AND PHORBOL MYRISTATE ACETATE ON THE INDUCTION OF DIFFERENTIATION IN MOUSE ERYTHROLEUKEMIC CELLS BY DIMETHYL SULFOXIDE, PROTEASES, AND OTHER COMPOUNDS*

William Scher and Samuel Waxman

Cancer Chemotherapy Foundation Laboratory
Division of Medical Oncology
Department of Medicine
Mount Sinai School of Medicine
New York, New York 10029

INTRODUCTION

Long term, cloned lines of erythroleukemia (MEL) cells, derived from Friend leukemia virus-infected mice, have been widely studied as a model system for the control of gene expression in eukaryotes in general and for those genes specific or relatively specific for erythrodifferentiation in particular (see Reference 1 for a list of reviews). Dimethyl sulfoxide (DMSO) was the first agent that was demonstrated to induce significant erythrodifferentiation in MEL cells.[1,2] This was the first example of induced in vitro erythrodifferentiation in a long term line. Since that time approximately 100 other agents have been shown to also induce MEL cell differentiation. Some of these agents are structurally related to the aprotonic, polar, planar solvent DMSO, such as N,N-dimethylformamide (DMF),[3] but most of them are not. Several of the other inducers fall into other classes of compounds that are structurally unrelated to DMSO such as short chain fatty acids, purines, short chain polymethylene diamides, cyclic and thioureas, lactams, and 2-pyridones. There is no known common structural or functional characteristic of all of these agents that has been definitively linked to the molecular mechanism responsible for their ability to induce differentiation. The mechanism is unknown. It has been suggested by several investigators that some of the inducers act by, at least partially, different mechanisms[4-7] (discussed below). In addition to the multitude of inducers known, several inhibitors of the process have been described in the hope that they would be useful in elucidating the mechanism of action of the inducers.[1,3,8] Of these dexamethasone (DEX) and phorbol 12-myristate 13-acetate (PMA) have been the most widely studied (see Reference 1 for reviews). DEX and other glucocorticoids are among the few types of potent inhibitors of DMSO induction that are effective in this system without cytotoxicity. PMA, although toxic, is of particular interest, since, in other systems, it acts as a powerful tumor promoter. A comparative study of the effects of these two inhibitors on the extent of differentiation induced by a variety of agents in two different, but related, commonly studied MEL cell lines was undertaken.[9] Lines 5-86[10] and DS-19[11] were each independently cloned in different laboratories from the same parent line, 745, without selective pressure other than that they were

*This work was supported in part by grants from the National Cancer Institute (CA 24402-03) and the National Institutes of Health (AM 16690-06).

highly inducible by DMSO. The level of inhibition of differentiation was found to be dependent upon both the clone of MEL cells and the types of inducers that were utilized.

MATERIAL AND METHODS

Chemicals

Tetramethyl urea (TMU) was obtained from Aldrich Chemical Co. (Milwaukee, Wisc.); actinomycin D, hemin chloride, and protease V8 from Calbiochem (San Diego, Calif.); isoton from Coulter Electronics, Inc. (Hialeah, Fla.); N,N-dimethyl acetamide (DMA), DMF, and hypoxanthine from Eastman Organic Chemicals (Rochester, N.Y.); H_2O_2 from Fisher Scientific Co. (Pittsburgh, Pa.); Na-isobutyrate, Na-n-propionate, and Na-n-valerate from ICN Pharmaceuticals (Plainview, N.Y.); Na-n-butyrate from Pfalz and Bauer, Inc. (Stamford, Conn.); benzidine $(HCl)_2$, n-butyrylcholine chloride, α-chymotrypsin, DMSO, L-ethionine, hydroxyurea, ouabain, PMA, and prostaglandin A_1 (PGA$_1$) from Sigma Chemical Co. (St. Louis, Mo.); prostaglandin E_1, (PGE$_1$) from Upjohn Co. (Kalamazoo, Mich.); and hexamethylene bisacetamide (HMBA) was a generous gift from Roberta C. Reuben, Cancer Center, Columbia University, N.Y. None of the solvents were allowed to come into contact with any plasticware or disposable glass pipets prior to being diluted.

All of the reagents used for inducing differentiation were dissolved in complete medium and generally used immediately, except the following compounds. Actinomycin D, butyrylcholine, ethionine, hemin, ouabain, and the prostaglandins were stored at $-20°C$. Actinomycin D was prepared in ethanol at 1 μg/ml, then dissolved in medium to yield a final concentration of 10 ng/ml. A stock solution of hemin was prepared by dissolving hemin in 0.2 M KOH. An equal volume of 1.0 M Tris HCl, pH 7.8 was added followed by sufficient 1 N HCl and water to bring the pH to 7.8 and the hemin concentration to 6.52 mg/ml.[12] Ouabain was first dissolved in ethanol, then diluted with medium so that the ethanol concentration did not exceed 0.01% (vol/vol). PGA$_1$ and PGE$_1$ were dissolved in ethanol and then medium so that the final ethanol concentration did not exceed 0.07% and 1.2%, respectively. Actinomycin D, hemin, and the prostaglandins were stored and utilized in the dark or in subdued light.

DEX was prepared in medium and stored at 4°C no longer than 1 month. PMA was dissolved in DMSO and diluted with medium so that the final concentration of DMSO from this source did not exceed 0.01% (vol/vol).

The amounts of ethanol and DMSO used as solvents for various reagents did not effect either differentiation or growth of the cells.

Cells

Cell clones (5-86)[10] and DS-19,[11] which were each derived from clone 745, and clone T3-Cl-2, which was derived from a different mouse strain,[13] were routinely passed and used in experiments as described[14,15] except that fetal bovine serum (15.0%, vol/vol) was obtained from Associated Biomedic Systems, Inc. (Buffalo, N.Y.), Microbiological Associates (Walkersville, Md.), or Rockland (Gilbertsville, Pa.). Experiments were initiated with cells that were in logarithmic growth, i.e., the cell concentration was not greater than 8×10^5 cells/ml after one or two days of growth in fresh medium. The trypan blue-exclusion test was used to determine the number of viable cells present in the cultures used for initiating experiments. Inducers and inhibitors were added just prior to seeding the cells. At the termination of each experiment, cell numbers were determined with the aid of a hemocytometer or a Coulter Electronics, Inc., Model Zf particle Counter. The percentage of cells containing hemoglobin was determined by a benzidine-H_2O_2 staining method.[14,16] Three hundred cells were examined on a slide approximately 5 min after 20 μl of an ice-cold benzidine-H_2O_2 solution [1.0 ml, 0.2% (vol/vol) benzidine($HCl)_2$ in 0.5 M acetic acid [stored for months at 4-8°C in a brown bottle] plus 20 μl freshly added [no more than 4 h] cold, 30% H_2O_2 (vol/vol) was added to 0.1 ml of a cell suspension. The percentage of hemoglobin-containing [benzidine-positive, B^+] cells [those that stained blue] was determined. Cells stimulated to differentiate with hemin were washed 5-10 times by adding 2 ml of phosphate-buffered saline, mixing 12 times up and down in a Pasteur pipet, and centrifuging at 250 × g for 10 min at 4°C as described.[17]

RESULTS

The effect of DEX on induction of differentiation in two cell lines by several compounds is given in TABLE 1. The extent of differentiation was determined by the percent of B^+ cells present after five days of treatment. DMSO, the classical inducer; some other aprotonic, polar, planar compounds; several inducers that are normal cellular constituents; and actinomycin D [the most potent inducer known in terms of effective molar concentration] were compared. The inducers

TABLE 1

EFFECT OF DEX ON ERYTHRODIFFERENTIATION*

Cell Line Inducer	Inducer Concentration (mM)	DS-19		5-86	
		Inducer Alone B^+ Cells (%)	Inducer + DEX B^+ Cells (% of Control)†	Inducer Alone B^+ Cells (%)	Inducer + DEX B^+ Cells (% of Control)
DMSO	250	91	12	90	10
DMA	30	72	25	88	7‡
DMF	130	81	14	93	7
TMU	8.3	82	16	79	9
HMBA	5	92	36	86	6
Hemin	0.1	64	22	43	22
Hypoxanthine	4	90	46	82	22
n-propionate	10	73	83	70	114
n-butyrate	1.5	44	111	40	107
isobutyrate	15	49	73	29	90
n-valerate	10	57	102	46	94
n-butyrylcholine	1.5	33	73	27	98
Actinomycin D	5.6×10^{-7}	74	70	10	—
PGE₁	0.1	65	84	42	53

*Cells were grown with the various inducers and with and without DEX [40 nM] for 5 days then scored for B^+ cells and counted as described in MATERIAL AND METHODS.

†% of control of B^+ cells: the percentage of B^+ cells in a culture treated with an inducer plus an inhibitor divided by the percentage of B^+ cells in a culture treated with the inducer alone times 100.

‡Cellular toxicity of >50%.

TABLE 2

EFFECT OF PMA ON ERYTHRODIFFERENTIATION

Cell Line Inducer†	Inducer + PMA* B⁺ Cells (% of Control)	
	DS-19	5-86
DMSO	16	82
DMA	2	39
DMF	3‡	28
TMU	23‡	66
HMBA	19‡	94
Hemin	20‡	22
Hypoxanthine	22‡	19
n-propionate	41‡	72
n-butyrate	118‡	65
isobutyrate	52	103
n-valerate	53‡	77
n-butyrylcholine	91‡	74‡
Actinomycin D	6‡	—
PGE1	19‡	53‡

*PMA at 160 nM.
†Inducer concentrations as in TABLE 1.
‡See TABLE 1 for footnotes.

studied generally stimulated 50% or more B⁺ cells. The percentage of B⁺ cells noted in untreated cultures was 0–2%. Butyrate, isobutyrate, and butyrylcholine induced less than 50% B⁺ cells in both cell lines, but were included in the study because of their relationships to normal cellular components. The most significant difference in inductive capability between cell lines was noted with actinomycin D treatment. This agent was a potent inducer in DS-19 cultures, but a weak one in those of 5-86. For this reason tests for the inhibitory effects of DEX and PMA on actinomycin D induction were not done in line 5-86. The effects of DEX were similar in both cell lines with most of the inducers tested. The greatest difference was found in combination with DMA where DEX (at 40 nM) was cytotoxic in 5-86, but not in DS-19 cells. In this case the effect on induction by DEX in 5-86 cultures cannot be meaningfully interpreted since it could have been due to specific inhibition of induction, inhibition of cell multiplication, or a combination of these effects. DEX inhibited induction due to HMBA, hypoxanthine, and PGE₁ substantially more in line 5-86 than in DS-19.

The effect of PMA on induction by the same agents is shown in TABLE 2. The concentration of PMA chosen for this study was the one generally used in prior reports by other investigators: 100 ng/ml, 160 nM (vide 1 for references). With this inhibitor major differences between the two lines were noted. Line 5-86 cells were not as sensitive to PMA as were DS-19 cells. For example, there was very little inhibition of induction by DMSO due to PMA in 5-86 cultures, whereas the inhibition was pronounced in those of DS-19. In fact inhibition by PMA of over 60% was only found with four inducers in 5-86 cultures. However, the significance of the extent of the inhibition of differentiation found in DS-19 cells, as noted in some of the studies described above, cannot be adequately assessed as attributable to the severe cytotoxicity of PMA (at the concentration tested) when added in combination with many of the inducers (all of them except, DMSO, DMA, and isobutyrate). Toxicity was seen in 5-86 cells only when PMA was tested in combination with butyrylcholine or PGE_1. In this cell line the pattern of inhibition by PMA was somewhat similar to that noted with DEX, i.e., PMA did not inhibit induction by butyrate or other fatty acids. The inhibition of induction and/or cell multiplication by DEX and PMA in combination with various inducers appear to be characteristic of these cell lines under the conditions utilized. However, some changes have been noted after long term passage of some lines that have not been subcloned.

Studies were initiated with other known MEL cell inducers: L-ethionine, hydroxyurea, oubain, and PGA_1. These compounds stimulated the appearance of less than 30% B^+ cells and/or were extremely cytotoxic in both of the cell lines noted as well as in MEL line T3-Cl-2 so that studies of DEX and PMA inhibition of induction due to these agents were not performed.

Tests with two other inducers, both serine-type proteases, have been started. A variety of proteases have been shown to stimulate MEL cell erythrodifferentiation and multiplication.[18] These include proteases with differing substrate specificities of the serine, thiol, and metallo-types obtained from bacteria, fungi, green plants, and mammals. The proteases are moderately strong inducers when used alone, and are synergistic for induction with low concentrations of DMSO and many other low molecular weight inducers.[18,19] DEX inhibited induction caused by α-chymotrypsin plus a low synergistic concentration of DMSO in DS-19 and 5-86 cells (TABLE 3) by 40% and 60%, respectively. Protease V8 induction was not strongly inhibited by DEX (even up to 10^{-5} M, not shown) in the presence or absence of DMSO in either DS-19 or 5-86 cultures. PMA, however, was inhibitory for both α-chymotrypsin and V8 induction in both cell lines. In the examples described of inhibition of induction due to proteases by DEX or PMA, no inhibition of the protease stimulation of cell multiplication occurred (not shown). Therefore, although it has not yet been tested directly, since induction and the stimulation of cell multiplication depend upon the proteolytic activity of these inducers, the inhibitors did not appear to act by inhibiting the proteolytic activity of the protease inducers.[18]

Because of the lack of the ability of DEX to inhibit induction by butyrate and its analogues, and because butyrate and DMSO are thought by several investigators to induce by different mechanisms[4-7,20] further comparative studies with these compounds have been initiated. As noted in TABLE 1, DEX did not inhibit butyrate-induced differentiation at concentrations that severely inhibited DMSO-induced differentiation in either DS-19 (FIGURE 1) cells or 5-86 cells (data

TABLE 3

EFFECTS OF INHIBITORS ON PROTEASE INDUCTION

	DS-19		5-86	
Inhibitor	Chymotrypsin, (400 μg/ml*)	Protease V8 (40 μg/ml)	Chymotrypsin (300 μg/ml)	Protease V8 (30 μg/ml)
DEX, 10^{-6} M	60†	100	40	100
PMA, 16×10^{-8} M	63	24	32	9

*Optimal concentrations for induction were used. DMSO (0.25%, vol/vol) was present in all samples. Individual chymotrypsin or protease V8 treatment yielded approximately 50% B^+ cells in both cell lines. See TABLE 1 footnotes.

†The values given are the percent of B^+ cells of cultures grown in the presence of an inducer and inhibitor compared to those grown in the presence of an inducer and the absence of an inhibitor (see footnotes of TABLE 1).

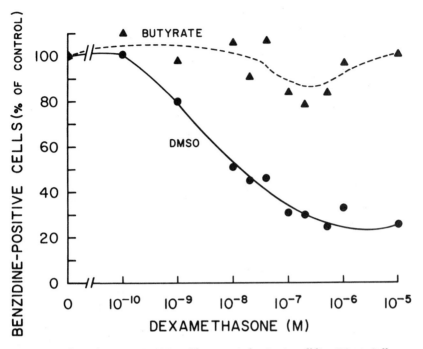

FIGURE 1. Effect of DEX on DMSO and butyrate induction in cell line DS-19. Cells were grown for 5 days as described in MATERIAL AND METHODS with either 250 mM DMSO or 1.5 mM butyrate and the concentrations of DEX indicated. The cells were tested for induction as described in MATERIAL AND METHODS and the percentage of B⁺ cells in cultures treated with DEX and butyrate or DMSO divided by the percentage of B⁺ cells in cultures treated with butyrate or DMSO alone × 100 was determined. DMSO, ●——● and butyrate, ▲---▲.

not shown). Some inhibition of DMSO-induced differentiation by DEX was noted at concentrations as low as 10^{-9} M. It caused a 50% inhibition at a concentration of approximately 70 × 10^{-9} M and 3 × 10^{-9} M in DS-19 and 5-86 cells, respectively. There was no DEX inhibition of butyrate induction in either cell line until at least 10^{-7} M DEX was utilized. In both cell lines there was an apparent stimulation of butyrate-induction at relatively low concentrations of DEX, i.e., in 5-86 cultures (not shown), the addition of 10^{-8} M DEX with butyrate increased the number of B⁺ cells by approximately 20% over those in cultures treated with butyrate alone. The effects of DEX on the percentage of B⁺ cells due to butyrate induction was similar in DS-19 and 5-86 cultures, except that at a relatively high concentration of DEX (10^{-5} M) in 5-86 cultures DEX did reduce the number of butyrate-induced B⁺ cells somewhat, i.e. to 68% of that in a culture treated with butyrate alone.

DEX, at concentrations greater than 10^{-9} M, modestly stimulated (20%) the growth of both cell lines while they were undergoing DMSO-induced differentiation. This is only shown for line DS-19 (FIGURE 2). In view of the stimulatory effect that DEX had on the growth of DMSO-treated cultures, the effect on butyrate-treated cultures was unexpected. The simultaneous treatment of cultures with butyrate plus DEX resulted in lower cell densities in both cell line DS-19 (FIGURE 2) and 5-86 (data not shown) compared to cultures treated with butyrate alone.

The inhibition by DEX of growth in butyrate-treated DS-19 cultures was first noted at 10^{-9} M DEX. At 10^{-8} M DEX it became moderately severe and at 10^{-5} M it reached 50% of that in cultures treated with butyrate alone. In 5-86 cultures, inhibition of growth (20%) by DEX during butyrate induction did not occur until a concentration of 10^{-8} M DEX was reached and severe inhibition of growth (40%) did not occur until the concentration was increased to 5×10^{-8} M. Therefore, butyrate-treated 5-86 cells were more resistant to growth inhibition by low concentrations of DEX than were DS-19 cells, but they were just as sensitive to high concentrations of DEX.

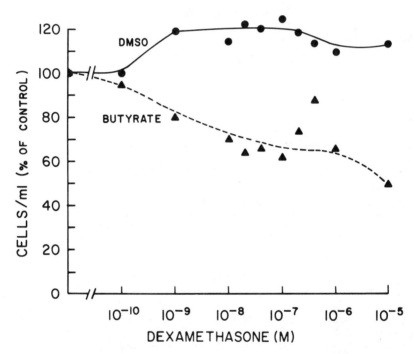

FIGURE 2. Effect of DEX on cell multiplication in cell line DS-19 during DMSO and butyrate treatment. Cells were grown as described in FIGURE 1 legend and the cell numbers determined as described in MATERIAL AND METHODS. The cells/ml in cultures treated with DEX and butyrate or DMSO divided by the cells/ml in cultures treated with butyrate or DMSO alone × 100 are depicted. DMSO, ●——● and butyrate, ▲---▲.

DISCUSSION

The effects of DEX and PMA on the induction of erythrodifferentiation and on cell multiplication by 15 reagents were studied (TABLES 1-3). DEX inhibited the induction caused by most of the compounds tested, but did not markedly inhibit induction due to the fatty acids or their analogues: propionate, butyrate, isobutyrate, valerate, or butyrylcholine. At certain concentrations of DEX there was even a small stimulation in the level of induction due to some of these fatty acids. These findings support the suggestion[4-7] that the mechanism of induction by fatty acids differs from that of DMSO and related compounds. The possibility of additional pathways of induction was suggested by the findings that induction due to actinomycin D or PGE_1 in clone DS-19 was only moderately inhibited by DEX.

Because of the differences seen in the ability of DEX to inhibit the effects of different classes of inducers, the effects of another inhibitor, PMA, were also investigated in the two clones of MEL cells. In cell line 5-86, PMA was, in general, either a non-inhibitor or a moderate inhibitor of induction whereas in cell line DS-19 inhibition of induction was usually associated with cytotoxicity.

Other investigators have reported the effects of PMA on induction due to some inducers other than DMSO. For example, PMA was found to inhibit induction by HMBA[21-23] and to acetamide and hypoxanthine.[24] Induction by butyrate originally was noted to be moderately inhibited by PMA in DS-19 cultures.[22] However, in another study, PMA was shown to inhibit butyrate induction by only 17% after 2 days of treatment.[20] In the present study, PMA was found to inhibit butyrate induction in 5-86 cells, but not in DS-19 cells. However, PMA was toxic in DS-19 cells in these studies. PMA was found by others[20] not to inhibit induction due to actinomycin D in experiments carried out for 3 days. In the present study, PMA did inhibit actinomycin D induction. However, the combination of actinomycin D and PMA in the 5-day studies used here was toxic and therefore valid comparisons cannot be made to the reported 3-day studies.[20]

Inhibition of MEL cell differentiation by DEX due to inducers other than DMSO has also been noted in other reports[20,25-28] that, in general, agree with the results reported here. However, the effect of DEX on hemin induction is somewhat controversial. It originally was reported that DEX inhibited the hemin-induced increase in globin mRNA in cell line T3-Cl-2 only 8%,[25] but in a subsequent report a marked inhibition of globin gene expression was noted[26] as found in the present study. Some of the differences noted may have been due to variations in the cell lines that were used. Although hemin induction is thought to follow a pathway that differs from that of DMSO induction, and that may be unique,[29-32] there appears to be similarity of actions in their capacities to be inhibited by DEX.

There have been some suggestions that phorbol ester-tumor promoters are related, both structurally and functionally, to glucocorticoids,[33] but glucocorticoids also have been shown to have effects that are the opposite of PMA.[34] In the studies reported here, DEX and PMA had more effects in common in relation to inhibition of induction in line DS-19 than in line 5-86. However, DEX and PMA had quite different effects on cell multiplication in the two cell lines. DEX (at 40 nM) was growth stimulatory or had no effect on growth in the presence of all inducers in both cell lines, while PMA was toxic in line DS-19 in the presence of most of the inducers. PMA was toxic in combination with only two of the inducers tested in line 5-86. However, PMA did not strongly inhibit induction in this line except with 5 of the inducers tested. Therefore, two of the best studied clones of MEL cells, DS-19 and 5-86, which were independently selected from the same parent clone for their capacity to be highly induced by DMSO, display several different properties.

As noted above, the effects of DEX on induction and growth were different in the presence of butyrate than in the presence of DMSO. These differences may reflect differences in the mechanisms of action of butyrate and DMSO as suggested by others,[4-7] but other explanations are possible. For example, butyrate might alter, block, or destroy DEX receptors or alter the metabolism of DEX in some other way so that the inhibitory effect of the steroid is nullified. Butyrate has been shown to reduce glucocorticoid receptor activity approximately 40% in

HeLa cells, although this was not sufficient to inhibit glucocorticoid effects in that system.[35] However, in MEL cells, it appears unlikely that butyrate directly interfered with DEX action since DEX was active in the presence of butyrate in this system. In these studies, DEX inhibited cell growth and altered modal cell volume (not shown). [Five days of treatment with DEX plus butyrate reduced the modal volume of MEL cells when compared to that of cells treated with butyrate alone (unpublished data)]. In addition, an altered metabolite of either butyrate or DEX, caused by the activity of the other compound, also could account for the lack of inhibition by DEX without invoking a different mechanism of action for the induction by butyrate.

SUMMARY

Lines DS-19 and 5-86, each derived from line 745, when tested for their responses to various inducers and inhibitors of differentiation, shared some characteristics, but differed in others. In particular, DS-19 was markedly induced to differentiate by actinomycin D whereas 5-86 was only slightly affected. The patterns of the ability of PMA to influence induction and cell multiplication by various inducing agents differed in the two lines.

The pattern of DEX inhibition of differentiation was similar in the two lines. Notably, DEX markedly inhibited induction due to all of the inducers tested except protease V8, actinomycin D, PGE_1, and butyrate and its fatty acid analogues that were tested.

DEX stimulated growth during its inhibition of induction by DMSO and many other inducers, but reduced cell multiplication in the presence of butyrate.

PMA inhibited induction by most of the inducers tested in DS-19 cells except for some of the fatty acids. The inhibition by PMA generally was accompanied by cytotoxicity in DS-19 cells, but not in 5-86 cells. PMA markedly inhibited differentiation by only 5 of the inducing agents tested in 5-86 cells, but was not as cytotoxic in this line.

Proteases, which have been shown to stimulate both MEL cell differentiation and growth,[18] are inhibited with respect to their effects on differentiation, but not with respect to those on growth by DEX and/or PMA. DEX did not have the same effect on induction stimulated by the two proteases studied.

Many of these findings indicate that at least some effects by inducers on cell multiplication in this system are not inextricably linked to differentiation. It is hoped that the further study of induction by proteases, which have known enzymatic activities, as well as of inhibitors of induction, will shed light on the molecular mechanism(s) of action of DMSO and other low molecular weight inducers.

ACKNOWLEDGMENTS

We thank Nella Hellinger for excellent technical assistance and Joan Remy for aid in typing this manuscript.

REFERENCES

1. SCHER, W., B. M. SCHER & S. WAXMAN. 1982. Nuclear events during differentiation of erythroleukemia cells. In Current Concepts in Erythropoiesis. C. D. R. Dunn, Ed.: 301–338. John Wiley & Sons. Chichester, England.

2. FRIEND, C., W. SCHER, J. G. HOLLAND & T. SATO. 1971. Hemoglobin synthesis in murine virus-induced leukemic cells in vitro. Stimulation by dimethyl sulfoxide. Proc. Natl. Acad. Sci. USA **68**: 378–382.

3. SCHER, W., H. D. PREISLER & C. FRIEND. 1973. Hemoglobin synthesis in murine virus-induced leukemia cells in vitro. III. Effects of 5-bromo 2′-deoxyuridine, dimethylformamide and dimethylsulfoxide. J. Cell. Physiol. **81**: 63–69.

4. KAMEJI, R., M. OBINATA, Y. NATORI & Y. IKAWA. 1977. Induction of globin gene expression in cultured erythroleukemia cells by butyric acid. J. Biochem. **81**: 1901–1910.

5. ROVERA, G. & S. SURREY. 1978. Use of resistant or hypersensitive variant clones of Friend cells in analysis of the mode of action of inducers. Cancer Res. **38**: 3737–3744.

6. EBERT, P. S., H. L. BONKOWSKY & A. DEISSEROTH. 1979. Evidence for multiple sites of regulation of heme synthesis in murine erythroleukemia cells. J Natl. Cancer Inst. **62**: 1247–1250.

7. ONO, T., K. MORIOKA, K. KOMITO, T. NOKUO & M. ISHIZAWA. 1979. Comparison of mechanisms for induction of hemoglobin synthesis in Friend leukemic cells by butyrate, dimethylsulfoxide, and hexamethylene bisacetamide. In Oncogenic Viruses and Host Cell Genes. Y. Ikawa & T. Okada, Eds.: 319–326. Academic Press. New York.

8. HUGUES, B. & H. B. OSBORNE. 1981. Dexamethasone inhibits a heme-independent event necessary for terminal differentiation of murine erythroleukemia cells. Biochem. Biophys. Res. Commun. **102**: 1342–1349.

9. SCHER, W. & S. WAXMAN. 1980. Further evidence that there are different biochemical mechanisms for the induction of hemoglobin synthesis in mouse erythroleukemia cells. Proc. 18th Congr. Int. Soc. Hematol. Montreal. No. 358, p. 88.

10. SCHER, W. & C. FRIEND. 1978. Breakage of DNA and alterations in folded genomes by inducers of differentiation in Friend erythroleukemic cells. Cancer Res. **38**: 841–849.

11. OHTA, Y., M. TANAKA, M. TERADA, O. J. MILLER, A. BANK, P. A. MARKS & R. A. RIFKIND. 1976. Erythroid cell differentiation: Murine erythroleukemia cell variant with unique pattern of induction by polar compounds. Proc. Natl. Acad. Sci. USA **73**: 1232–1236.

12. RUTHERFORD, T. R. & D. J. WEATHERALL. 1979. Deficient heme synthesis as the cause of noninducibility of hemoglobin synthesis in a Friend erythroleukemia cell line. Cell **16**: 415–423.

13. IKAWA, Y., M. AIDA & Y. INOUE. 1976. Isolation and characterization of high and low differentiation-inducible Friend leukemia lines. Gann **67**: 767–770.

14. SCHER, W., D. TSUEI, S. SASSA, P. PRICE, N. GABELMAN & C. FRIEND. 1978. Inhibition of dimethyl sulfoxide-stimulated Friend cell erythrodifferentiation by hydrocortisone and other steroids. Proc. Natl. Acad. Sci. USA **75**: 3851–3855.

15. SCHER, W., D. TSUEI & C. FRIEND. 1980. The structural basis for steroid modulation of DMSO-stimulated erythrodifferentiation. Leukemic Res. **4**: 217–229.

16. ORKIN, S. H., F. I. HAROSI & P. LEDER. 1975. Differentiation in erythroleukemic cells and their somatic hybrids. Proc. Natl. Acad. Sci. USA **72**: 98–102.

17. BENOFF, S., S. A. BRUCE & A. I. SKOULTCHI. 1980. X-linked control of globin mRNA and hemoglobin production in erythroleukemia-lymphoma cell hybrids. Somat. Cell Genet. **6**: 15–28.

18. SCHER, W., B. M. SCHER & S. WAXMAN. 1982. Protease stimulate mouse erythroleukemia cell differentiation and multiplication. Biochem. Biophys. Res. Commun. **109**: 348–354.

19. SCHER, W., B. M. SCHER & S. WAXMAN. 1983. Proteases act synergistically with low molecular weight inducers to stimulate mouse erythroleukemia cell differentiation. Exp. Hematol. **11**: No. 6. (In press.)

20. GAZITT, Y. & C. FRIEND. 1980. Polyamine biosynthesis enzymes in the induction and inhibition of differentiation in Friend erythroleukemia cells. Cancer Res. **40**: 1727–1732.

21. FIBACH, E., R. GAMBARI, P. A. SHAW, G. MANIATIS, R. C. REUBEN, S. SASSA, R. A. RIFKIND & P. A. MARKS. 1979. Tumor promotor-mediated inhibition of cell differentiation: Suppression of the expression of erythroid functions in murine erythroleukemia cells. Proc. Natl. Acad. Sci. USA **76**: 1906–1910.

22. YAMASAKI, H., E. FIBACH, U. NUDEL, I. B. WEINSTEIN, R. A. RIFKIND & P. A. MARKS. 1977. Tumor promotors inhibit spontaneous and induced differentiation of murine erythroleukemia cells in culture. Proc. Natl. Acad. Sci. USA **74:** 3451-3455.
23. YAMASAKI, H., R. A. MUFSON & I. B. WEINSTEIN. 1979. Phorbol ester induced prostaglandin synthesis and ^{3}H-TPA metabolism by TPA-sensitive and TPA-resistant Friend erythroleukemia cells. Biochem. Biophys. Res. Commun. **89:** 1018-1025.
24. MIAO, R., A. H. FIELDSTEEL & D. W. FODGE. 1978. Opposing effects of tumour promoters on erythroid differentiation. Nature **274:** 271-272.
25. LO, S.-C., R. AFT & G. C. MUELLER. 1978. Separation of globin gene expression and terminal differentiation in Friend erythroblastic leukemia cells. J. Cell Biol. **79:** 35a.
26. LO, S.-C., R. AFT, J. ROSS & G. C. MUELLER. 1978. Control of globin gene expression by steroid hormones in differentiating Friend leukemia cells. Cell **15:** 447-453.
27. GAMBARI, R. 1982. Differential effect of dexamethasone on Friend leukemia cells induced to differentiate by hexamethylene bisacetamide or butyric acid. Cell Biol. Internatl. Rep. **6:** 341.
28. EISEN, H., F. KEPPEL-BALLIVET, C. P. GEORGOPOULOS, S. SASSA, J. GRANICK, I. PRAGNELL & W. OSTERTAG. 1978. Biochemical and genetic analysis of erythroid differentiation in Friend virus-transformed murine erythroleukemia cells. *In* Differentiation of Normal and Neoplastic Hematopoietic Cells. A. Book, B. Clarkson, P. A. Marks & J. E. Till, Eds.: 277-294. Cold Spring Harbor Laboratory. Cold Spring Harbor, N.Y.
29. GUSELLA, J. F., S. C. WEIL, A. S. TSIFTSOGLOU, V. VOLLOCH, J. R. NEUMANN, C. KEYS & D. E. HOUSEMAN. 1980. Hemin does not cause commitment of murine erythroleukemia (MEL) cells to terminal differentiation. Blood **56:** 481-487.
30. LOWENHAUPT, K. & J. B. LINGREL. 1979. Synthesis and turnover of globin mRNA in murine erythroleukemia cells induced with hemin. Proc. Natl. Acad. Sci. USA **76:** 5173-5177.
31. ALTER, B. P. & S. C. GOFF. 1978. Variable globin chain synthesis in mouse erythroleukemia cells. Blood **52:** 1047-1057.
32. ROVERA, G., D. ADEN & S. SURREY. 1978. Allylisopropylacetamide restricts expression of β minor globin gene in Friend cells. Nature **272:** 172-175.
33. WILSON, S. R. & J. C. HUFFMAN. 1976. The structural relationship of phorbol and cortisol: a possible mechanism for the tumor promoting activity of phorbol. Experientia **32:** 1489-1490.
34. YUSPA, S. H., U. LICHTI, H. HENNINGS, T. BEN, E. PATTERSON & T. J. SLAGA. 1978. Tumor promotor-stimulated proliferation in mouse epidermis in vivo and in vitro: Mediation by polyamines and inhibition by the antipromotor steroid fluocinolone acetonide. *In* Carcinogenesis. Mechanisms of Tumor Promotion and Cocarcinogenesis. T. J. Slaga, A. Sivak & R. K. Boutwell, Eds. **2:** 245-255. Raven Press. New York.
35. LITTLEFIELD, B. A., N. B. CIDLOWSKI & J. A. CIDLOWSKI. 1980. Modulation of glucocorticoid effects and steroid receptor binding in butyrate-treated HeLa S$_3$ cells. Arch. Biochem. Biophys. **201:** 174-184.

COMBINED PHARMACOLOGIC AND SURGICAL TREATMENTS FOR ACUTE SPINAL CORD TRAUMA

Nolan C. Rucker*

Comparative Neuroscience Research Institute
Bel-Rea Institute of Animal Technology
Denver, Colorado 80231

William V. Lumb and Robert J. Scott

Surgical Laboratory
Colorado State University
Fort Collins, Colorado 80523

INTRODUCTION

Acute spinal cord trauma was induced by the Allen method at T_{12} in 48 dogs. Six groups of 7 dogs each were treated with combinations of pharmacologic and surgical treatments; a seventh group of 6 dogs remained as traumatized untreated controls. Results indicate an additive therapeutic effect in those animals treated with myelotomy and dimethyl sulfoxide. Dexamethasone, reserpine, and perfusion with hypertonic dextrose solution were of no benefit.

Acute spinal cord trauma is an often encountered clinical entity in both people and animals in our mechanized society. Few reports have been made about the combined activity of proven pharmacologic and surgical treatments. The objective of the present report is to describe concurrent treatment with several techniques, all of which have previously been thought to have beneficial effects.

Since 1911, when Allen[1] first introduced his method for inducing spinal cord trauma and noted improved recovery rates after myelotomy, there have been many attempts by investigators to increase recovery of neurologic function. Meritorious properties have been attributed to many pharmacologic, surgical, and physical modalities for sparing the spinal cord from permanent autolytic changes. Corticosteroids,[2-4] vasoactive antagonists,[5-7] hyperosmolar solutions,[8] hypothermia,[4-9,11] spinal cord perfusion,[12] hyperbaric oxygen,[13-15] myelotomy,[1,16-18] rhizotomy,[19] and decompressive laminectomy have been extolled, along with many other modalities. The common goal of these treatments was to prevent time-related progressive hemorrhagic necrosis associated with spinal cord trauma.

The objective of the present study was to evaluate the efficacy of combinations of agents and surgical procedures, all of which had been thought to be of value in prevention of trauma-induced spinal cord deficit.

MATERIALS AND METHODS

Surgical Procedure

Forty-eight healthy male and female dogs, ranging from 7.2 to 15 kg (mean 10.9), were randomly allotted to 7 groups. Each dog was fasted and given chloramphenicol (Chloromycetin) (49.5 mg/kg; i.m.) 12 hours before surgical

*Send correspondence to N.C.R., % Bel-Rea Institute of Animal Technology, 9870 East Alameda Avenue, Denver, Col. 80231.

0077-8923/83/0411-0191 $01.75/0 © 1983, NYAS

manipulation. Atropine sulfate (0.22 mg/kg) was given subcutaneously 20 minutes before induction with 4% thiamylal sodium (Surital). General anesthesia was maintained on halothane (Fluothane), using positive pressure ventilation. Each dog was placed in ventral recumbency on a flat surgical table and adjusted horizontally to ensure that the spinal cord was level. An i.v. drip of lactated Ringer's solution (55 ml/kg) was administered throughout the surgical procedure. Rectal thermistor and ECG leads were attached to monitor core body temperature and cardiac activity. A heating pad was placed under the animal to maintain body heat.

The left peroneal nerve was isolated and two clip electrodes were attached. The skin was closed over the nerve and electrodes to prevent drying during the remainder of the procedure. A second incision was made over the dorsal midline of the head, and the temporal muscle was reflected ventrally to expose the right calvarium. Two holes, 6 mm in diameter, were drilled through the bone over the postcentral gyrus, 0.5 cm apart. Both holes were tapped and 6-mm screws with attached electrodes were inserted. Care was taken to avoid puncturing the dura mater. The lead wires were exited subcutaneously at the caudal base of the skull, and the incisions were closed. A baseline cortical-evoked potential (CEP) from the left peroneal nerve to the right sensory cortex of the cerebral hemisphere was recorded. Stimulating current was 4 mA and a pulse width, 0.5 msec at 2/sec; 128 stimuli were averaged.

A dorsal midline incision was made from T_{10}-L_1. A pneumatic bur (3M Co.) was used to expose the spinal cord from T_{11}-T_{13}, taking care to preserve the cranial and caudal articular facets of vertebrae. Final exposure was accomplished using a rongeur, being cautious not to contuse the cord. Epidural fat around the dura mater and associated spinal nerve roots was removed by suction. An extension of the incision was made laterally in the lamina of T_{12} to the floor of the canal to ensure that no bony impediment would exist for the impounder. A dorsal midline durotomy was made from T_{11}-T_{13} with release of CSF. The dura-arachnoidea was permitted to retract laterally, exposing the pial surface of the cord.

The drop apparatus was leveled and positioned over the middle of the T_{12} spinal segment. Succinylcholine (Sucostrin), (0.08 mg/kg) was given i.v.; the respirator was stopped and the animal was hyperventilated manually (by hand bagging) for 20 sec. During the period of respiratory arrest, the Teflon impounder (7.98 g) was centered over the T_{12} spinal cord segment in direct contact with the dorsal pial surface. The pin holding the impounder in the drop tube was removed and any distraction was corrected by moving the vernier knobs to ensure correct cord contact. A 24.2309-g center-vented weight was allowed to fall 23.9 cm before striking the 1.27 cm diameter face of the Teflon impounder. The impounder's flat circular surface (7 mm diameter) impacted on the cord. Velocity of the weight was measured by an attached photoelectric apparatus with two openings into the drop tube at the distal end, corresponding to the impact point on the Teflon impounder. Velocity determinations allowed calculation of energy impacting the impounder (mean 529 g-cm ± 30 SD).

The impounder was immediately removed from the spinal cord and the respirator was started. Total respiratory arrests rarely exceeded 20 to 30 sec.

Treatments

Moist surgical towels were placed over the laminectomy site and 60 minutes after spinal cord trauma, treatment regimens were begun (TABLE 1). This 60-minute interval was intended to simulate the most ideal circumstances where aggressive treatment of a spinal cord injury might be instituted in a clinical environment. The CEP recordings were made at this time.

Dexamethasone

Dexamethasone (Dexasone) (DM) was given i.v. at a dosage of 2.2 mg/kg. Subsequently, it was administered i.m. twice daily for 5 days after trauma at the following dosage rates (per kg of body weight): day 1, 0.55 mg; day 2, 0.26 mg; day 3, 0.13 mg; day 4, 0.0666 mg; and day 5, 0.022 mg.

Dimethyl Sulfoxide

Dimethyl sulfoxide (DMSO) was administered (i.v.) at a dosage of 0.623 g/kg as a 40% solution; the DMSO was also given once daily during the first 2 postoperative days, as follows: day 1, 0.495 g/kg; and day 2, 0.385 g/kg.

TABLE 1

TREATMENT OF DOGS WITH INDUCED SPINAL CORD TRAUMA

Dog Groups (N = No. of Dogs)	Treatment				
	DM	DMSO	RP	PF	MT
A (N = 6)*					
B (N = 7)	X	X	X	X	X
C (N = 7)		X	X	X	X
D (N = 7)	X		X	X	X
E (N = 7)	X	X		X	X
F (N = 7)	X	X	X		X
G (N = 7)	X	X	X	X	

*Control

Reserpine

Reserpine (Serpasil) (RP) was administered either in a 25% dextrose perfusion solution (by subarachnoidally placed catheter) or, in the absence of perfusion, as one single i.v. injection 60 minutes after trauma was induced. Dosage of RP was 0.88 mg/kg, regardless of route, and only one dose was given.

Perfusion

Perfusion (PF) of the cranial and caudal parts of the spinal cord was accomplished by passing a 1.5-mm diameter catheter 10 cm cranially and caudally in the subarachnoidal space. The catheter was attached to a Harvard-type pump that delivered 25% dextrose, at the rate of 4 ml/minute for 1 hour. Excess perfusate was removed by suction from the operative site.

Myelotomy

A dorsal midline myelotomy (MT) was performed from T_{11} to T_{13} to the level of the central spinal cord canal. A razor blade was used to make the incision, and the depth was judged visually.

By using internal suction with perfusion, all incisions were closed at approximately the same time in each group. No attempt was made to close or cover the dura mater. Polyglycolic acid suture (2–0) was used to close the superficial fascia and subcutaneous tissues. Skin incisions were closed with 3–0 monofilament nylon suture. Rolled gauze tent bandages were affixed to the skin with 2–0 silk to prevent postoperative seromas. All dogs were given chloromycetin (49.5 mg/kg) for 3 days after trauma. They were then given a prophylactic dose of penicillin-streptomycin (1 ml/9 kg; i.m.) twice daily to prevent urinary sepsis and abscessation associated with decubital ulcers. Each animal was kept on a sheep fleece-type cage liner to aid in prevention of decubital ulcers.

TABLE 2

TARLOV RATINGS AND NUMBER OF DOGS WALKING AT 42 DAYS

(N = No. of Dogs)	Tarlov Ratings*		No. of Dogs Walking at End of 42 Days
	For Individual Dogs	Sum	
A (N = 6)†	1,1,1,1,1,1	6	0
B (N = 7)	1,1,2,1,2,3,4	14	2
C (N = 7)	1,1,1,1,3,1,3	11	2
D (N = 7)	1,1,1,1,2,1,1	8	0
E (N = 7)	3,4,4,1,1,1,1	15	3
F (N = 7)	4,1,5,4,1,5,1	21	4
G (N = 7)	1,1,1,1,1,1,1	7	0

*Numerical ratings: 1 = some muscle tone; 2 = reflex standing; 3 = walking with deficit; 4 = walking, running with deficit; and 5 = normal, full recovery.
†Control.

Evaluation of Treatment

Results of the neurologic deficits created by the spinal cord trauma were evaluated by four criteria: neurologic examination, CEP, gross lesions, and histopathologic changes. Serial neurologic examinations were made on each dog preceding euthanasia at 42 days after surgical manipulation. Each animal was assigned a numerical value based on the modified Tarlov scale[3] as follows: 1 = some muscle tone; 2 = reflex standing; 3 = walking with deficit; 4 = walking, running with deficit; and 5 = normal, full recovery.

At necropsy, each animal was given (i.v.) sodium pentobarbital (0.44 mg/kg) while attached to a respirator and was maintained at a surgical plane of anesthesia. The CEP were made from the previously implanted skull electrodes by stimulating the peroneal nerve of the left limb. Control data were obtained by stimulating the radial nerve of the left thoracic limb, proximal to the trauma site at T_{12}. Terminally, a vasopressor-potentiated solution was perfused into the animal (120 mm Hg) via the aorta, to fix the CNS.[1] The entire spinal cord of each dog was examined and tissue sections were made based on severity of cavitation, apparent axolysis, and inflammatory reaction. Each section was assigned a value ranging from 1 to 4 with 4 being the most severely affected.

Analysis of data from the treatment groups was performed, using the confidence interval approach.[20] The CEP data (amplitudes and latencies) were processed by discriminant analysis and principal component analysis.[21]

TABLE 3

PROBABILITY OF RECOVERY WITH VARIOUS THERAPY REGIMENS

Treatment Group	Probability of Recovery	Approximate 95% Confidence Limits	
		Lower	Upper
A	0/6 = 0.000		
B	2/7 = 0.285	0.030	0.600
C	2/7 = 0.285	0.030	0.600
D	0/7 = 0.000	0.000	0.400
E	3/7 = 0.429	0.070	0.700
F	4/7 = 0.570	0.120	0.750
G	0/7 = 0.000	0.000	0.400

RESULTS

Visual Observations

Postoperatively, all animals had flaccid paralysis of the pelvic limbs with urine retention and atonic anal sphincters, while maintaining spinal segmental reflexes (patellar and pedal withdrawal). Most animals developed reflex bladder control after 7 to 10 days. Many animals (Tarlov ratings of 0, 1) continued to have urinary and fecal incontinence throughout the 42-day observation period. Improvement of dogs with Tarlov ratings of 2 or greater was gradual throughout the 42 days (TABLE 2).

The 6 dogs in the control group (group A) remained paraplegic throughout the 42-day period and had Tarlov ratings of 1. Two groups (D and G) had no dogs that exceeded Tarlov 2 rating. Two other groups (B and C) each had 2 dogs that walked. Group B also had 2 dogs that could stand reflexly. Group E had 2 dogs that could walk and run and a third that walked with deficit. Group F, which had the best results, contained 2 dogs that were normal and 2 that could walk and run with some deficit.

TABLE 3 gives the estimated probabilities of recovery for each of the treatment groups along with the 95% confidence limits. Hypotheses concerning no differences among treatment groups need not be tested, because of overlap of the confidence intervals. However, the estimated probabilities can be ranked and compared with the control data (TABLE 4). Those treatment groups for which the confidence limits do not include zero can be said to show a statistically significant probability of recovery greater than that for the control group.

TABLE 4

RANKING OF TREATMENTS

Rank	Treatment Group	Probability of Recovery
1	D	0.000
2	G	0.000
3	B	0.285
4	C	0.285
5	E	0.429
6	F	0.570

Gross and Microscopic Examination

At necropsy, all spinal cords were covered with a dense fibrous connective tissue callus. It was firmly adherent to the cord and extended the length of the durotomy incision. Cavitation at T_{12} was noted in most specimens, with the fibrous callus extending into the cavernous area. If MT had been performed, there was noticeably less cavitation with greater continuity of the cord parenchyma. Many MT specimens had a yellow discoloration in the dorsal half of the cord parenchyma, which extended into the cord tissue.

Microscopically, various degrees of meningeal fibroplasia were noted dorsal to the durotomy site. Serial sections made through T_{11}, T_{12}, and T_{13} revealed cratering and extensive loss of cord tissue in the T_{12} area. Central necrosis and intact ventral white matter were noted with dilated myelin sheaths and malacic areas.

Correlation was not possible between severity of histopathologic lesions, gross lesions, and the success or failure of any treatment group to regain function of the pelvic limbs.

TABLE 5

DISCRIMINANT ANALYSIS OF CEP RECORDINGS MADE FROM EXPERIMENTALLY TRAUMATIZED DOGS

	1 Hour		2 Hours		42 Days	
Item	NA	A	NA	A	NA	A
Number of dogs	46		45		44	
Nonambulatory (NA)	14		11	23	24	9
Ambulatory (A)	0	12	0	11	0	11
Accuracy	38%		32%		55%	

At 1 hour, 32 dogs (20 + 12) were indicated to be ambulatory by discriminant analysis. Of this number, 12 (38%) were clinically ambulatory at 42 days after trauma. No dogs that were declared ambulatory subsequently were nonambulatory.

Analyses of CEP

Discriminant analysis was performed on the CEP recordings at 1 and 2 hours and 42 days after trauma. This method is designed to separate dogs that subsequently will become ambulatory from those that will remain paralyzed. Using a discriminant function that allowed no mistake in the ambulatory category, we were only able to separate ambulatory from nonambulatory dogs with 38% accuracy at 1 hour, 32% accuracy at 2 hours, and 55% accuracy at 42 days (TABLE 5). Principal component analysis was also performed and tended to confirm the important CEP variables used in discriminant analysis.

DISCUSSION

A more extended recuperative period could possibly have resulted in greater numbers of recoveries, since return of neuronal function is slow. Our thought was that by using a high g-cm impact force, the beneficial effects of any treatment combination would be accentuated.

One need not do a statistical test if one accepts the statement that the probability for recovery in control subjects is indeed zero. That is, any recovery in an experimental group indicates a significant effect, and thus there exists evidence of benefits from treatment regimes of groups B, C, E, and F only.

Certain inferences concerning treatments can be made. The DMSO and MT are present in all regimens where recovery occurs. When either one is missing, there is no indication of recovery. Thus, the two treatments combined significantly and appreciably enhanced the probability for recovery.

Whenever treatments RP and RF are both present, the recovery probability is either zero or reduced when treatments DMSO and MT are present. When one or the other of treatments RP and PF are missing and treatments DMSO and MT are present, the recovery potential is maximum. Thus, the inference may be made that treatments RP and PF represent a negative effect for recovery. Strong evidence does not exist that DM affects recovery.

From these data, it appears that DMSO was a critical contributor to the higher group scores. This is supported by the work of de la Torre et al.[3] and Kajihara et al.[22] who have reported positive effects from DMSO following spinal cord trauma. Transmembrane drug-carrying capability, cell membrane penetrability, membrane stabilization, antiinflammatory, vasodilatory, and diuretic effects have all been attributed to DMSO.[3,23,24] Finney et al.[25] have shown a sparing effect of DMSO on O_2 consumption by myocardial cells. Theoretically, this antihypoxic effect could sustain traumatized neuronal tissues during the period of low blood flow. Electron micropic studies have shown the sparing effect of DMSO on biological membranes following oxygen deprivation.

Myelotomy is one of the oldest methods proposed for treatment of contused cord tissue. Allen,[1] in his classic report of 1911, reported recovery of 5 of 5 dogs traumatized with 540 g-cm when MT was performed after trauma. Other investigators have repeated Allen's original work and found MT to have a positive effect on recovery from spinal trauma.[16,18,25] Theories of action include release of increased intramedullary pressure, increased oxygen interface with exposed surface area, and release of noxious vasoactive amines trapped within the trauma site.

These two treatments (DMSO and MT) are directed toward control of a local anaerobic environment while normal vascular responses can be reinstated in this segment of injured tissue. In essence, treatment of a local shock phenomenon at the cellular level in a restricted area of the body becomes the primary objective. Temporary protection of neuronal tissues from the ischemia resulting from impaired spinal cord blood supply may well be the beneficial effect of DMSO and MT.[26-32]

Although DM is routinely used clinically in treatment of central nervous system trauma, its use has been questioned.[33] Black and Markowitz[2] reported that DM had a protective effect against cord trauma in monkeys. Lewin et al.[34] reported that DM had a beneficial effect in spinal-injured cats, perhaps due to prevention of potassium loss from injured cord. Cooper et al.,[35] in a double-blind study of traumatic head injuries in persons, could find no difference in recovery between placebo- and DM-treated patients. The fact that DM did not appreciably contribute to recovery in our study is, therefore, not surprising.

Osterholm et al.[7] showed that recovery was greater in cats that were treated with RP before spinal cord trauma. They theorized that vasoactive amine release at the trauma site decreased spinal cord blood flow with cellular hypoxia. Sparing effects of RP have been attributed to norepinephrine depletion, thus avoiding elevated levels of catecholamines at the spinal cord injury site. Others, however, have rejected the catecholamine hypothesis.[36-38] Our work tends to confirm their results.

Although our results appear very favorable for the combination of DMSO (given i.v.) and MT, one should accept these cautiously, because of the small number of animals used in the present experimental groups. Further investigation should be done with larger numbers to prove the additive therapeutic effect of this combination.

REFERENCES

1. ALLEN, A. R. 1911. Surgery of experimental lesion of spinal cord equivalent to crush injury of fracture dislocation of spinal column—A preliminary report. J. Am. Med. Assoc. **57**: 878–880.
2. BLACK, P. & R. S. MARKOWITZ. 1971. Experimental spinal cord injury in monkeys: Comparison of steroids and local hypothermia. Surg. Forum **22**: 409–411.
3. DE LA TORRE, J. C., C. M. JOHNSON, D. J. GOODE et al. 1975. Pharmacologic treatment and evaluation of permanent experimental spinal cord trauma. Neurology **25**: 508–514.
4. DUCKER, T. B. & H. F. HAMIT. 1969. Experimental treatments of acute spinal cord injury. J. Neurosurg. **30**: 693–697.
5. HILL, H. F. & J. L. OSTERHOLM. 1974. Noradrenergic mediation of experimental spinal injury. Review of current research on spinal cord injury. J. Neurosurg. **40**: 5–33.
6. MENDENHALL, H. V., P. LITWAK, D. J. YTURRASPE et al. 1976. Aggressive pharmacologic and surgical treatment of spinal cord injuries in dogs and cats. J. Am. Vet. Med. Assoc. **168**: 1026–1031.
7. OSTERHOLM, J. L., G. F. MATHEWS, J. D. IRIN et al. 1972. Antinorepinephrine therapy against traumatic hemorrhagic necrosis of the spinal cord: Preliminary report. Clin. Neurol. **20**: 382–399.
8. JOYNER, J. & L. W. FREEMAN. 1963. Urea and spinal cord trauma. Neurology **13**: 69–72.
9. ALBIN, M. S., R. J. WHITE, G. ACOSTA-RUA et al. 1968. Study of functional recovery produced by delayed localized cooling after spinal cord injury in primates. J. Neurosurg. **29**: 113–120.
10. ALBIN, M. S., R. J. WHITE, G. S. LOCKE et al. 1967. Localized spinal cord hypothermia. Anesthe. Analg. (Cleveland) **46**: 8–15.
11. THIENPRASIT, P., H. BANTLI, J. R. BLOEDEL et al. 1975. Effect of delayed local cooling on experimental spinal cord injury. J. Neurosurg. **42**: 150.
12. TATOR, C. H. & L. DEECKE. 1973. Value of normothermic perfusion, hyperthermic perfusion, and durotomy in the treatment of experimental acute spinal cord trauma. J. Neurosurg. **39**: 52–64.
13. HARTZOG, T. J., R. G. FISHER & C. SNOW. 1969. Spinal cord trauma: Effect of hyperbaric oxygen therapy. Proc. Spinal Cord Injury Conf. **17**: 70–71.
14. KELLY, D. L., K. R. L. LASSITER, A. VONGSVIVUT et al. 1972. Effect of hyperbaric oxygenation the tissue oxygen studies in experimental paraplegia. J. Neurosurg. **36**: 425–429.
15. YEO, J. D., S. STABBACK & B. MCKINZIE. 1977. A study of the effect of hyperbaric oxygen on the experimental spinal cord injury. Med. J. Aust. **2**: 145–147.
16. CAMPBELL, J. B., V. DECRESCITO, J. J. TOMASULA et al. 1973. Experimental treatment of spinal cord contusion in the cat. Surg. Neurol. **1**: 102–106.
17. FREEMAN, L. W. & T. W. WRIGHT. 1953. Experimental observations of concussion and contusion of the spinal cord. Ann. Surg. **137**: 433–443.
18. RIVLIN, A. S. & C. H. TATOR. 1979. Effect on vasodilators and myelotomy in recovery after acute spinal cord injury in rats. J. Neurosurg. **50**: 349–352.
19. OSTERHOLM, J. L. 1974. The pathophysiological response to spinal cord injury. J. Neurosurg. **40**: 5–33.
20. MOOD, A. M., F. A. GRAYBILL & D. C. BOES. 1974. Introduction to the Theory of Statistics. 3rd Edit. p. 395. McGraw-Hill Book Co. New York.

21. KENDALL, M. 1975. Multivariate Analysis. Hafner Press. New York.
22. KAJIHARA, K., J. KAWANAGA, J. C. DE LA TORRE & S. MULLAN. 1973. Dimethyl sulfoxide in the treatment of experimental acute spinal cord injury. Surg. Neurol. **1:** 16–22.
23. KLIGMAN, A. M. 1965. Topical pharmacology and toxicology of dimethyl sulfoxide— Part 1. J. Am. Med. Assoc. **193:** 796–804.
24. NARULA, P. N. 1975. The comparative penetrant-carrier action of dimethyl sulfoxide and ethyl alcohol *in vivo*. Ann. N.Y. Acad. Sci. **37:** 277–278.
25. FINNEY, J. W., H. C. URSCHEL & G. A. BALLA. 1967. Protection of the ischemic heart with DMSO alone or DMSO with hydrogen peroxide. Ann. N.Y. Acad. Sci. **141:** 231–241.
26. DOHRMANN, G. J., F. C. WAGNER, JR. & P. C. BUCY. 1971. The microvasculature in transitory traumatic paraplegia. J. Neurosurg. **35:** 263–271.
27. DUCKER, T. B. & P. L. PEROT. Spinal cord oxygen and blood flow in trauma. Surg. Forum. **22:** 413–415.
28. FAIRHOLM, D. J. & I. M. TURNBULL. 1971. Microangiographic study of experimental spinal cord injuries. J. Neurosurg. **35:** 277–286.
29. GRIFFITHS, I. R. 1975. Vasogenic edema following acute and chronic spinal cord compression in the dog. J. Neurosurg. **42:** 155–165.
30. GRIFFITHS, I. R., N. BURNS & A. R. CRAWFORD. 1978. Early vascular changes in the spinal grey matter following impact injury. Acta Neuropathol. **41:** 33–39.
31. RIVLIN, A. S. & C. H. TATOR. 1978. Regional spinal cord blood flow in rats after severe cord trauma. J. Neurosurg. **49:** 844–853.
32. SENTER, H. J. & J. L. VENES. 1978. Altered blood flow and secondary injury in experimental spinal cord trauma. J. Neurosurg. **46:** 569–578.
33. TATOR, C. H. & D. W. ROWED. 1979. Current concepts in the immediate management of acute spinal cord injuries. Can. Med. Assoc. J. **121:** 453–464.
34. LEWIN, M. G., R. R. HANSEBOUT & H. M. PAPPIUS. 1974. Chemical characteristics of traumatic spinal cord edema in cats. Effect of steroids on potassium depletion. J. Neurosurg. **40:** 65–75.
35. COOPER, P. R., S. MOODY, W. K. CLARK *et al.* 1979. Dexamethasone and severe head injury. J. Neurosurg. **51:** 307–316.
36. RAWE, S. E., R. H. ROTH, M. BOADLE-BIBER *et al.* 1977. Norepinephrine levels in experimental spinal cord trauma. Part I: Biochemical study of hemorrhagic necrosis. J. Neurosurg. **46:** 342–349.
37. RAWE, S. E., R. H. ROTH & W. F. COLLINS. 1977. Norepinephrine levels in experimental spinal cord trauma. Part II: Histopathological study of hemorrhagic necrosis. J. Neurosurg. **46:** 350–356.
38. SCHOULTZ, T. W. 1977. Microscopic analysis of early histopathological spinal cord alterations following trauma in normal and catecholamine-depleted cats. J. Neurol. Sci. **32:** 283–295.

ULTRASTRUCTURAL STUDIES OF RAT FASCICULI GRACILIS UNMYELINATED FIBERS AFTER CONTUSION AND DMSO TREATMENT*

Pamela K. Hill, J. C. de la Torre,† Susannah M. Thompson,
Sheila Rosenfield-Wessels, and Mary L. Beckett

Department of Anatomy
Eastern Virginia Medical School
Norfolk, Virginia 23501

INTRODUCTION

Morphological changes in the spinal cord are generally seen within several hours following the onset of insult.[9,15] This period is unquestionably the time when the central nervous system (CNS) is most vulnerable to subcellular destruction and must be protected as soon after injury as possible to prevent irreversible loss of function.

Ultrastructural preservation of the monkey brain after ischemic injury was shown by de la Torre and Hill[12] to be enhanced by using DMSO when compared to dexamethasone or saline treatment. The subcellular features of the brain receiving a physically induced trauma and DMSO treatment were not compared with the results of the previous study that used an ischemic model. In another study, de la Torre and co-workers[13] showed a correlation of somatosensory evoked potentials with return of motor function in 7 out of 8 dogs receiving contusion of the spinal cord and DMSO treatment. The response of dorsal funicular fibers to DMSO treatment was not examined ultrastructurally in that study and has not been described by other investigators.

These findings prompted us to examine the ultrastructure of the adult rat spinal cord following contusion and DMSO treatment. The specific objective was to describe the ultrastructural features of fasciculi gracilis unmyelinated fibers during the early stages of recovery (first 4 days) after contusion and treatment with DMSO and saline. The implications of preserving such fibers for potential functional return were considered and will be discussed subsequently.

EXPERIMENTAL PROCEDURES

Experimental Design and Surgical Procedures

The experimental design is summarized in TABLE 1. Group C (control) rats underwent L-1 laminectomy only and 4 days of saline treatment. Group SC (saline control) rats underwent L-1 laminectomy, contusion of the L1-2 level of the spinal cord and 4 days of saline treatment. Group D (DMSO treated) rats underwent L-1 laminectomy, contusion of the L1-2 level of the spinal cord, and 4 days of DMSO treatment. The treatments in all three groups were administered

*Supported by the Eastern Paralyzed Veterans Association.

†Dr. Jack C. de la Torre's present address is: Northwestern University Medical School, Division of Neurosurgery, Chicago, Illinois 60611.

200

by osmotic mini-pump. Animals in all three groups were assigned to their respective group after surgery and mini-pump implantation.

Three groups of 6 female Sprague-Dawley rats (250–300 g) were included in this study. All animals were anesthetized with an intraperitoneal injection of sodium pentobarbital (Nembutal, from Abbott Laboratories, 36 mg/kg) and laminectomy was performed with a microdrill under sterile conditions at the L-1 level of the spinal cord. The microdrill was used to transect the L-1 laminae in such a way that both neural arches were removed as an intact unit. The result was that the dorsal surface of the spinal cord was protected from trauma and the amount of bleeding and surgical time was minimized. Bladders were expressed twice daily in group SC and D by applying manual pressure to the suprapubic area. Loose stools were present in animals in both group SC and D thereby alleviating the necessity of manually evacuating the bowels. The first post-operative day, animals in all three groups were given an intraperitoneal injection of 1–2 ml of water containing 5% dextrose. For the duration of the experiments, animals in all three groups were given an intramuscular injection of penicillin G (1 ml containing 250,000 U per injection) twice daily.

The contusion injury was produced with the impactor of a custom-designed apparatus modified from that described by Allen.[1] The impactor was positioned lightly over the dorsal aspect of the exposed L1-2 segment of the spinal cord. A

TABLE 1

SUMMARY OF EXPERIMENTAL DESIGN

Group	Number	Injury	Treatment	Period (Days)
C (Control)	6	—	Saline + pump	4
SC (Saline control)	6	+	Saline + pump	4
D (DMSO treated)	6	+	DMSO + pump	4

10 g weight was then dropped a distance of 20 cm through the column of the contusion apparatus. Calibration of the impactor was done electrophysiologically according to Molt and co-workers[27] and it was estimated that the impact of 200 g-cm striking the cord was equivalent to 0.17640 newtons.

To allow for continuous perfusion over the dorsal surface of the exposed spinal cord of either saline or DMSO at a rate of 1 μl/h, a sterile Alzet osmotic mini-pump #2001 (Alza Corp.) was implanted after laminectomy in group C animals and after laminectomy and contusion in animals of group SC and group D (Figure 1). The implantation procedure followed that described by de la Torre and Gonzalez-Carvajal[11] with some modifications as specified in FIGURE 1. To ensure systemic levels of both drugs, the animals in groups SC and D also received an intraperitoneal injection of saline or DMSO from Research Industries, Inc. (1.5 g/kg body weight in a 50% saline solution), respectively. The injections were given 1 h after contusion, every 4 hours for the first day and twice daily thereafter for 4 days.

Ultrastructural Preparation

Spinal cords were processed for ultrastructural study as described previously.[20] The right and left dorsal funiculi were dissected microscopically from L1-2 as well as 1 cm proximal (T11-13) and 1 cm distal (L3-5) to that area. The dorsal medial half of each posterior funiculus (fasciculus gracilis) was then selected to avoid any possible overlap with fibers of the ventrally located cortico-spinal tract[16,28] or with fibers of the laterally located fasciculus cuneatus.[28] After processing the tissue according to the method of Hill and co-workers,[20] ultrathin sections were examined with the Philips EH-301 transmission electron microscope.

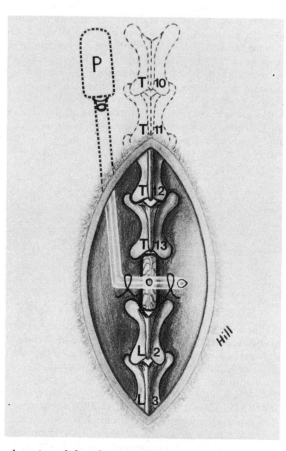

FIGURE 1. Implantation of the Alza osmotic mini-pump. All implantation procedures were performed with the aid of the Zeiss operating microscope model #615. Paraspinal muscles were retracted from the T-13 to L-2 vertebral level after L-1 laminectomy and a 45° angle "tunnel" made through the center of the left muscle group with an 18 gauge hypodermic needle. The Alzet minipump #2001 (p) filled with either saline or DMSO was positioned subcutaneously and laterally to the left of the T-10 through T-13 segments of the vertebral column. A 6-cm length of PE-60 tubing was connected to the pump, slipped through the "tunnel" and bent 45° at its left distal end to span the dorsal aspect of the spinal cord. To prevent potential damage to the cord, the overriding tubing was secured bilaterally with 4-0 Ethiflex suture to the inner aspect of the paraspinal muscles. Prior to positioning of the tubing, small openings were made with an ophthalmic cautery in its dorsal and ventral surfaces for maximum fluid release over the cord. The paraspinal muscles and skin incision were sutured separately and the pump allowed to function for 4 days.

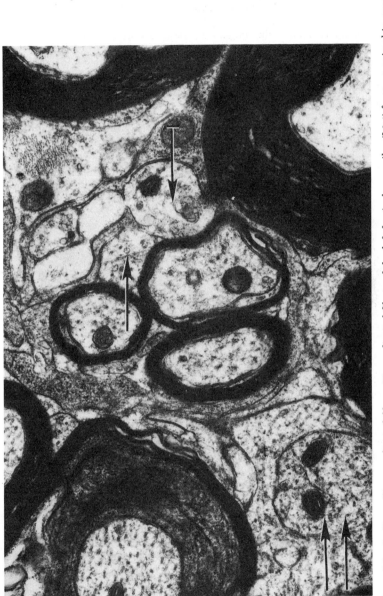

FIGURE 2. Normal fasciculi gracili unmyelinated fibers. Unmyelinated fibers of the left fasciculus gracilus [L3,4] from an animal in group C represent the usual clustering arrangement of small (→), medium-sized (⊦→), and large fibers (⇒) that range in diameter from 0.2–0.4 μm, 0.5–0.8 μm, and 0.9–1.5 μm, respectively. Note the presence of filamentous type mitochondria (m) in the medium-sized and large fibers. 38,000 ×, with 95% figure reduction.

RESULTS

General Observations

Normal Fasciculi Gracilis Unmyelinated Fibers of Group C

Unmyelinated fibers of the normal rat fasciculi gracilis occurred in clusters of several fibers (1–5) or in groups containing a large number of fibers (10–30) scattered between myelinated fibers. The diameter of unmyelinated fibers ranged from 0.2–0.4 µm for small fibers, 0.5–0.8 µm for medium-sized fibers, and 0.9–1.5 µm for large fibers (FIGURE 2). No synaptic connections were associated with any of the three groups. Mitochondria of all three groups of unmyelinated fibers were of the filamentous type. No subcellular differences were observed between right and left sides of the group C fasciculi gracilis unmyelinated fibers. No gross nor subcellular abnormalities were seen using the osmotic mini-pump implantation to either the right or left fasciculus gracilis of animals in group C.

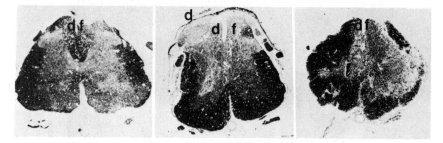

FIGURE 3. Histological examination of the contusion injury. The lesion site at the L1-2 level of the spinal cord (center) demonstrates complete loss of myelinated fibers and severe neuropil distortion in both the dorsal funiculi (df) and dorsal-lateral funiculus. Note that the dura (d) remains intact dorsally as do myelinated fibers in more distal segments of the dorsal roots. The entire gray matter also displays severe disruption of neuropil and vasculature. One centimeter proximal to the lesion site (left), the myelinated fibers of the dorsal funiculi (df) are intact although severely disrupted by edema. One centimeter distal to the lesion site (right), any recognizable fibers of the dorsal funiculus (df) appear to be replaced with glial proliferation. 6 µm paraffin sections stained with luxol fast blue and counterstained with cresyl violet. 9.5 ×, with 75% figure reduction.

Experimental Groups SC and D

Lesion site. Histological examination of the lesion site (L1-2) 4 days after injury demonstrated the presence of a severe, symmetrical lesion characterized by replacement of completely degenerated gray matter with gliosis. All areas of white matter at the lesion site were less severely affected than gray matter, although extracellular edema and gliosis was present throughout and particularly destructive to the dorsal funiculi and dorsal-lateral funiculi (FIGURE 3).

Gliosis at the lesion site was less extensive in group D animals than in those of group SC. Obliteration of the dorsal median septum by extracellular edema and gliosis occurred more frequently in group SC animals than in those of group D. Erythrocytes were seen in edematous areas of gliosis at the lesion site in group SC animals but appeared less numerous in the same area of group D animals.

Proximal and distal to the lesion site. Less gross distortion of fasciculi gracilis unmyelinated fibers by extracellular edema and gliosis was evident 1 cm proximal and distal to the lesion site in group D animals when compared with control tissues of group SC (FIGURE 2). In group D, the distal segment generally showed a lesser amount of extracellular fluid accumulation than did the proximal segment. No such distinction was observed between proximal and distal segments of group SC animals.

Specific Observations

Lesion Site: L1-2

The gross clustering arrangement of unmyelinated fibers at the lesion site was better preserved in group D fasciculi gracilis unmyelinated fibers than in those of group SC. The neuropil of group D tissues contained sporadic, minimal accumulation of extracellular edema (FIGURE 4a) while group SC tissues were often uniformly distorted by the increased extracellular fluid (FIGURE 4b). Large unmyelinated fibers of both groups showed a greater degree of gross disruption from extracellular edema than did medium-sized and small unmyelinated fibers. Clusters of medium-sized and small unmyelinated fibers in group D animals were maintained without apparent alteration. Large, medium-sized, and small unmyelinated fibers of group SC fasciculi gracilis frequently showed severe distortion of the gross clustering arrangement, with the small fibers being the least affected. In both groups, astrocytic processes appeared occasionally to be "protecting" the gross arrangement of unmyelinated fibers by circumscribing clusters of fibers (FIGURE 5).

Ultrastructural intracellular changes were present in small and medium-sized unmyelinated fibers of group D animals to a much lesser extent than those in group SC. The subcellular components of the small unmyelinated fibers of group D animals (FIGURE 6a) remained unaltered while medium-sized fibers occasionally displayed asymmetrical aggregation of clear-type synaptic vesicles and attenuation of axoplasm. The neurofilaments and neurotubules in the latter group were usually spared degenerative changes and synaptic contacts were maintained. Examination of medium-sized fibers of group SC and group D showed a significantly greater degree of subcellular integrity in the latter group. Large unmyelinated terminals in group D animals frequently showed the same ultrastructural changes described in the subsequent paragraph for large terminals of group SC. Synaptic connections frequently remained intact in the large terminals of group D animals, although occasionally the axo-dendritic contacts manifested either a loss or thickening of synaptic membranes (FIGURE 6a, inset).

Changes in subcellular organelles and axoplasmic constituents were noted in both groups as a result of intracellular fluid accumulation. In group SC (FIGURE 6b), most medium-sized and large unmyelinated fibers demonstrated asymmetrical aggregation of clear-type synaptic vesicles and attenuation of axoplasm often accompanied by degeneration of neurofilaments and neurotubules. Mitochondria in some fibers frequently showed densification of matrix and swelling of cristae. In several instances, the mitochondrial matrix was severely attenuated and cristae were obliterated. The most dramatic changes present in group SC were complete loss of synaptic vesicles in many severely dilated terminals and frequent absence of synaptic connections between such terminals. The small unmyelinated fibers in group SC appeared to be resistant to the intracellular

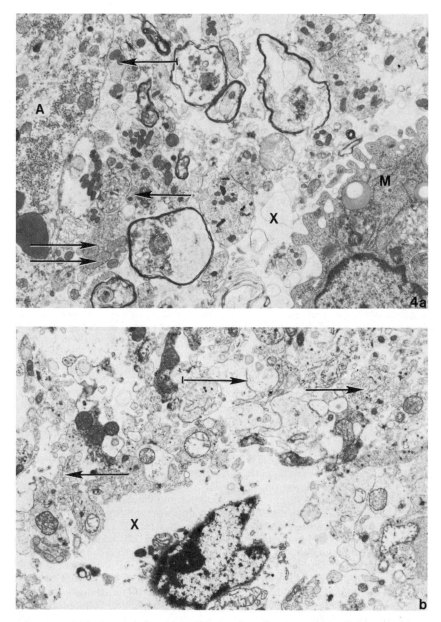

FIGURE 4. (a) Lesion site of group D. Clusters of small (→), medium-sized (↦), and large (⇉) unmyelinated fibers are preserved despite the sporadic presence of extracellular edema (x). Note the presence of a microglial cell (M) and the perikaryon of an astrocyte (A). 9,690 ×, with 70% figure reduction.

(b) Lesion site of group SC. Clustering of small unmyelinated fibers remains intact in some areas of the lesion site (arrows) of saline-treated animals despite the uniform, severe distortion of the neuropil by extracellular edema (x). Note the fragmentation of what may have been large unmyelinated fibers (↦) 9,690 ×, with 70% figure reduction.

alterations described in the medium-sized and large terminals. No subcellular differences were observed between right and left sides of the lesion site in group SC and group D fasciculi gracilis unmyelinated fibers.

Proximal to the Lesion Site: T11-13

The gross clustering arrangement of unmyelinated fibers located proximal to the lesion site at T11-13 was better preserved in the DMSO-treated animals than in the saline-treated group. Extracellular edema was present sporadically and

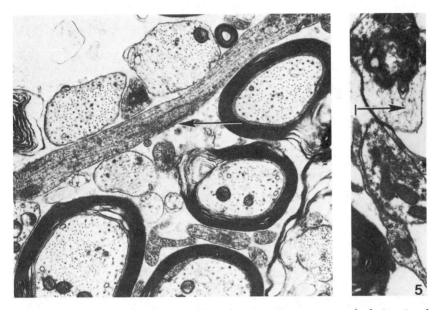

FIGURE 5. Protection of unmyelinated fibers by astrocytic processes at the lesion site of group D and group SC. The presence of astrocytic processes (arrow) in close association with unmyelinated fibers at the lesion site seemed to provide "protection" of these fibers from intracellular fluid accumulation and/or subcellular degenerative changes in both group D and group SC (inset). Note in the inset that an unmyelinated fiber (|→) adjacent to the "protected" fiber shows an absence of neurotubules, densification of mitochondria, and the presence of what appears to be an aggregation of degenerating intracellular membranous structures (|→). 30,000 ×; 30,000 ×, inset; with 70% figure reduction.

generally minimal throughout the neuropil in the former whereas the neuropil was often uniformly distorted by extracellular fluid accumulation in the latter. Small unmyelinated fibers of both groups showed the least degree of gross distortion from extracellular edema when compared with medium-sized and large unmyelinated terminals. Medium-sized and large unmyelinated terminals showed severe disruption of the gross clustering arrangement in group SC animals (FIGURE 7b). Despite a moderate, sporadic accumulation of extracellular fluid in the neuropil of group D animals (FIGURE 7a), the gross clustering of

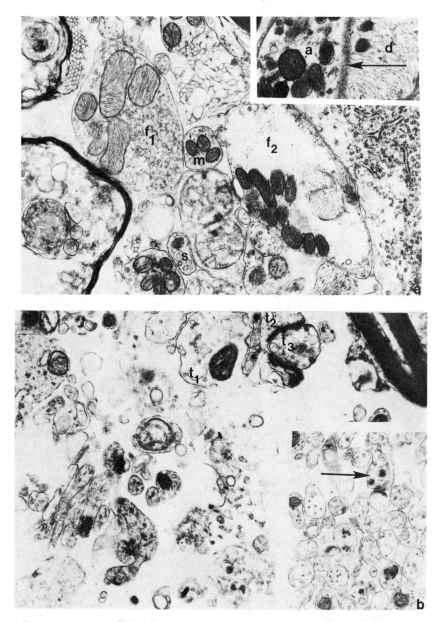

FIGURE 6. (a) Intracellular changes in unmyelinated fibers at the lesion site of group D. Small, medium-sized, and large unmyelinated fibers are present in this area of the lesion site in group D fasciculi gracilis. The small (s) and medium-sized (m) terminals show a normal composition and arrangement of mitochondria, neurotubules, and neurofilaments. One large fiber (f₁) possesses normal mitochondria and symmetrical distribution of clear-type synaptic vesicles. Another large fiber (f₂) has undergone an asymmetrical aggregation of mitochondria and clear-type synaptic vesicles presumably caused by an increased

medium-sized and large unmyelinated fibers remained intact in most instances. Large myelinated fibers in group D, however, occasionally demonstrated disruption of clustering because of extracellular edema.

Changes in subcellular organelles and axoplasmic constituents were noted in both groups SC and D as a result of intracellular fluid accumulation and were similar to those described for unmyelinated fibers at the lesion site. Synaptic contacts were better preserved in group D than in group SC animals. Fragmented synapses were seen in both groups but with less frequency in the terminals of group D animals. In large fibers of both groups that showed intracellular fluid accumulation, clear and dense-cored vesicles were usually aggregated asymmetrically as were microtubules and neurofilaments (FIGURE 7a). No subcellular differences were observed between right and left sides proximal to the lesion site in group SC and group D fasciculi gracilis unmyelinated fibers.

Distal to the Lesion Site: L3-5

The most outstanding gross and subcellular ultrastructural responses to DMSO treatment of fasciculi gracilis unmyelinated fibers in our study were present 1 cm distal to the lesion site at the level of L3-5. The gross clustering of all sizes of unmyelinated fibers in group D animals was intact despite sporadic accumulation of extracellular fluid (FIGURE 8a). The presence of extracellular edema in group SC fasciculi gracilis caused disruption of the gross arrangement of medium-sized and large unmyelinated fibers but appeared to spare the small unmyelinated fibers (FIGURE 9a).

Intracellular accumulation of fluid and/or loss of axoplasmic constituents occurred in all sizes of unmyelinated fibers in group SC fasciculi gracilis often causing severe ultrastructural alterations (FIGURE 9b). In several instances, extreme distortion of unmyelinated fibers made it impossible to determine their original size. Fragmentation of synaptic contacts was frequently observed in these fibers. A few large unmyelinated terminals in group D displayed mild intracellular dilation resulting in attenuation of axoplasm and non-uniform distribution of synaptic vesicles (FIGURE 8b). In such cases, however, synaptic contacts were always intact. No subcellular differences were observed between right and left sides distal to the lesion site in group SC and group D fasciculi gracilis unmyelinated fibers.

---

accumulation of intracellular fluid. The inset illustration represents the synaptic connection between an axon (a) and dendrite (d) at the lesion site of group D fasciculi gracilis. The pre- and post-synaptic membranes appear to be thickened (arrow) and several mitochondria seem to be degenerating in the axon. 30,000 ×; 30,000 ×, inset; with 70% figure reduction.

(b) Intracellular changes in fasciculi gracilis unmyelinated fibers at the lesion site of group SC. Despite the presence of severe extracellular edema, the small unmyelinated fibers at the lesion site in group SC (inset) have retained their normal clustering arrangement and intracellular integrity in most instances. Several fibers illustrated by the inset contain dense-core vesicles (→) but are noticeably lacking synaptic connections. Large terminals represented by t_1 frequently show fragmentation of the axolemma and asymmetrical aggregation of axoplasmic constituents. Note the retraction of the synaptic membrane of t_1 (→). Several medium-sized terminals (t_2; t_3) show similar asymmetrical aggregation of axoplasmic constituents as does t_1, although the pre- and post-synaptic connections between t_2 and t_3 appear to be intact. 25,500 ×; 25,500 ×, inset; with 70% figure reduction.

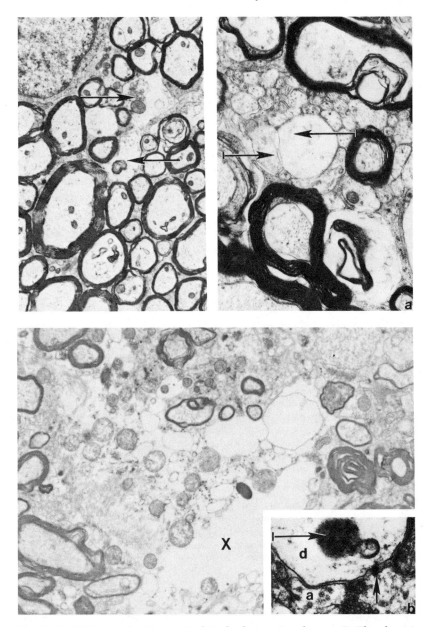

FIGURE 7. (a) One centimeter proximal to the lesion site of group D. The clustering arrangement of fasciculi gracilis unmyelinated fibers 1 cm proximal to the lesion site of group D is well preserved despite asymmetrical aggregation of synaptic vesicles in several large fibers (→, left). Note the absence of extracellular edema in the neuropil (left and right). A higher magnification illustration to the right shows the intact arrangement of small unmyelinated fibers as they surround several medium-sized fibers (⊢→). 11,400 ×; 30,000 ×, inset; with 70% figure reduction.

DISCUSSION

Gross and Histological Features of the Lesion

To ensure reproducibility of an irreversible, symmetrical lesion at the L1-2 level of the spinal cord, only rats that demonstrated bilateral spreading of hemorrhage and swelling of the cord from the mid-dorsal to the lateral dorsal surfaces within 15 minutes after contusion were included in the study. Histological examination of the lesion site in untreated animals (FIGURE 3) revealed that the contusion caused severe damage to the entire L1-2 segment of the spinal cord. The most extensive distortion, however, occurred to the dorsal funiculi presumably because of the direct impact on the dorsal surface of the spinal cord. The lesion site in group D animals showed considerably less distortion of the tissue histologically than that of group C presumably because of the potent diuretic effect[6,8,14,21] and vasodilatory characteristics[14] of DMSO.

By convention, investigators working with experimental spinal cord injury models express the contusion "force" as g-cm, which is not a true measurement of force.[27] For this reason, it was estimated according to the method of Molt and co-workers[27] that the impact of 200 g-cm striking the cord was equivalent to 0.17640 newtons. Although this a theoretical value for the impact force, it provides a more accurate description of the force used to produce the contusion injury than does g-cm.

Ultrastructural Response of Fasciculi Gracilis Unmyelinated Fibers to DMSO Treatment

Adequate fixation of mammalian spinal cord for ultrastructural studies is undoubtedly one of the most difficult challenges in neuroanatomical research mainly because of the variable density and dimension of the intrinsic microvasculature. The problem becomes particularly apparent when suitable preservation of the dorsal funiculi is hampered by the fact that the normal blood flow to that region is one of the lowest of any area in the adult rat spinal cord.[19,30] The situation is complicated further in the contused spinal cord because of a compromised intrinsic microvasculature. We have dealt with this problem as described in a previous study[20] and used the osmotic mini-pump to ensure delivery of drugs to the injured tissue.

The striking presence of synapses in association with medium-sized and large unmyelinated fibers and the noticeable absence of such connections between small fibers poses the interesting question of why are these structures present in the contused fasciculi gracilis and absent in noninjured tissue? Perhaps these connections reflect an attempt by injured axons to reestablish continuity with

---

(b) One centimeter proximal to the lesion site in group SC. Fasciculi gracilis unmyelinated fibers 1 cm proximal to the lesion site in saline-treated animals show loss of their usual clustering arrangement by extracellular edema (x) except for those of the small caliber. At higher magnification (inset), the remnant of synaptic membranes (→) between a dendrite (d) and an axon (a) seems to be the only remaining connection between the two terminals. Note the presence of a dense, osmophilic body (⊢→) within the dendrite that probably represents the breakdown product of intracellular membranous structures. 11,400 ×; 30,000 ×, inset; with 70% figure reduction.

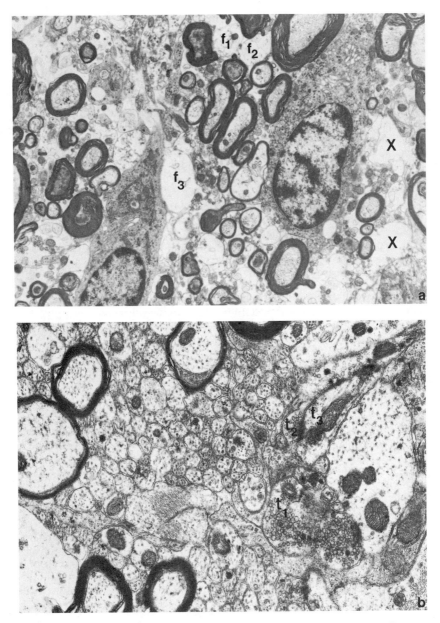

FIGURE 8. (a) One centimeter distal to the lesion site of group D. The gross clustering arrangement of all sizes of fasciculi gracilis unmyelinated fibers is well preserved even in a few areas that display some dilation of extracellular space by edema (x). Note that some large fibers (f_1; f_2; f_3) show attenuation of axoplasm while that of medium-sized and small fibers seems to be spared such an alteration. 11,400 ×, with 70% figure reduction.

(b) Intracellular changes in fasciculi gracilis unmyelinated fibers distal to the lesion site of group D. The outstanding feature of fasciculi gracilis unmyelinated fibers distal to the lesion site in group D represented in this illustration is that fibers of all three calibers generally retained their normal intracellular features. Notice the symmetrical arrangement of synaptic vesicles in terminals t_1 and t_2 and the synaptic connection (→) between t_2 and t_3. 30,000 ×, with 70% figure reduction.

other parts of the spinal cord, particularly distal to the lesion site of DMSO-treated animals. Although the mechanism of how DMSO preserves membrane stability following injury is unknown,[25] that property is of obvious value during the early period of spinal cord injury in preventing fragmentation of nerve fiber axolemmas and the limiting membrane of their respective organelles. This preservation was also observed in myelinated fibers by Kajihara and co-workers[22] who showed that there was less demyelination and damage to axons of contused dog spinal cord white matter following treatment with DMSO as compared to other treatments.

The next intriguing question is where do these terminals that contain synaptic connections originate? They may be collaterals from either the dorsal column postsynaptic tract,[2,4,6,32,35] primary afferents,[18,29] or descending projections from the dorsal column nuclei.[7] In regard to the small unmyelinated fibers that lack synapses, without doing an extensive serial-section examination of these fibers one may assume that they are axons *en passant* traversing the dorsal column neuropil. Degeneration and/or tracer studies would have to be done in order to prove the exact origin of all three sizes of fibers in our particular study.

The gradation in severity of damage from negligible to complete devastation of small, medium-sized, and large unmyelinated fibers, respectively, may be explainable on the basis of gross arrangement and fiber size. The clustering arrangement of small fibers may afford them greater physical protection from trauma then medium-sized or large myelinated fibers because of their close association to each other and their being sequestered among myelinated fibers to a greater extent than other fibers. By comparison, the medium-sized unmyelinated fibers may be more vulnerable and the large unmyelinated fibers at greatest risk to physical damage because their gross arrangement in the fasciculi gracilis neuropil does not provide as sheltered a milieu as it does for the small fibers. Those medium-sized and large unmyelinated fibers that received DMSO treatment were certainly spared severe degenerative changes often present in saline control animals.

The damage of fasciculi gracilis unmyelinated fibers is obviously more severe at the site of impact than at areas proximal and distal to the lesion in group SC and D. The greater preservation of all three areas of fasciculi gracilis in rats treated with DMSO when compared with control tissues correlates well with our previous findings that traumatized CNS tissue can be spared irreversible alterations if treated with DMSO during the early phase of recovery.[12] We postulate that the ability of DMSO to act as a potent diuretic[14,21] and antiedema drug[6,8] probably reduces the extracellular fluid that accumulates so rapidly several hours following spinal cord injury. By diminishing extracellular edema with DMSO treatment, intracellular fluid balance can be subsequently maintained to a greater degree.

The most outstanding gross and subcellular ultrastructural responses to DMSO treatment of fasciculi gracilis unmyelinated fibers were present 1 cm distal to the lesion site at the level of L3-5. All three sizes of unmyelinated fibers in group D were spared the devastating subcellular changes so frequently observed in the same fibers of group SC fasciculi gracilis. One possible explanation for this observation is a greater perfusion of blood supplied to that area by the artery of Adamkiewicz.[34] Alternatively, regeneration of the microvasculature, which is known to occur by three days following contusion,[3] may be enhanced in those animals treated with DMSO. Our findings (unpublished data) indicate that the tight junctions between endothelial cells and the ultrastructural integrity of the same cells in venules particularly are preserved to a greater degree in

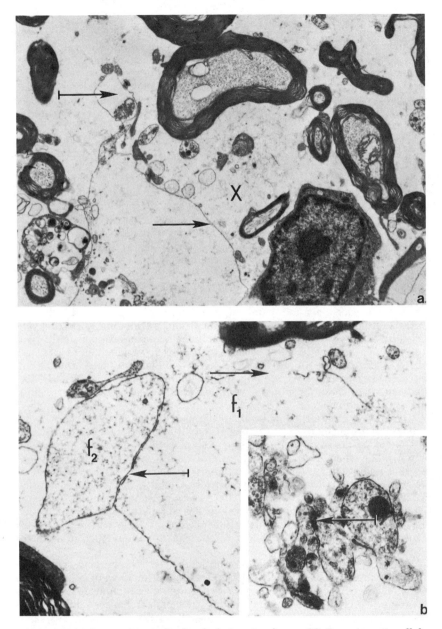

FIGURE 9. (a) One centimeter distal to the lesion site of group SC. Excessive extracellular edema (x) has resulted in severe distortion of the fasciculi gracilis neuropil. Several apparent unmyelinated fibers (→) display intracellular dilation accompanied by attenuation of axoplasm and asymmetrical aggregation of degenerating intracellular constituents (↦). 11,400 ×, with 70% figure reduction.

DMSO-treated animals than in those receiving saline. The ability of DMSO to maintain patency of cerebral blood vessels after occlusion[14] and to improve cerebral blood flow[6] results in a more homeostatic milieu by providing oxygen and nutrients required by CNS tissue for viability after injury. Although the reason for the apparent ability of DMSO to preserve the microvasculature or to possibly facilitate regeneration of such vessels in our study is unknown, it is logical to speculate that there is a positive relationship between maintenance of vascular integrity and preservation of fasciculi gracilis unmyelinated fibers.

Implications for Potential Functional Return

We have demonstrated ultrastructurally the presence of three distinct sizes of unmyelinated fibers in the adult rat fasciculi gracilis with the medium-sized and large fibers being most vulnerable to degenerative changes during the first 4 days following contusion. Despite not knowing the origin of these fibers, particularly those associated with synaptic connections, it is of interest to speculate about a functional discrimination of these fibers, i.e. does each size fiber subserve a specific sensory submodality for either temperature or pain? For example, could each of the three unmyelinated fibers carry three different sensations of coldness such as mild, moderate, and severe? Angaut-Petit[2] proposes that the dorsal column postsynaptic tract is composed of A delta and C fibers both of which are known to be associated with transmission of temperature sensation and nociception, particularly in the cat. If the fibers in our study constitute part of this second order dorsal column pathway and are related to transmission, temperature, and nociception, the presence of synapses within the fasciculi gracilis could represent the "third relay" for injured fibers to reestablish these sensory connections between the denervated hind limb and higher centers.

If one defines regeneration in the CNS as the reestablishment of structural and functional components after injury, there is some evidence that regeneration can occur in the adult rat dorsal columns. Lampert and Cressman[24] described regeneration of myelinated axons as early as 4 days following myelotomy in the rat but do not comment on unmyelinated fibers. Gelderd and co-investigators[17] have shown that myelinated and unmyelinated axons are increased in the scarred transection site of rats receiving hyperbaric oxygen and DMSO after injury. Although further studies are required to determine the origin of these fibers, the correlation of their presence with coordinated hindlimb movement in some of the animals may suggest that regenerative activity is fostered by the use of hyperbaric oxygen and DMSO.[17] Rucker and co-workers[31] as well as McCallum and Bennett[26] provide further evidence that DMSO is far more efficacious in promoting functional return after experimental SCI when compared with dexamethasone or dextrose.

Since our study has shown how fasciculi gracilis unmyelinated fibers respond

---

(b) Intracellular changes in fasciculi gracilis unmyelinated fibers distal to the lesion site of group SC. Severe intracellular edema has resulted in axoplasmic attenuation of one fiber (f_1) and fragmentation of its axolemma (→). Dilatation and attenuation of the axoplasm is also present in an adjacent fiber (f_2). Notice the fragmented synaptic membrane between f_1 and f_2 (⊢→). Despite these severe intracellular changes, some unmyelinated terminals retain their synaptic connections (insert, ⊢→) and often display axoplasmic densification. 22,000 ×; 25,500 ×, inset; with 70% figure reduction.

subcellularly to DMSO treatment during the early period of recovery from contusion, further studies defining the origin of axons associated with synaptic connections should provide insight into how the mammalian CNS attempts to compensate and recover from injury.

ACKNOWLEDGMENTS

We wish to express our gratitude to the Eastern Paralyzed Veterans Association for their support of this project. We would also like to thank Mr. James Slusser and Ms. Karen Wark for their assistance in preparing the illustrations. We also wish to thank Dr. J. T. Molt, Dr. Kent Sanders, and Mr. Paul Sullivan for their assistance in construction of the contusion apparatus. Our appreciation is also extended to Ms. Helen Bolger for typing this manuscript.

REFERENCES

1. ALLEN, A. R. 1911. Surgery of experimental lesion of spinal cord equivalent to crush injury of fracture dislocation of spinal column. J. Am. Med. Assoc. (Sept. 9): 878–880.
2. ANGAUT-PETIT, D. 1975. The dorsal column system. II. Functional properties and bulbar relay of the postsynaptic fibres of the cat's funiculus gracilis. Exp. Brain Res. 22: 471–493.
3. BEGGS, J. L. & J. D. WAGGENER. 1979. Microvascular regeneration following spinal cord injury: the growth sequence and permeability properties of new vessels. Adv. Neurol. 22: 192–206.
4. BENNETT, G. J., Z. SELTZER, M. J. HOFFERT, G. W. LEE, N. NISHIKAWA & R. DUBNER. 1981. The morphology and location of the cells of origin of the dorsal column postsynaptic tract (DCPST). Annual Meeting of the Society for Neuroscience 7: 611 (Abstract #199.7).
5. BROWN, A. G. 1981. In Organization in the Spinal Cord. The Anatomy and Physiology of Identified Neurons. pp. 122–129. Springer-Verlag. New York.
6. BROWN, F. D., L. M. JOHNS & S. MULLAN. 1980. Dimethyl sulfoxide in experimental brain injury, with comparison to mannitol. J. Neurosurg. 53: 58–62.
7. BURTON, H. & A. D. LOEWY. 1977. Projections to the spinal cord from medullary somatosensory relay nuclei. J. Comp. Neurol. 173: 773–792.
8. CAMP, P. E., H. E. JAMES & R. WERNER. 1981. Acute dimethyl sulfoxide therapy in experimental brain edema: Part 1. Effects on intracranial pressure, blood pressure, central venous pressure and brain water and electrolyte content. Neurosurg. 9(1): 28–33.
9. DE LA TORRE, J. C. 1981. Spinal cord injury: Review of basic and applied research. Spine 6(4): 1–21.
10. DE LA TORRE, J. C. & J. E. BOGGAN. 1980. Spinal cord injury and physiological recording in the rat. Exp. Neurol. 70: 356–370.
11. DE LA TORRE, J. C. & M. GONZALEZ-CARVAJAL. 1981. Steady state drug or fluid delivery to injured or transected spinal cord of rats. Lab. Anim. Sci. 31(6): 700–702.
12. DE LA TORRE, J. C. & P. K. HILL. 1976. Ultrastructural studies on formation of edema and its treatment following experimental brain infarction in monkeys. In Dynamics of Brain Edema. H. M. Pappius & W. Freindel, Eds.: 306–314. Springer-Verlag. Berlin.
13. DE LA TORRE, J. C., H. M. KAWANAGA, D. J. GOODE, C. M. JOHNSON, K. KAJIHARA, D. W. ROWED & S. MULLAN. 1975. Dimethyl sulfoxide in CNS trauma. Ann. N.Y. Acad. Sci. 243: 362–389.
14. DE LA TORRE, J. C., J. W. SURGEON, P. K. HILL & T. KHAN. 1977. DMSO in the treatment of brain infarction: Basic considerations. In Air Embolism and Acute Stroke. J. M. Hallenbeck & L. J. Greenbaum, Eds.: 138–161. Undersea Medical Society. Report No. 11-15-17.

15. DUCKER, T. B., G. W. KINDT & L. G. KEMPE. 1971. Pathological findings in acute experimental spinal cord trauma. J. Neurosurg. **35**: 700-708.
16. GANCHROW, D. & J. J. BERNSTEIN. 1981. Projections of caudal fasciculus gracilis to nucleus gracilis and other medullary structures and Clarke's necleus in the rat. Brain Res. **205**(2): 383-390.
17. GELDERD, J. B., D. W. WELCH, W. P. FIFE & D. E. BOWERS. 1980. The therapeutic effects of hyperbaric oxygenation and dimethyl sulfoxide following spinal transection in rats. Undersea Biomed. Res. **7**: 305-319.
18. GLEES, P. & J. SOLER. 1951. Fibre content of the posterior column and synaptic connections of nucleus gracilis. Zeitschrift für Zellforschung, Bd. **36**, S: 381-400.
19. HAYASHI, N., J. C. DE LA TORRE & B. GREEN. 1980. Regional spinal cord flow and tissue oxygen content after spinal cord trauma. Surg. Forum **31**: 461-463.
20. HILL, P. K., J. C. DE LA TORRE, S. M. THOMPSON, D. F. BULLOCK & S. ROSENFIELD-WESSELLS. 1981. A comparison study of E-M fixation procedures for the adult rat spinal cord based on regional blood flow. J. Neurosc. Meth. **5**(1-2): 23-31.
21. JACOB, S. W., M. BISCHEL & R. J. HERSCHLER. 1964. Dimethyl sulfoxide (DMSO): a new concept on pharmacotherapy. (Editorial). Curr. Ther. Res. **6**: 134-135.
22. KAJIHARA, K., H. KAWANAGA, J. C. DE LA TORRE & S. MULLAN. 1973. Dimethyl sulfoxide in the treatment of experimental acute spinal cord injury. Surg. Neurol. **1**: 16-22.
23. KUMAZAWA, T. & E. R. PERL. 1976. Differential excitation of dorsal horn and substantia gelatinosa marginal neurons by primary afferent units with fine (A and C) fibers. *In* Sensory Functions of the Skin in Primates, with Special Reference to Man. Y. Zutterman, Ed.: 67-88. Pergamon Press. New York.
24. LAMPERT, P. & M. CRESSMAN. 1964. Axonal regeneration in the dorsal columns of the spinal cord of adult rats. Lab. Invest. **13**: 825-839.
25. LIM, R. & S. MULLAN. 1975. Enhancement of resistance of glial cells by dimethyl sulfoxide against sonic disruption. Ann. N.Y. Acad. Sci. **243**: 358-361.
26. McCALLUM, J. E. & M. H. BENNETT. 1976. DMSO as a therapeutic agent in chronic spinal cord compression. Program Abstracts of the 26th Annual Meeting of the Congress of Neurological Surgeons (New Orleans). p. 166.
27. MOLT, J. T., L. R. NELSON, D. A. POULOS & R. S. BOURKE. 1979. Analysis and measurement of some sources of variability in experimental spinal cord trauma. J. Neurosurg. **50**: 784-791.
28. RANSON, S. W. 1913. The fasciculus cerebro-spinalis in the albino rat. Am. J. Anat. **14**(4): 411-425.
29. RETHELYI, M. & J. SZENTIAGOTHAI. 1973. Distribution and connections of afferent fibers in the spinal cord. *In* Handbook of Sensory Physiology. Vol. II, Somatosensory System. A. Iggo, Ed.: 207-252. Springer-Verlag. New York.
30. RIVLIN, A. S. & C. H. TATOR. 1978. Regional spinal cord blood flow in rats after severe cord trauma. J. Neurosurg. **49**: 844-853.
31. RUCKER, N. C., W. V. LUMB & R. J. SCOTT. 1981. Combined pharmacologic and surgical treatments for acute spinal cord trauma. Am. J. Vet. Res. **42**: 1138-1142.
32. RUSTIONI, A. 1973. Non-primary afferents to the nucleus gracilis from the lumbar cord of the cat. Brain Res. **51**: 81-95.
33. TREVINO, D. S., J. D. COULTER & W. D. WILLIS. 1973. Location of cells of origin of the spinothalamic tract in lumbar enlargement of the monkey. J. Neurophysiol. **36**: 750-761.
34. TVETEN, L. 1976. Spinal cord vascularity. IV. The spinal cord arteries in the rat. Acta Radiologica **17**(4): 385-398.
35. UDDENBERG, N. 1968. Functional organization of long, second order afferents in the dorsal funiculus. Exp. Brain Res. **4**: 377-382.

SPINAL CORD TRANSECTION IN RATS: THE THERAPEUTIC EFFECTS OF DIMETHYL SULFOXIDE AND HYPERBARIC OXYGEN*

John B. Gelderd,† W. P. Fife,‡ D. E. Bowers,¶ S. H. Deschner,†
and D. W. Welch‡

†Department of Anatomy
College of Medicine
‡Department of Biology
College of Science
Texas A&M University
College Station, Texas 77843
¶Section of Anatomy
School of Dental Medicine
Southern Illinois University
Alton, Illinois 62014

INTRODUCTION

Experimental spinal cord injury in mammals, induced either by contusion or transection, typically results in secondary destruction of neuropil adjacent to the injury. This phenomenon was first described by Ramón y Cajal[1] in the early part of this century and subsequently reported by others.[2-6] Following the initial injury, necrosing neuropil adjacent to the injury is gradually replaced by small cysts that coalesce to form large fluid-filled cavitations immediately rostral and caudal to the injury site. In the rat, these cavitations can eventually occupy over 90% of the cross-sectional area of the spinal cord adjacent to the lesion.[7] Since spinal cord cavitations present an incompatible biological environment for regenerating nerve fibers, any neural regeneration that may occur is forced to the periphery of the spinal cord where, in the case of spinal cord transection, the collagenous scar is extensive. Thus, cavitation formation appears to be a major factor in the abortive regeneration and permanent paralysis typically seen following mammalian spinal cord injury. Although a variety of factors may be involved in the ultimate destruction of neuropil surrounding a spinal cord injury, evidence indicates that there is a severe compromise of regional spinal cord microvasculature following contusion, compression, or transection injuries.[8-11] Lack of regional blood flow results in ischemia, hypoxia, and eventual neuronal death.

Previous data from a variety of investigators indicate that hyperbaric oxygen (HBO) therapy can be effective in reducing the debilitating effects of spinal cord injury both in humans[12-15] and experimental animals,[16-18] presumably by increasing oxygen levels in ischemic neuropil adjacent to a lesion. It has also been reported that dimethyl sulfoxide (DMSO) treatments have therapeutic value following experimental brain injuries or spinal cord contusions.[19-27] Investigators have reported that DMSO protected axons and their myelin sheaths,[11-28] reduced edema,[19,21] increased blood flow,[11,29] and accelerated return of function.[11,21,23] Although many of the animals in the above studies underwent behavioral testing, histological data from the lesion site in the spinal cord studies were derived from

*Supported by a grant from Paralysis Cure Research Foundation.

0077-8923/83/0411-0218 $01.75/0 © 1983, NYAS

short term animals. Thus, the purpose of the following series of experiments was to critically evaluate histological and behavioral effects of HBO and DMSO therapy in spinal cord injured rats following extended post-lesion recovery periods.

MATERIAL AND METHODS

Surgery

Adult, Long-Evans Hooded rats were used in all groups. Under chloral hydrate anesthesia (5 mg/kg), a midline dorsal incision was made in the mid-thoracic region and the dorsal musculature dissected free of the vertebral column. Following laminectomy, spinal cords were transected with a #12 scapel either at the T5 or T8 vertebral level. To ensure complete transections, the scalpel was passed through the transection site four times. Following a saline rinse and establishment of hemostasis with Gelfoam, the completeness of the transection was further verified with the aid of an Olympus MTX operating microscope. The musculature and skin were then sutured shut in layers.

Postoperative Care

Immediately after surgery, all animals received a 0.1 ml intramuscular injection of a broad spectrum antibiotic (Combiotic) in the hip. In addition, the hindquarters of all operated animals were dipped in 1% picric acid to retard autocannibalism. For two weeks following surgery, the urinary bladders of all operated animals were manually expressed every twelve hours and each animal received daily oral administration of nitrofurantoin to prevent urinary bladder infection. For the remainder of the postoperative periods, all animals were checked daily for urine retention and cleanliness.

Treatment Schedules

Following surgery, animals were separated into groups. With the exception of the transected control group (Group I), treatment began within fifteen minutes following surgery.

Group I. *Transected Controls* (N = 34). These animals received only normal postoperative care as described above.

Group II. *HBO Treatments* (N = 10). Animals were placed in a hyperbaric chamber and the pressure increased to 2.82 atmospheres absolute, which is equivalent to the pressure encountered at a depth of 60 feet of seawater. Chamber air was then replaced by a mixture of 80% oxygen (O_2) and 20% nitrogen (N) for twenty minutes, then switched back to air for five minutes. The transition time between the oxygen-nitrogen mixture and air was approximately 1 minute. This cycle (20 minutes O_2-N, 5 minutes air) was repeated until the animals were exposed to enriched levels of oxygen for a total of 90 minutes. Animals were then switched back to air and chamber pressure was reduced to normal atmospheric levels. This treatment regimen was repeated for 47–54 consecutive days. To ensure consistency of treatment parameters, chamber temperature was maintained below 26°C and a carbon dioxide (CO_2) scrubber maintained CO_2 levels at less than 0.03%.

Group III. HBO Treatments (N = 24). This group of animals received the identical HBO treatments given animals in Group II, except half of this group received treatments for fifteen consecutive days and the other half for thirty consecutive days.

Group IV. HBO Treatments (N = 24). Twelve of these animals received HBO treatments as described in Group II, except the treatment pressure was increased to 3.73 atmospheres for fifteen consecutive days. The other twelve animals received HBO treatments at 3.73 atmospheres for thirty consecutive days.

Group V. DMSO (N = 10). Animals received subcutaneous injections of DMSO over the lesion every 12 hours for ten consecutive days. All injections consisted of a 50% solution of DMSO in normal saline with a dosage schedule as follows: 2 g/kg every 12 hours for two days; 1 g/kg every 12 hours for days 3 through 10.

Group VI. HBO + DMSO (N = 10). This group received the combined treatments as described for Groups II and V.

Group VII. DMSO (N = 15). Animals received a 0.5 ml subcutaneous injection of 20% DMSO in phosphate buffer (pH 8.0) over the lesion site every 12 hours for fifteen consecutive days.

Gruop VIII. DMSO/Trypsin (N = 15). This group received the identical treatments given Group VII with the addition of 0.4 mg trypsin included in each injection medium.

Group IX. DMSO/Trypsin/HBO (N = 15). These animals received the identical treatments given to Group VIII in addition to daily HBO treatments for fifteen consecutive days as described for Group II.

Behavior

Following surgery, all animals were checked daily for return of coordinated hindlimb movements. In addition, systematic behavioral testing was accomplished either on a weekly or monthly basis, depending upon the length of the postoperative period. Motor function was tested by placing individual animals on a flat surface and carefully observing them for coordinated hindlimb movements that coincided with simultaneous movements of the forelimbs. Nociceptive pathways and hindlimb reflexes were tested by pinching both hind feet and tails.

Sacrifice Schedule and Histological Procedures

All animals were killed by intracardiac perfusion with fixatives after postoperative survival periods ranging from 60–200 days. Animals were perfused with either 10% buffered formalin for light microscopy or 3% glutaraldehyde and 4% paraformaldehyde in a 0.01 M phosphate-sucrose buffer for transmission and scanning electron microscopy. In the animals prepared for light microscopy, a 2-cm section of spinal cord containing the lesion site was removed from each animal and stored in 10% buffered formalin for a minimum of 30 days. Following paraffin embedding, longitudinal serial sections were cut at 12 microns with a rotary microtome and mounted on slides. Sections were stained using the Bodian Silver technique[30] for nerve fibers and Gomori's trichrome technique[31] for connective tissue elements. In animals perfused for transmission electron microscopy, a 1-cm section of spinal cord containing the lesion was removed and cut into 4 cross-sectional blocks. Tissue blocks were postfixed in 1% osmium tetroxide, dehydrated and embedded in an epoxy-resin mixture. Thick sections (1 µm) were stained in 1% toluidine blue for orientation. Thin sections for electron micros- copy were stained with lead citrate and uranyl acetate. For scanning electron microscopy, 0.5-cm sections of tissue were cut either in midsagittal section or cross section, dehydrated in ethanol, followed by immersion in acetone. Tissue was transferred from acetone to a Denton DCP-1 critical-point dryer. Dried specimens were mounted on aluminum stubs and sputter-coated with gold palladium in a Hummer II sputter coater.

RESULTS

Histology

Group I (Controls)

At the light microscopic level, spinal cords from control animals typically revealed a relatively dense collagenous scar at the transection site, which was bounded rostrally and caudally by large, fluid-filled cavitations (FIGURE 1A). The scar usually contained clusters of ependymal cells along the rostral and caudal edges. Glial cells and fibroblasts were abundant within the scar with collagen fibrils typically arranged transverse to the long axis of the spinal cord. A few nerve fibers were seen within the scar. At the center of the scar, nerve fibers were usually seen as single entities or small fascicles. Toward the periphery of the scar, where the collagen was more dense, nerve fibers appeared as tightly packed fascicles. Electron microscopy of the scar revealed that most nerve fibers were myelinated, although occasional unmyelinated axons were seen (FIGURE 1B). Myelinated axons within the scar were predominantly wrapped by Schwann cells, which were surrounded by a basal lamina. A small rim of neuropil was usually seen adjacent to the lesion immediately deep to the meninges. Nerve fibers were routinely observed within this preserved rim of neuropil but few nerve fibers penetrated the scar.

Groups II, III, IV (HBO Treatments)

Although there was some variability in the size of the cavitation within and between HBO groups, HBO animals routinely revealed less cavitation formation than untreated control animals (FIGURE 2A). With the preservation of neuropil adjacent to the lesion, viable neurons were commonly seen adjacent to the scar (FIGURE 4B). Although dilatation and disruption of the central canal were also routinely seen in HBO animals, in most cases the disruption was not as severe. In contrast to the scar seen in control animals, HBO animals typically exhibited well-vascularized scars containing densely packed collagen fibers (FIGURE 2A,B), In addition, there was also an increase in the rostro-caudal extent of the scar. At the light microscopic level, numerous axons were seen in the preserved neuropil adjacent to the scar. Those axons that entered the scar were predominantly

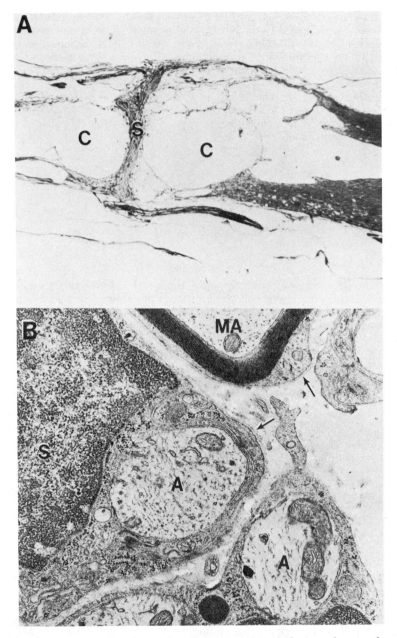

FIGURE 1. Transected control animals. A: low-power view of a horizontal section through the lesion site at 90 days postlesion. The typical large cavitations (C) can be seen both rostral and caudal to the collagenous scar (S) (Bodian stain ×8). B: electron micrograph of the scar, showing a small fascicle of unmyelinated .(A) and myelinated (MA) axons, which are surrounded by Schwann cell cytoplasm and its associated basement membrane (arrows). The nucleus (N) of a nearby Schwann cell can also be seen (×24,600). Figure reduction of 70%.

arranged as tightly packed fascicles (FIGURE 3B). As in control animals, some nerve fibers turned to course along the edge of the scar. However, many others were seen penetrating the scar parallel to the long axis of the spinal cord (FIGURE 2C). Electron microscopy of the scar area also revealed many tightly packed fascicles containing myelinated, unmyelinated, and naked axons (FIGURE 3C).

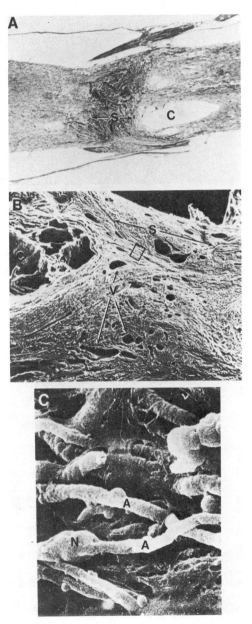

FIGURE 2. HBO-treated animals (Groups II–IV). A: low-power view of a horizontal section through the lesion site, showing an increase in the collagenous density and rostro-caudal extent (arrows) of scar (S) as compared to control animals. Neuropil adjacent to the lesion is also preserved, resulting in reduction of cavitation (C) formation (Gomori's trichrome ×6). B: low-power scanning electron micrograph of a sagittal section through the lesion site, showing the typical scar (S) penetrated by a number of blood vessels (V). Some cavitations (C) are present rostral to the lesion. However, considerable preserved neuropil can be seen both surrounding these cavitations and in the area immediately caudal to the scar (×16). C: high-power view of the area within box in C, showing myelinated axons (A) traversing the lesion. The large fusiform swelling (N) on one of the axons is presumably the nucleus of a Schwann cell (×3,400). Figure reduction of 70%.

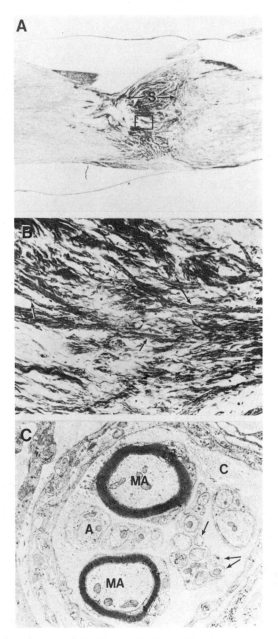

FIGURE 3. HBO-treated animals (Groups II–IV). A: low-power horizontal view of the lesion area showing the dense collagenous scar (S), and preserved neuropil adjacent to the lesion (Bodian stain ×6). B: high-power view of area in the box in A, showing tightly packed fascicles of axons (arrows) growing through the lesion site (×580). C: electron micrograph of a typical fascicle of axons found within the scar of HBO animals, showing myelinated (MA), unmyelinated (A), and naked axons (arrows) surrounded by collagen fibrils (C) (×12,100). Figure reduction of 70%.

Group V (50% DMSO in Saline)

The lesion areas in these animals closely resembled those of animals treated with HBO (Groups II, III, and IV) with the exception of the scar. Usually the scar appeared as a relatively loose cellular matrix containing randomly arranged collagen fibers. The rostro-caudal extent and vascularity of the scar was similar to HBO animals (FIGURE 4A). In some animals the central canal became considerably dilated, but remained intact to end at the rostral and caudal surfaces of the scar as large terminal dilatations (FIGURE 4A). Nerve fibers were seen routinely penetrating the loose scar. In contrast to HBO animals, nerve fibers that entered the scar exhibited random orientation within the scar. Typically, nerve fibers were seen both as loosely arranged fascicles and single entities. As in the HBO animals, many myelinated, unmyelinated, and naked nerve fibers were routinely seen within the scar (FIGURE 4C). Neurons were also consistently seen in the preserved neuropil adjacent to the lesion (FIGURE 4B).

Group VI (HBO + DMSO)

Qualitatively, the lesion area in this group appeared similar to the DMSO groups (Group V). Numerous myelinated, unmyelinated, and naked nerve fibers were seen growing into the loose, well-vascularized scar from the preserved neuropil at both rostral and caudal stumps of spinal cord. As with other groups that showed preserved neuropil adjacent to the lesion, viable neurons were routinely observed in the vicinity of the scar.

Groups VII, VIII, and IX (20% DMSO in PO$_4$ Buffer; DMSO/Trypsin; DMSO/Trypsin/HBO)

With the exception of the animals in Group IX, the spinal cord at the lesion site in these groups typically resembled the lesion area of untreated control animals. However, animals in Group IX occasionally showed some sparing of neuropil adjacent to the lesion in addition to an increase in the rostro-caudal diameter and collagenous density of the scar, typical of HBO-treated animals.

Behavior

A summary of the behavioral results is presented in TABLE 1. Approximately 88% of all operated animals survived the entire postoperative period designated for each group. All operated animals exhibited typical spinal shock (flaccid paralysis, hypotonus, hyporeflexia) for 3–10 days following surgery. During the remainder of the postoperative period, some animals developed spastic paraplegia consisting of hyperreflexia, muscle fasciculations, spastic circumduction of hindlimbs, and clonus. None of the animals that developed spastic paraplegia exhibited persistent coordinated hindlimb movements, hindlimb weight-bearing ability, or sensory return caudal to the lesion. Locomotion was achieved by the forelimbs while dragging the caudal portion of the body. The hindlimbs were typically extended behind the animals with the plantar surfaces of the feet facing upwards and the digits flexed.

Animals that eventually showed return of hindlimb function usually began

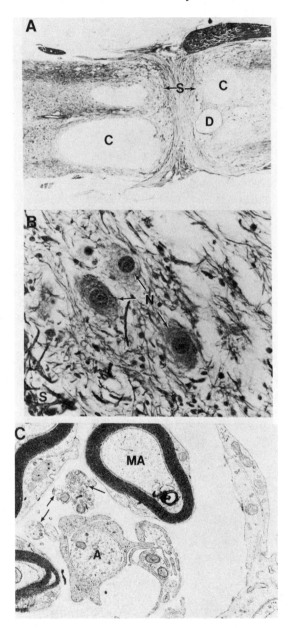

FIGURE 4. DMSO-treated animals (Group V). A: low-power horizontal view of lesion site showing a relatively loose scar (S), reduced cavitation formation (C) as compared to controls, and a terminal dilatation (D) of the central canal. Preservation of the central canal was routinely seen in both DMSO and HBO animals (Gomori's trichrome ×6). B: high-power view of neurons (N) routinely found in preserved neuropil adjacent to the scar (S). This phenomenon was also seen in HBO animals. C: loose fascicle of nerve fibers routinely found within the scar showing myelinated (MA), unmyelinated (A), and naked axons (arrows) (×12,100). Figure reduction of 70%.

TABLE 1

SUMMARY OF BEHAVIORAL RESULTS

Treatment Groups	Number of Animals Showing Strong Coordinated Hindlimb Movements (Number of Animals/Group)	Number of Animals Showing Hindlimb Weight-Bearing Ability	Number of Animals Squealing and Biting in Response to Nociceptive Stimuli Applied Caudal to the Lesion
I Transected controls	1 (34)		
II HBO (2.82 atmos. for 47–54 days)*	3 (10)	1¶	
III {HBO (2.82 atmos. for 15 days)†	2 (9)		
{HBO (2.82 atmos. for 30 days)	2 (9)		
IV {HBO (3.73 atmos for 15 days)‡	3 (9)	1¶	
{HBO (3.73 atmos. for 30 days)‡	3 (8)	1¶	
V DMSO (50% soln. in saline)	2 (9)	2¶	
VI HBO + DMSO*	6 (10)	2¶	2¶
VII DMSO (20% in phosphate buffer; pH 8.0)‡	0 (13)		
VIII DMSO/trypsin‡	0 (13)		
IX DMSO/trypsin/HBO‡	0 (14)		

*Adult, male rats, sacrificed 60–70 days postlesion.
†Adult, female rats, sacrificed 90–100 days postlesion.
‡Adult, female rats, sacrificed 180–200 days postlesion.
¶These animals are derived from groups showing strong coordinated hindlimb movements. In Group VI, the same animals that showed weight-bearing ability also showed sensory return.

exhibiting coordinated hindlimb movements 35–45 days postlesion. HBO animals typically gained maximum return of function 50–60 days postlesion and retained that level through the remainder of a given postoperative period. A similar recovery period was recorded for animals showing return of hindlimb function following combined HBO/DMSO treatments (Group VI). However, DMSO-treated animals (Group V) that recovered some hindlimb function typically did not exhibit coordinated hindlimb movements until 70–80 days postlesion. Two animals in Group VI that attained weight-bearing ability and sensory return were also observed standing on their hind legs in their cages, using their front legs to balance themselves against the cage wall.

Although some animals from Groups II–VI exhibited coordinated alternating hindlimb movements and weight-bearing ability, none of the animals regained normal hindlimb function. The caudal portion of their bodies appeared unstable and the animals frequently lost their balance, falling to the side. However, they were able to right themselves to stand again.

Comparison of Histological and Behavioral Data

All animals that exhibited return of hindlimb function also revealed reduction of spinal cord cavitations and large numbers of fibers traversing the scar. However, not all animals that showed cavitation reduction regained use of their hindlimbs. FIGURE 5A shows the spinal cord of an animal treated with DMSO (Group V) that did not show return of function. Although this animal revealed cavitation reduction and a relatively loose collagenous scar typical of DMSO-treated animals, careful perusal of the lesion at the light microscopic level revealed few nerve fibers penetrating the scar. Nerve fibers found within the scar were loosely arranged, randomly oriented, and appeared to cease their growth shortly after penetrating the scar (FIGURE 5B). Similar findings were also observed in groups treated with HBO or combined HBO/DMSO. However, in HBO-treated animals, nerve fibers that penetrated the dense scar were typically seen as small, tightly packed fascicles.

DISCUSSION

A number of hypotheses have been offered to explain the etiology of spinal cord cavitations. Kao[6,32–36] and his associates suggest that cavitations form due to the release of lysosomal enzymes from severed axons or from axon tips that rupture while attempting to grow. Release of lysosomal enzymes into the surrounding neuropil presumably cause neural destruction and subsequent cavitation formation. Another theory by Osterholm and his associates[8] proposes that toxic levels of norepinephrine accumulate in spinal cord neuropil following injury, causing destruction of the spinal cord gray matter with the concomitant formation of spinal cord cavitations. Feringa and his associates[37–39] suggest that cavitation formation is caused by an autoimmune reaction to CNS antigens released following injury. Free radical formation[40] may also be involved in producing spinal cord cavitation. Spinal cord injury may produce superoxide and/or hydroxyl free radicals in such numbers that available enzymatic activity cannot remove them, thus resulting in destruction of neuropil.

De la Torre[10,11] has recently offered a detailed theory to explain the events that lead to cavitation formation following spinal cord injury. Briefly stated, he

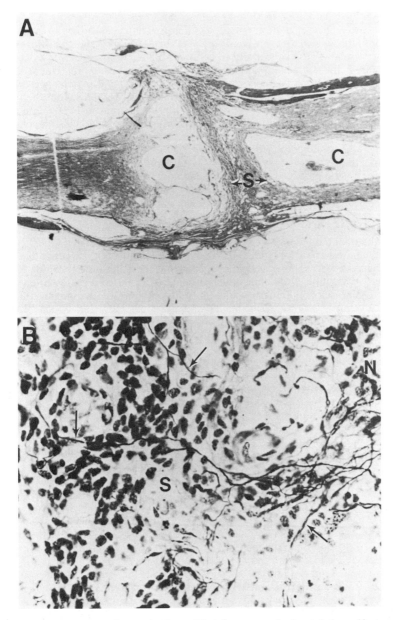

FIGURE 5. DMSO-treated animals (Group V). A: low-power horizontal view of lesion site showing typical scar (S) and reduction of cavitation (C) formation (Bodian stain ×8). B: high-power view of interface between neuropil (N) and scar (S) of animal in A. A few nerve fibers (arrows) penetrate the scar from the adjacent neuropil. After entering the scar, the nerve fibers have a random orientation and appear to penetrate only a short distance into the scar, which is occupied by many leukocytes. Figure reduction of 70%.

suggests that the source of spinal cord cavitation resides in the compromise of spinal cord microvasculature resulting in decreased oxygen supply to spinal cord neuropil, thus reducing mitochondrial oxidative phosphorylation, causing reduction of cellular ATP levels. Reduced cellular ATP levels are followed by calcium production and the eventual activation of phospholipases that leads to the production of substances known to promote vasospasm and platelet aggregation. The above events culminate in extensive platelet aggregation within the microvasculature, thereby further compromising the blood supply to adjacent neuropil, causing cell death. De la Torre's theory seems compelling in light of data that have been published concerning the effects of HBO treatments in humans and animals with various spinal cord or head injuries.[12-18] In view of the fact that administration of HBO increases oxygen levels in rat spinal cord,[41,42] it is reasonable to assume that the positive results seen following HBO therapy are partially due to increased oxygen concentrations in the ischemic neuropil adjacent to the lesion. Increased levels of oxygen may reverse tissue ischemia and prevent destruction of the neuropil until revascularization can occur.

A possible hindrance to the effectiveness of HBO therapy following experimental spinal cord injury lies in the ability of HBO to increase the collagenous density and rostro-caudal extent of the scar.[43-45] It should also be noted that HBO can cause oxygen toxicity at high pressures and long duration, resulting in lung damage, CNS injury, seizures, and eventual death.[41,42] Conversely, if oxygen is used within established therapeutic limits, no problems of lung damage or CNS toxicity occur.[14,46] Moreover, it has been shown that HBO can be an effective, noninvasive method capable of preserving adjacent neuropil and reducing the debilitating effects of spinal cord injury.[12-18,47,48]

Previous data indicate that DMSO is well suited as a therapeutic agent to preserve neuropil following CNS injury, since it protects axons and their myelin sheaths,[25,28] reduces tissue edema and inflammation,[10,22] increases blood flow through its properties as an anticoagulant, hemodilutant, and vasodilator,[25,29] and accelerates return of function.[20,23,25,27] Moreover, DMSO has been shown to stabilize lysosomal membranes[49] and is an effective scavenger of free radicals.[50] Since scar density may also be a factor that can hinder nerve fiber growth through the lesion, DMSO may act to promote nerve fiber regeneration by reducing the collagenous density of the scar through its abilities to inhibit fibroblast proliferation[51] and block the synthesis and metabolism of collagen.[52]

Despite an earlier report[53] that described regeneration and return of function in trypsin-treated rats, and another report[54] that described enhanced enzymatic activity when DMSO was combined with trypsin as described for Groups VIII and IX, we were unable to determine any therapeutic effects following these treatment regimens. Previous data from our laboratory[55] and published reports by others[56,57] indicate that enzyme therapy may be of questionable value following experimental spinal cord injury.

The appearance of naked axons in the scars of animals at 90-100 days postlesion is particularly significant because it indicates continual axonal growth. Since growth of axons is typically aborted within a few days following spinal cord transection, the presence of naked axons at 90-100 days postlesion suggests that HBO and DMSO treatments can prolong the regenerative process for extended periods following injury.

Although spinal cord cavitation should be viewed as an important factor preventing neural regeneration and return of function in mammals, other factors must be considered such as the role of glial and ependymal cells in the regenerative process, the establishment of functional synapses by axons growing through the injury site to areas rostral and caudal to the lesion, the enhancement of the growth potential of central nervous system axons, and the knowledge of which spinal cord nerve tracts are mandatory for meaningful, volitional return of function. The causative factors and underlying mechanisms leading to the formation of spinal cord cavitations and related subsequent pathophysiology are complex. However, the results of our recent studies, which have been summarized in this text, lend support to the theory of ischemia as the fundamental cause of spinal cord cavitation. However, further careful studies, utilizing a variety of anatomical and physiological techniques, are required to enhance our knowledge of the pathophysiological processes that result in spinal cord cavitation. Such studies might eventually lead to an effective treatment for the debilitating permanent effects of spinal cord injury.

ACKNOWLEDGMENTS

The authors give special thanks to the personnel at the Texas A&M Hyperbaric Physiology Laboratory for their expertise and assistance, Ms. Nadine Stuth for her excellent histological techniques, and Ms. Janet Natowitz for her patience and typing skills.

REFERENCES

1. RAMON Y CAJAL, S. 1928. Degeneration and Regeneration of the Nervous Systems. Vols. 1 and 2. Oxford University Press. London.
2. GUTH, L. 1975. History of central nervous system regeneration research. Exp. Neurol. **48**(3, Pt. 2): 3–15.
3. GUTH, L. & W. F. WINDLE. 1970. The enigma of central nervous regeneration. Exp. Neurol. Suppl. **5**: 1–43.
4. GUTH, L. & W. F. WINDLE. 1973. Physiological, molecular, and genetic aspects of central nervous regeneration. Exp. Neurol. **39**: iii–xvi.
5. WINDLE, W. F. 1980. The Spinal Cord and Its Reaction to Traumatic Injury. Marcel Dekker. New York.
6. KAO, C. C. , R. P. BUNGE & P. J. REIER, Eds. 1983. Spinal Cord Reconstruction. Raven Press. New York.
7. GELDERD, J. B., M. A. MATTHEWS, M. F. ST. ONGE & C. L. FACIANE. 1980. Qualitative and quantitative effects of ACTH, Piromen, Cytoxan and isobutyl-2-cyanoacrilate treatments following spinal cord transection in rats. Acta Neurobiol. Exp. (Warsz.). **40**: 489–500.
8. OSTERHOLM, J. L. 1978. The Pathophysiology of Spinal Cord Trauma. Charles C. Thomas. Springfield, Ill.
9. GOLDSMITH, H. S., E. STEWARD, W. F. CHEN & S. DUCKETT. 1983. Application of intact omentum to the normal & traumatized spinal cord. *In* Spinal Cord Reconstruction. C. C. Kao, R. P. Bunge, & P. J. Reier, Eds.: 235–244. Raven Press. New York.
10. DE LA TORRE, J. C. 1980. Chemotherapy of spinal cord trauma. *In* The Spinal Cord and its Reaction to Traumatic Injury. W. Windle, Ed.: 291–310. Marcel Dekker. New York.
11. DE LA TORRE, J. C. 1981. Spinal cord injury: Review of basic and applied research. Spine **6**: 315–355.
12. HARTZOG, J. T., R. G. FISHER & C. SNOW. 1969. Spinal cord trauma: Effect of hyperbaric oxygen therapy. Proc. Ann. Clin. Spinal Cord Inj. Cong. **17**: 70.
13. HOLBACH, K. H., H. WASSMANN & D. LINKE. 1977. The use of hyperbaric oxygenation in the treatment of spinal cord lesions. Exp. Neurol. **16**: 213–221.
14. JONES, R. F., I. P. UNSWORTH & J. E. MARASSZEKY. 1978. Hyperbaric oxygen and acute spinal cord injuries in humans. Med. J. Aust. **2**: 573–575.

15. LINKE, D., K. H. HOLBACH, H. WASSMANN & K. L. HOHELUCHTER. 1975. Electromyographic surveillance of hyperbaric oxygenation treatment (HO) of spinal lesions. *In* Forensic Problems in Neurosurgery. W. Klug, M. Brock, M. Klinger & O. Spoerri, Eds.: 268-271. Springer-Verlag. New York.

16. KELLY, D. L., JR. K. R. L. LASSITER, A. VONGSWIVERT & J. M. SMITH. 1972. Effects of hyperbaric oxygenation and tissue oxygen studies in experimental paraplegia. J. Neurosurg. **36:** 425-429.

17. YEO, J. D., B. MCKENZIE, B. HARDWOOD & A. KIDMAN. 1976. Treatment of paraplegic sheep with hyperbaric oxygen. Med. J. Aust. **1:** 538-540.

18. YEO, J. D., S. STABBACK & B. MCKENZIE. 1977. A study of the effects of hyperbaric oxygen on the experimental spinal cord injury. Med. J. Aust. **2:** 145-147.

19. BROWN, F. D., L. M. JOHNS & S. MULLAN. 1980. Dimethyl sulfoxide in experimental brain injury, with comparison to mannitol. J. Neurosurg. **53:** 58-62.

20. DE LA TORRE, J. C., K. KAJIHARA, D. W. ROWED, J. M. KAWANAGA & J. F. MULLAN. 1972. Modification of experimental head and spinal cord injuries using dimethyl sulfoxide. Trans. Amer. Neurol. Assoc. **97:** 203-233.

21. DE LA TORRE, J. D., C. M. JOHNSON, L. H. HARRIS, K. KAJIHARA & S. MULLAN. 1974. Monoamine changes in experimental head and spinal cord trauma: Failure to confirm previous observations. Surg. Neurol. **2:** 5.

22. DE LA TORRE, J. D., C. M. JOHNSON, D. J. GOODE & S. MULLAN. 1975. Pharmacologic treatment and evaluation of permanent experimental spinal cord trauma. Neurology **25:** 508-514.

23. DE LA TORRE, J. C., H. M. KAWANAGA, D. W. ROWED, C. M. JOHNSON, D. L. GOODE, K. KAJIHARA & S. MULLAN. 1975. Dimethyl sulfoxide in central nervous system trauma. Ann. N.Y. Acad. Sci. **243:** 362-389.

24. DE LA TORRE, J. C. & J. W. SURGEON. 1976. Dexamethasone and DMSO in experimental transorbital infarction. Stroke **7**(6): 577-583.

25. DE LA TORRE, J. C., J. W. SURGEON, P. K. HILL & T. KHAN. 1977. DMSO in the treatment of brain infarction: Basic considerations. *In* Arterial Air Embolism and Acute Stroke. J. M. Hallenbeck & L. Greenbaum, Eds.: 138. Undersea Med. Soc. Bethesda, Md.

26. KAJIHARA, K., H. KAWANAGA, J. C. DE LA TORRE & S. MULLAN. 1973. Dimethyl sulfoxide in the treatment of experimental acute spinal cord injury. Surg. Neurol. **1:** 16-22.

27. MCCALLUM, J. E. & M. H. BENNETT. 1976. DMSO as a therapeutic agent in chronic spinal cord compression. Program. Abstr. 26th Ann. Mtg. Cong. of Neurol. Surg. p. 166. New Orleans.

28. LIM, R. & S. MULLAN. 1975. Protective effect of dimethyl sulfoxide on brain cells against sonic stress. Ann. N.Y. Acad. Sc. **243:** 358-361.

29. MEAD, C. O., R. A. MOODY, S. RUAMSUKI & S. MULLAN. 1970. Effect of isovalemic hemodilution of cerebral blood flow following experimental head injury. J. Neurosurg. **32:** 40-50.

30. BODIAN, D. 1936. A new method for staining nerve fibers and nerve endings in mounted paraffin sections. Anat. Rec. **65:** 89-97.

31. GOMORI, G. 1950. A rapid one step trichrome stain. Am. J. Clin. Pathol. **20:** 661-664.

32. KAO, C. C. & L. W. CHANG. 1977. The mechanism of spinal cord cavitation following spinal cord transection. I. A correlated histochemical study. J. Neurosurg. **46:** 197-209.

33. KAO, C. C., L. W. CHANG & J. M. B. BLOODWORTH. 1977. The mechanism of spinal cord cavitation following spinal cord transection. II. Electron microscopic observations. J. Neurosurg. **40:** 745-756.

34. KAO, C. C., L. W. CHANG & J. M. B. BLOODWORTH. 1977. The mechanism of spinal cord cavitation following spinal cord transection. III. Delayed grafting with and without spinal cord retransection. J. Neurosurg. **46:** 757-766.

35. KAO, C. C., L. W. CHANG & J. M. B. BLOODWORTH. 1977. Axonal regeneration across transected mammalian spinal cords: An electron microscopic study of delayed microsurgical nerve grafting Exp. Neurol. **54:** 591-615.

36. KAO, C. C. 1980. Spinal cord cavitation after injury. *In* The Spinal Cord and its Reaction to Traumatic Injury. W. F. Windle, Ed.: 249-270. Marcel Dekker. New York.

37. FERINGA, E. R., J. S. WENDT & R. D. JOHNSON. 1974. Immunosuppressive treatment to enhance spinal cord regeneration in rats. Neurology (Minneapolis) **24**: 287–293.
38. FERINGA, E. R., R. D. JOHNSON & J. S. WENDT. 1975. Spinal cord regeneration in rats after immunosuppressive treatment. Arch. Neurol. **22**: 676–683.
39. FERINGA, E. R., W. K. KINNIN & A. G. BRITTEN. 1976. Recovery in rats after spinal cord injury. Neurology (Minneapolis) **26**: 839–843.
40. MICHELSON, A. M., J. M. McCORD & I. FRIDOVITCH, Eds. 1977. Superoxide and Superoxide Dismutases. Academic Press. New York.
41. OGILVIE, R. W. & J. D. BALENTINE. 1973. Oxygen tensions in the deep gray matter of rats exposed to hyperbaric oxygen. Adv. Exp. Med. Biol. **37**: 299–304.
42. OGILVIE, R. W. & J. D. BALENTINE. 1975. Oxygen tension in spinal cord gray matter during exposure to hyperbaric oxygen. J. Neurosurg. **43**: 156–161.
43. CLEMENTE, C. D. 1955. Structural regeneration in the mammalian central nervous system and the role of neuroglia and connective tissue. *In* Regeneration in the Central Nervous System. W. F. Windle, Ed.: 147–161. Charles C. Thomas. Springfield, Ill.
44. HUNT, T. K., J. NUNIKOSKI, B. H. ZEDERFELDT & I. A. SILVER, 1977. Oxygen in wound healing enhancement; cellular effects of oxygen. *In* Hyperbaric Oxygen Therapy. J. C. Davis & T. K. Hunt, Eds. Undersea Med. Soc. Bethesda, Md.
45. JUVA, K., D. J. PROCKOP, G. W. COOPER & J. W. LASH. 1966. Hydroxylation of proline and the intracellular accumulation of a polypeptide precursor of collagen. Science **152**: 92.
46. HART, G. B. 1976. Indications and contraindications for hyperbaric oxygen therapy. J. Am. Med. Assoc. **236**: 1892.
47. GELDERD, J. B., D. W. WELCH, W. P. FIFE & D. E. BOWERS, JR. 1980. Therapeutic effects of hyperbaric oxygen and dimethyl sulfoxide following spinal cord transection in rats. Undersea Biomed. Res. **7**: 305–320.
48. GELDERD, J. 1983. Hyperbaric oxygen and dimethyl sulfoxide therapy following spinal cord injury. *In* Spinal Cord Reconstruction. C. C. Kao, R. P. Bunge & P. J. Reier, Eds. Raven Press. New York.
49. WEISSMAN, G., G. SESSA & V. BEVANS. 1967. Effect of DMSO on the stabilization of lysosomes by cortisone and chloroquine *in vitro*. Ann. N.Y. Acad. Sci. **141**: 326–332.
50. EDERBAUM, A. I., E. DICKER, E. RUBIN & G. COHEN. 1977. The effect of dimethyl sulfoxide and other hydroxyl radical scavengers on the oxidation of ethanol by rat liver microscomes. Biochem. Biophys. Res. Commun. **78**(4): 1254–1262.
51. BERLINER, D. L. 1967. The influence of dimethyl sulfoxide on fibroblastic proliferation. Ann. N.Y. Acad. Sci. **141**: 159–164.
52. GRIES, G. 1971. Some effects of DMSO on connective tissue. *In* Dimethyl Sulfoxide. S. W. Jacob, E. E. Rosenbaum & D. C. Wood, Eds.: 325–336. Marcel Dekker. New York.
53. MATINIAN, L. A. & A. S. ANDREASIAN. 1976. Enzyme Therapy in Organic Lesions of the Spinal Cord. E. Tanasescu, Transl. Brain Information Service. University of California. Los Angeles, Calif.
54. RAMMLER, D. H. 1971. Use of DMSO in enzyme-catalyzed reactions. *In* Dimethyl Sulfoxide. S. W. Jacob, E. E. Rosenbaum & D. C. Wood, Eds. Marcel Dekker. New York.
55. GELDERD, J. B. & M. F. ST. ONGE. 1977. The effect of L-thyroxine and enzyme treatments following spinal cord transection in rats: A light microscopic study. Anat. Rec. **187**: 586.
56. GUTH, L., E. ALBUQUERQUE, S. S. DESPHANDE, C. P. BARRETT, E. J. DONATI & J. E. WARNICK. 1980. Ineffectiveness of enzyme therapy on regeneration in the transected spinal cord of the rat. J. Neurosurg. **52**: 73–86.
57. FERINGA, E. R., T. F. KOWALSKI, H. L. VAHLSING & R. A. FRYE. 1979. Enzyme treatment of spinal cord transected rats. Ann. Neurol. **2**: 203–206.

ANTIPLATELET EFFECT OF DIMETHYL SULFOXIDE, BARBITURATES, AND METHYL PREDNISOLONE

Manuel Dujovny, Rodney Rozario, Nir Kossovsky,*
Fernando G. Diaz, and Ricardo Segal†

Department of Neurological Surgery
Henry Ford Hospital
Detroit, Michigan 48202

*University of Chicago
Pritzker School of Medicine
Chicago, Illinois 60637

†Veterans Administration
Medical Center
Pittsburgh, Pennsylvania 15240

INTRODUCTION

Despite advances in instrumentation, suture materials, and operative techniques, thrombus formation at the anastomotic site in small vessels remains a major factor that compromises surgical results.[1-3] Adjunctive pharmacological attempts to reduce thrombus formation intraoperatively have been studied, but the effectiveness of these agents remains to be established in microsurgery.[4-7] The present study was undertaken to compare and evaluate the antiplatelet properties of dimethyl sulfoxide (DMSO), pentobarbital, and methyl prednisolone in altering the thrombotic response inflicted by surgical trauma.

METHOD

Sixty Sprague-Dawley rats, weighing between 350 and 500 g, were selected and divided into a control group of 12 animals and an experimental group of 48 animals. The experimental group was further divided into four subgroups (A, B, C, and D) of 12 animals each. The rats were anesthetized with acetopromazine (19 mg/kg i.m.), ketamine hydrochloride (60 mg/kg i.m.), and atropine (0.4 mg subcutaneous).

The ventral side of the neck was shaved, and the carotid arteries were exposed bilaterally by means of microsurgical techniques through a midline incision. In the control group, a Vari-Angle‡ aneurysm clip was applied for 1 hour to the right carotids of 6 animals, while the remaining 6 received a transverse arteriotomy and suture repair. No pharmacological agents were used in the control group. After the clips were removed, blood flow was restored for 20 minutes. Proximal and distal ligatures were then secured, and the carotid arteries were excised under the Zeiss OPMI operating microscope (Carl Zeiss, Inc., New York, N.Y.; Zeiss setting, 25×), opened longitudinally, and gently washed with Ringer's solution. The open arteries were fixed with buffered 2% glutaraldehyde

‡Vari-Angle Aneurysm Clip System (Cat. 20-1152) Codman & Shurtleff, Inc., Randolph, Massachusetts 02368.

0077-8923/83/0411-0234 $01.75/0 © 1983, NYAS

(pH 7.2) for 5 minutes and stored in the same solution for 24 hours. The specimens were then dehydrated by serial passage through 30%, 50%, 75%, and 95% ethanol. Preparation of the specimens for scanning electron microscopy (SEM) included critical-point drying in a vacuum chamber with carbon dioxide for complete dehydration. Each specimen was then mounted on a circular aluminum stub and coated with gold palladium 1 to 4 μm thick. The endothelial surfaces were examined using the AMR (AMR Scanning Electron Microscope manufactured by Advanced Metal Research, 149 Middlesex Turnpike, Burlington, Mass.) SEM at 40 to 16,000×.

Experimental groups A, B, C, and D were subjected to the same surgical procedures as the control group. In addition, group A was treated with DMSO (2 g/kg) infused intravenously for 1 hour, beginning just before the vascular occlusion. Group B was treated with pentobarbital (90 mg/kg i.v.), Group C with thiopental (90 mg/kg i.v.). The animals treated with pentobarbital were intubated and maintained on ventilatory support throughout the experiments. The animals in group D were treated with methyl prednisolone (40 mg/kg i.v.) in an identical fashion as those in group A.

The experimental specimens were prepared as described for the control group. Two criteria were used to evaluate the lesions induced by the aneurysm clip: the degree of endothelial damage and the configuration of the lesion. The degrees of endothelial damage (in ascending order) were endothelial fold realignment, endothelial fold flattening, endothelial layer fracture, exposure of the media, crater formation, and characteristics of thrombus formation. The microscopic appearance of the platelets was also evaluated. The lesion configurations were either oval (corner mirror) or linear (transverse).

We graded the characteristics of the thrombus in the following manner: 0, no thrombus visible in the suture line or over the sutures; +, presence of thrombus over the suture line or over the suture material; + +, thrombus covering the suture line and the suture material and protruding slightly into the lumen of the artery; + + +, thrombus covering the suture line and the suture material, with important protrusion in the lumen. Three of the four authors separately reviewed all photographs, analyzed, and graded them with the scale described above. The chi square test for nominal data was used for statistical analysis, and p value less than .05 was considered significant.

RESULTS

In the control group, all left carotid arteries occluded by the aneurysm clip revealed endothelial flattening, realignment, and fracture with copious thrombus formation. The six control specimens subjected to arteriotomy and suture repair showed heavy deposits of platelet, fibrin, and red blood cell clumps at the arteriotomy site (FIGURE 1). In all specimens from experimental group A (occluded by the aneurysm clip and treated with DMSO) endothelial shredding, flattening, realignment, and fracture with exposure of the subendothelium were seen. However, no thrombus formation was observed. Specimens that had the arteriotomy showed minimal signs of platelet fibrin clumping at the suture line. The platelets appeared spherical with no pseudopod formation. The adjacent endothelium appeared intact (FIGURE 2).

In experimental group B (treated with pentobarbital) platelet fibrin deposits were seen at both the clip and arteriotomy sites. The amount of thrombus formation was greater than that seen in the group treated with DMSO, and the suture line was completely covered by platelet fibrin deposits.

The vessels that were treated with thiopental (group C) showed results that were similar to the pentobarbital group, but to a milder degree. Fibrin deposition was slightly less, and thrombus formation was comparable (FIGURE 3). In experimental group D (treated with methyl prednisolone) abundant platelet fibrin and RBC deposits were seen, similar to those observed in the control group.

Statistical analysis was based on the comparison of two identically designed tests that were blindly rated on a scale of 0 to + + +. The chi square analysis of the

FIGURE 1. Control.

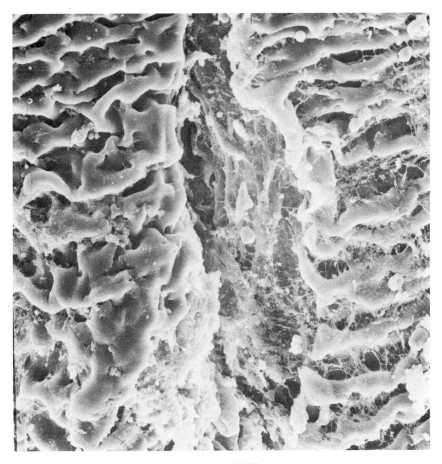

FIGURE 2. DMSO.

damage mediated by the clip shows that the protection offered by DMSO (group A) is significant over all that of other groups with a p < .01. The pentobarbital and thiopental groups are probably the same (p < 1.0), but they are both significantly different from the control group (p < .05).

The chi square analysis of the vascular damage at the arteriotomy site showed that the groups treated with DMSO and thiopental offered significant protection over controls (p < .05). The pentobarbital group, although significantly different from either the DMSO or thiopental group, also offered significant protection over controls (p < .05). Methyl prednisolone specimens did not differ from the control samples in either of the two tests.

DISCUSSION

Though technical expertise remains the most important factor in assuring patency after microvascular anastomosis, the search continues for an ideal

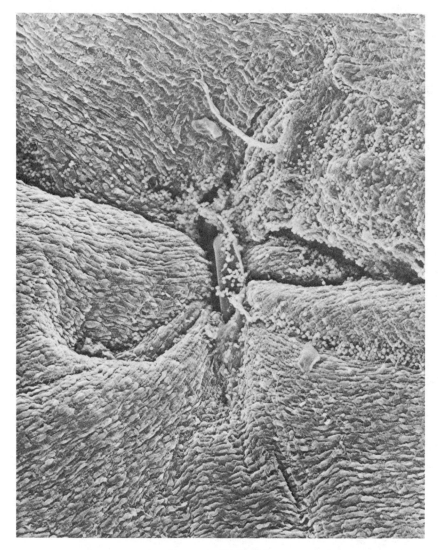

FIGURE 3. Thiopental.

antiplatelet agent that can decrease the initial thrombotic response and, consequently, improve the patency rate.[8-12]

Experimentally, pharmacological agents with known antiplatelet properties have been assessed by various authors (TABLE 1). Some have used the SEM to evaluate thrombus formation at the anastomotic site, and others have reported on the gross observation of patency rates. None of the agents, however, has gained clinical popularity.

DMSO was discovered by Alexander Saytzeff in 1866, but it was only in the 1940s that it became popular as an industrial solvent. In 1961, Herschler noted that odd property of DMSO to enhance plant growth by 15–20%. He also drew attention to its cryopreservative properties and its potential use to store transplantable organs and blood components. Shortly thereafter, Jacob introduced DMSO into medicine for the treatment of burns, frostbite, and arthritis.[13-15] In neurosurgery, DMSO was experimentally shown to be of benefit in the treatment of head and spinal cord trauma and in focal cerebral ischemia and reperfusion.[14,16,17] These encouraging results have led to its trial as an adjunctive mode of therapy in severe cerebrospinal trauma in a few selected medical centers.[18]

DMSO has a simple molecular structure with a molecular weight of 78.13. It can readily penetrate tissue membranes without causing significant damage. This property may be related to its relatively polar nature, its capacity to accept hydrogen bonds, and its small, compact structure.

Physiologically, DMSO has been demonstrated to be a potent diuretic and respiratory stimulant, to decrease oxygen consumption, and to stabilize lysosomal membranes.[19-21] In addition to its ability to rapidly permeate the cell membranes, it possesses the added property of facilitating the transport of several drugs.[22-24]

In 1966, Deutsch[25] showed that DMSO had an antiplatelet effect. *In vitro* experimentation has subsequently shown that DMSO decreases platelet aggregation to various stimuli, such as adenosine diphosphate (ADP), epinephrine, and thrombin. In addition, it has no permanent adverse effect on platelet function.[26,27] Human cryopreserved platelets treated with DMSO and stored for as long as 400 days and subsequently retransfused have been shown to be hemostatically effective.[28-32]

Although the mechanism of action of DMSO is still unknown, various authors have proposed possible sites of action. Holtz and others had suggested that DMSO, acting as a sulfhydryl inhibitor, prevents platelet-to-platelet bonding.[33-35] Panganamala et al.[46] showed that DMSO inhibited arachidonic-acid–induced aggregation and suggested that it acted as an inhibitor of prostaglandin biosynthesis. Wieser[37] demonstrated that DMSO was capable of elevating cyclic AMP by inhibiting phosphodiesterase in a nonplatelet cell system. Investigation is still

TABLE 1

PHARMACOLOGICAL AGENTS USED TO INCREASE PATENCY

Author	Drug	Results
Rosenblum & Sundt[12]	Heparin	Thrombus SEM evaluation
	ASA	No quantitative change in thrombus SEM evaluation
Laha et al.[6]	ASA	Thrombus SEM evaluation
	Dipyridamole	No change from control SEM evaluation
	Prostaglandin D_2	No change from control SEM evaluation
Ketchum et al.[4]	Pluronic F.68	Control = 54.8% Experimental = 86%
Kolar et al.[5]	Acenocumarin	Control = 31% Experimental = 70%
Acland[1]	Magnesium sulfate	Control = 30% Experimental = 90%
Nomoto et al.[7]	Magnesium sulfate	Control = 90% Experimental = 100%

needed to determine whether DMSO exerts its protective effect in cerebral ischemia and reperfusion by an antiplatelet effect or by protecting the endothelium, and thus maintaining its ability to synthesize prostacyclin, a known vasodilator and potent antiaggregant.

Our SEM studies have shown that DMSO significantly decreased platelet fibrin thrombi at the site of endothelial injury. This observation raises the possibility that the beneficial effects noted in the experimental studies with DMSO on head trauma and cerebral ischemia with DMSO, may have improved survival by exerting a protective effect on the microcirculation by decreasing platelet aggregation, thus modifying the evolution of the no re-flow phenomenon.

Clinically and experimentally, the barbiturates have shown some beneficial effect in the treatment of head trauma[38] and focal and global cerebral ischemia.[39-41]

TABLE 2

THE EFFECT OF BARBITURATES ON PLATELETS

Author	Drug	Dose	Experimental Group	Antiplatelet Effect
Vario[47]	Pentobarbital	25 mg/kg	Rabbit	platelet
	Thiopental	15 mg/kg	in vitro	agg. to ADP
Bologna[50]	Thiopental	4×10^{-3}	Human PRP	None in vitro
Rosenblum[48]	Thiopental	6 mg/kg	Mouse in vivo	Agg. prolonged
McKenzie[48]	Pentobarbital	60 mg/kg	Rabbit in vitro in vitro	↓ platelet agg. to ADP microemboli
Demopoulous[42,43]	Methohexital	25 mg/kg	Cat in vivo	SEM ↓ platelet adherence
Present study	Pentobarbital	90 mg/kg	Rat in vivo	SEM platelet adherence

Using the SEM, Demopoulous and Flamm[42] have recently found that platelet fibrin deposition decreased in the ischemic middle cerebral artery territory when they used methohexital in the experimental treatment of focal ischemia. They postulated that the barbiturates protected the endothelial membrane and preserved its integrity and ability to synthesize prostacyclin by quenching free radicals at the site of ischemia, thus inhibiting platelet aggregation.[43-44]

Various in vivo and in vitro experiments have shown that platelet aggregation is decreased by pentobarbital,[45] pentothal,[46] and methohexital.[42] Vairo et al.[47] showed reduced platelet aggregation to ADP and thrombin in the in vivo rabbit experimental model when the animal was treated with either pentobarbital (25 mg/kg i.v.) or pentothal (15 mg/kg i.v.) infused over a 2-minute period. The study by Rosenblum,[48] using the mouse as an in vivo model, also demonstrated that platelet aggregation was prolonged on the endothelial surface of cerebral arteries exposed to filtered ultraviolet light when the animal was anesthetized with pentobarbital 6 mg/100 g, as compared to the animal anesthetized with urethane 2

Dujovny *et al.*: Antiplatelet Effects 241

mg/g intraperitoneally. Using the ruby laser discharge to induce endothelial damage in the rabbit ear chamber preparation, McKenzie *et al.*[49] found that sodium pentobarbital (30 mg/kg) reduced the number of microemboli from the site of endothelial damage. Concurrently, evaluating platelet aggregation *in vitro*, he also found a decreased aggregation response to ATP.

The only study we are aware of in which human platelet response to barbiturates was assessed was Bologna's study[50] in 1978. He showed no significant antiplatelet aggregation effect with pentothal in human platelet-rich plasma. Whether this represents a species difference, a dose-related phenomenon, or a manifestation of the type of barbiturate administered will require further investigation (TABLE 2). In the present study, we also observed a decrease in platelet fibrin deposition in pentothal-treated animals, although less than the effect seen with DMSO.

Statistically, the DMSO treatment, thiopental, and pentobarbital treatments have all been significant. Although thiopental and pentobarbital were not as effective as DMSO in protecting the vascular endothelium, they were both equally effective.

Various theories have been postulated to explain why methyl prednisolone tends to inhibit platelet aggregation in *in vitro* experimentation.[14,51-58] Recently, corticosteroids have been shown to inhibit phospholipase A_2 activity and prevent the release of arachidonic acid, limiting the substrate for the prostaglandin synthetase system.[58-60] However, corticosteroids have also been shown to inhibit the synthesis of prostacyclin by the vessel wall, an effect presumably resulting from limiting the cyclic endoperoxide, the precursor for prostacyclin synthesis.[61,62] This would eliminate the protection afforded by the vessel wall in preventing platelet aggregation. Perhaps this inhibiting effect on prostacyclin synthesis may explain the results observed in the current experiment, in which we found no significant difference between the group of animals treated with methyl prednisolone and the control group.

The recent knowledge of prostaglandin biosynthesis and its intimate relationship with both platelet and vessel wall interaction has now indicated that both these systems will have to be evaluated concurrently if we are to successfully manipulate this intricate biochemical system to our advantage in microvascular surgery and the treatment of cerebrovascular disease.

1. ACLAND, R. 1972. Prevention of thrombosis in microvascular surgery by the use of magnesium sulfate. Br. J. Plast. Surg. **25:** 292–299.
2. DUJOVNY, M., N. WACKENHUT, N. KOSSOVSKY, C. W. GOMES, R. K. LAHA, L. LEFF & D. NELSON. 1979. Minimum vascular occlusive force. J. Neurosurg. **51:** 662–668.
3. GERTZ, S. D., M. L. RENNELS & E. NELSON. Endothelial cell ischemic injury: protective effect of heparin or aspirin assessed by scanning electron microscopy. Stroke **6:** 375–380.
4. KETCHUM, L. D., W. W. WENNEN, F. W. MASTER & D. W. ROBINSON. 1970. Experimental use of pluronic F68 in microvascular surgery. Plast. Reconstr. Surg. **53:** 288–292.
5. KOLAR, L., J. WIEBERDINK & R. S. RENEMAN. 1973. Anticoagulation in microvascular surgery. Eur. Surg. Res. **5:** 52–57.
6. LAHA, R. K., M. DUJOVNY, S. DE CASTRO & J. PHILIPS. 1980. Antiplatelet agents in microvascular surgery. Vasc. Surg. **14:** 39–48.
7. NOMOTO, H., H. J. BUNCKE & N. L. CHATER. 1976. Improved patency rate in microvascular surgery when using magnesium sulfate and a silicone rubber vascular cleft. Plast. Reconstr. Surg. **54:** 157–160.

8. BLOOCK, H. W. & J. M. FREDERICKSON. 1972. The effect of heparin on thrombosis at microvenous anastomotic site. Arch. Otolaryngol. 95: 68–71.
9. GREGORIUS, K. F. 1978. Applications of scanning electron microscopy to microvascular surgery. In Microsurgery. 2nd edit. R. W. Rand, Ed. Chapt. 21, pp. 325–338. C. V. Mosby Co. St. Louis, Mo.
10. O'BRIEN, B. M. 1977. Microvascular Reconstructive Surgery. pp. 46–48, 71–76. Churchill, Livingstone. Edinburgh.
11. OSGOOD, C. P., M. DUJOVNY, R. FAILLE, P. J. BARRIONUEVO, E. Z. LONGA & R. MATTA. 1976. Early scanning electron microscopic evaluation of microvascular meneuvers. Angiology 27: 96–105.
12. ROSENBAUM, R. J. & R. M. SUNDT. 1977. Thrombus formation and endothelial alterations in microarterial anastomoses. J. Neurosurg. 47: 430–441.
13. JACOB, S. W., M. BISCHEL & R. J. HERSCHLER. 1964. Dimethyl sulfoxide: effects on the permeability of biological membranes. Preliminary report. Curr. Ther. Res. 6: 193–198.
14. LAHA, R. K., M. DUJOVNY, P. J. BARRIONUEVO, S. C. DeCASTRO, H. R. HELLSTROM & J. C. MAROON. 1978. Protective effects of methyl prednisolone and dimethyl sulfoxide in experimental middle cerebral artery embolectomy. J. Neurosurg. 49: 508–516.
15. WOOD, D. C. & J. WOOD. 1975. Pharmacologic and biochemical consideration of dimethyl sulfoxide. Ann. N.Y. Acad. Sci. 243: 7–19.
16. DE LA TORRE, J. C. & J. W. SURGEON. 1976. Dexamethasone and DMSO in experimental transorbital cerebral infarction. Stroke 7: 577–583.
17. DE LA TORRE, J. C., H. M. KAWANAGA, C. M. JOHNSON, D. W. ROWED, D. J. GOODE, K. KAJIHARA & S. MULLAN. 1975. Dimethyl sulfoxide in central nervous system trauma. Ann. N.Y. Acad. Sci. 243: 362–389.
18. WALLER, F. T., P. E. CAMP, H. O. PAXTON, C. T. TANABE & S. W. JACOB. 1979. Reduction of intracranial pressure with dimethyl sulfoxide. (Abstract) 29th Annual Meeting. Congress of Neurological Surgeons. Las Vegas.
19. ASHWOOD-SMITH, M. J. 1967. Radioprotective and cryoprotective properties of dimethyl sulfoxide in cellular systems. Ann. N.Y. Acad. Sci. 141: 45–62.
20. FINNEY, J. W., H. C. URSCHEL, G. A. BALLA, G. J. RACE, B. E. JAY, H. P. PINGREE, A. L. DORMAN & J. T. MALLAMS. 1967. Protection of the ischemic heart with DMSO alone or DMSO with hydrogen peroxide. Ann. N.Y. Acad. Sci. 141: 231–241.
21. Weissmann, G., G. SESSA & V. BEVANS. 1967. Effect of DMSO on the stabilization of lysosomes by cortisone and cloroquine in vitro. Ann. N.Y. Acad. Sci. 141: 326–332.
22. ALLEN, J. P. & C. F. ALLEN. 1975. The effect of dimethyl sulfoxide on hypothalamic-pituitary-adrenal functions in the rat. Ann. N.Y. Acad. Sci. 243: 325–336.
23. MAYNARD, J. R., D. J. FINTEL, F. A. PIHICK & Y. NEMERSON. 1976. Tissue factor in cultured cells. Pharmacologic effects. Lab. Invest. 35: 550–557.
24. VAN DER MEER, C., P. W. VALKENBURG & M. REMMELTS. 1963. Experiment on the radioprotective action of dimethyl sulphoxide. Int. J. Radiat. Biol. 6: 151–155.
25. DEUTSCH, E. 1966. Borinflussung des Blutgerinnung dusch DMSO and Kombinationen mit Heparin. In DMSO Symposium. p. 144. Saladruck, Vienna.
26. DAVEY, M. G. & E. F. LUSCHER. 1968. Effects of dimethyl sulfoxide and of vitamin A on human platelets. Thromb. Diath. Haemorrhag. 19: 12–17.
27. VALARIE, C. R., C. G. ZAROULIS, J. C. ROGERS, R. F. HANDIN & L. D. MARCHIONNI. 1972. Prostaglandins in the preparation of blood components. Science 175: 539–549.
28. CROWLEY, J. P., A. RENE & C. R. VALERI. 1974. Changes in platelet shape and structure after freeze preservation. Blood 44: 599–603.
29. SCHIFFER, C. A., J. AISNER & P. H. WIERNIK. 1976. Clinical experience with transfusion of cryopreserved platelets. Br. J. Haematol. 34: 377–385.
30. SCHIFFER, C. A., C. L. WHITAKER, M. SCHMUKLER, J. AISNER & S. L. HILBERT. 1976. The effect of dimethyl sulfoxide on in vitro platelet function. Thromb. Haemost. 36: 221–229.
31. SCHIFFER, C. A., J. AISNER & P. H. WIESNIK. 1978. Frozen autologous platelet transfusion for patient with leukemia. N. Engl. J. Med. 239: 7–12.
32. VALERI, C. R., H. FEINGOLD & L. D. MARCHIONNI. 1974. A simple method for freezing

human platelets using 6% Dimethylsulfoxide and storage at −80°C. Blood **43**: 131–136.

33. HARRISON, M. J. G., P. R. EMMONS & J. R. A. MITCHELL. 1966. The effect of sulphydryl and enzyme inhibitors on platelet aggregation in vitro. Thromb. Haemost. **15/16**: 122–133.

34. HOLTZ, G. C. & R. B. DAVIS. 1972. Inhibition of human platelet aggregation by dimethyl sulfoxide, dimethylacetamide, and sodium glycerophosphate. Proc. Soc. Exp. Biol. Med. **141**: 244–248.

35. ROBINSON, C. W., R. G. MASON & R. H. WAGNER. 1963. Effect of sulfhydryl inhibitors on platelet agglutinability. Proc. Soc. Exp. Biol. Med. **113**: 857–861.

36. PANGANAMALA, R. V., H. M. SHARMA, R. E. HEIKKILA, J. C. GEER & D. G. CORNWELL. 1976. Role of hydroxyl radical scavengers dimethyl sulfoxide, alcohols and methional in the inhibition of prostaglandin biosynthesis. Prostaglandins **11**: 599–606.

37. WIESER, P. B., M. A. ZEIGLER & J. N. FAIN. 1978. Effects of dimethylsulfoxide on cyclic AMP accumulation. Lipolysis and glucose metabolism of fat cells. Biochem. Pharmacol. **26**: 775–778.

38. MARSHAL, L. F. & H. M. SHAPIRO. 1977. Barbiturate control of intracranial and other conditions. Acta Neurol. Scand. Suppl. **64**: 156–157.

39. BLEYAERT, A. L., E. M. NEMOTO, P. A. SAFAR, W. S. STEROSKI, J. MOSSY, G. R. RAO & J. MICKELL. 1977. Thiopental amelioration of post-ischemic encephalopathy in monkeys. Acta Neurol. Scand. Suppl. **64**: 144–145.

40. NEMOTO, E. M., A. W. KOFKE, P. KESSLER, K. A. HOSSMAN, W. S. STEZOWSKI & P. A. SAFAR. 1977. Studies on the pathogenesis of ischemic brain damage and the mechanism of its amelioration by thiopental. Acta Neurol. Scand. Suppl. **64**: 142–143.

41. NORDSTRON, C. H., G. CALDERINI, S. REHNCRONA & B. K. SIESJO. 1977. Effects of phenobarbital anesthesia on postischemic cerebral blood flow and oxygen consumption in the rat. Acta Neurol. Scand. Suppl. **64**: 146–147.

42. DEMOPOULUS, H. B., E. S. FLAMM & M. YODER. 1979. Mechanism of barbiturate protection of ischemic endothelium: A scanning electron microscopy study. Proc. Am. Assoc. Neurolog. Surgeons. Paper **19**: 35–36.

43. DEMOPOULOS, H. B., E. S. FLAMM, M. D. SELICMAN, E. JORGENSEN & J. RANSOHOFF. 1977. Antioxidant effects of barbiturates in model membranes undergoing free radical damage. Acta Neurol. Scand. Suppl. **64**: 152–153.

44. FLAMM, E. S., H. B. DEMOPOULUS, M. L. SELIGMAN & J. RANSOHOFF. 1977. Possible molecular mechanisms of barbiturate-mediated protection in regional cerebral ischemia. Acta Neurol. Scand. Suppl. **64**: 150–151.

45. CORKILL, G., O. K. CHIKOVANI, I. MCLEISH, L. W. MCDONALD, & J. R. YOUMANS. 1976. Timing of pentobarbital administration for brain protection in experimental stroke. Surg. Neurol. **5**: 147–149.

46. HOFF, J. T., L. H. PITTS, R. SPETZLER & C. B. WILSON. 1977. Barbiturates for protection from cerebral ischemia in aneurysm surgery. Acta Neurol. Scand. Suppl. **64**: 158–159.

47. VAIRO, G., F. ROSSI, M. A. SCAIURO, G. RUSSO, P. PEDONE & A. A. SOMMA. 1978. Narcosi aggregazione delle piastrine e risveglianti. Arch. Sci. Med. **135**: 245–248.

48. ROSENBLUM, W. I. & F. ELSABBAN. 1977. Platelet aggregation in the cerebral microcirculation effect of aspirin and other agents. Circ. Res. **40**: 320–328.

49. MCKENZIE, F. N. & E. SVENSJO. 1972. Effect of sodium pentobarbital anesthesis on platelet behavior in vitro. Microvasc. Res. **4**: 42–50.

50. BOLOGNA, E. & A. RANIERI. 1978. Effetti del pentothal, della prostigmina e della D-Tubocuranina sull' aggregazione piastrinica in vitro. Boll. Soc. Ital. Biol. Sper. **54**: 1229–1234.

51. PETTY, C. & T. BAGEANT. 1974. In vitro manipulation of 2,3-diphosphoglycerate levels in acid-citrate dextrose blood with steroids. Life Sci. **14**: 1279–1283.

52. CAZENAVE, J. P., J. A. DAVIES, A. F. SENYI, M. A. BLAJCHMAN, J. HIRSCH & J. F. MUSTARD. 1976. Effects of methylprednisolone on platelet adhesion to damage aorta, bleeding time and platelet survival. Blood **48**: 1009.

53. BUSUTTIL, R. W., W. J. GEORGE & R. L. HEWITT. 1975. Protective effect of methylpredni-solone on the heart during ischemic arrest. J. Thorac. Cardiovasc. Surg. **70:** 955-965.
54. IATRIDIS, S. G., P. G. IATRIDIS, S. G. MARKIDOU, & B. H. RAGATZ. 1975. 2,3-Diphosphoglycerate. A physiological inhibitor of platelet aggregation. Science **187:** 259-261.
55. MCGRAW, C. P., D. F. FLEMING & J. H. SPRUIL, JR. 1974. Effect of methylprednisolone on experimental cerebral infarction in the Mongolian gerbil. Stroke **5:** 444-446.
56. MITAMURA, D., A. IOPPOLO, M. L. SELIGMAN, E. S. FLAMM, J. RANSHOFF & H. B. DEMOPOULOS. 1977. Loss of cerebral cholesterol in CNS injury and modulation by corticosteroids. Presented at the Meeting of American Association of Neurological Surgeons. Toronto. April 24-28.
57. NELSON, W. R. & G. A. TAYLOR. 1975. In vitro inhibition of endotoxin induced platelet aggregation with hydrocortisone sodium succiate (soler-cortef) Scand. J. Haematol. **15:** 35-44.
58. SANDER, W. J., A. ROSENBERG & J. HAWIGER. 1976. Human platelet function under the influence of methylprednisolone inhibition of aggregation serotonin release and clot-promoting. Phospholipid irrespective of membrane receptors involved. Clin. Res. **24:** 48A.
59. BLAJCHMAN, M. A., A. F. SENYL, J. HIRSH, Y. SURYA & M. BUCHANAN. 1979. Shortening of the bleeding time in rabbits by hydrocortisone caused by inhibition of prostacyclin generation by the vessel wall. J. Clin. Invest. **63:** 1026-1035.
60. HONG, S. L. & L. LEVIN. 1976. Inhibition of arachidonic acid release from cells as the biochemical action of anti-inflammatory corticosteroids. Proc. Natl. Acad. Sci. USA **73:** 1730-1734.
61. FLOMAN, Y., N. FLOMAN & U. ZOR. 1976. Inhibition of prostaglandin E release by anti-inflammatory steroid. Prostaglandins **11:** 591-594.
62. GRYGLEWSKI, R. J., B. PANCZENKO, R. KORBUT, L. GRODZINSKAL & A. OCETKIEWICZ. 1975. Corticosteroids inhibit prostaglandin release from perfused mesenteric blood vessels of rabbit and from perfused lungs of sensitized guinea pig. Prostaglandins **10:** 343-347.

DIMETHYL SULFOXIDE THERAPY FOLLOWING PENETRATING BRAIN INJURY

Frederick D. Brown, Lydia Johns, and Sean Mullan

Section of Neurosurgery
Department of Surgery
The University of Chicago Hospitals and Clinics
Chicago, Illinois 60637

In earlier experiments, control cerebral missile injuries were produced in rhesus monkeys.[1,2] Treatment of similarly injured animals with mannitol resulted not only in greater survival, but also in significantly improved cerebral blood flow (CBF) and metabolism.[3-5] These positive therapeutic results were obtained with mannitol given either 15 minutes or 1 hour after trauma. It was postulated that the improvement may have been based, in part, on a mannitol-induced increase in cardiac output.[4,5]

Dimethyl sulfoxide (DMSO) has been shown to be effective therapy in models of cerebral infarction[6-8] and trauma.[9] It may provide a protective effect against mechanical disruption,[10] as well as improve CBF and control intracranial pressure (ICP).[9] We, therefore, decided to test this therapeutic agent in our gunshot wound model. In the present study, we have examined the effects of DMSO initiated 1 hour following trauma.

MATERIALS AND METHODS

Seven rhesus monkeys, weighing 5 to 9 kg, were included in this study. Each was anesthetized with 1 to 2 mg/kg of phencyclidine hydrochloride, repeated as required. A cuffed endotracheal tube was inserted. A polyethylene catheter was passed into the femoral artery to monitor mean arterial blood pressure (MAP) and heart rate, and to obtain samples for hematocrit, lactate, and blood gases. A femoral vein was catheterized for administration of maintenance saline and DMSO doses. Respirations were recorded with a pneumograph, and body temperature was maintained at 38° to 39°C with a heating pad. The animals were held in a stereotaxic frame in the sphinx position.

An epidural balloon was inserted through a parietal burr hole to monitor ICP. A 3-mm hole was made over the torcula Herophili to obtain cerebral venous blood gases and lactates; except during sampling, this hole was occluded with bone wax. A 7-mm hole was made in the right occipital area 10 mm above the nuchal line and 12 mm to the right of the midline. A 310-mg spherical BB pellet was fired through this hole on a line 5° divergent from the midline. The bullet typically stopped at the upper outer quadrant of the right orbit. This path was chosen to avoid direct brain-stem, ventricular, and major blood vessel damage.

For determination of CBF, a direct injection of ^{133}Xe was made into the common carotid artery after ligation of the external carotid branches and placement of a single detector over each hemisphere. The flow was calculated by the initial-slope clearance technique.[11] Cerebral perfusion pressure (CPP), cerebral vascular resistance (CVR), arterial-venous oxygen content difference (a-vO$_2$), cerebral metabolic rate of oxygen consumption (CMRO$_2$), and cerebral

245

0077-8923/83/0411-0245 $01.75/0 © 1983, NYAS

metabolic rate of lactate production (CMRL) were calculated as previously described.[1,2] Means, standard error of means (SEM), and *t*-tests were calculated in conventional fashion.

Following baseline observations, a missile was fired at 90 m/sec (kinetic energy of 1.26 joules) through the right cerebral hemisphere with a Crossman 160 air rifle attached to a stereotaxic frame. The burr hole was then sealed with methyl methacrylate. All observations were repeated at 1, 10, and 30 minutes following injury and then hourly until death or the end of 6 hours. One hour following injury, DMSO was started as a 0.5 g/kg bolus in a 50% solution. The bolus was repeated up to every 15 minutes, as much as necessary, whenever the ICP rose above 20 mm Hg.

RESULTS

Immediately after trauma, there occurred a reduction in respiratory rate and an increase in tidal volume but no significant change in arterial blood gases. The respiratory pattern returned to baseline within a few minutes and was unaffected by DMSO. The heart rate was initially slow after injury but returned to normal in 30 minutes and was unaffected by the DMSO given at 1 hour.

In the untreated animals, the MAP rose initially and then, commencing at 15 minutes, decreased progressively (FIGURE 1). Treatment with DMSO at 1 hour dramatically reversed this hypotensive trend. The MAP was 109 ± 7.7 mm Hg at 2 hours, which was insignificantly higher than the baseline value of 99.8 mm Hg and significantly higher (p < 0.05) than the untreated value at 2 hours (78 mm Hg). By 4 hours, the MAP in the DMSO group was 116 ± 3.2 mm Hg.

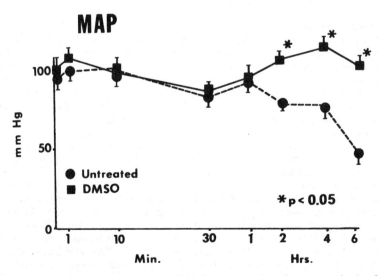

FIGURE 1. The changes in mean arterial blood pressure (MAP) for untreated animals and for those treated with DMSO given 1 hour after injury. An asterisk denotes a significant difference between the DMSO group and the untreated animals.

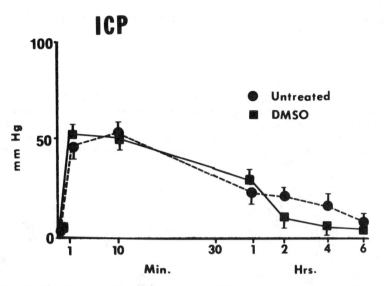

FIGURE 2. The changes in intracranial pressure (ICP) for untreated animals and for those treated with DMSO given 1 hour after injury. There were no significant differences between the groups at any time.

The ICP in the untreated animals rose immediately after injury to a peak value of 59 ± 7 mm Hg at 1 minute (FIGURE 2). It then gradually fell to 41 mm Hg by 1 hour, and then stabilized at a mildly elevated level of 27 mm Hg at 2 hours. The ICP of the DMSO group (16.5 ± 2.5 mm Hg) was insignificantly lower than the untreated 2-hour value. A mean of 5.2 boluses of DMSO, 0.5 g/kg, was required per animal to maintain an ICP of 20 mm Hg or less.

The CPP fell to nearly half of the baseline values at 10 minutes after injury (45.3 ± 5.6 mm Hg), and remained near this level in the untreated group. This trend was reversed by DMSO, so that by 2 hours the CPP of 92.6 ± 7.2 mm Hg was essentially the same as the baseline value of 88.6 mm Hg, and significantly higher (p < 0.05) than the untreated 2 hour value of 51 mm Hg (FIGURE 3).

In the untreated animals, CBF fell from a baseline of 42.6 ml/100 g/min to 16 ml/100 g/min at 30 minutes (FIGURE 4). It then rose slightly but remained below 30 ml/100 g/min for the entire observation period. Administration of DMSO increased CBF to 37.0 ± 4.0 ml/100 g/min by 2 hours, a value not significantly less than baseline.

In the untreated animals, the CVR was very unstable (FIGURE 5). Shortly after drug administration, the CVR was stabilized at virtually baseline levels.

The $CMRO_2$ changes paralleled those of CBF in the untreated and treated animals (FIGURE 6). The 6-hour $CMRO_2$ value for DMSO was 2.76 ± 0.7 ml/100 g/min, which was virtually the same as baseline. The a-vO_2 differences showed very little fluctuation in the untreated or treated group (FIGURE 7).

The CMRL, which had risen to 150% of baseline at 1 hour posttrauma, returned to normal within 5 hours with DMSO treatment at 1 hour.

The mortality for the DMSO group was 14% compared to 45% for the untreated group. None of the animals had an intracranial extravascular blood collection of more than 1 ml.

DISCUSSION

There are many possible explanations for the DMSO group withstanding trauma better than the untreated animals. Weissmann et al.[12] have shown that DMSO stabilizes lysosomal membranes, which would prevent cellular enzymatic breakdown. Lim and Mullan[10] demonstrated that DMSO will enhance the resistance of glial cells against sonic disruption. Dimethyl sulfoxide is a diuretic

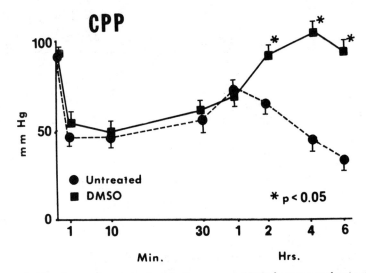

FIGURE 3. The changes in cerebral perfusion pressure (CPP) for untreated animals and for those treated with DMSO given 1 hour after injury. An asterisk denotes a significant difference between the DMSO group and the untreated animals.

agent[13,14] and has been shown to be an effective antiedema drug.[14,15] The diuretic and antiedema effects may account for the ability of DMSO to lower ICP as demonstrated by de la Torre et al.[9] with an epidural brain compression model. More recently, the same ability of DMSO to lower ICP was demonstrated by Camp et al.[16] in a cryogenic edema model. In the epidural brain compression model, an apparent increase in flow was seen through a cortical window following DMSO therapy.[9] In addition to increased flow, DMSO may induce an increase of oxygen diffusion into tissue.[17] When rats are pretreated with DMSO, they have improved survival from experimental hypoxia.[18]

In addition to trauma, DMSO has been effective in treating experimental stroke. De la Torre and Surgeon[6] demonstrated improved neurological recovery when DMSO was given following experimental middle cerebral artery occlusion.

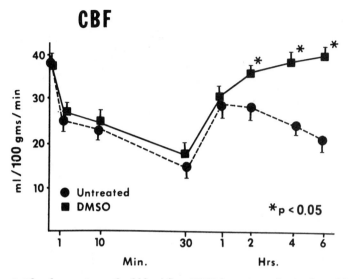

FIGURE 4. The changes in cerebral blood flow (CBF) for untreated animals and for those treated with DMSO given 1 hour after injury. An asterisk denotes a significant difference between the DMSO group and the untreated animals.

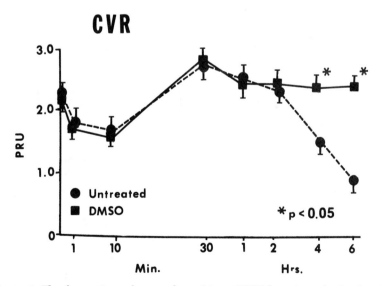

FIGURE 5. The changes in cerebrovascular resistance (CVR) for untreated animals and for those treated with DMSO given 1 hour after injury. An asterisk denotes a significant difference between the DMSO group and the untreated animals. PRU = peripheral resistance units.

Similarly, McGraw and Lawson[8] noted that gerbils subjected to common carotid artery ligation had a smaller infarct size if treated with DMSO. In addition, Laha et al.[7] found that DMSO significantly reduced the incidence of infarct during experimental middle cerebral artery embolectomy. Weber et al.[19] found a higher patency in previously frozen vein grafts if they were pretreated with DMSO; the DMSO-treated grafts showed less endothelial disruption.

In previous papers, we have described an increase in survival after a cerebral missile injury to monkeys treated with mannitol. An improvement in MAP, CPP, CBF, and $CMRO_2$ was noted. It was suggested that the basis of these improvements may have been an increase in cardiac output.[3-5] Cardiac output was not measured in the present series of experiments, but DMSO has been reported to have a positive inotropic effect in some species.[20] Considering the vast improvement in MAP in animals with DMSO treatment, even over that achieved with mannitol, it is possible that DMSO may increase the cardiac output, which could account for the improvement of many of the parameters.

The improvement in CBF may be related to many factors. It is certainly related to the increase in MAP. Severe cerebral trauma would be expected to cause some loss of autoregulation, so that flow would passively rise and fall with perfusion pressure. Although the ICP was not significantly helped with DMSO, the intracranial compliance might have been. If it were, we would have an explanation for the increase in MAP without a commensurate rise in ICP—the best combination for maximum CBF and $CMRO_2$. The DMSO may have further augmented flow on a rheological basis, for it has been suggested to have an anticoagulant effect at high concentrations,[21] and to lessen platelet adhesiveness[22] and aggregation.[23] It has been thought to increase flow through its potent histamine-liberating property,[24] which would produce vasodilation and a

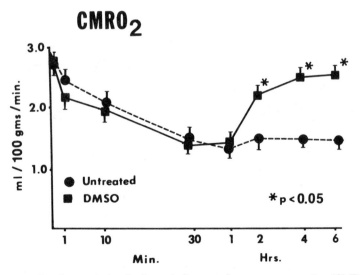

FIGURE 6. The changes in cerebral metabolic rate of oxygen consumption ($CMRO_2$) for untreated animals and for those treated with DMSO given 1 hour after injury. An asterisk denotes a significant difference between the DMSO group and the untreated animals.

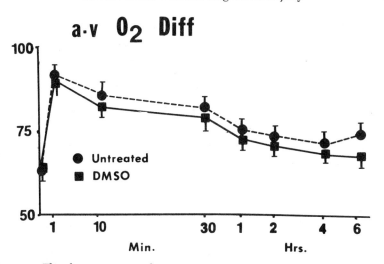

FIGURE 7. The changes in arterial-venous oxygen content differences (a-v O_2 Diff) for untreated animals and for those treated with DMSO given 1 hour after injury. There were no significant differences between the groups at any time.

decrease in CVR. This mechanism may not be a factor in our experiments, however, because CVR actually increased with DMSO.

Perhaps the most interesting of our results is the improvements in $CMRO_2$ following DMSO treatment. By 6 hours after trauma (5 hours after initiation of DMSO), the $CMRO_2$ returned to normal pretrauma levels. Similarly, the CMRL returned to normal levels by 6 hours posttrauma. Thus, the metabolic activity of the brain, which is one of the best indices of cellular viability, returned to normal. This metabolic recovery appeared to be more complete with DMSO than with mannitol. The $a-vO_2$ differences do not significantly vary among the DMSO-treated mannitol-treated, or untreated animals; from FIGURES 4 and 6 it can be seen that the improvement in $CMRO_2$ with DMSO paralleled the changes in CBF. Therefore, we feel that the improvement in $CMRO_2$ was largely secondary to the rise in CBF, which followed the rise in MPA and CPP.

The difference in survival with mannitol at 1 hour (75%) as compared with DMSO (86%) is not significant, but the significantly higher MAP, CPP, CBF, and $CMRO_2$ are suggestive that DMSO may be superior to mannitol in this model. Actually, the results obtained with DMSO at 1 hour after injury appear to be just as good as those obtained with mannitol given at 15 minutes following an identical injury.[3-5] From the practical standpoint, treatment at 1 hour following injury is more relevant than at 15 minutes. Certainly, one cannot extrapolate data from monkeys to humans, but we feel DMSO should be compared to mannitol in clinical trials with severe head injury.

REFERENCES

1. CROCKARD, H. A., F. D. BROWN, A. B. CALICA, et al. 1977. Physiological consequences of experimental cerebral missile injury and use of data analysis to predict survival. J. Neurosurg. **46:** 784–794.

2. CROCKARD, H. A., F. D. BROWN, L. M. JOHNS, et al. 1977. An experimental cerebral missile injury model in primates. J. Neurosurg. **46:** 776-783.
3. BROWN, F. D., L. M. JOHNS, H. A. CROCKARD, et al. 1979. Response to mannitol following experimental cerebral missile injury. In Neural Trauma. A. J. Popp, R. S. Nelson, L. R. Nelson, et al., Eds. pp. 281-287. Raven Press. New York.
4. BROWN, F. D., L. M. JOHNS, J. J. JAFAR, et al. 1979. Detailed monitoring of the effects of mannitol following experimental head injury. J. Neurosurg. **50:** 423-432.
5. BROWN, F. D., L. M. JOHNS, J. J. JAFAR, et al. 1978. Systemic and cerebral hemodynamic response to mannitol after cerebral missile injury. Surg. Forum **29:** 525-527.
6. DE LA TORRE, J. C. & J. W. SURGEON. 1976. Dexamethasone and DMSO in experimental transorbital cerebral infarction. Stroke **7:** 577-583.
7. LAHA, R. K., M. DUJOVNY & P. J. BARRIONUEVO. 1978. Protective effects of methyl prednisolone and dimethyl sulfoxide in experimental middle cerebral artery embolectomy. J. Neurosurg. **49:** 508-516.
8. McGRAW, C. P. & J. W. LAWSON. 1977. The effect of dimethyl sulfoxide on cerebral infarction in the Mongolian gerbil. (Abstract) Stroke **8:** 6.
9. DE LA TORRE, J. C., D. W. ROWED, H. M. KAWANAGA, et al. 1973. Dimethyl sulfoxide in the treatment of experimental brain compression. J. Neurosurg. **38:** 345-354.
10. LIM, R. & S. MULLAN. 1975. Enhancement of resistance of glial cells by dimethyl sulfoxide against sonic disruption. Ann. N.Y. Acad. Sci. **243:** 358-361.
11. OLESEN, J., O. B. PAULSON & N. A. LASSEN. 1971. Regional cerebral blood flow in man determined by the initial slope of the clearance of intraarterially injected ^{133}Xe. Stroke **2:** 519-540.
12. WEISSMANN, G., G. SESSA & V. BEVANS. 1967. Effect of DMSO on the stabilization of lysosomes by cortisone and chloroquine in vitro. Ann. N.Y. Acad. Sci. **141:** 326-332.
13. FORAMENEK, K. & T. SUCKERT. 1966. Diuretische Wirkung von DMSO. In G. Laudahn & K. Gertich, Eds.: 18. Dimethyl Sulfoxide Symposium. Vienna. Berlin. Saladruk.
14. JACOB, S. W., M. BISHCEL & R. J. HERSCHLER. 1964. Dimethyl sulfoxide (DMSO) a new concept on pharmacotherapy. Curr. Ther. Res. **6:** 134-135.
15. FORAMENEK, K. & W. KOVAI. 1966. DMSO bei Experimentallen Rattenpfotemodeman. In Dimethyl Sulfoxide Symposium. G. Laudahn & K. Gertich, Eds.: 21. Vienna. Berlin. Saladruk.
16. CAMP, P. E., H. E. JAMES & R. WERNER. 1981. Acute dimethyl sulfoxide therapy in experimental brain edema: Part I. Effects on intracranial pressure, blood pressure, central venous pressure, and brain water and electrolyte content. Neurosurgery **9:** 28-33.
17. FINNEY, J. W., H. C. URSCHEL, G. A. BALLA, et al. 1967. Protection of the ischemic heart with DMSO alone or DMSO with hydrogen peroxide. Ann. N.Y. Acad. Sci. **141:** 231-241.
18. DE LA TORRE, J. C. & D. W. ROWED. 1974. DMSO: A new respiratory stimulant? J. Clin. Pharmacol. **14:** 345-353.
19. WEBER, T. R., S. M. LINDENAUER, T. L. DENT, et al. 1976. Long-term patency of vein grafts preserved in liquid nitrogen in dimethyl sulfoxide. Ann. Surg. **184:** 709-712.
20. SHLAFER, M., J. L. MATHENY & A. M. KAROW, JR. 1974. Cardiac inotropism of dimethyl sulfoxide: osmotic effects and interactions with calcium ion. Eur. J. Pharmacol. **28:** 276-287.
21. DAVIS, H. L., N. L. DAVIS & A. L. CLEMONS. 1967. Procoagulant and nerve-blocking effects of DMSO. Ann. N.Y. Acad. Sci. **141:** 310-325.
22. DEUTSCH, E. 1966. Beinflussung der Blutgerinnung durch DMSO und Komlinationen mit Heparin. Dimethyl Sulfoxide Symposium in G. Laudahn & K. Gertich, Eds.: 144. Vienna. Berlin. Saladruk.
23. GOROG, P. 1971. Cited in S. W. Jacob. Pharmacology of DMSO. In Dimethyl Sulfoxide. M. Dekker, Ed.: 108. New York.
24. ADAMSON, J. E., H. H. CRAWFORD & C. E. HORTEN. 1966. The action of dimethyl sulfoxide on the experimental pedicle flap. Surg. Forum **17:** 491-492.

DIMETHYL SULFOXIDE IN BRAIN EDEMA
AND INTRACRANIAL PRESSURE*

Hector E. James,†‡ William Cornell,† Marc del Bigio,†‡
and Rita Werner†

†Division of Neurosurgery
‡Departments of Surgery and Pediatrics
University of California
San Diego, California 92103

INTRODUCTION

There are presently many therapeutic agents employed for the management of brain edema and for the acute reduction of intracranial pressure (ICP) in clinical practice. The primary forms of therapy presently available to the clinician are hyperventilation, hypertonic diuretics (such as mannitol), and nephron-blocking diuretics (such as furosemide). More recently, barbiturates have been shown to be very effective agents for the control of ICP. One of the side effects of barbiturates is that they may reduce systemic blood pressure, consequently interfering with cerebral perfusion pressure and thus leading to cerebral ischemia. In previous work, we had confirmed the findings of other authors of the reduction of ICP after bolus administrations of dimethyl sulfoxide (DMSO) in two models of experimental brain edema in albino rabbits.[4] The administrations of bolus dosage of DMSO had been noted not to affect systolic arterial pressure (SAP) and various dosages and varying concentrations of DMSO were noted to sustain SAP as ICP was reduced.[25]

Because of the positive effect on blood pressure of DMSO, it was decided to observe the response of a DMSO infusion in the face of a pentobarbitone infusion, with the hopes that there would be an enhancement of the reduction of ICP with these agents, and at the same time the DMSO could counteract the barbiturates' effect of reducing SAP, thus maintaining cerebral perfusion pressure.

With the above hypothesis in mind, 3-hour infusions of DMSO and 3-hour infusions of DMSO with pentobarbital were undertaken in an experimental model of brain edema.

MATERIALS AND METHODS

The experimental preparation with albino rabbits consisted of (1) untreated controls (sham-operated, $N = 15$); (2) cryogenic left hemisphere injury and metabolic (cytotoxic) insult ($N = 24$); (3) the therapy group (cryogenic left hemisphere lesion and metabolic lesion) which was treated with DMSO; and finally, (4) the DMSO-pentobarbital simultaneous therapy group.

Albino rabbits weighing 2.5 to 3.5 kg were anesthetized with intravenous sodium thiopental (20 mg/kg) through the marginal vein of the ear. With the head located in a stereotactic device, a midline scalp incision was made under local

*Supported in part with research funds of the Division of Neurosurgery (U.C.S.D.) and U.C.S.D. Academic Senate support (R-E60-M, R-B86-M).

anesthesia (lidocaine 1%), the calvarium was exposed, and a 12.5 diameter circular trephine hole was made over the left parieto-occipital cortex. A stainless steel probe (area 64 mm^2) equilibrated with liquid nitrogen, was then applied to the intact dura for 90 seconds. The skull defect was then closed by suturing the bone remnant into its position and the skin incision was sutured. Evans blue (1 mg/kg of a 2% solution) was administered intravenously. 120 mg/kg of 6-aminonicotinamide (6-ANA) was injected intraperitoneally to create a cytotoxic lesion.[1,15] A group of animals had the operation, but received no freeze lesion and no 6-aminonicotinamide (sham operation). Therapy trials commenced 24 hours after the lesion. As with the sham-operated and untreated control groups, the treated rabbits were then briefly re-anesthetized with sodium thiopental, tracheostomized, and ventilated with a small-animal respirator (Harvard Apparatus Co., Inc., Millis, Mass.) with a mixture of oxygen (50%) and nitrous oxide (50%). They were then paralyzed with pancuronium (0.5-1 mg) intravenously, and femoral, venous, and arterial catheterizations were performed. The arterial blood gases were maintained so that the PaCO$_2$ was in the range of 37-43 torr. The animals were then positioned in the stereotactic head-holding device, and a 20 gauge plastic catheter was inserted into the cisterna magna for continuous ICP recording; the reference point for this was the interaural line. ICP, SAP, and central venous pressure (CVP) were monitored continuously through appropriate strain gauge transducers and were recorded on a multichannel polygraph (Gilson Model CMH; West Coast Science Co., Oakland, Calif.). Bilateral, anterior, and posterior screws were placed in the calvarium for electroencephalographic (EEG) recording, which was displayed simultaneously with the other parameters. The sham-operated population and the untreated controls were ventilated until the PaCO$_2$ stabilized and then were killed 45 minutes later. The third group, after stabilization of the PaCO$_2$, received 2 g/kg of a 20% solution of DMSO in dextrose and water (Tera Pharmaceutical Inc., Research Industries Corp., Pharmaceutical Division, Salt Lake City, Utah) in a 3-hour infusion. The fourth group received simultaneously 1-2 g/kg infusion of a 20% solution of DMSO in dextrose and water, with a pentobarbital infusion (60 mg/kg of a 40% solution). Prior to this experimental group, another group of animals had DMSO administered simultaneously with higher dosages of pentobarbital (120 mg/kg, 90 mg/kg) but because of severe systemic hypotension, the dose of 60 mg/kg was arrived at, since this dosage produced less reduction in SAP when combined with DMSO.

At the end of the experimental period, all animals were killed by intravenous air embolization and their brains were removed by rapid craniectomy. The cerebral hemispheres were isolated, and two samples of brain tissue, each weighing 0.76 ± 0.27 (SD) including white and gray matter, but excluding areas of lesion necrosis or hemorrhage, were taken from the region of the surrounding brain in the left hemisphere. Homologous samples were dissected systematically from the contralateral hemisphere. The brain water content was calculated after drying the tissue at 110°C constant temperature for three measurements. Gross pathology was assessed by looking at the extent of distribution of Evans blue, to indicate blood-brain barrier breakdown, hemorrhage and necrosis, and the extent of the same in the left hemisphere.

RESULTS

Behavior

Behavior in the sham-operated group was normal. In the cryogenic lesion plus 6-ANA subgroups, severe hypoactivity was noted in 85% of the animals 24 hours after the lesions, with a 30% mortality on the night of lesioning.

Gross Pathology

In the sham-operated animals there was no extravasation of Evans blue dye, and no gross pathological changes were noted. In the cryogenic and cytotoxic lesion subgroups, there was an area of hemorrhage and necrosis created by the cold injury, which averaged 13 mm in diameter at the cortical surface and generally extended 3-4 mm into the underlying brain parenchyma. Evans blue extravasation was noticed to extend in a 5-8 mm radius into the injured hemisphere, beyond the area of hemorrhage and necrosis. Frequently, Evans blue dye was seen in the white matter of the right hemisphere and at times a light bluish hue was seen in both lateral ventricles. There was no difference in the gross pathology between the untreated controls, the DMSO, and the DMSO and pentobarbital subgroups.

EEG

In the sham-operated group, fast activity was present over both hemispheres 24 hours later. In the group with cryogenic lesion plus 6-ANA, there was pronounced slowing and very poor activity over the left hemisphere in 90% of the animals. The right hemisphere demonstrated an almost isoelectric recording in 40%, 50% had diffuse slowing, and the remaining 10% were normal. After administration of DMSO alone, there seemed to be an improvement of the tracing of the left hemisphere in four of the seven animals. In the DMSO-pentobarbital group, burst suppression secondary to the barbiturate infusion was noted over both hemispheres, more noticeable over the right. This pattern started 15-20 minutes after the initiation of the therapy, and although it decreased in intensity, it remained visible until the end of the experimental run in some of the animals.

Intracranial Pressure

The mean ICP for the sham-operated animals was 2.65 ± 2.2 (SD) torr. In the untreated control group, it was 15.8 ± 8 torr. This ICP remained at that level in the animals that had recordings for 2-3 hours following stabilization of the $PaCO_2$ at 37-43 torr ($N = 6$).

The mean ICP before DMSO at a $PaCO_2$ of 37-42 in the therapy group was 12.9 ± 4.8 (SD) torr. The mean initial ICP for the DMSO-pentobarbital infusion was 11.9 ± 2.8 (SD) torr. There was no statistical difference between these two initial values. The mean ICP decreased throughout the infusion in both subgroups, so that at 150 and 180 minutes into the infusion in both groups, it was statistically significant from zero time ($p < 0.005$). However, there was no difference in the mean ICP at the end of the run between both therapy subgroups. FIGURE 1 illustrates the ICP response during infusion.

Systolic Arterial Pressure

The SAP in the sham-operated group, as well as in the untreated controls at a $PaCO_2$ of 37-42 torr, ranged between 170 and 85 torr.

In the DMSO group it was 116.4 ± 8.5 (SD) torr before therapy, and it remained unchanged throughout treatment. However, in the DMSO-pentobarbital infu-

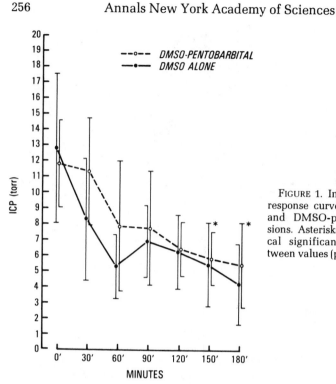

FIGURE 1. Intracranial pressure response curves to DMSO alone and DMSO-pentobarbital infusions. Asterisks represent statistical significant differences between values (p < 0.005).

sion, there was a steady decrease of SAP throughout the run that became significant at 120 minutes (p < 0.025) and then it remained so until the end of the run. The SAP at 180 minutes into the infusion ranged from 95 to 175 torr in the DMSO alone group, and between 50 to 150 torr in the DMSO-pentobarbital group. FIGURE 2 shows the response of SAP in both therapy subgroups.

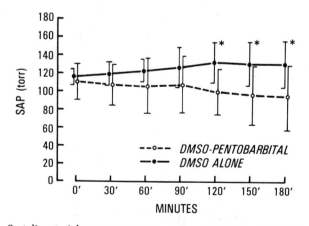

FIGURE 2. Systolic arterial pressure response curves to DMSO and DMSO-pentobarbital infusions. Asterisks represent statistical significant differences between values (p < 0.025).

Central Venous Pressure

The CVP before DMSO therapy was 6.4 ± 1.7 torr (SD) and its completion, was 6.7 ± 1.5 torr. In the DMSO-pentobarbital group, the CVP was 7.5 ± 1.9 torr, at the initiation of the infusion (not significant from DMSO-alone), and at the end of the infusion it was 7.1 ± 2.3 torr (not significant from DMSO-alone). FIGURE 3 shows the response of the CVP to the infusion in the therapy subgroups.

Brain Water Content

The sham-operated animals had a mean water content of 79.2 ± 1.3 (SD) for the left hemisphere and 79 ± 1.2% in the right hemisphere. In the untreated control group, it was 82.8 ± 1.1% for the left and 81.1 ± 1.4% for the right. After DMSO-alone, it was 82.1 ± 0.9 for the left and 80.2 ± 0.6% for the right

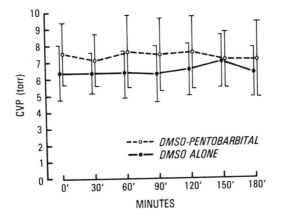

FIGURE 3. Central venous pressure response curves to DMSO and DMSO-pentobarbital infusions.

hemisphere. The difference between untreated controls and the therapy groups was significant for the right hemisphere only (p < 0.005). The difference between the left and right hemispheres in the water content for the DMSO-alone group was also significant (p < 0.005). In the DMSO with pentobarbital subgroup, the water content for the left hemisphere was 81.1 ± 1.9% and 79.1 ± 1.5% for the right. The difference was statistically significant to the DMSO-alone group, for the left (p < 0.01) and for the right (p < 0.005).

DISCUSSION

DMSO is known to be an effective agent in the acute management of cerebral infarction,[10,13,17,19] brain compression,[8] and intracranial hypertension due to penetrating missile injury.[2,3] Brown et al. had noted that in the penetrating-missile brain-injury model, repeated doses of 0.5 g of a 50% solution of DMSO per kg were required to maintain a low ICP.[3] In a previous study, we had noticed a tendency of ICP to rise during the hour after the DMSO bolus was given.[4] Because of this, an infusion was subsequently chosen, and this demonstrated a steady decrease of ICP during the infusion with stabilization of SAP.[11] A subacute toxicity study in the rhesus monkey was reported by de la Torre et al. in which animals were administered DMSO at 3 g/kg of a 40% solution over nine consecutive days, subsequently monitoring the animals for four months.[9] This study showed no deleterious effects from the administration of the agent in a subacute form. Therefore, the known alterations that can occur with DMSO in bolus administrations seem to have been minimized by a subacute administration of the drug. The alterations previously noted have been of the blood coagulation,[6,12] hemolysis accompanying potassium leakage,[7] and alteration of platelet

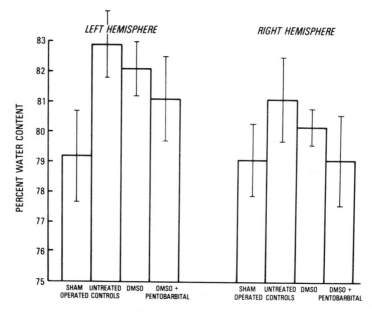

FIGURE 4. Brain water content of the left and right hemispheres in the various experimental subgroups. There is a significant difference between the sham-operated and the untreated controls for both hemispheres ($p < 0.005$). There is a statistical significant decrease for both hemispheres for the left and right hemispheres for the DMSO-pentobarbital group, when compared to the DMSO alone runs (see RESULTS).

function.[21] Thus, it was felt that the infusion could be better tolerated and that the fact that SAP was sustained in the face of steady reduction of ICP, makes DMSO an ideal agent for maintaining cerebral perfusion pressure.

Barbiturates are presently employed for the control of experimental and severe clinical intracranial hypertension.[5,18,20,23,24] ICP may be reduced as a consequence of a fall in the cerebral blood volume due to reduced cerebral metabolism, or it may be a result of direct vasoconstriction of the cerebral arterioles caused by the barbiturate. Go et al. demonstrated in the cat that variations in vascular tone of the cerebral arterioles resulted in significant changes in water content of the edematous brain.[14] Clasen et al. also demonstrated improvement of cryogenic brain edema with pentobarbital and furosemide.[5] Matsumoto *et al.* pointed out that the well documented reduction of water content in cryogenic edema with barbiturates may be a direct consequence of a reduction of systemic arterial pressure, and due to such a reduction there is a fall of the hydraulic pressure across the blood-brain barrier.[18] This could explain why the water content was lower in the DMSO-pentobarbital group when compared to the DMSO-alone therapy subgroup. Despite this significant difference in the reduction of water content, the fall of ICP was statistically not different between both subgroups.

One of the limitations of the application of barbiturates in clinical work for the control of intracranial hypertension is the known effect of barbiturates in reducing SAP. Because of this, a reduction of cerebral perfusion pressure can occur and this can adversely affect the cerebral metabolism of an already injured brain, by superimposing ischemic damage and edema on a primary insult. Brain edema may be magnified by hypotension owing to the fact that when cerebral blood flow reaches 10–15 ml/100 g/minute, it can by itself create an ischemic form of edema.[22]

It was our desire to stabilize SAP while administering barbiturates by applying a DMSO infusion. Unfortunately, the possible positive inotropic effect of the DMSO was not sufficient to counteract the negative effect of the barbiturate. Thus, SAP was reduced out of proportion to the changes that occurred with DMSO, in the face of a similar reduction of ICP. Therefore, no beneficial effect was noted on adding pentobarbital to DMSO therapy for the reduction of intracranial hypertension. Further, the reduction in ICP would have a deleterious effect on cerebral perfusion and consequently, brain edema may be worsened by an ischemic secondary insult from the reduction of cerebral blood flow. In previous work, an even lower dose of pentobarbital in the same experimental animal (40 mg/kg 30 minute infusion) created a reduction in SAP that though not statistically significant from the beginning of the experiment, was markedly different from what occurred when 1 g/kg of a 10% solution of DMSO was administered by intravenous bolus. We therefore conclude that there is no advantage of adding the effects of DMSO onto pentobarbital for the management of intracranial hypertension. Even though a reduction of water in the edematous brain may occur with DMSO-pentobarbital combination (over DMSO alone) this may in itself not counteract the deleterious effect of the reduction of SAP when DMSO-pentobarbital simultaneous therapy is given.

ACKNOWLEDGMENTS

We acknowledge the patient and excellent secretarial work performed by Yvette Cabrera.

REFERENCES

1. BAETHMANN, A. & A. VAN HARREVELD. 1973. Water and electrolyte distribution in gray matter rendered edematous with a metabolic inhibitor. J. Neuropathol. Exp. Neurol. **32:** 408–423.
2. BROWN, F. D., L. M. JOHNS & J. F. MULLAN. 1979. DMSO treatment in an experimental cerebral missile injury. Surg. Forum **30:** 444–445.
3. BROWN, F. D., L. M. JOHNS & S. MULLAN. 1980. Dimethyl sulfoxide in experimental brain injury, with comparison to mannitol. J. Neurosurg. **53:** 58–62.

4. CAMP, P. E., H. E. JAMES & R. WERNER. 1981. Acute dimethyl sulfoxide therapy in experimental brain edema: Part I. Effects on intracranial pressure, blood pressure, central venous pressure, and brain water and electrolyte content. Neurosurgery **9:** 28–33.

5. CLASEN, R. A., S. PANDOLFI & D. CASEY, JR. 1974. Furosemide and pentobarbital in cryogenic cerebral injury and edema. Neurology (Minneap.) **24:** 642–648.

6. DAVIS, H. E., N. L. DAVIS & A. L. CLEMONS. 1967. Procoagulant and nerve-blocking effects of DMSO. Ann N.Y. Acad. Sci. **141:** 310–325.

7. DEBRUIJNE, A. W. & J. VAN STEVENINCK. 1972. Lysis of yeast cells and erythrocytes by dimethyl sulfoxide. Biochem. Pharmacol. **21:** 153–162.

8. DE LA TORRE, J. C., D. W. ROWED, H. M. KAWANAGA & S. MULLAN. 1973. Dimethyl sulfoxide in the treatment of experimental brain compression. J. Neurosurg. **38:** 345–354.

9. DE LA TORRE, J. C., T. ERNEST & R. WOLLMAN. 1981. Subacute toxicity of intravenous dimethyl sulfoxide in rhesus monkeys. J. Tox. Environ. Health. **7:** 49–57.

10. DE LA TORRE, J. C. & J. W. SURGEON. 1976. Dexamethasone and DMSO in experimental transorbital cerebral infusion. Stroke **7:** 577–583.

11. DEL BIGIO, M., H. E. JAMES, P. E. CAMP, R. WERNER, L. F. MARSHALL & H. TUNG. 1982. Acute dimethyl sulfoxide therapy in brain edema. Part 3: Effect of a 3-hour infusion. Neurosurgery **10:** 86–89.

12. DISTEFANO, V. & J. J. KLAHN. 1965. Observations on the pharmacology and hemolytic activity of dimethyl sulfoxide. Toxicol. Appl. Pharmacol. **7:** 660–666.

13. DUJOVNY, M., P. J. BARRIONUEVO, R. K. LAHA, C. P. OSGOOD, S. DeCASTRO, J. MAROON & R. HELLSTROM. 1977. Experimental middle cerebral artery microsurgical embolectomy. *In* Microsurgery for Stroke. P. Schmiedek, Ed.: 91–97. Springer-Verlag. New York.

14. GO, K. G., W. ZIJLSTRA, A. FLANDERIJN, & F. ZUIDERVEEN. 1974. Circulatory factors influencing exudation in cold-induced cerebral edema. Exp. Neurol. **42:** 332–338.

15. JAMES, H. E., D. A. BRUCE & F. WELSH. 1978. Cytotoxic edema produced by 6-aminonicotinamide and its response to therapy. Neurosurgery **3:** 196–200.

16. JAMES. H. E., P. E. CAMP, R. D. HARBAUGH, L. F. MARSHALL & R. WERNER. 1982. Comparison of the effects of DMSO and pentobarbitone on experimental brain Oedema. Acta Neurochirurg. **60:** 245–255.

17. LAHA, R. K., M. DUJOVNY, P. J. BARRIONUEVO, S. C. DeCASTRO, H. R. HELLSTROM, & J. C. MAROON. 1978. Protective effects of methyl prednisolone and dimethyl sulfoxide in experimental middle cerebral artery embolectomy. J. Neurosurg. **49:** 508–516.

18. MATSUMOTO, A., K. KOGURE, Y. UTSUNOMIYA, R. BUSTO, P. SCHEINBERG & O. M. REINMUTH. 1975. Energy metabolism and CSF in cold induced brain edema: Comparison of the effect of dexamethasone under nitrous oxide and under pentobarbital anesthesia. *In* Blood Flow and Metabolism in the Brain. A. M. Harper, W. B. Jennett, J. D. Miller & J. O. Rowan, Eds.: 629–630. Churchill-Livingston. Edinburgh.

19. McGRAW, C. P. 1977. The effect of dimethyl sulfoxide (DMSO) on cerebral infarction in the Mongolian gerbil. Acta Neurol. Scand. [Suppl] **64:** 160–161.

20. MICHENFELDER, J. E. & R. A. THEYE. 1973. Cerebral protection by thiopental during hypoxia. Anesthesiology **39:** 510–517.

21. SCHIFFER, C. A., C. L. WHITAKER, M. SCHMUKLER, J. AISNER & S. L. HILBERT. 1976. The effect of dimethyl sulfoxide on in vitro platelet function. Thomb. Haemostas. **36:** 221–229.

22. HOSSMAN, K. A. & F. J. SCHUIER. 1980. Experimental brain infarcts in cats. Stroke **11**(6): 583–601.

23. SHAPIRO, H. M., S. R. WYTE & J. LOESER. 1974. Barbiturate-augmented hypothermia for reduction of persistent intracranial hypertension. J. Neurosurg. **40:** 90–100.

24. SMITH, A. L. & J. J. MARQUE. 1976. Anesthetics and cerebral edema. Anesthesiology **45:** 897–901.

25. TSURUDA, J., H. E. JAMES, P. E. CAMP & R. WERNER. 1982. Acute dimethyl sulfoxide therapy in experimental brain edema. Part 2: Dose and concentration on intracranial pressure, blood pressure, and central venous pressure. Neurosurgery **10**(3): 355–359.

DIMETHYL SULFOXIDE AND OTHER THERAPIES IN EXPERIMENTAL PRESSURE-INDUCED CEREBRAL FOCAL ISCHEMIA*

Maurice S. Albin, Leonid Bunegin, and Philip Helsel

Department of Anesthesiology
University of Texas Health Science Center
San Antonio, Texas 78284

During the past seven years,[1] our research group has been delineating the physiopathological responses of brain to graded brain retraction pressure (BRP) under a variety of conditions including normotension and induced arterial hypotension.[2-7] We have noted that the pressure threshold for the development of histological changes after one hour of retraction at normotensive arterial levels was greater than 20 torr and at induced hypotensive levels, greater than 10 torr. We have shown the correlation of somatosensory cortically evoked responses (SER) to the development of lesions and to cerebral perfusion pressures (CPP), with a higher CPP showing a smaller decrease in SER and a greater resistance to histopathological changes. We have also positively correlated decreases in SER with decreases in local cortical blood flow, especially in the face of induced hypotension to 50 torr.[5] Interestingly, the application of 20 torr BRP for a period of one hour on one somatosensory cortex has revealed a corresponding increase of intracranial pressure (ICP) on the contralateral side. Concurrently, a decrease in mean hemispheric and local cortical blood flow in the retracted and contralateral areas was considerably greater under induced hypotension than in the normotensive animals. Under these conditions, there was a loss of autoregulation in the hypotensive animals. By using the brain retraction pressure technique, we have been able to produce focal ischemia in the experimental animals (canine, cat, monkey) with definable, reproducible behavioral, histological, and survival characteristics. The objective of this study was to evaluate neurobehavioral and histological responses to dimethyl sulfoxide (DMSO) and other therapeutic modalities with graded BRP under induced arterial hypotension to 50 torr.

METHODS

Using light pentobarbital, endotracheal anesthesia in acclimated mongrel canines, a craniectomy was performed over the right temporal-parietal cortex. Each animal was monitored for the ECG, mean arterial blood pressure (MAP), central venous pressure (CVP), discontinuous arterial blood gases and electrolytes, obtained through previously inserted catheters, monitoring leads, and discontinuous arterial blood samples.

The dura was then incised and reflected, exposing an area over the somatosensory cortex. A 12.0 mm De Martel retractor blade was fixed onto a micromanipulator to control placement and movement of the retractor onto brain.

A thin-sleeved Albin-Bunegin pressure sensor was fixed over the retractor

*Supported in part by grants from The Distilled Spirits Council and The Moody Foundation.

261

and connected to the Codman® pressure monitor (FIGURES 1 and 2). A minute quantity of sterile air is pumped by the pressure monitor into the plastic sleeve sensor, which contains two contact electrodes. The amount of air pressure needed to separate the electrodes is proportional to the pressure exerted by the retractor. The pressure monitor cycles at least 20 times a minute so that an almost continuous reading of BRP can be obtained from this counter-pressure pneumoelectronic system.

The animals were randomly assigned to one of eight groups (seven treatment plus control) and subdivided into 0, 10, and 30 torr of BRP for one hour under sterile conditions with the MAP reduced to 50 torr using a titrated intravenous solution of trimetaphan. Following the hour, the retractor and monitoring system were then removed, the incisions closed, and the animals observed in an intensive care environment for seven days after which euthanasia occurred. The brains were then removed and placed in formalin for light microscopy study.

The neurobehavioral status (N.S.) was determined using the following five point rating scale: 0 = death before 7 days, 1 = paralysis, 2 = not paralyzed but unable to stand, 3 = standing with weakness, and 4 = normal standing and walking.

The randomized therapy included: (1) DMSO, 0.25 g/kg i.v. prior to retraction followed by 0.2 g/kg every 12 hours for 3 days. (2) Furosemide, 1.0 mg/kg i.v. during craniectomy and 0.5 mg/kg i.v. prior to closure of incision. (3) Hypothermia, using surface cooling to 30°C and maintained until termination of 1 hour of BRP. (4) Barbiturates, 15 mg/kg/h thiopental, sodium, by i.v. infusion until termination of surgical procedure. (5) Mannitol, 2.0 g/kg at craniectomy, then 1.0

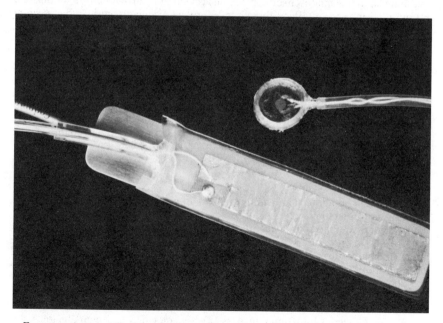

FIGURE 1. A 12-mm De Martel retractor blade encased in a plastic Albin-Bunegin brain retraction pressure sensor.

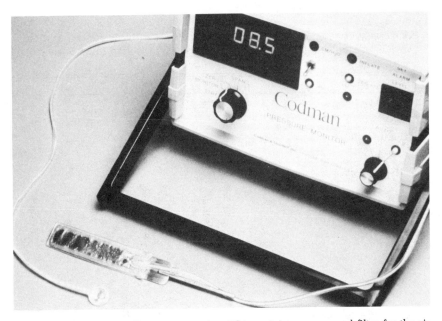

FIGURE 2. The Codman® pressure monitor. This contains a pump and filter for the air pressure source, a pressure transducer to give an electronic indication of pressure, and the solenoids and electronic control circuitry.

g/kg one-half hour prior to incision closure. (6) Dextran (low molecular weight) 10 ml/kg at beginning of craniectomy, followed by 10 ml/kg daily for 3 days postoperatively. (7) Methylprednisolone, 30 mg/kg daily (in 2 doses) for 3 days before, and 3 days after incision closure. (8) Control, no therapy but BRP of 0, 10, and 30 torr for 1 hour.

The experimental design included randomization of therapies and application during MAP at 50 torr and 0, 20, and 30 torr BRP.

The individual N.S. scores from each group (controls and treated animals) were compared first by analysis and variance and then each treatment group was compared to the controls by Dunnett's *t* test.

RESULTS

As can be noted in TABLE 1, 130 animals (N) were treated and rated, the N.S. being expressed as a mean score. The severest challenge to the brain is to be found when 30 torr of BRP was applied for one hour with the MAP at 50 torr; allowing for CPP of only 20 torr during the hour period of focal ischemia. It can be seen (TABLE 2) that the DMSO scoring was significant against control with hypothermia approaching significance. Combining the 10 and 30 BRP torr again indicates the better grading of DMSO and hypothermia. The only other therapy with survival scoring was mannitol. It was thought that the barbiturate group was

TABLE 1

NEUROBEHAVIORAL SCORING, BRAIN RETRACTION PRESSURES AT 0, 10, AND 30 TORR
WITH THERAPIES. THE MEAN ARTERIAL PRESSURE WAS REDUCED TO 50 TORR WITH
TRIMETAPHAN IN ALL ANIMALS.

Group	BRP/Torr	N.S.	N
DMSO	0	3.9	5
	10	3.0	5
	30	2.5	6
Furosemide	0	2.4	5
	10	3.4	7
	30	1.4	5
Hypothermia	0	3.0	5
	10	3.0	5
	30	2.2	5
Barbiturates	0	1.7	5
	10	0.6	6
	30	0.0	5
Mannitol	0	3.0	6
	10	2.5	4
	30	2.0	6
Dextran	0	2.9	7
	10	1.6	5
	30	1.4	5
Methylprednisolone	0	3.0	6
	10	1.8	5
	30	0.6	5
Control	0	3.8	5
	10	1.2	5
	30	0.9	7
			130 Total

not evaluated adequately because of a breakdown in the intensive care management of the 10 and 30 BRP/torr groups.

The histolgical study tended to reinforce the findings of the neurobehavioral
scoring. The lesion volumes in the 30 BRP/torr control group averaged about 3.0
ml ± 1.0 with severe focal swelling in the right parietal cortex with white matter

TABLE 2

THE NEUROBEHAVIORAL SCORING COMPARED TO CONTROLS AT 30 TORR BRAIN
RETRACTION PRESSURE

Therapies	N.S.	α
DMSO	2.57	0.05
Mannitol	2.00	NS
Furosemide	1.40	NS
Methylprednisolone	0.60	NS
Hypothermia	2.22	0.09
Dextran	1.40	NS
Barbiturates	0.00	NS
Control	0.85	

edema, focal necrosis, and cavitation occurring. Some edema and cortical hemorrhage could be seen on the left side as well.

The DMSO animals showed a much smaller lesion volume than control (<2.0 ml), slight to moderate focal swelling on right parietal cortex, mild white matter edema, superficial hemorrhage with a small amount of necrosis in right parietal region, and minimal edema on the left side. The histology in the 30 BRP/torr hypothermia group was similar to DMSO except for a slightly larger lesion volume. The remaining therapies appeared similar to control in lesion volumes, cavitation, necrosis, and edema.

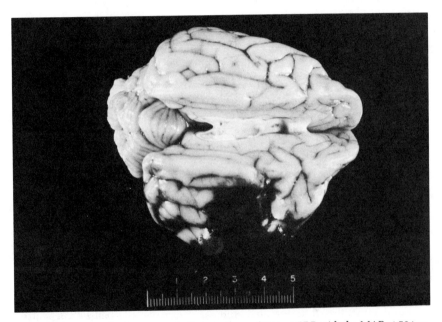

FIGURE 3. Canine brain one week after one hour of 30 torr BRP with the MAP at 50 torr. The lesion volume was calculated at 3.5 ml.

DISCUSSION

Although this experimental model of producing focal ischemia involves surgical manipulation of brain and exposure to air,[8] it has a validity based on surgical reality in the human and gives a reproducible lesion (FIGURE 3) that has many characteristics found after compression injury to brain. Our findings with this model relating to changes in blood flow and lesion development after BRP have been validated by Rosenorn and Diemer in a similar study in rats.[9]

Induced arterial hypotension is often used in neurosurgical vascular procedures with concomitant brain retraction.[10] It is important to realize that the critical factor causing the development in the pathology is the net reduction in regional cerebral perfusion pressure (rCPP). The maximal result occurs at a BRP of 30 torr when the MAP is reduced to 50 torr, the net rCPP being 20 torr (TABLE 3). In early experimental work,[2,3] we noted no local histological or SER reaction when a BRP of 50 torr was instituted for one hour in a group of animals whose MAP was greater than 150 torr.

The therapies tested in this study are those that have been, or are being used in the treatment of increased intracranial pressure, cerebral edema, cerebral ischemia, and for the enhancement of flow through the cerebral microcirculation.[10] In controlled animal studies, barbiturates[11] have been used to protect the brain against cerebral infarction. Unfortunately, it is felt that our barbiturate data are not valid because of difficulties involved in taking care of these animals in the intensive care environment.

TABLE 3

PHYSIOPATHOLOGICAL RESPONSES TO BRAIN RETRACTION PRESSURES OF 30, 20, AND 10 TORR WITH THE MEAN ARTERIAL PRESSURE AT 50 TORR USING TRIMETAPHAN

Retractor Pressure (torr)	Evoked Responses				72 Hours		
	30 Min	60 Min	120 Min	72 H	BBB	Path.	Neurology
30	+ +	–	–	–	+ + +	Infarc.	Pleg. Atax.
20	+ +	–	–	–	+ + +	Infarc.	Pleg. Atax.
10	+ +	+	+	±	–	Swell.	Normal

BBB is blood brain barrier permeability; Pleg. is plegia; Atax. is ataxia; infarc. is infarction; and swell. is swelling.

Our data appear to indicate that behavioral and histological improvement occurred in the 30 torr BRP groups that were subjected to DMSO and hypothermia when compared to the control. It also appears possible that statistical significance with hypothermia might occur if the N would be increased. There is no question that the DMSO-treated group at 30 torr BRP did better than control. Five of the six animals survived the seven-day period with better neurobehavioral scores and smaller, more superficial lesions.

While one can speculate that hypothermia exerts its protective effect because of a reduction in metabolic demand, the mechanism concerning DMSO is even more elusive. Experimental data have indicated that DMSO may affect the prostacyclin-prostaglandin system (PGE$_1$, PGE$_2$, and PGF$_{2\alpha}$);[12,13] inhibit platelet aggregation by increasing cAMP[14] and reducing platelet ADP;[15] increase spinal cord and cerebral blood flow in ischemic states; act as a hydroxyl-trapping agent;[16] and possibly stabilize cell membranes after mechanical damage.[17] A better description of these mechanisms can be seen in the review by de la Torre.[18]

We think that the ability of DMSO to scavenge free radicals may be an important factor in understanding its mechanisms of action. Our laboratory is now evaluating the ability of DMSO to attenuate lesion formation after ethanol infusion and pressure-induced focal ischemia under normotension and induced hypotension. It has been suggested that lipid free-radical damage may occur because of the lipophilic properties of ethanol, and Flamm and co-workers[19] have shown that ethanol potentiates central nervous system trauma.

We infused ethanol in anesthetized animals for a period of one hour so that the blood level was between 150-200 mg% and assigned then to 30 torr BRP with normotension and induced hyoptension and also with DMSO. Our preliminary data indicate:[20] (1) The lesion volume in the 30 torr BRP, ethanol, hypotensive group was five times larger than in the 30 torr BRP group without ethanol. (2) The lesion volume in the 30 torr BRP, ethanol, hypotensive group followed by DMSO appeared to be attenuated since it was not greater than twice the volume of the 30 torr BRP control without ethanol.

We feel that this information suggests that free-radical scavenging by DMSO might be its major mode of action. In terms of rapid therapeutic delivery from a variety of routes, DMSO has a most decided advantage over hypothermia where special techniques and equipment are needed and a time delay necessary before therapeutic temperatures can be reached.

CONCLUSION

In evaluating seven different therapies, DMSO appears to be most effective in attenuating neurobehavioral signs and histological responses to pressure-induced focal ischemia with the cerebral perfusion pressure lowered to 20 torr. It seems that free-radical scavenging may be the critical mechanism of action by DMSO.

REFERENCES

1. ALBIN, M. S., L. BUNEGIN, M. DUJOVNY, M. H. BENNETT, P. J. JANNETTA, & H. M. WISOTSKEY. 1975. Brain retraction pressure during intracranial procedures. Surg. Forum **26:** 199-200.
2. ALBIN, M. S., L. BUNEGIN, M. H. BENNETT, M. DUJOVNY & P. J. JANNETTA. 1977. Clinical and experimental brain retraction pressure monitoring. Acta Neurolog. Scand. (Suppl 64) **56:** 522-523.
3. BENNETT, M. H., L. BUNEGIN, M. S. ALBIN, M. DUJOVNY, H. HELLSTROM & P. J. JANNETTA. 1977. Evoked potential correlates of graded brain retraction pressure. Stroke **8:** 487-492.
4. LAHA, R. K., M. DUJOVNY, S. RAO, P. S. BARRIONUEVO, L. BUNEGIN, H. R. HELLSTROM, M. S. ALBIN & F. H. TAYLOR. 1979. Cerebellar retraction: Significance and sequelae. Surg. Neurol. **12**(3): 209-215.
5. ALBIN, M. S., L. BUNEGIN, P. HELSEL, A. MARLIN & M. BABINSKI. 1980. Intracranial pressure and regional cerebral blood flow responses to experimental brain retraction pressure. *In* Intracranial Pressure IV. K. Shulman, A. Marmaru, J. Miller, D. Becker, G. Hochwald & M. Brock, Eds.: 131-134. Springer-Verlag. Berlin.
6. BUNEGIN, L., M. S. ALBIN, P. HELSEL & R. D. BELL. 1980. Changes in somatosensory evoked responses and cerebral blood flow following induced hypotension. Anesthesiology **53:** 546.
7. ALBIN, M. S., L. BUNEGIN, A. MARLIN, P. HELSEL, W. PHILLIPS & M. BABINSKI. 1980. Brain retraction pressure and cerebral perfusion. Anesthesiology **53:** S117.
8. DIAZ, F. G. & J. L. AUSMAN. 1980. Experimental cerebral ischemia. Neurosurgery. **6:** 436-445.
9. ROSENORN, J. & H. H. DIEMER. 1982. Reduction of regional cerebral blood flow during brain retraction pressure in the rat. J. Neurosurg. **56:** 826-829.
10. ALBIN, M. D. 1978. Neuroanesthesiology. *In* Microsurgical Treatment of Neurovascular Disease. Neurosurgery (Supplement) **3:** 285-337.

11. SMITH, A., J. HOFF, S. NIELSEN & C. LARSON. 1975. Barbiturate protection against cerebral infarction. In Cerebral Circulation and Metabolism. T. Langfit, L. McHenry, Jr., C. M. Reivich & H. Wollman., Eds.: 347–348. Springer-Verlag, New York.
12. LEHANN, T. R. & A. HORITA. Effects of dimethyl sulfoxide (DMSO) on prostaglandin synthetase. Proc. West. Pharmacol. Soc. **18:** 81–82.
13. RAO, CH. V. 1977. Differential effects of detergents and dimethyl sulfoxide on membrane prostaglandin E_1 and F_2 receptors. Life Sci. **20:** 2013.
14. WIESER, P. B., M. A. ZEIGER & J. N. FAIN. 1977. Effects of dimethyl sulfoxide on cyclic AMP accumulation, lipolysis and glucose metabolism of fat cells. Biochem. Pharmacol. **26:** 775–778.
15. SCHIFFER, C. A., C. L. WHITAKER, M. SCHMUKLER, J. AISNER & S. L. HILBERT. 1976. The effect of dimethyl sulfoxide on in vitro platelet function. Thrombos. Haesmostas. (Stuttg.) **36:** 221–229.
16. PANGAMALA, R. V., H. M. SHARMA & R. E. HEIKKILA. 1976. Role of hydroxyl radical scavengers, dimethyl sulfoxide, alcohols and methonal in the inhibition of prostaglandin synthesis. Prostaglandins **11:** 599–607.
17. LIM, R. & S. MULLAN. 1975. Enhancement of resistance of glial cells by dimethyl sulfoxide against sonic disruption. Ann. N.Y. Acad. Sci. **243:**358–361.
18. DE LA TORRE, J. 1980. Chemotherapy of spinal cord trauma. In The Spinal Cord and Its Reaction to Traumatic Injury. W. F. Windle, Ed.: 291–310. Marcel Dekker. New York.
19. FLAMM, E. S., H. B. DEMOPOULOS, M. L. SELIGMAN, J. J. TOMASULA, V. DECRESCITO & J. RANSOHOFF. 1977. Ethanol potentiation of central nervous system trauma. J. Neurosurg. **46:** 328–335.
20. ALBIN, M. S., L. BUNEGIN & J. GELINEAU. 1982. Alcohol enhances enlargement of intracranial focal ischemic lesions. Anesthesiology **57:** A309.

INEFFECTIVENESS OF DMSO IN TREATING
EXPERIMENTAL BRAIN ISCHEMIA*

John R. Little, Robert F. Spetzler,† Richard A. Roski,† Warren R.
Selman,† Joseph Zabramski,† and Ronald P. Lesser

Department of Neurosurgery
Cleveland Clinic Foundation
Cleveland, Ohio 44106

†*Department of Neurosurgery*
Case Western Reserve University
Cleveland, Ohio 44106

INTRODUCTION

The effects of treatment of acute focal cerebral ischemia with dimethyl sulfoxide (DMSO) are controversial. Some experimental studies have shown improvement in morbidity and mortality;[1-3] whereas, other studies have not.[4,5] The objective of the present investigation was to study the effects of DMSO on acute focal cerebral ischemia in two established experimental models.

METHODS

Middle Cerebral Artery Occlusion in Cats

Twenty adult male cats (*Felix catus*) were anesthetized with ketamine hydrochloride (40 mg/kg intraperitoneally). The administration of ketamine hydrochloride took place two or more hours before middle cerebral artery (MCA) occlusion. Additional doses of ketamine hydrochloride were not given.

A tracheostomy was performed and mechanical ventilation instituted. Skeletal muscle paralysis was achieved with D-tubocurare (1.5 mg/kg i.v.). A small catheter was inserted into the right carotid artery through the lingual artery for the subsequent injection of radionuclides.

Arterial blood gases were intermittently determined to maintain the $PaCO_2$ in the 30–35 torr range and the PaO_2 above 100 torr. Arterial blood pressure was monitored continuously. A heating pad was placed over the trunk to keep the core temperature at 37°C as measured by a rectal temperature probe. The right MCA was exposed through a transorbital approach. The proximal segment of the right MCA was dissected from the adjacent structures in preparation for the application of a miniature aneurysm clip.

The scalp and temporalis muscle were removed bilaterally from the skull. Small stainless steel bolt electrodes were screwed into holes drilled bilaterally 1 cm from the midline in the midfrontal, posterior frontal, and parietal regions. Another hole was drilled in the midline over the frontal air sinus and a screw was inserted for use as a reference electrode. The temporalis muscle was used for the

*Supported in part by grants from the American Heart Association (Northeast Ohio Affiliate) and National Institutes of Health grant 1 R01 NS15411-10A1.

ground. EEG tracings were obtained at regular intervals before and after right MCA occlusion.

An index of erythrocyte flow was determined by measuring the transit of technetium-99 (^{99}Tc) labeled erythrocytes.[6] A collimated 1.5 cm sodium iodide crystal was applied to the skull overlying the right Sylvian cortex. The ^{99}Tc-labeled erythrocytes (0.5 ml containing 100 μCi) were injected rapidly into the right carotid artery through the lingual artery catheter. Measurements were recorded on a paper strip recorder.

Regional cerebral blood flow (rCBF) was measured by the xenon-133 (^{133}Xe) clearance technique. The sodium iodide crystal placement was similar to that used for the ^{99}Tc erythrocyte transit studies. The ^{133}Xe (200 μCi in 0.5 ml of normal saline) was injected rapidly into the right carotid artery through the lingual artery catheter. Measurements were recorded on a multichannel analyzer for a 10-minute period. The partition coefficient was adjusted for the hemoglobin value of each animal. Kinetic analysis was used to calculate the rCBF.

The erythrocyte transit and rCBF studies were performed immediately before right MCA occlusion. The studies were repeated immediately after occlusion and again at 3 and 6 hours.

The right MCA was occluded with a miniature aneurysm clip after the completion of the initial radionuclide and EEG studies. The clip remained in place for 6 hours.

Treatment Groups

The 20 cats were assigned alternately to the control and treatment groups. Ten cats were not treated. They received 25 ml of normal saline intravenously during a 15-minute period beginning at the time of right MCA occlusion. Ten cats were treated with medical grade DMSO (2.5 g/kg). Normal saline was added to the DMSO to a combined volume of 25 ml (i.e., 30–50% DMSO concentration). The solution was administered intravenously over a 15-minute period beginning at the time of right MCA occlusion.

Examination of the Brains

Thirty minutes before carbon-fixative perfusion, sodium fluorescein (i.e., 0.5 ml of a 10% solution) and Evans blue dye (i.e., 0.5 ml of a 10% solution) were given intravenously. Intra-arterial carbon-fixative perfusion was carried out at the end of the 6-hour ischemic period after the completion of the radionuclide studies. A midline thoracotomy was performed. The right MCA was reopened by removing the aneurysm clip to improve the delivery of the carbon-fixative solution to the ischemic tissue. The animals were perfused with 50 ml of isotonic saline followed by a mixture of colloidal carbon (250 ml) and phosphate-buffered formaldehyde (250 ml) at a constant pressure of 100 mm Hg. The brains were removed and placed in 10% buffered formalin for 48 hours.

The brains were sliced coronally and the presence or absence of fluorescein and Evans blue dye was recorded. The distribution and intensity of carbon staining were graded according to a previously described system.[7] Grade "0" indicated normal vascular filling; Grade "1" referred to a few circumscribed foci of poor filling, not more than 3 mm in diameter; Grade "2" indicated a large area of improper subcortical filling; and Grade "3" referred to an extensive cortical and subcortical region of impaired filling.

Thin (i.e., 10 μm) semi-serial coronal sections were prepared from paraffin-embedded slices of both hemispheres, stained with hematoxylin and eosin and periodic acid Schiff stains, and examined with a light microscope. The cross-sectional areas of gray matter were moderate and severe neuronal alterations (i.e., Grades 2 and 3[8]) predominated were determined in coronal sections of the right cerebral hemispheres 3 mm posterior to the temporal lobe tip. The percentage of gray matter surface area where severe ischemic neuronal alterations predominated (i.e., ischemic gray area/total gray area $\times 100$) was determined.

Middle Cerebral Artery Occlusion in Baboons

Fifteen male baboons (*Papio anibus*) were anesthetized with ketamine hydrochloride. An inflatable balloon occluder was placed around the left MCA through a transorbital approach.[9] The cuff was positioned immediately distal to the origin of the left MCA and proximal to the lenticulostriate branches.

After implantation of the occluding device, the baboons were prepared for intensive care monitoring. Percutaneous femoral catheterization was employed to introduce long and short arterial lines and two central venous lines. Two sets of symmetrically placed (frontal, occipital, earlobe) EEG needle electrodes were inserted into the scalp. A rectal probe was inserted for temperature monitoring. All animals were placed in a primate restraint chair and allowed to recover for at least 24 hours after implantation for subsequent experimentation to assure that no neurological deficit had occurred secondary to surgery. All animals were awake and free from the effects of anesthetics at the time of MCA occlusion.

Treatment Groups

The 15 baboons were assigned alternately to the untreated and treated groups. Seven baboons undergoing 6 hours of temporary left MCA occlusion were not treated. These baboons had the same intensive care as the treated baboons.

Four baboons undergoing 6 hours of temporary left MCA occlusion were treated with DMSO and pentobarbital. They were given DMSO (1 g/kg i.v.) 30 minutes and 2 hours after occlusion. These animals subsequently received a continuous infusion of DMSO during the next 8 hours (i.e., 1 g/kg i.v. over 8 hours). Pentobarbital therapy was begun 4 hours after MCA occlusion. A loading dose of 30 mg/kg was administered by slow intravenous infusion. Continuous barbiturate infusion was then begun and titrated to maintain an isoelectric EEG (less than 2 μV potentials) while not allowing a reduction of arterial blood pressure of more than 15%. Aramine (metaraminol hydrochloride) was administered for the occasional periods of hypotension that could not be controlled by decreasing the barbiturate infusion. The treated animals were intubated and ventilated to maintain normocarbia (PaCO$_2$ 32–38 torr) and normoxia (PO$_2$ 90–120 torr). Barbiturate coma was maintained for 96 hours. The pentobarbital was then discontinued.

Four baboons undergoing 12 hours of temporary left MCA occlusion were treated with DMSO alone. The regimen for DMSO administration was similar to the 6-hour group treated with DMSO and pentobarbital.

After the period of intensive care observation, the baboons were returned to their cages. The final neurological evaluation was performed in surviving animals one week after left MCA occlusion. Neurological examination was based on a 100-point scale that allowed evaluation of unrestrained primates.[9] Lower scores represented worse outcomes, with a score of 0 indicating death before the end of the 1 week observation period.

Examination of the Brains

The surviving baboons were killed humanely one week after occlusion with intravenous KCl, and the brains removed and placed in 10% buffered formalin for one week. The morphological examination was based on a 100-point scale to evaluate the percentage of grossly infarcted hemisphere, the presence of gross shift of midline structures, and the microscopic appearance of the neural tissue and microvasculature.[10] Lower scores represented more severe morphological changes.

The brains of those animals that died before the end of the intensive care monitoring were removed immediately. These brains were analyzed in the same fashion as described in the preceding paragraph.

RESULTS

Middle Cerebral Artery Occlusion in Cats

Vital Signs

Systemic stability was maintained in all cats. Physiological monitoring parameters, including blood pressure, PaO_2, $PaCO_2$, and temperature were similar in the untreated and treated groups. The mean hematocrit was $34 \pm 3\%$ in the untreated group and $32 \pm 4\%$ in the treated group.

Radionuclide Studies

The results of the erythrocyte transit studies were similar in the untreated and treated groups. Erythrocyte transit times in the untreated group were 10 ± 1 sec before occlusion, 13 ± 4 sec immediately after occlusion, 16 ± 3 sec at 3 hours, and 18 ± 5 sec at 6 hours. Erythrocyte transit times in the treated group were 10 ± 2 sec before occlusion, 15 ± 4 sec immediately after occlusion, 19 ± 6 sec at 3 hours, and 19 ± 5 sec at 6 hours.

A significant difference in rCBF was not demonstrated between the untreated and treated groups. Eight cats in the untreated and treated groups had rCBF values below 18 ml/100 g/min on at least one occasion following MCA occlusion. The rCBF (ml/100 g/min) in the untreated group was 46 ± 10 before occlusion, 15 ± 8 immediately after occlusion, 14 ± 4 at 3 hours, and 11 ± 3 at 6 hours. The rCBF (ml/100 g/min) in the treated group was 45 ± 11 before occlusion, 16 ± 6 immediately after occlusion, 15 ± 9 at 3 hours, and 15 ± 6 at 6 hours.

EEG Studies

The amplitude of EEG activity was reduced in the right cerebral hemisphere immediately after right MCA occlusion in 8 untreated cats and 7 treated cats. In all cats there was a tendency over a period of hours for the EEG voltage to gradually diminish bilaterally in addition to whatever focal changes occurred after occlusion. Overall, no significant differences were found between the untreated and treated groups. In 2 untreated cats and 3 treated cats, there was no significant alteration in the relationship between the EEG backgrounds in the two hemispheres after occlusion. The rCBF was consistently greater than 18 ml/100 g/min in the 2 untreated cats and in 2 of the 3 treated cats without EEG changes.

Morphological Studies

Macroscopic findings. The right MCA and its major branches were well filled with carbon-fixative solution. This confirmed the reopening of the right MCA after removal of the miniature aneurysm clip. Gross swelling of cerebral tissue in

TABLE 1

DISTRIBUTION OF COLLOIDAL CARBON IN THE RIGHT CEREBRAL HEMISPHERES OF CATS UNDERGOING RIGHT MIDDLE CEREBRAL ARTERY OCCLUSION

Carbon Distribution Grade	Untreated Cats (10)	Treated Cats (10)
0	0	1
1	1	0
2	1	1
3	8	8

the right MCA territory was present in 8 untreated cats and 8 treated cats. The mean right-to-left shift of midline structures was 1.0 ± 0.5 mm in both groups. The distribution of carbon filling in the right cerebral hemisphere is listed in TABLE 1. Evans blue staining was invariably present in areas of gray matter pallor and had a patchy distribution. Fluorescein staining was present in the same areas, but was less intense.

Microscopic findings. The percentage of gray matter cross-sectional area where severe ischemic neuronal alterations predominated was $45 \pm 12\%$ in the untreated group and $51 \pm 14\%$ in the treated group. Two untreated cats and 2 treated cats had severe ischemic changes involving less than 20% of the gray matter area. A significant difference was not identified.

Middle Cerebral Artery Occlusion in Baboons

Vital Signs

Physiological monitoring parameters, including blood pressure, PaO_2, $PaCO_2$, and temperature were similar in the three groups.

Neurological Findings

Analysis of the neurological scores indicated that treatment with DMSO and pentobarbital coma or DMSO alone did not improve the outcome (TABLE 2) when compared with untreated baboons in the present and previous studies.[10,11] Similar observations had been made in the evaluation of baboons undergoing 6 hours of MCA occlusion with 96 hours of pentobarbital coma starting 4 hours after occlusion.[10]

Morphological Studies

Analysis of morphological changes also demonstrated that treatment with DMSO and pentobarbital coma or DMSO alone failed to reduce ischemic

TABLE 2

NEUROLOGICAL AND PATHOLOGICAL SCORES IN 15 BABOONS UNDERGOING LEFT MIDDLE CEREBRAL ARTERY OCCLUSION

Treatment Groups (Number of Baboons)	Neurological Score	Pathological Score
	47	40
	27	20
	17	20
Untreated baboons (7)	17	10
	0	0
	0	0
	0	0
DMSO-Pentobarbital Treated baboons (4)	70	60
	0	0
	0	0
	0	0
DMSO-Treated Baboons (4)	90	80
	0	0
	0	0
	0	0

Neurological score: 100 (no deficit) ↔ 0 (death)
Pathological score: 100 (no infarct) ↔ 0 (extensive infarct/edema)

cerebral edema and the size of the infarct (TABLE 2). Similar observations had been made in the brains of baboons undergoing 6 hours in MCA occlusion with 96 hours of pentobarbital coma starting 4 hours after occlusion.[10]

DISCUSSION

Dimethyl sulfoxide has been heralded as a potent therapeutic agent capable of providing benefit in a wide range of conditions. The mechanisms of action, however, have not been clearly established. Findings of previous studies suggest that DMSO can accumulate free radicals, stabilize lysosomes, protect cell membranes, disaggregate platelets, reduce tissue edema, stimulate diuresis, reduce intracranial pressure, and increase cellular resistance to anoxia and ischemia.[1-3,12-17]

A beneficial effect of DMSO in the treatment of acute focal cerebral ischemia has not been clearly established. De la Torre and Surgeon[1] treated 5 rhesus monkeys with DMSO (2.5 g/kg i.v.) 4 hours after acute, unilateral MCA occlusion. The MCA was reopened after 17 hours of occlusion, and the monkeys were killed seven days later. The treated monkeys showed "significant protection from the severe neurological deficits" seen in an untreated group of 5 monkeys. Reduction in brain swelling and tissue injury in the DMSO-treated group was reported; however, the rCBF changes were not altered.

The results of the study of de la Torre and Surgeon[1] did not allow firm conclusions about the efficacy of DMSO in the treatment of acute focal cerebral ischemia. The number of treated monkeys (i.e., 5) was small. As well, DMSO administration was begun 4 hours after MCA occlusion, that is, at a time when microcirculatory insufficiency would have impaired delivery of the agent and when irreversible neuronal injury would have been present.[8,18-20]

In another investigation, de la Torre and associates[2] treated 10 squirrel monkeys with DMSO (1 g/kg i.v.) 15 minutes after MCA occlusion. Two treated monkeys died within 4 days, whereas 6 of 10 untreated monkeys died. No other parameters were reported. However, the results suggested some protection from the effects of cerebral swelling secondary to infarction.

Laha and associates[3] studied the effects of DMSO (2 g/kg i.v.) in dogs undergoing embolic occlusion of the MCA. DMSO was given to 6 dogs beginning at the time of embolization. The embolus was removed from the MCA using microsurgical techniques 6 hours after embolization. Three weeks later the dogs were killed and the brains were examined. The neurological deficits and pathological findings in the treated dogs were less severe than those in the 9 untreated dogs.

The embolization technique used for MCA occlusion of the dog by Laha and associates,[3] although mimicking the human situation, is more difficult to control and probably less reliable than direct compression occlusion of the artery with a clip or balloon occluding device. Cortical infarction, when it occurs, is usually hemorrhagic.[21-23] As well, MCA occlusion in dogs has not been shown to consistently produce cortical and subcortical ischemic infarction.[23-25] Consequently, more than 6 dogs would have to be used in order to make any firm conclusions.

McGraw and Larsen[4] were unable to demonstrate a beneficial action of DMSO in acute focal cerebral ischemia. They treated 20 mongolian gerbils with DMSO (0.5 ml of a 50% solution) one hour after unilateral ligation of the carotid artery. There was no significant difference in infarct production or morbidity from that in the untreated group, which received saline. However, increased permeability to Trypan blue dye was found more frequently in untreated animals. The studies suggested that treatment with DMSO favorably modified permeability changes in the blood-brain barrier.

In the present study, treatment with DMSO did not adversely affect the physiological parameters in either the cats or baboons. No improvement of EEG findings, erythrocyte transit, rCBF, blood-brain permeability, or morphological findings were demonstrated in the DMSO-treated cats undergoing 6 hours of MCA occlusion. The use of DMSO also failed to favorably modify the neurological or morphological outcome in baboons undergoing 12 hours of MCA occlusion.

Previous studies by Selman and associates[10,11] have shown that barbiturate coma effectively improves the neurological and pathological scores in baboons undergoing 6 hours of MCA occlusion when treatment is started within 30 minutes of occlusion. Treatment with barbiturates starting 4 hours after MCA occlusion did not result in improvement. In the present study, DMSO was started 30 minutes after MCA occlusion and pentobarbital coma was initiated 3.5 hours later. This protocol was selected to determine a simple method of protecting the ischemic brain when pentobarbital coma is started at a time when pentobarbital therapy alone may be ineffective, that is, a situation commonly encountered clinically. Unfortunately, the use of DMSO in conjunction with pentobarbital coma failed to improve the outcome.

SUMMARY

A beneficial effect of dimethyl sulfoxide (DMSO) in the treatment of acute focal cerebral ischemia has not been proven. In the present study, two established experimental models of acute focal cerebral ischemia were treated with DMSO. Twenty adult cats lightly anesthetized with ketamine hydrochloride underwent right middle cerebral artery (MCA) occlusion for 6 hours. Ten cats were not treated and 10 cats received DMSO (2.5 g/kg i.v.) immediately after occlusion. No improvement of EEG findings, erythrocyte transit, regional cerebral blood flow (rCBF), blood-brain barrier permeability, or morphological findings were demonstrated in the DMSO-treated cats. In a second study, 15 conscious adult baboons underwent temporary left MCA occlusion (6 or 12 hours) using an implanted occluding device. Seven baboons were not treated and 8 baboons received continuous intravenous infusions of DMSO for 10 hours beginning 30 minutes after occlusion. Four of the baboons that were treated with DMSO also were treated with pentobarbital coma for 96 hours starting 4 hours after occlusion. Analysis of the neurological scores after 1 week survival indicated that treatment with DMSO alone and DMSO and pentobarbital coma did not improve the outcome. Morphological changes were similar in the 3 groups. The findings of our investigation indicate that DMSO is ineffective in treating acute focal cerebral ischemia.

ACKNOWLEDGMENTS

The authors express their appreciation to Dr. Arthur L. Scherbel, Department of Rheumatology, for his advice and guidance in this project.

REFERENCES

1. DE LA TORRE, J. C. & J. W. SURGEON. 1976. Dexamethasone and DMSO in experimental transorbital cerebral infarction. Stroke 7: 577–583.
2. DE LA TORRE, J. C., H. M. KAWANAGA, D. W. ROWED, C. M. JOHNSON, D. J. GOODE, K. KAJIHARA & S. MULLAN. 1975. Dimethyl sulfoxide in central nervous system trauma. Ann. N.Y. Acad. Sci. 243: 362–389.
3. LAHA, R. K., M. DUJOVNY, P. J. BARRIONUEVO, S. C. DeCASTRO, H. R. HELLSTROM & J. C. MAROON. 1978. Protective effects of methyl prednisolone and dimethyl sulfoxide in experimental middle cerebral artery embolectomy. J. Neurosurg. 49: 508–516.

4. McGraw, C. P. & J. W. Lawson. 1977. The effect of dimethyl sulfoxide on cerebral infarction in the mongolian gerbil. Stroke **8:** 6.

5. Little, J. R., A. Cook & R. P. Lesser. 1981. Treatment of acute focal cerebral ischemia with dimethyl sulfoxide. Neurosurgery **9:** 34–39.

6. Little, J. R., A. Cook, S. A. Cook & W. J. MacIntyre. 1981. Microcirculatory obstruction in focal cerebral ischemia. Albumin and erythrocyte transit. Stroke **12:** 218–223.

7. Crowell, R. M. & Y. Olsson. 1973. Observations on the microvasculature in focal cerebral ischemia and infarction. *In* Eighth Conference in Cerebrovascular Disease. F. H. McDowell & R. W. Brennen, Eds. **8:** 77–88. Grune & Stratton. New York.

8. Little, J. R. 1980. Morphological changes in acute focal ischemia: Response to osmotherapy. Adv. Neurol. **28:** 443–457.

9. Spetzler, R. F., W. R. Selman, P. Weinstein, J. Townsend, M. Mehdorn, D. Telles, R. C. Crumrine & R. Macko. 1980. Chronic reversible cerebral ischemia: Evaluation of a new baboon model. Neurosurgery **7:** 257–261.

10. Selman, W. R., R. F. Spetzler, R. A. Roski, V. R. Roessmann, R. Crumrine & R. Macko. 1982. Barbiturate coma in focal cerebral ischemia. J. Neurosurg. **56:** 685–690.

11. Selman, W. R., R. F. Speltzer, V. R. Roessmann, J. I. Rosenblatt & R. Crumrine. 1981. Barbiturate-induced coma therapy for focal cerebral ischemia. J. Neurosurg. **55:** 220–226.

12. Ashwood-Smith, M. J. 1975. Current concepts concerning radioprotective and cryoprotective properties of dimethyl sulfoxide in cellular systems. Ann. N.Y. Acad. Sci. **243:** 246–256.

13. Deutsch, E. & M. Kock. 1966. Zur Wirkung von DMSO auf de Blutgerinnung. *In* Dimethylsulfoxyd-DMSO Internationales Symposium. pp. 144–149. Saladruck. Berlin.

14. Finney, J. W., H. C. Urschel, G. A. Balla, G. J. Race, B. E. Jay, H. P. Pingree, H. L. Dorman & J. J. Mallams. 1967. Protection of the ischemic heart with DMSO alone or DMSO with hydrogen peroxide. Ann. N.Y. Acad. Sci. **141:** 231–241.

15. Franz, T. J. & J. T. Van Bruggen. 1967. A possible mechanism of action of DMSO. Ann. N.Y. Acad. Sci. **141:** 302–309.

16. Panganamala, R. V., H. M. Scharma, R. E. Heikkila, J. C. Geer & D. G. Cornwell. 1976. Role of hydroxyl radical scavengers dimethyl sulfoxide, alcohols, and methional in the inhibition of prostaglandin biosynthesis. Prostaglandins **11:** 599–607.

17. Weismann, G., G. Sessa & V. Bevens. 1967. Effect of DMSO on the stability of lysosomes by cortisone and chloroquine in vitro. Ann. N.Y. Acad. Sci. **141:** 326–332.

18. Hossman, K.-A. & F. J. Schuier. 1980. Experimental brain infarcts in cats: I. Pathophysiological observations. Stroke **11:** 583–592.

19. Little, J. R., T. M. Sundt & F. W. L. Kerr. 1974. Neuronal alterations in developing cortical infarction: An experimental study in monkeys. J. Neurosurg. **40:** 186–198.

20. Little, J. R., F. W. L. Kerr & T. M. Sundt. 1975. Microcirculatory obstruction in focal cerebral ischemia: Relationship to neuronal alterations. Mayo Clin. Proc. **50:** 264–270.

21. Dujovny, M., C. P. Osgood, P. J. Barrionuevo, R. Hellstrom & R. K. Laha. 1976. Middle cerebral artery microneurosurgical embolectomy. Surgery **80:** 336–339.

22. Hill, N. G., C. H. Millikan, K. G. Wakin & G. P. Sayre. 1955. Studies in cerebrovascular disease. VII. Experimental production of cerebral infarction by intracarotid injection of homologous blood clot. Mayo Clin. Proc. **30:** 625–633.

23. Molinari, G. F. 1970. Experimental cerebral infarction. II. Clinicopathological model of deep cerebral infarction. Stroke **1:** 232–244.

24. Diaz, F. G., A. R. Mastri, J. Ausman & S. N. Chou. 1979. Acute cerebral revascularization: Part 1. Cerebral ischemia experimental animal model. Surg. Neurol. **12:** 353–362.

25. Shibata, S., C. P. Hodge & H. M. Pappius. 1974. Effect of experimental ischemia on cerebral water and electrolytes. J. Neurosurg. **41:** 146–159.

TREATMENT OF CEREBRAL INFARCTION WITH DIMETHYL SULFOXIDE IN THE MONGOLIAN GERBIL*

C. Patrick McGraw

Division of Neurological Surgery
Department of Surgery
University of Louisville School of Medicine
Louisville, Kentucky 40292

INTRODUCTION

Ischemic cerebral infarction is one of the leading causes of morbidity and mortality in the United States. It can be a serious secondary effect of cardiac dysfunction or thrombus generation from cardiac maladies. Dimethyl sulfoxide (DMSO) has been shown to have multiple actions that can improve morbidity and mortality rates in acute focal cerebral ischemia.

Decreased Intracranial Pressure

DMSO has been reported to acutely decrease intracranial pressure (ICP) in experimental animal injury models.[1,2] One gram of a 10% solution of DMSO[1] significantly decreased the ICP within five minutes in rabbits with cryogenic lesions. However, the baseline ICP or wave was less than 20 mm Hg. De la Torre et al.[2] produced supratentorial extradural compression with a balloon until they observed apnea, dilated pupils, bilaterally flat EEG, a self-sustaining rise in intracranial pressure and blood pressure, and reduced carotid blood flow. All animals subsequently began gasping respirations. The balloon was decompressed at one hour in the surviving animals. One group was treated with 2.2 g/kg DMSO.† The animals' ICP returned to baseline within a few minutes following DMSO injection.[2]

Brown et al.[5] found that ICP increased following cerebral missile injury and that this elevated pressure was decreased with DMSO treatment in a manner similar to treatment with mannitol or saline infusion. They[5] reported that DMSO therapy resulted in a higher blood pressure, higher cerebral perfusion pressure, higher blood flow, and higher oxidative metabolism than in untreated or mannitol-treated animals.

DMSO has also been reported to have many effects that may prove useful in the treatment of elevated ICP produced by cerebral edema. These effects, discussed in more detail below, include anti-inflammation, diuresis and antiedema, antiplatelet aggregation, vasodilation, respiratory stimulation, lysosmal membrane stabilization, blood-brain barrier penetrations, and nonspecific increased resistance to insult.

*Supported in part by the North Carolina Heart Association (Chapel Hill, N.C.) and in part by National Institute of Neurologic Disease (Washington D.C.) Grant NS 06655-11.

†While the single-dose LD$_{50}$ given monkeys is between 4 and 8 g/kg,[3] DMSO has been administered topically to humans in doses of 1 g/kg for 90 days without serious side effects.[4]

0077-8923/83/0411–0278 $01.75/0 © 1983, NYAS

Anti-inflammatory Effect

DMSO has been shown to have an anti-inflammatory effect in many tissues.[6-8] De la Torre and Surgeon[9] have reported a protective effect with experimental transorbital infarction in rhesus monkeys. Laha et al.[10] in a similar study, using an experimental dog model of middle cerebral artery embolism, reported that low dose methyl prednisolone and dimethyl sulfoxide both provided some protective effects. They found that in control animals the average size of brain infarction was 1.45 cm. The animals treated with methylprednisolone (2 mg/kg) or with DMSO 2 g/kg had no brain infarction. However, animals treated with methyl prednisolone (30 mg/kg) suffered cerebral infarction similar to the untreated animals.

Diuretic and Anti-edema Effect

Dimethyl sulfoxide has been reported to produce diuresis,[9,11,12] which reduces blood volume and should decrease the elevated ICP often associated with cerebral ischemia. It has been reported to protect against cellular disruption.[28] Dimethyl sulfoxide reduces tissue edema,[34,11] which should decrease necrosis of brain tissue caused by edema and, therefore, should reduce the size of the lesion. De la Torre et al.[9] measured brain dry and wet weights as a measure of cerebral edema following cerebral infarction. They found that there was no swelling of the traumatized hemisphere in DMSO-treated rhesus monkeys. Camp et al.[1] found that therapy with DMSO plus 6-aminonicotinamide for cryogenic lesions produced a significant decrease in the water content of both hemispheres of the brain.

Vasodilatory Effect

Several studies present indirect evidence that DMSO may produce vasodilation. These include increased pedicle-flap survival following treatment with DMSO,[13] the histamine-liberating properties of DMSO,[14] and the smooth muscle relaxing properties of DMSO.[15]

Some studies indicate that DMSO increases cerebral blood flow following injury.[5,12] De la Torre et al.[12] reported that in the rhesus monkey, DMSO improved cortical blood flow within 30 minutes and improved carotid blood flow within 10 minutes of its administration. This increase in blood flow should facilitate the passage of nutrients to the ischemic area, and enhance the protective effects of DMSO. Dimethyl sulfoxide has also been reported to increase tissue oxygenation[16,17] or reduce oxygen consumption.[18] Other studies report no change in cerebral blood flow with DMSO administration.[9,19] In a later study, de la Torre and Surgeon[9] reported that in rhesus monkeys subjected to experimental cerebral infarction, DMSO-treated animals had less brain damage than control animals and they also had greater protection from the severe neurological deficits seen in control animals.

In each of these studies, mean arterial pressure and ICP changed with treatment. No data were provided with which to calculate cerebral vascular resistance. It is not possible to determine if DMSO produced cerebral vasodilation in these studies.

Respiratory Stimulant Effect

De la Torre and Rowed[20] have demonstrated that DMSO is a potent respiratory stimulant. They administered DMSO intravenously 2.0 g/kg in a 50% vol/vol solution, intravenously to rhesus monkeys. One minute after injection, the respiratory minute volume was depressed for an average of 54%. The respiratory rate increased by an average of 16%. After three minutes, the respiratory minute volume had risen to almost 300% control value and the respiratory rate had increased by almost 50% of control value.[20] The respiratory minute ventilation remained elevated for about 30 minutes following a single injection. This respiratory stimulation alone may be sufficient enough to cause a decrease in ICP. Dimethyl sulfoxide has also been reported to increase tissue oxygenation[16,17] or to reduce oxygen consumption.[18]

Stabilization of Lysosomal Membranes

Weissman et al.[21] reported that the concentration of steroids and chloroquine necessary to stabilize lysosomes are reduced from 10- to 1000-fold when the steroid is dissolved in DMSO. The authors[21] suggest that DMSO may render steroids more available to their targets within tissues. In two in vitro studies, DMSO has been shown to affect lysosomal membranes, but in both of these studies the concentration of DMSO was about 10%, which is much higher than might be expected to be achieved therapeutically.[22,23] Dimethyl sulfoxide also prevents the release of lysosomal enzymes.[21,24]

Penetration of the Blood-Brain Barrier

Brink and Stein[25] reported that DMSO crosses many biological membranes. They also reported that DMSO facilitated the entry of ^{14}C-pemoline into the brain of rats. They postulated that DMSO resulted in a partial breakdown of the blood-brain diffusion barrier in vivo.

De la Torre[26] studied the penetration of L-dopa and 5-HTP (hydroxytryptophan) through the rat blood-brain barrier using DMSO as a transport vehicle. He reported that DMSO was able to transport L-dopa, and, much less effectively, 5-HTP, across the blood-brain barrier. He speculated that the carrier mechanism was probably rapid because in the brain, L-dopa is rapidly converted to dopamine, which does not cross the blood-brain barrier. Such an ease of transport across the blood-brain barrier could ensure that DMSO will enter the ischemic region, thus exerting a direct effect on the tissue involved.

Dimethyl sulfoxide has been reported to increase the penetration of adrenaline and noradrenaline across the blood-brain barrier of the neonatal chick.[27] Moreover, DMSO (10–15% i.v. and i.p.) has been shown to reversibly open the blood-brain barrier of mice to horseradish peroxidase and stimulate the pinocytosis of horseradish peroxidase by the cerebral endothelium.[28]

Nonspecific Enhancement of Resistance

Several investigators have shown that DMSO, by some unknown mechanism, can protect cells from insult. In 1959, Lovelock and Bishop demonstrated the

DMSO protected bull spermatozoa and bovine red cells from freezing damage.[29] Later, Ashwood-Smith[30] demonstrated a radioprotective effect of DMSO in mice. Asher[27] found that at room temperature the compound action potential was broadened and delayed by DMSO. Nerves with or without perineural sheaths normally do not survive 0.5 hour exposure of -20 or $-30°C$. Dimethyl sulfoxide in 5% or 10% concentration offered protection for up to a two-hour exposure.[31] Lim and Mullan[32] studied the effect of DMSO on rat astrocytoma cells subjected to sonic stress. They found that cells immersed in media with 10% DMSO survived sonic stress better than several other treatments. De la Torre and Rowed[17] studied 210 seconds of nitrogen-induced anoxia in rats. The rats, pretreated with DMSO 3.5 g/kg in a 50% vol/vol solution or doxapram 25 mg/kg, had significant survival rates as compared to those pretreated with ethamivan 10 mg/kg or phenobarbital 6 mg/kg. The mechanism by which DMSO provides protection from such varied insult is not known. DMSO has been shown to scavenge hydroxyl radicals.[33]

Decreased Platelet Aggregation

Dimethyl sulfoxide has been shown to decrease platelet aggregation[8,34,35] and possibly disaggregate platelets in vessels.[36] Decreased platelet aggregation would be expected to improve blood flow and reduce ischemic damage to the brain.

In summary, DMSO has been shown to reduce ICP in experimental animals following head injury. This may be the result of one or more of the effects described above.

STUDY

The gerbil is a particularly good model in which to study cerebral ischemia because it lacks a blood vessel corresponding to the posterior communicating artery and thus has an incomplete circle of Willis.[37,38] This absence of one of the routes for collateral circulation may account for the high incidence of ipsilateral cerebral infarction that can be produced in gerbils by unilateral ligation of a common carotid artery. The incidence of experimental infarction in gerbils when one carotid artery is ligated ranges from 33%[39] to 84%,[33] and is fatal in from 37% to 65%.[41]

METHODS

Three hundred and two young adult Mongolian gerbils of both sexes weighing 40 to 60 g were utilized. The animals were divided into three groups as follows: Group 1 (240 animals operated on, one-half DMSO-treated and one-half saline-treated); Group 2 (50 animals sham operated, one-half DMSO-treated and one-half saline-treated); and Group 3 (12 animals not operated on but DMSO-treated). The animals operated on were anesthetized with ether or ketamine. A ventral midline cervical incision was made from the mental protuberance of the mandible to the manubrium. The left common carotid artery was located by blunt dissection, care being taken not to injure the jugular vein, or the adjacent nerves. In Group 1 animals, the artery was doubly ligated with 5-0 monofilament nylon suture and was transected between the ligatures. Then, in all animals, the incision was closed with 9 mm stainless steel autoclips. Each animal was then given a 1 ml intraperitoneal injection of 1% trypan blue solution.

Postoperatively, one-half of the animals in Groups 1 and 2 were given DMSO intraperitoneally in a double-blind manner following the schedules listed in TABLE 1. The remaining animals received saline on the same dose schedule. The 12 control animals were given DMSO. Clinical signs of infarction were recorded.[42]

The animals were killed at the end of the 120-hour postoperative period and an autopsy was done. Their brains were removed for gross examination. The presence and extent of infarction were determined by the amount of trypan blue staining.

In order to compare the animals receiving DMSO with the control animals receiving saline, life tables were constructed by actuarial methods to indicate the cumulative probability of dying as influenced by a specific time following infarction.

TABLE 1

DOSE SCHEDULE FOR DMSO ADMINISTRATION IN TREATED GERBILS

Groups	Number of Animals	Anesthesia	DMSO Regimen
1a	20	Ether	5 g/kg 50% solution at 1 h post-
2a	5		op. and every 8 h thereafter for 72 h
1b	20	Ketamine	5 g/kg 25% solution at 1 and 8 h
2b	5		post-op. and 2.5 g/kg 25% solution every 8 h thereafter for 72 h
1c	20	Ketamine	5 g/kg 25% solution at 1 h post-
2c	5		op. and 2.5 g/kg solution every 8 h thereafter for 72 h
1d	60	Ether	2.5 g/kg 25% solution at 1 h and
2d	10		2.5 g/kg every 24 h thereafter

Totals: 120 + 25 = 145 DMSO treated, +145 saline treated, +12 not operated on = 302 OR Group 1 (240 left common carotid ligations) + Group 2 (50 operated controls) + Group 3 (12 non-operated controls) for a total of 302 gerbils.

RESULTS

At any dose, DMSO had no significant effect on the number of infarctions that developed or on mortality when compared to animals receiving saline. However, in those animals with infarction, those treated with DMSO had a significantly smaller (p < 0.05) amount of trypan blue staining. The kind of anesthesia used did not appear to be relevant in any of the findings. The morbidity rate in DMSO-treated animals as compared to that in saline-treated animals was affected by dose size, there being a 10% incidence of drug toxicity in animals receiving the higher dose. Morbid indications included eyes that were matted shut, generalized pulmonary hyperemia and edema, renal and hepatic necrosis, and lymphadenitis. At the lowest doses of DMSO, the actuarial tables showed a decreased probability of dying after the first 48 hours, which was not significant.

DISCUSSION

Studies by de la Torre and co-workers[9,12] indicated reduced mortality and morbidity from cerebral infarction following unclipping of the middle cerebral artery in rhesus monkeys. However, in the gerbil the critical vessel was not recanalized, which may account for the difference between de la Torre's[9,12] results and ours. It may be that DMSO is most valuable in the transitional period of occlusion before recanalization is completed. This would suggest that recanalization is necessary for adequate DMSO to get to the lesion to disaggregate platelets in vessels,[36] reduce tissue edema,[11,12] protect against cellular disruption,[32] and prevent the release of lysosomal enzymes.[18,36]

DMSO may temporarily prevent the formation of edema in ischemic areas, thereby decreasing cell necrosis. However, since gerbils drink relatively little water and their urine is highly concentrated, doses of DMSO that are nontoxic in other species are more likely to be toxic in gerbils. Therefore, the antiedema benefit of DMSO may be decreased in this animal model.

DMSO has also been reported to increase tissue oxygenation[37,38] or to reduce oxygen consumption.[18] Such benefits would make it necessary for DMSO to arrive at the tissues of adequate quantity to transport oxygen. While such a process may be facilitated by the capability of DMSO to penetrate the blood-brain barrier, these benefits both require that adequate oxygen reach the cells, and, for adequate oxygen to reach the cell, recanalization is necessary. Therefore, in this and other studies that are models with permanent vessel occlusion, the demonstrated benefit of DMSO may be transient.

In conclusion, in gerbils, DMSO did not change the mortality or morbidity of cerebral infarction caused by ligation of a common carotid artery, but did decrease the amount of trypan blue staining in animals with infarcts. This information, combined with results reported by other investigators leads us to believe that DMSO may have a temporary protective effect in cerebral ischemia, similar to that shown with the use of pentobarbital;[40] thus DMSO should be studied further.

SUMMARY

Dimethyl sulfoxide (DMSO) has been reported to have beneficial effects in the treatment of central nervous system trauma, possibly due to its reported anti-inflammatory, antiedemic, anticoagulate, diuretic, hypothermic, vasodilatory, and respiratory stimulatory effects as well as an ability to correct membrane instability and penetrate the blood-brain barrier. In this paper we discussed these properties, and how they may be of benefit in ischemic cerebral infarction and elevated intracranial pressure. We also described a study we performed to determine if treatment with DMSO would decrease the morbidity and mortality from experimental cerebral infarction.

REFERENCES

1. CAMP, P. E., H. E. JAMES & R. WERNER. 1981. Acute dimethyl sulfoxide therapy in experimental brain edema. Neurosurgery 9: 28–33.
2. DE LA TORRE, J. C., D. W. ROWED, H. M. KAWANAGA & S. MULLAN. 1973. Dimethyl

sulfoxide in the treatment of experimental brain compression. J. Neurosurg. **38:** 345-352.

3. MUTHER, R. S. & W. M. BENNETT. 1980. Effects of dimethyl sulfoxide on renal function in man. J. Am. Med. Assoc. **244:** 2081-2083.
4. BROBYN, R. D. 1975. The human toxicology of dimethyl sulfoxide. Ann. N.Y. Acad. Sci. **245:** 497-506.
5. BROWN, F. D., L. M. JOHNS & S. MULLAN. 1980. Dimethyl sulfoxide in experimental brain injury, with comparison to mannitol. J. Neurosurg. **53:** 58-62.
6. GOROG, P. & I. B. KOVAKS. 1968. Effect of dimethyl sulfoxide on various experimental inflammations. Curr. Therapy Tex. **10:** 486-492.
7. PREZIOSI, P. & U. SCAPAGNINI. 1966. Action of dimethyl sulfoxide on acute inflammatory reactions. Curr. Therapy Tex. **8:** 261-265.
8. BROWN, J. H. & H. K. MACKEY. 1968. Further studies on the erythrocyte anti-inflammatory assay. Proc. Soc. Exp. Bio. Med. **128:** 504.
9. DE LA TORRE, J. C. & J. W. SURGEON. 1976. Dexamethasone and DMSO in experimental transorbital cerebral infarction. Stroke **7:** 577-583.
10. LAHA, R. K., M. DUJOVNY, B. J. BARRIONUEVO, S. C. DECASTRO, H. R. HELLSTROM & J. C. MAROON. 1978. Protective effects of methyl prednisolone and dimethyl sulfoxide in experimental middle cerebral artery embolectomy. J. Neurosurg. **49:** 508-516.
11. FORMANEK, K. & S. SUCKERT. 1966. Diuretische Wirkuns von DMSO. In Procedings of the DMSO Symposium. Vienna. p. 21. Saladruck. Berlin.
12. DE LA TORRE, J. C., H. M. KAWANAGA, D. W. ROWED, C. M. JOHNSON, D. J. GOODE, K. KAJIHARA & S. MULLAN. 1975. Dimethyl sulfoxide in central nervous system. Ann. N.Y. Acad. Sci. **243:** 362-389.
13. ADAMSON, J. E., C. E., HORTON, H. H. CRAWFORD & W. T. AYERS. 1966. The effects of dimethyl sulfoxide on the experimental pedical flap: A preliminary report. Plastic. Reconstruct. Surg. **37:** 105-107.
14. KLIGMAN, A. M. 1965. Topical pharmacology and toxicology of dimethyl sulfoxide. J. Am. Med. Assoc. **193:** 796-805.
15. ZETLER, G. & L. H. LANGHOF. 1971. Dimethyl sulfoxide, a reversible inactivator of receptor-effector systems in the isolated guinea pig ileum. Arch. Exp. Pathol. Pharm. **270:** 361-365.
16. FINNEY J. W., H. C. URSCHEL & G. A. BALLA. 1967. Protection of the ischemic heart with DMSO alone or DMSO with hydrogen peroxide. Ann. N.Y. Acad. Sci. **141:** 231-241.
17. VAN DER MEER C., P. W. VALKENBURG & M. REMMELTS. 1963. Experiments on the radioprotective action of dimethyl sulfoxide. Int. J. Radiat. Biol. **6:** 151-155.
18. FRANZ T. J. & J. T. VAN BRUGGEN. 1967. A possible mechanism of action for DMSO. Ann. N.Y. Acad. Sci. **141:** 302-309.
19. LITTLE, J. R., A. COOK & R. P. LESSER. 1981. Treatment of acute focal cerebral ischemia with dimethyl sulfoxide. Neurosurgery **9:** 34-38.
20. DE LA TORRE, J. C. & D. W. ROWED. 1974. DMSO: A new respiratory stimulant. J. Clin. Pharmacol. **14:** 345-353.
21. WEISSMAN, G., G. SESSA & V. BEVANS. 1967. Effect of DMSO on the stabilization of lysosomes by cortisone and chloraquine in vitro. Ann. N.Y. Acad. Sci. **141:** 326-332.
22. MISCH, D. W. & M. S. MISCH. 1975. The effect of dimethyl sulfoxide on a lysosomal membrane. Ann. N.Y. Acad. Sci. **243:** 54-59.
23. LEE, D. 1971. The effect of dimethyl sulfoxide on the permeability of the lysosomal membrane. Biochim. Biophys. Acta **233:** 619-623.
24. LITTLE J. R., W. L. KERR & T. M. SUNDT. 1974. The role of lysosomes in the production of ischemic nerve cell changes. Arch. Neurol. **30:** 448-455.
25. BRINK, J. J. & D. G. STINE. 1967. Pemoline levels in brain: Enhancement by dimethyl sulfoxide. Science **158:** 1480-1497.
26. DE LA TORRE, J. C. 1970. Active penetration of L-dopa and 5-HTP through the brain barrier using dimethyl sulfoxide. Experientia **26:** 1117-1118.
27. HANIG, J. P., J. M. MORRISON & S. KROP. 1971. Increase of blood-brain barrier permeability to catecholamines by dimethyl sulfoxide in the neonate chick. J. Pharm. Pharmac. **23:** 386-387.

28. BROADWELL, R. D., M. SALCMAN & R. S. KAPLAN. 1982. Morphologic effect of dimethyl sulfoxide on the blood-brain barrier. Science **217:** 164-166.
29. LOVELOCK, J. E. & M. W. J. BISHOP. 1959. Protection of freezing damage to living cells by dimethyl sulfoxide. Nature **183:** 1394-1397.
30. ASHWOOD-SMITH, M. J. 1967. Radioprotective and cryoprotective properties of dimethyl sulfoxide in cellular systems. Ann. N.Y. Acad. Sci. **141:** 45-62.
31. ASHER, I. M. 1972. Effects of DMSO on the electrical response of humarus nerves frozen to -20 degrees C, -30 degrees C and at room temperature. Cryobiology **9:** 153-162.
32. LIM R. & S. MULLAN. 1975. Enhancement of resistance of glial cells by dimethyl sulfoxide against sonic disruption. Ann. N.Y. Acad. Sci. **243:** 358-361.
33. PANGANAMALA, R. V., H. M. SHARMA, R. E. HEIKKILA, J. C. GREER & D. G. CORNWELL. 1976. Role of hydroxyl radical scavengers dimethyl sulfoxide alcohols and methional in the inhibition of prostaglandin biosynthesis. Prostaglandins **11:** 599-607.
34. GOROG, P. 1975. Antiarthritic and antithrombotic effects of topically applied dimethyl sulfoxide. Ann. N.Y. Acad. Sci. **243:** 91-97.
35. ROSENBLUM, W. I. & F. EL-SABBAN. 1982. Dimethyl sulfoxide and glycerol, hydroxyl radical scavengers, impair platelet aggregation within and eliminate the accompanying vasodilation of, injured mouse pial arterioles. Stroke **13:** 35-39.
36. DEUTSCH, E. 1966. Beeinflussung det Blutgerinnung durch DMSO and Kombinationen mit Heparin. In DMSO Symposium. p. 144, Vienna. Saladruck. Berlin.
37. LEVINE, S. & H. PAYAN. 1966. Effects of ischemia and other procedures on the brain and retina of the gerbil (Meriones unguiculatus). Exp. Neurol. **16:** 255-262.
38. KAHN, K. 1972. The natural course of experimental cerebral infarction in the gerbil. Neurology (Minneapolis) **22:** 510-515.
39. DONLEY, R. F. & T. M. SUNDT. 1973. The effect of dexamethasone on the edema of focal cerebral ischemia. Stroke **4:** 148-155.
40. HARRISON M. J. G., D. BROWNBILL, P. D. LEWIS & R. W. R. RUSSEL. 1973. Cerebral edema following carotid artery ligation in the gerbil. Arch. Neurol. **28:** 389-391.
41. HARRISON M. J. G. & R. W. R. RUSSELL. 1972. Effect of dexamethasone on experimental cerebral infarction in the gerbil. J. Neurol. Neurosurg. Psychiat. **35:** 520-521.
42. MCGRAW, C. P. 1977. Experimental cerebral infarction effects of pentobarbital in mongolian gerbils. Arch. Neurol. **34:** 334-336.

TREATMENT OF ELEVATED INTRACRANIAL PRESSURE WITH DIMETHYL SULFOXIDE

Frederick T. Waller, Calvin T. Tanabe, and Harold D. Paxton

Division of Neurosurgery
Oregon Health Sciences University
St. Vincent Hospital and Medical Center
Portland, Oregon 97201

INTRODUCTION

Intracranial pressure (ICP) has been recognized as an important physiological parameter relating to brain function in patients with a variety of intracranial abnormalities.[2,9,16] Persistently elevated ICP can result in increased morbidity and mortality rates, especially in patients with serious head injuries.[1,13,14,15] There has consequently been a great deal of clinical and experimental interest in the treatment of intracranial hypertension. Management usually consists of reduction of the arterial carbon dioxide (pCO_2) level, reduction of cerebral blood volume and hence ICP, restriction of exogenous fluids to minimize cerebral edema, and administration of osmotic diuretics, such as mannitol and urea, to reduce edema fluid in the brain. These measures are sometimes not adequate to control the ICP in cases of severe intracranial hypertension.

Intravenous barbiturates can be given to reduce elevated ICP in some of these severe cases, possibly acting by way of a direct effect on the cerebral vasculature.[14] However, in doses required for effective control of elevated ICP, intravenous barbiturates reduce cardiac output, systemic arterial pressure, and consequently cerebral perfusion pressure (mean systemic arterial pressure less ICP). Additionally, such doses result in a state of iatrogenic coma. The failure rate of intravenous pentobarbitol in such severe cases is reported to be approximately 25%.[13,14]

It is clear, therefore, that there is a need for additional therapeutic modalities in the treatment of severely elevated ICP. Dimethyl sulfoxide (DMSO) has shown promise in this regard in the experimental treatment of brain trauma, brain infarction (stroke), and brain edema.[3-8,11,17] This report outlines our experience with the use of DMSO in a clinical setting to control elevated ICP of diverse etiology refractory to other therapeutic measures.

MATERIALS AND METHODS

A total of eleven patients were treated with intravenous DMSO for intracranial hypertension. Intracranial hypertension is defined as intracranial pressure greater than 20 millimeters of mercury (mm Hg) for more than thirty minutes, as measured by a subarachnoid pressure bolt[18] placed three to four centimeters lateral to the midline of the skull over the coronal suture. The reasons for the elevation in intracranial pressure in these patients were varied and are outlined below (TABLE 1). The patients were divided into two subgroups based upon treatment administered prior to the initiation of intravenous DMSO therapy.

Group A consists of five patients, termed barbiturate nonresponders. Three had elevated intracranial pressure following head trauma, one following sub-

286

0077-8923/83/0411-0286 $01.75/0 © 1983, NYAS

arachnoid hemorrhage and one due to encephalitis. The three trauma patients had intracranial hematomas that were surgically evacuated shortly after hospital admission. The patient with subarachnoid hemorrhage was comatose and decerebrate; the source of his hemorrhage was never identified. Patient #3 had biopsy-proven herpes simplex encephalitis, diagnosed following the onset of coma and transtentorial herniation. All patients were given a Glasgow coma scale score[10] of five at the time of initiation of treatment for elevated intracranial pressure. Conventional treatment consisted of: hyperventilation to reduce pCO_2 and cerebral blood volume (pCO_2 26–30 torr, pO_2 greater than 90 torr), intravenous dexamethasone (4 mg every six hours), and intravenous mannitol (0.25 mg/kg body weight of 20% mannitol every 2–4 hours as needed for ICP greater than 20 mm Hg). All had uncontrollable intracranial pressure despite the above treatments. They were then started on intravenous pentobarbital with a 3 mg/kg loading dose, followed by a 1 mg/kg per hour maintenance dose to achieve a

TABLE 1

Patient	Age	Sex	Diagnosis	Glasgow Score
Group A				
1	28	M	Subarachnoid hemorrhage	5
2	34	M	Epidural hematoma	5
3	19	M	Herpes simplex encephalitis	5
4	39	F	Acute subdural hematoma	5
5	27	M	Acute subdural hematoma	5
Group B				
6	27	M	Acute subdural hematoma	5
7	47	M	Hypertensive intracerebral hemorrhage	6
8	48	F	Subarachnoid hemorrhage	5
9	57	F	Subarachnoid hemorrhage, intracerebral hematoma	5
10	5	M	Arteriovenous malformation, intracerebral hematoma	6
11	19	F	Temporal lobe contusion	4

serum pentobarbitol level of 2.5–3.5 mg percent.[14] In all five patients this combined therapy including intravenous barbiturates failed to control the intracranial pressure, and they were treated with intravenous DMSO following 48–72 hours of nonresponse to barbiturate therapy.

DMSO was given as a 40% concentration in 5% dextrose in water (D5W) at a total dose of 1.0 gram DMSO per kilogram body weight, administered rapidly intravenously. The infusion was repeated every six hours as needed to reduce the intracranial pressure to a level less than 20 mm Hg. All other previously initiated treatment modalities were continued. DMSO was only administered if transiently increased hyperventilation or additional mannitol failed to reduce the ICP. Intracranial pressure response to each DMSO infusion, rate of diuresis following the infusion, and mean systemic arterial pressure were monitored and tabulated.

Group B, termed conventional therapy nonresponders, consisted of six patients with elevated intracranial pressure. Two patients had sustained head trauma (one required evacuation of an intracranial hematoma) and four had experienced spontaneous intracranial hemorrhage (three required evacuation of intracerebral hematomas). They were treated as were the patients in Group A with hyperventilation, dexamethasone, and intravenous mannitol, but failed to have sustained reduction of elevated intracranial pressure. At this point, they were given intravenous DMSO, instead of being treated with intravenous barbiturates, and received 10% DMSO in D5W at a dose of 1.0 g/kg of body weight (compared to a 40% solution given to Group A patients). Again, DMSO was given only if they failed to respond to further transient reduction of pCO_2 or additional mannitol. Response to treatment was monitored.

RESULTS

Change in Intracranial Pressure

DMSO effectively reduced the intracranial pressure in both Group A (barbiturate nonresponders) and Group B (conventional therapy nonresponders). These results were tabulated in TABLE 2. The maximum reduction of ICP per infusion of DMSO occurred thirty minutes following each infusion and averaged 22.9 mm Hg for patients given a 40% DMSO concentration (Group A) and 22.7 mm Hg reduction for patients given a 10% DMSO concentration (Group B). There was no significant difference in effectiveness based upon concentration, the total dose of 1.0 g/kg of body weight being identical in both groups. The maximum reduction in intracranial pressure following a single infusion was 56 mm Hg (patient #3). Of a total of 39 separate DMSO infusions there was only one failure to reduce intracranial pressure; this patient responded to a subsequent infusion six hours later (patient #2). There was no instance of ICP rising as a result of an infusion of DMSO.

While DMSO will acutely reduce elevated ICP, the effect is not sustained and it must be repeated in most cases. Nine of the eleven patients required more than one infusion to keep their average ICP below 20 mm Hg (TABLE 2). The duration of effectiveness per infusion averaged 4–6 hours, although in some cases it was much shorter. Patients #3 and #5 (simultaneous barbiturate therapy) experienced sustained ICP reduction to below 20 mm Hg for only 2–3 hours.

Diuresis Post-infusion

DMSO produced a brisk diuresis in all cases, despite prior fluid restriction and treatment with mannitol (TABLE 2). The average two-hour urine volume following infusion of a 10% concentration was 346 ml, and 282 ml following infusion of a 40% concentration of DMSO.

It should be noted, however, that a 10% solution of DMSO amounts to approximately 700 ml volume for an average man.

Effectiveness of Repetitive Infusions

DMSO remained effective in reducing elevated intracranial pressure with repetitive administrations, producing a consistent reduction in ICP after multiple

TABLE 2

Patient	Infusion #	DMSO Conc.	Pre-infusion ICP (mm Hg)	Post-infusion ICP (mm Hg)	ICP Reduction (mm Hg)	2-Hour Post-infusion Diuresis
1	1	40%	30	2	28	240
2	1	40%	54	42	8	600
	2	40%	20	20	0	300
	3	40%	22	6	16	240
	4	40%	22	1	21	220
	5	40%	32	6	26	225
	6	40%	22	8	14	210
	7	40%	20	12	8	290
3	1	40%	44	8	32	160
	2	40%	42	6	36	40
	3	40%	42	18	24	475
	4	40%	28	2	26	60
	5	40%	58	2	56	100
	6	40%	42	6	36	235
4	1	40%	22	2	20	50
	2	40%	24	6	18	260
	3	40%	20	4	16	170
	4	40%	28	5	23	340
	5	40%	24	20	4	200
5	1	40%	40	4	36	110
	2	40%	55	5	50	425
	3	40%	28	22	6	250
	4	40%	32	12	20	720
	5	40%	36	10	26	485
6	1	10%	28	20	8	320
	2	10%	30	26	4	280
7	1	10%	28	10	18	375
	2	10%	22	12	10	160
	3	10%	24	18	6	80
8	1	10%	100	46	54	450
	2	10%	54	12	42	525
	3	10%	24	6	18	170
9	1	10%	22	18	4	260
	2	10%	30	10	20	440
	3	10%	40	6	34	325
	4	10%	30	18	12	250
	5	10%	28	4	24	150
10	1	10%	28	6	22	90
	2	10%	40	15	25	180
	3	10%	35	16	17	90
11	1	10%	40	4	36	875

administrations (TABLE 3). Additionally, the rate of diuresis was not significantly changed after multiple administrations (TABLE 3).

Adverse Effects

Administration of a 40% concentration produced red cell hemolysis and hemoglobinuria. However, there was no significant change in hematocrit or hemoglobin and renal function was not impaired. With a 10% concentration of DMSO, hemolysis did not occur.

Bleeding time was prolonged to 1.5 times normal in patients receiving a 40% concentration of DMSO although all other clotting parameters, including platelet function, were unchanged. Bleeding time prolongation did not occur with a 10%

TABLE 3
EFFECTIVENESS OF REPETITIVE INFUSIONS

Infusion #	Total Number of Infusions	Average ICP Reduction 30-min Post-infusion (mm Hg)	Average Diuresis 2-h Post-infusion (ml)
1	11	24.2	301
2	9	24.1	290
3	8	17.1	225
4	5	20.4	318
5	5	27.2	232
6	1	19.3	301
7	1	8.0	290

concentration. We did not observe any adverse clinical effects in those patients with a prolonged bleeding time.

Beneficial Factors

DMSO does not alter the level of consciousness as do intravenous barbiturates in the general anesthetic dosages required to reduce intracranial pressure. Consequently, it is possible to assess patients by serial clinical examination as well as follow the course of intracranial pressure during treatment.

There was no change in systemic arterial pressure following infusion of DMSO. Cerebral perfusion pressure consequently improved as the intracranial pressure was reduced. There was no demonstrable change in serum electrolytes or hepatic function as a result of DMSO administration.

Survival

Three patients (#5, 10, 11) survived and have all made a good recovery, returning to work and school. The remaining patients died despite normalization of their intracranial pressure.

Discussion

DMSO has been successfully used experimentally to reduce cerebral edema and intracranial pressure in a variety of animal models including trauma[3,5,6] and cryogenic lesions,[4,17] as well as reduction of cerebral infarct volume[7,8,11] although the results in this regard are not always consistent.[12] The mechanism of action remains unknown but may involve diuresis, a direct metabolic effect on brain tissue, or vasoactive changes in the cerebral circulation relating to prostaglandin functions.[4]

Our experience demonstrates that DMSO can effectively be used in a clinical setting to control elevated ICP where other modalities have failed. The consistent diuretic effect following administration of DMSO (Table 1) suggests that diuresis might be the primary mechanism responsible for ICP reduction. However, the maximal fall in ICP occurs within 30 minutes of administration of DMSO, suggesting that a more direct action, possibly vessel mediated, might be responsible. Additionally, the volume of the infusion itself resulted in a transiently positive fluid balance.

We initially utilized a 40% concentration of DMSO at a dose of 1.0 g/kg of body weight and found that it effectively reduced ICP but at the expense of red cell hemolysis and hemoglobinuria. Consequently, the concentration was reduced to 10%, with no change in the total dose, and was found to be equally effective but without side effects. While we did not vary the total dose administered, recent experimental work by Camp *et al.*,[4,17] suggests that a 1.5 g/kg dose of DMSO might provide a more sustained duration of ICP reduction.

Our group of patients were being simultaneously treated by multiple modalities for intractable intracranial hypertension. A reasonable question might be whether a synergistic effect between DMSO and these other agents was a significant factor in the successful reduction of ICP. Experimental work supports the efficacy of DMSO as a primary agent,[4] but clinical confirmation would depend upon a randomized trial comparing DMSO to mannitol and barbiturates alone and in combination.

The patients treated in Group A (barbiturate nonresponders) were not expected to survive. The fact that one patient (#5) did survive, improving after ICP reduction by DMSO, is very encouraging and suggests that DMSO has a valid role in the clinical management of patients with intracranial hypertension refractory to other management. However, control of ICP alone will not assure a good outcome, as our nonsurvivors died despite normalized ICP. The degree of immediate irreversible brain injury, on whatever basis, determines that certain individuals will not recover no matter what is done. The goal of ICP management is prevention of secondary injury to the brain by the reduction of cerebral edema that occurs as a result of the initial insult. As ICP reflects cerebral edema formation, DMSO would appear to be effective in altering the course of this subsequent injury.

Because DMSO does not result in a state of deep iatrogenic coma as do intravenous barbiturates, patient assessment by clinical examination remains possible. Additionally, cardiac output and cerebral perfusion pressure are not reduced, assuring maximal possible perfusion of the brain during treatment for elevated ICP. It may well be that DMSO should be used as more primary treatment, prior to the initiation of barbiturate treatment, to avoid those potential problems. Our success with Group B patients suggests this is reasonable.

Clearly, there are many unknown factors relating to how and why DMSO reduces ICP, but its effectiveness in doing so seems clear. This limited experience should serve as a validation of the potential usefulness of DMSO in a clinical setting and indicates the need for further in-depth investigation.

REFERENCES

1. BECKER, D. P., J. D. MILLER, J. D. WARD, R. P. GREENBERG, H. F. YOUNG & R. SAKALAS. 1977. The outcome of severe head injury with early diagnosis and management. J. Neurosurg. **47:** 491–502.
2. BECKER, D. P., H. F. YOUNG, J. K. VRIES & R. SAKALAS. 1975. Monitoring in patients with brain tumors. *In* Clinical Neurosurgery. R. Wilkins, Ed. **22:** 364–388. Waverly Press. Baltimore, Md.
3. BROWN, F. D., L. M. JOHNS & S. MULLAN. 1980. Dimethyl sulfoxide in experimental brain injury, with comparison to mannitol. J. Neurosurg. **53:** 58–62.
4. CAMP, P. E., H. E. JAMES & R. WERNER. 1981. Acute dimethyl sulfoxide therapy in experimental brain edema. Part I. Neurosurgery **9:** 28–33.
5. DE LA TORRE, J. C., D. W. ROWED, H. M. KAWANAGA & S. MULLAN. 1973. Dimethyl sulfoxide in the treatment of experimental brain compression. J. Neurosurg. **38:** 345–354.
6. DE LA TORRE, J. C., D. W. ROWED, M. D. KAWANAGA & S. MULLAN. 1972. Modification of experimental head and spinal cord injuries with dimethyl sulfoxide. Trans American Neurological Assn. **97:** 230–233.
7. DE LA TORRE, J. C. & J. W. SURGEON. 1976. Dexamethasone and DMSO in experimental transorbital infarction. Stroke **7:** 577–583.
8. DUJOVNY, M., P. J. BARRIONUEVO, R. K. LAHA, C. P. OSGOOD, S. DECASTRO, J. MAROON & R. HELLSTROM. 1977. Experimental middle cerebral microsurgical embolectomy. *In* Microsurgery for Stroke. P. Schmiedek, Ed.: 91–97. Springer-Verlag. New York.
9. FISHMAN, R. A. 1975. Brain edema. N. Engl. J. Med. **293:** 706–711.
10. JENNETT, B. & M. BOND. 1975. Assessment of outcome after severe brain damage. A practical scale. Lancet **1:** 480–484.
11. LAHA, R. K., M. DUJOVNY, P. J. BARRIONUEVO, S. C. DECASTRO, R. HELLSTROM & J. MAROON. 1978. Protective effects of methyl prednisolone and dimethyl sulfoxide in experimental middle cerebral artery embolectomy. J. Neurosurg. **49:** 508–516.
12. LITTLE, J. R., A. COOK & R. P. LESSER. 1981. Treatment of acute focal cerebral ischemia with dimethyl sulfoxide. Neurosurgery **9:** 34–39.
13. MARSHALL, L. F., R. W. SMITH & H. M. SHAPIRO. 1979. The outcome with aggressive treatment in severe head injuries. Part I: The significance of intracranial pressure monitoring. J. Neurosurg. **50:** 20–25.
14. MARSHALL, L. F., R. W. SMITH & H. M. SHAPIRO. 1979. The outcome with aggressive treatment in severe head injuries. Part II: Acute and chronic barbiturate administration in the management of head injury. J. Neurosurg. **50:** 26–30.
15. MILLER, J. D., D. P. BECKER, J. D. WARD, H. G. SULLIVAN, W. E. ADAMS & M. J. ROSNER. 1977. Significance of intracranial hypertension in severe head injury. J. Neurosurg. **47:** 503–516.
16. NORNES, H. 1975. Monitoring of patients with intracranial aneurysms. *In* Clinical Neurosurgery. R. Wilkins, Ed. **22:** 321–331. Waverly Press. Baltimore, Md.
17. TSURUDA, J., H. E. JAMES, P. E. CAMP & R. WERNER. 1982. Acute dimethyl sulfoxide therapy in experimental brain edema. Part II. Neurosurgery **10:** 355–359.
18. VRIES, J. K., D. P. BECKER & H. F. YOUNG. 1973. A subarachnoid screw for monitoring intracranial pressure. J. Neurosurg. **39:** 416–419.

ROLE OF DIMETHYL SULFOXIDE IN PROSTAGLANDIN-THROMBOXANE AND PLATELET SYSTEMS AFTER CEREBRAL ISCHEMIA

J. C. de la Torre

Division of Neurosurgery
Northwestern University Medical School
Chicago, Illinois 60611

Between the ideas and the reality
Between the motion and the act
Falls the Shadow.
                    T. S. Eliot

INTRODUCTION

In the U.S., approximately 395,000 persons every year experience a thromboembolic stroke. About 40% of this number die within 30 days and one half of the survivors require special care due to moderate or severe functional disabilities.

Cooper and Rice[1] estimated the cost of embolic stroke in 1972 at 6.2 billion dollars and that figure is certain to have risen considerably during the past 10 years. The magnitude of this problem makes it essential to search and find the pathological causes and a viable therapy to reverse acute stroke episodes.

A growing body of evidence points to a role by the prostanoids (prostaglandins and thromboxanes) and platelets as agents associated with cerebral infarction[2-13] and vasospasm.[14-20]

Studies have shown that mammalian vasculature and specifically, cerebral microvessels, can synthesize prostaglandin (PG) I_2, $PGF_{2\alpha}$, PGE_2, and thromboxane A_2 (TXA_2).[8,21,22]

A substantial number of reports show that pharmacological manipulation of the prostaglandin-thromboxane (PG-TX) system can affect the outcome of experimentally induced ischemia and vasospasm.[9,23-29]

Other studies initiated in this laboratory have shown that dimethyl sulfoxide (DMSO) is able to reduce intracranial pressure[30-42] and increase cerebral blood flow (CBF)[3,33,37,43] following assorted lesions in mammalian brain, including human.[44,45] These lesions were induced experimentally in brain by balloon compression,[30,33] cryogenic probe with chemicals,[34,36] cryogenic probe,[38] high velocity missile,[37] cerebrovascular infarction,[31,39-41,43] and retraction pressure.[42] Clinical lesion studies have included cerebral hemorrhage and closed-head injuries.[44-45]

PATHOCHEMISTRY OF ISCHEMIA

The object of this study is to discuss corollaries between actual findings and empirical observations that may explain the actions of DMSO on brain following trauma, specifically as they relate to the PG-TX and platelet systems. For this

293

0077-8923/83/0411-0293 $01.75/0 © 1983, NYAS

purpose, a heuristic model of actual and theoretical activity by DMSO on biochemical pathways and organ physiology is presented.

FIGURE 1 illustrates the presumed cascade of biochemical events leading to the elaboration of PG-TX and platelet aggregation after an ischemic injury, for example, from an experimental cerebral infarction. Assuming that the lesion is of sufficient magnitude to initiate pathological changes in the brain, one of the initial

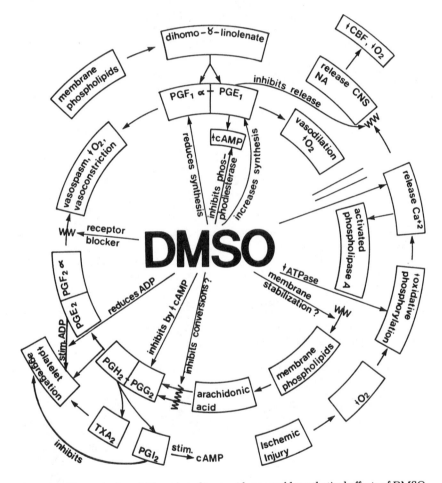

FIGURE 1. Theoretical model based on direct evidence and hypothetical effects of DMSO activity on prostaglandin synthesis following ischemic injury. The biochemical cascade proceeding after ischemic injury has been worked out in other investigations. The chief actions of DMSO on these substances are as follows: reduction of ATPase activity; reduction of calcium release (*); receptor block of PGF$_{2\alpha}$ (*); reduction of ADP-induced platelet aggregation (*); increase of cAMP (†); increase of PGE$_1$ (†); reduction of synthesis, PGF$_{1\alpha}$ (*); reduction of synthesis of PGG$_2$ by increasing cAMP (†); and indirect reduction of noradrenaline release (*). Biochemical reactions involved in thrombogenic activity are shown by (*) while those involved in anti-thrombogenic activity are represented by (†). See text for details.

TABLE 1

ENZYMES AND HORMONES AFFECTING ISCHEMIA

Vasoconstrictor/PA	Vasodilator/PD
PGE_2	PGE_1
TXA_2	PGI_2
ADP	cAMP

ADP: adenosine diphosphate; cAMP: cyclic adenosine monophosphate PA = platelet aggregator; PD = platelet deaggregator.

reactions seen to occur is an immediate reduction of oxygen delivery to the tissue. As this happens, mitochondrial oxidative phosphorylation is negatively affected, and results in a reduction of ATP, the major source of cellular energy. As ATP concentration decreases, sequestered calcium is released to activate mitochondrial and microsomal phospholipases. The phospholipases chemically attack long-chain phospholipids, thus uncoupling esterified free fatty acids. At the same time, inhibition of mitochondrial oxidation results in further build-up of free fatty acids. Polyunsaturated C_{20} free fatty acids provide the substrate for conversion to prostaglandins. There are three ways that prostaglandins can be elaborated. The monoenoic pathway forms PGE_1 and $PGE_{1\alpha}$ from dihomo-γ-linolenate. The bisenoic pathway leads to the elaboration of the endoperoxides (PGG_2, PGH_2), which are the controlling agents in sub-pathways producing PGI_2, TXA_2, and PGE_2. One can see from Table 1 that PGI_2 (prostacyclin) and, to a lesser extent, PGE_1 act as vasodilators and platelet deaggregators. The antiplatelet aggregation activity by PGI_2 and PGE_1 results from their increase of cAMP levels in platelets.[9,10,22] The other products, especially TXA_2, are potent vasoconstrictors and platelet aggregators. There is a third trienoic pathway derived from eicosapentaenoic acid, which originates with the membrane-bound fatty acid. We will not review this pathway because little is known about the effects of its products, TXA_3 and PGI_3, on cerebral vascular bed. However, it is of interest that the vascular/platelet action of PGI_3 is similar to that of PGI_2, although TXA_3 is not analogous to TXA_2 since it can increase the levels of cAMP in platelets, thus neutralizing their aggregation.[46,47]

It has been proposed that the lower incidence of vascular disease seen in some Eskimos may be due to their metabolic shift to the trienoic pathway resulting from dietary factors. By contrast, vascular disorders presumably occur more readily in Western culture where the pro-thrombotic bisenoic pathway is prevalent.[48]

There are at least three major biochemical reactions that can worsen ischemia: release of calcium and hydroxyl radicals, release of thromboxane A_2 (TXA_2), and formation of $PGF_{2\alpha}$ or PGE_2.

We have seen how the release of sequestered Ca^{2+} will activate phospholipases to form free fatty acids in the system. Calcium can also be released from platelets after trauma to increase muscle coat contractility in microvessels thus reducing tissue blood flow perfusion.

Ca^{2+} can also induce release of noradrenaline (NA) from neuronal terminals.[51] The release of this transmitter may activate alpha receptors in the cerebral vasculature, resulting in increased vasoconstriction, lowered blood flow, and reduced oxygen delivery to the tissue.[49,50] Calcium ion flux in myocardial tissue cells may be a key pathological element following ischemic infarction. The regulation of this Ca^{2+} intracellular flux forms the basis for calcium channel-blocking pharmacotherapy in preventing cardiac arrythmias.[83]

The presence of TXA_2 in blood will cause strong vasoconstriction and platelet aggregation. Similarly, the formation of $PGF_{2\alpha}$ or PGE_2 will also affect the vascular/platelet system but the reaction will not be as severe as with TXA_2.[18,20,29] Formation of PGE_2 can stimulate the levels of adenosine diphosphate (ADP), a mild platelet aggregator, and of noradrenaline.[51] Vascular constriction and platelet clumping can be antagonized if PGI_2 is released from endothelial cells in the microvasculature.[9,10,13] PGI_2 appears to do this by stimulating adenylate cyclase, leading to an increase in cAMP levels in platelets.[9,22] Cyclic AMP is a powerful platelet deaggregator.[22]

DMSO AND PLATELET-INDUCED ISCHEMIA

FIGURE 1 shows a scheme of both investigated and theoretical actions of DMSO on the biochemical events generated after an ischemic injury. We previously proposed this hypothetical model to help conceptualize how DMSO, or similar drugs, might affect the pathochemical balance that results in lack of tissue perfusion following trauma.[3]

A similar relationship between DMSO and the vascular system in the presence of trauma is presented in FIGURE 2.

The biochemical and vascular responses to injury appear to have a cause and effect relationship that can be integrated in terms of substances that either increase or decrease blood flow. The substance's effect can be *physical*, i.e., reduce or increase the vessel lumen obstruction, or *chemical*, reduce or increase the vessel lumen diameter (vasoconstriction/vasodilation).

Platelets for example, can induce both conditions. Obstruction of the vessel lumen can result from platelet adhesion (platelet buildup in damaged vessel lining) or platelet aggregation. Platelet damage moreover, can cause vasoconstriction or vasospasm by liberating vasoactive substances locally within the blood vessel or perivascularly, if penetrating damage to the vessel has occurred. There are two storage sites within platelets that contain most of these vasoactive substances. The alpha granules contain fibrinogen, while the dense bodies store ATP, ADP, serotonin, and calcium, which can be secreted by the platelet into the circulation by a canalicular system.[52] Thromboxane A_2 has also been shown to be manufactured in the microsomal fraction of animal and human platelets.[10] All these vasoactive substances (with the exception of ATP) can cause significant reduction of blood flow by physical or chemical reactivity on the vasculature.

DMSO can antagonize a number of these vasoactive substances released by the platelets, which could consequently induce vasoconstriction, vasospasm, or obstruction of vessel lumen. For example, a study has shown that DMSO can inhibit ADP and thrombin-induced platelet aggregation *in vitro*.[53] It may presumably do this by increasing the levels of cAMP (a strong platelet deaggregator) through inhibition of its degradative enzyme, phosphodiesterase.[54] DMSO is reported to deaggregate platelets *in vivo* following experimental cerebral ischemia.[55-58] This effect may be fundamental in view of the finding that cerebral ischemia produces transient platelet abnormalities thay may promote microvascular aggregate formation and extend the area of ischemic injury.[2]

The biochemical picture is further complicated by the possible activity of DMSO on other vasoactive substances secreted by the platelets during injury or ischemia. For example, the release of calcium from cells or platelets and its effect on arteriolar-wall muscle spasm may be antagonized by circulating DMSO.[59,60]

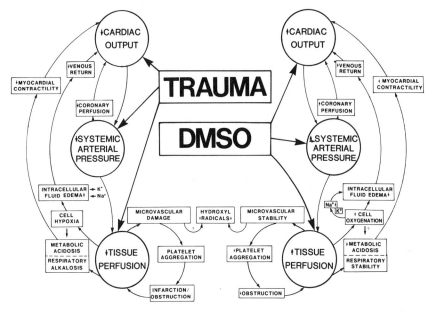

FIGURE 2. Cycle of events following traumatic injury resulting in ischemia. The cascade of metabolic changes after trauma begins with a reduction of tissue perfusion, which may continue on its own cycle by affecting the microcirculation, platelet aggregation, and further reduction of blood flow by obstruction. These changes will lead to cell hypoxia and metabolic acidosis and affect cardiac output and systemic arterial pressure. A reduction of systemic arterial pressure may continue to lower tissue and coronary perfusion and eventually affect cerebral autoregulation. DMSO has been shown to increase tissue perfusion (see text for details) thus affecting the microcirculation, platelet stasis, and blood flow. With increased tissue perfusion, cell oxygenation improves, metabolic acidosis is neutralized, and intracellular fluid retention is diminished. Cardiac output increases after DMSO. This increase is probably caused by DMSO activity on myocardial contractility and tissue perfusion. Systemic arterial pressure is either slightly increased or remains unaffected. DMSO appears to neutralize the cellular damage caused by circulating hydroxyl radicals, an effect that may directly improve microcirculatory status. For an explanation of how DMSO may increase tissue perfusion, see FIGURES 1 and 3. Key: ↑ = increases; ↓ = decrease; → = no change.

Collagen release by platelets may be likewise neutralized by DMSO,[61,62] thus preventing platelet adhesion.

DMSO AND PG-TX SYSTEM

The possible role of DMSO in the PG-TX and platelet system is illustrated in FIGURES 1-3. Little is known about the actions of DMSO on prostaglandins. Studies have reported that DMSO can increase the synthesis of PGE_1, a moderate vasodilator.[63] PGE_1 can reduce platelet aggregation by increasing cAMP levels and also inhibit the calcium-induced release of noradrenaline in nerve terminals, an effect that may antagonize vasoconstriction and reduction of cerebral blood flow.[3,64]

DMSO, it will be recalled, also has a direct effect on cAMP. It increases cAMP presumably by inhibiting phosphodiesterase,[54] although an indirect action on PGI_2-induced elevation of platelet cAMP by DMSO should not be ruled out. Any process that increases platelet cAMP will exert strong platelet deaggregation.

It has also been reported that DMSO can block $PGF_{2\alpha}$ receptors and reduce PGE_2 synthesis.[65] Both these compounds can cause moderate platelet aggregation and $PGF_{2\alpha}$ is known to induce vasoconstriction.[47] (FIGURE 1). The effects of DMSO on thromboxane synthesis is unknown. It could however, inhibit TXA_2 biosynthesis in much the same way as hydralazine or dipyridamole,[66] since it shares a

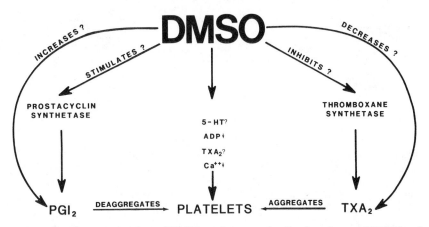

FIGURE 3. Theoretical actions of DMSO on the prostaglandin-thromboxane (PG-TX) and platelet systems. DMSO may make PGI_2 (prostacyclin) available in the microvasculature after ischemia by stimulating PGI_2 synthetase or directly protecting the vascular endothelium of blood vessels where PGI_2 is stored.

An increase of PGI_2 synthesis or availability at the vessel wall would have a positive and direct effect on ischemia by antagonizing platelet aggregation and vasoconstriction. DMSO may also antagonize the synthesis (as hydralazine[66]) or release of thromboxane A_2 (TXA_2) and thus indirectly counteract platelet aggregation and vasoconstriction. Antagonistic action of DMSO on ADP and calcium secreted from platelets after injury is supported by indirect findings. The effects of DMSO on the other platelet aggregatory and thrombogenic secretions, such as 5-HT and TXA_2, are unknown.

number of similar properties with these agents, specifically, their increase of cAMP levels (FIGURE 3).

DMSO and Cell Membrane Protection

The ability of DMSO to protect cell membrane integrity in various injury models is well documented.[67-70]

Cell membrane preservation by DMSO might help explain its ability to improve cerebral and spinal cord blood flow after injury.[37,44,71] DMSO could be preventing impairment of cerebrovascular endothelial surfaces where PGI_2 is elaborated and where platelets can accumulate following injury. The effects by DMSO may be twofold: reduction of platelet adhesion by inhibiting collagen[61,62] and reduction of platelet adhesion by protecting the vascular endothelium and ensuring PGI_2 release.

DMSO, HYDROXYL RADICALS, AND CALCIUM

Although many hormones, chemical transmitters, peptides, and numerous enzymes can be found in mammalian circulation at any given time, it is the hydroxyl radicals that have drawn attention as playing an important role in the pathogenesis of ischemia.[72,73] Free radicals can be elaborated by peroxidation of cellular membrane-bound lipids when oxygen delivery is not totally abolished, as in ischemia and hypoxia, or when oxygen is resupplied after an ischemic episode.[74]

One of the significant sites where hydroxyl radicals can form following ischemia is in mitochondria. DMSO is known to be an effective hydroxyl radical scavenger.[75-77] Since it has been shown that DMSO can improve mitochondrial oxidative phosphorylation, it has been suggested that DMSO may act to neutralize the cytotoxic effects of hydroxyl radicals in mitochondria themselves.[78] Oxidative phosphorylation is the process responsible for the elaboration of ATP, the major source of cellular energy, and is one of the primary biochemical activities to be negatively affected following ischemic injury (FIGURE 1). DMSO has also been reported to reduce ATPase activity in submitochondrial particles,[79,80] an effect that can lower oxygen utilization during cellular ischemia.

It has been proposed that DMSO may reduce the utilization of oxygen by an inhibiting effect on mitochondrial function.[80] In that experiment, the energy loss due to inhibition of oxidative activity after brain tissue was perfused with DMSO was compensated by an increase in glycolysis.[80]

It seems probable that the neutralizing action of DMSO on hydroxyl radical damage following injury could diminish the negative outcome of ischemia. However, the formation of hydroxyl radicals is dependent on time and oxygen availability, but the development of ischemia is immediate and its reversal may depend on more prevalent subsystems such as the PG-TX and platelet interactions. In our judgement, maintaining the balance of these subsystems appears more critical in predisposing the outcome of cerebral ischemia.

Another interesting effect of DMSO is on calcium. When isolated rat hearts are perfused with a calcium-free solution followed by reperfusion with a calcium-containing solution, a massive release of creatine kinase (indicating cardiac injury) is observed. This creatine kinase level increase is accompanied by electrocardiographic (EKG) changes and ultrastructural cell damage.[81] DMSO has been reported to significantly reduce the release of creatine kinase and prevent EKG and ultrastructural changes if it is present during reperfusion of the isolated rat heart with a calcium-containing solution.[59] Moreover examination of the heart tissue by electron microscopy showed that DMSO-treated preparations prevented mitochondrial swelling and contraction band formation, induced by the re-entry of calcium, when compared to non-treated control cells.[59] These findings are supported by another investigation showing that DMSO can block calcium-induced degeneration of isolated myocardial cells.[60] This protective effect by DMSO on myocardial tissue may be critical during ischemic myocardial infarction when evolutionary EKG changes, elevated serum creatine kinase levels, and myocardial necrosis can develop rapidly.

A

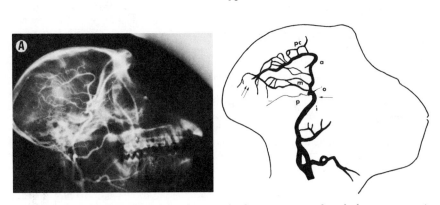

FIGURE 4. A. Normal rhesus monkey cerebral arteriogram taken before surgery. A schematic trace is shown on the right to illustrate normal vascular diameters of major branches and their anatomoses. Key: i = internal carotid artery, p = posterior cerebral artery, o = ophthalmic artery, m = middle cerebral artery, a = anterior cerebral artery, and pc = pericallosal artery. Posterior-occipito-parietal (POP) vascularization (↑↑), and internal carotid at the level of the siphon (↑) are shown.

B

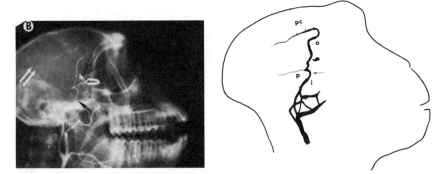

FIGURE 4. B. Representative arteriogram seen in all monkeys 4 hours after middle cerebral artery (MCA) occlusion, immediately prior to treatment. Note absence of POP (↑↑) and MCA filling as well as narrowing of internal carotid (↑).

Moreover, since platelets are known to release calcium from their dense bodies storage sites following ischemia, DMSO may antagonize the myocontractile effect of calcium on arteriolar smooth muscle,[82] a condition that could develop into severe vasospasm and neural tissue hypoxia. This is supported by our finding that DMSO is able to reverse internal carotid vasospasm or vasoconstriction in monkeys subjected to middle cerebral artery occlusion.[3,31,32]

C

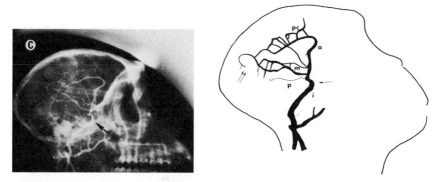

FIGURE 4. C. DMSO-treated monkey 17.5 hours after occlusion. Clip was removed 30 minutes prior to arteriogram. Note POP (↑↑) and pericallosal artery (pc) revascularization is similar to pre-occlusion arteriogram. Internal carotid narrowing (↑) has been reversed.

D

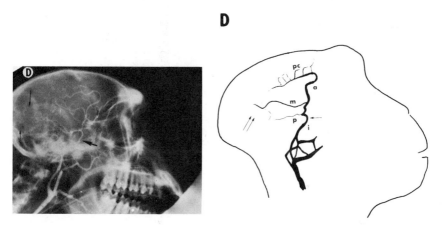

FIGURE 4. D. Representative arteriogram of dexamethasone- or saline-treated monkey 17.5 hours after occlusion. Clip was removed 30 minutes prior to arteriogram. Note poor POP (↑↑) and pericallosal artery (pc) filling after revascularization. Internal carotid narrowing (↑) is still present.

This is also the biochemical basis behind the present treatment of coronary artery vasospasm using calcium-channel blockers such as verapamil.[83] Although the mechanism of transmembrane calcium ion flux is complex, isolated heart preparations show that calcium channel antagonists can inhibit calcium and sodium transport across myocardial cell membranes.[84] It would be very useful to know whether DMSO exerts similar effects or whether its activity on isolated heart preparations is achieved through other mechanisms (see DMSO IN EXTRA-CEREBRAL ISCHEMIA).

DMSO IN CEREBRAL ISCHEMIA

Experimental cerebral ischemia, induced by clipping of the middle cerebral artery (MCA), can be reversed when DMSO is given 4 hours after occlusion. When rhesus monkeys underwent MCA clip occlusion through a transorbital approach, treatment was begun after 4 hours and the MCA clip was removed after 16 hours. The monkeys were treated with i.v. saline, dexamethasone (3 mg/kg), or DMSO (2.5 g/kg, 50% solution). FIGURE 4A shows the normal angiographic picture of monkeys prior to MCA occlusion. FIGURE 4B shows the typical narrowing of the internal carotid artery (ICA) and blockade of MCA perfusion to parietal and posterior brain regions seen in all animals prior to treatment.

FIGURE 4C shows the typically treated DMSO monkey after 17.5 hours; no narrowing of the ICA is evident and the perfusion of posterior-occipital-parietal (POP) regions (FIGURE 4C) is comparable to the pre-occlusion angiogram. By contrast, dexamethasone or saline-treated monkeys still retain narrowing of the ICA and poor perfusion of the POP area (FIGURE 4D). Function returned after 7 days, showed good to excellent recovery in DMSO-treated animals and poor recovery in all saline or dexamethasone-treated monkeys.[43] Morphological examination of the cerebral tissue after 7 days showed significantly better preservation of structure in DMSO than with the other two treatments.

These results indicate that DMSO increases cerebral perfusion after ischemia and can reverse ICA narrowing (vasospasm?) following MCA occlusion. This observation is supported by other findings showing an increase in measured cerebral blood flow after experimental brain compression and infarction,[3,30,33] high velocity missile injury,[37] and cerebral hemorrhage in patients.[44]

Although cerebral blood flow was not measured, it presumably increased when DMSO was used after experimental carotid artery occlusion,[40] MCA infarction,[39,41] cryogenic lesions,[34-36,38] and brain retraction pressure.[42] No improvement was obtained in one study[85] after 2.5 g/kg i.v. DMSO was used in cats with MCA occlusion. Cats, however, make experimental models since they have an unusual sensitivity to DMSO, particularly after anesthesia. For example, 200 mg/kg of DMSO given to cats will induce transient apnea, with a fall in blood pressure and heart rate in a dose-response fashion.[86,87] A single i.v. dose of 400–600 mg/kg in the anesthetized cat is generally fatal.[30,86,87]

DMSO IN EXTRACEREBRAL ISCHEMIA

Previous studies have shown that DMSO can reduce the infarct size in porcine hearts subjected to coronary artery ligation[88] and maintain myocardial contractile strength after hypoxia in a dose-dependent fashion.[89] DMSO was also reported to reduce myocardial necrosis induced by isoproterenol and to prevent the formation of ventricular aneurysms.[90]

More recent studies have reported that i.v. infusion of DMSO caused an increase in cardiac output, heart rate, pulmonary capillary wedge pressure, and pulmonary arterial pressure when compared to equal volumes of saline.[91] These values returned to normal 10 minutes following DMSO infusion. In globally induced ischemic heart, DMSO was reported to significantly improve mitochondrial state 3, respiratory rates, and oxidative phosphorylation, thus preventing the usual pathogenic changes seen in mitochondria following ischemia.[78]

In circumflex coronary artery ligation in dogs, DMSO prevented cyclic reduction of coronary blood flow caused by platelet aggregation at the site of occlusion.[92]

When ischemia was induced experimentally in other organs, the response to DMSO administration was similar to brain and heart. For example, experimentally induced ischemic acute renal failure (ARF) was reversed by i.v. DMSO.[93] The ARF was induced by subjecting rats to unilateral nephrectomy, then tying off the remaining renal artery 7 days later. The prevention of ARF in DMSO-treated rats appeared to be more pronounced than treatment with propranolol or chronic saline loading.[93]

DMSO has also been reported to reverse experimentally induced intestinal ischemia.[94]

These findings complement those reported in cerebrovascular injuries following the administration of DMSO. The implication is that similar mechanisms are involved in cerebral and extracerebral organ ischemia. (FIGURE 1–3).

More importantly, the collective conclusion drawn after assessing the effects of DMSO in cerebral and extracerebral ischemia produced in different models and experimental paradigms, is the potential action of this drug on various clinical disorders. It may or may not appear an understatement to point out that DMSO may have therapeutic value not only in cerebral ischemia but also in myocardial ischemia and infarction, transient ischemic attacks (TIAs), acute renal failure, and platelet-induced vascular abnormalities, to name but a few major disorders. Further experimental and clinical trials should resolve this issue.

SUMMARY

Direct and empirical evidence indicates that intravenous administration of DMSO can arrest or reverse cerebral and extracerebral ischemia following experimental or clinical injury.

When the delivery of oxygen and nutrients to the tissue is deficient or unavailable (as in ischemia), cell damage or death with all its attending pathological consequences becomes an end-point. In the brain, this equates to a build-up of intracranial pressure, impairment of neural transmission to vital centers, and loss of function or death.

We have reviewed a number of studies that show the usefulness of DMSO in preventing significant pathology from developing in various experimental injury models and in clinical subjects.

We have proposed that the action of DMSO in biochemical, morphological, and functional subsystems is not specific but rather interactive.

FIGURE 5 illustrates this point. Any one effect by DMSO on these subsystems that does not affect the others seems highly unlikely. How DMSO or similar drugs affect these systems, could provide important clues in clarifying the pathogenesis of ischemia and in reducing its severity.

We conclude from the available evidence that ischemic injury is a dynamic process constantly promoting biochemical, vascular, and morphological changes and that DMSO is able to intervene at various levels of this pathochemical cascade.

DMSO may do this by its ability to normalize tissue perfusion when this is lacking or impaired. We speculate that this effect by DMSO is predominantly on the PG-TX and platelet systems, since these appear to be the most important candidates implicated in vessel occlusion and spasm. It is further concluded from the available and theoretical evidence presented here, that clinical trials using

POSSIBLE ROLE OF DMSO
ON SUBSYSTEM PATHOLOGY AFTER ISCHEMIA

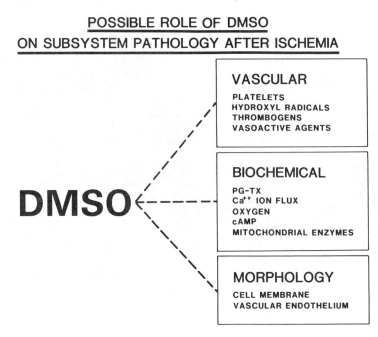

FIGURE 5. Following ischemic injury, DMSO acts on three major subsystems: vascular, biochemical, and structural. Its vascular and biochemical actions may be on receptors, enzyme synthesis, cellular fluid exchange (see text), while its action on the cell membranes and intracellular organelles may be to protect their morphological integrity.

DMSO in cerebral and extracerebral organ ischemia should be designed in order to evaluate the efficacy of this compound to other antithrombogenic therapies. It is reasonable to assume that DMSO may provide a primary approach to the treatment of cerebral, myocardial, renal, and platelet-induced ischemic disorders.

REFERENCES

1. COOPER, B. S. & D. P. RICE. 1976. The economic cost of illness revisited. Social Security Bull. (Feb.)
2. DOUGHERTY, J. H., D. E. LEVY & B. B. WEKSLER. 1979. Experimental cerebral ischemia produces platelet aggregates. Neurology 29: 1460–1465.
3. DE LA TORRE, J. C., J. W. SURGEON, P. K. HILL & T. KHAN. 1977. DMSO in the treatment of brain infarction: Basic considerations. In Arterial Air Embolism and Acute Stroke. J. M. Hallenbeck & L. Greenbaum, Eds.: 138–161. Report No. 11/15/77. Undersea Medical Society. Bethesda, Md.
4. DENTON, I. C., R. P. WHITE & J. T. ROBERTSON. 1972. The effects of prostaglandins E_1, A_1 and F_2 in the cerebral circulation of dogs and monkeys. J. Neurosurg. 36: 34–42.
5. FIELDS, W. S., N. A. LEMAK, R. F. FRANKOWSKI & R. J. HARDY. 1977. Controlled trial of aspirin in cerebral ischemia. Stroke 8: 301–314.
6. FURLOW, T. W. & N. H. BASS. 1976. Arachidonate-induced cerebro-vascular occlusion in the rat. The role of platelets and aspirin in stroke. Neurology 26: 297–304.

7. HAGEN, A. A., J. N. GERBER, C. SWEELEY, R. P. WHITE & J. T. ROBERTSON. 1977. Pleocytosis and elevation of prostaglandin F_2 and E_2 in cerebrospinal fluid after intracisternal injection of thrombin. Stroke **8**: 236–238.
8. HAGEN, A. A., R. P. WHITE & J. T. ROBERTSON. 1979. Synthesis of prostaglandins and thromboxane B_2 by cerebral arteries. Stroke **10**: 306–309.
9. MONCADA, S. & J. R. VANE. 1979. The role of prostacyclin in vascular tissue. Fed. Proc. **38**: 66–71.
10. NEEDLEMAN, P., S. MONCADA, S. BUNTING, J. R. VANE, M. HAMBERG & B. SAMUELSSON. 1976. Identification of an enzyme in platelet microsomes which generates thromboxane A_2 from prostaglandin endoperoxides. Nature **261**: 558–560.
11. SINZINGER, H., K. SILBERBAUER, M. WINTER & P. CLOPATH. 1979. Effects of experimental atherosclerosis on prostacyclin (PGI_2) generation in arteries of miniature swine. Artery **5**: 448–462.
12. WHITE, R. P., D. A. TERRAGNO, N. A. TERRAGNO, A. A. HAGEN & J. T. ROBERTSON. 1977. prostaglandins in porcine cerebral arteries. Stroke **8**; 135.
13. NEEDLEMAN, P., M. MINKES & A. RAZ. 1976. Thromboxanes: selective biosynthesis and distinct biological properties. Science **193**: 163–165.
14. DEMBINSKA-KIEC, A., T. GRYGLEWSKA, A. ZMUDA & R. J. GRYGLEWSKI. 1977. The generation of prostacyclin by arteries and by the coronary vascular bed is reduced in experimental atherosclerosis in rabbits. Prostaglandins **14**: 1025–1034.
15. MAEDA, Y., E. TANI & T. MIYAMOTO. 1981. Prostaglandin metabolism in experimental cerebral vasospasm. J. Neurosurg. **55**: 779–785.
16. AU, T. L. S., G. A. COLLINS, C. J. HARVIE & M. J. A. WALKER. 1980. Actions of prostaglandin-I_2 and prostaglandin-E_2 on coronary occlusion-induced arrhythmias in the rat. In Advances in Prostaglandin and Thromboxane Research. **8**: 647–650. Raven Press. New York.
17. SASAKI, T., S. MUROTA, S. WAKAI, T. ASANO & K. SANO. 1981. Evaluation of prostaglandin biosynthetic activity in canine basilar artery following subarachnoid injection of blood. J. Neurosurg. **55**: 771–778.
18. PENNINK, M., R. P. WHITE, J. R. CROCKARELL & J. T. ROBERTSON. 1972. Role of prostaglandin F_2 in the genesis of experimental cerebral vasospasm. Angiographic study in dogs. J. Neurosurg. **37**: 398–406.
19. ROSENBLUM, W. I. 1975. Effects of prostaglandins on cerebral blood vessels: Interaction with vasoactive amines. Neurology **25**: 1169–1171.
20. WHITE, R. P. 1971. Prostaglandin F_2 and experimental cerebral vasospasm in dogs. Pharmacologist **13**: 292.
21. MAURER, P., M. A. MOSKOWITZ, L. LEVINE & E. MELAMED. 1980. The synthesis of prostaglandins by bovine cerebral microvessels. Prostagl. Med. **4**: 153–161.
22. GORMAN, R. R., S. BUNTING & O. V. MILLER. 1977. Modulation of human platelet adenylate cyclase by prostacyclin (PGX). Prostaglandins **13**: 377.
23. AIKEN, J. W., R. J. SHEBUSKI & R. R. GORMAN. 1980. Blockage of partially obstructed coronary arteries with platelet thrombi; comparison between its prevention with cyclooxygenase inhibitors versus prostacyclin. In Advances in Prostaglandin and Thromboxane Research. **8**: 635–640. Raven Press. New York.
24. DIX, R. K., G. J. KELLINER, N. JURKIEWICZ & T. LAWRENCE. 1979. The influence of prostacyclin on coronary occlusion induced arrhythmia in cats. Prostagl. Med. **3**: 173–184.
25. JUGDUTT, B. I., G. M. HUTCHINS, B. H. BULKLEY & L. C. BECKER. 1979. Infarct size reduction by prostacyclin after coronary occlusion in conscious dogs. Clin. Res. **27**: 177A.
26. OGLETREE, M. L. & A. M. LEFER. 1978. Prostaglandin induced preservation of the ischemic myocardium. Circ. Res. **42**: 218–224.
27. SINZINGER, H., J. KALIMAN, K. WIDHALM, O. PACHINGER & P. PROBST. 1981. Valve of platelet sensitivity to antiaggregatory prostaglandin (PGI_2, PGE, PGD_2) in 50 patients with myocardial infarction at young age. Prostagl. Med. **7**: 125–132.
28. SMITH, E. F. III, J. B. SMITH & A. M. LEFER. 1979. Role of arachiadonic acid products in early myocardial ischemia. Fed. Proc. **38**: 1037.
29. SPAGNUOLO, C., L. SAUTEBIN, G. GALLI, G. RACAGNI, C. GALLI, S. MAZZARI & M. FINESSO.

1979. PGF$_2$, thromboxane B$_2$, and HETE levels in gerbil brain cortex after ligation of common carotid arteries and decapitation. Prostaglandins **18**: 53-61.

30. DE LA TORRE, J. C., D. W. ROWED, H. M. KAWANAGA & S. MULLAN. 1973. Dimethyl sulfoxide in the treatment of experimental brain compression. J. Neurosurg. **38**: 345-354.

31. DE LA TORRE, J. C., H. K. KAWANAGA, P. K. HILL & J. W. SURGEON. 1975. Experimental therapy after middle cerebral artery occlusion. Surg. Forum **26**: 489-492.

32. DE LA TORRE, J. C. & P. K. HILL. 1976. Ultrastructural studies on formation of edema and its treatment following experimental brain infarction in monkeys. In Dynamics of Brain Edema. H. Pappius & W. Feindel, Eds: 306-314. Spinger-Verlag. New York.

33. DE LA TORRE, J. C., H. M. KAWANAGA, D. J. GOODE, C. M. JOHNSON, K. KAJIHARA, D. W. ROWED & S. MULLAN. 1975. Dimethyl sulfoxide in CNS trauma. Ann. N.Y. Acad. Sci. **243**: 362-389.

34. CAMP, P. E., H. E. JAMES & R. WERNER. 1981. Acute dimethyl sulfoxide therapy in experimental brain edema: Part 1. Effects on intracranial pressure, blood pressure, central venous pressure and brain water and electrolyte content. Neurosurgery **9**: 28-33.

35. TSURUDA, J., H. E. JAMES, P. E. CAMP & R. WERNER. 1982. Acute dimethyl sulfoxide therapy in experimental brain edema: Part 2. Effect of dose and concentration on intracranial pressure, blood pressure and central venous pressure. Neurosurgery **10**: 355-359.

36. DEL BIGIO, M., H. E. JAMES, P. E. CAMP, R. WERNER, L. MARSHALL & H. TUNG. 1982. Acute dimethyl sulfoxide therapy in brain edema. Part 3: Effect of a 3-hour infusion. Neurosurgery **10**: 86-89.

37. BROWN, F. D., L. M. JOHNS & S. MULLAN. 1980. Dimethyl sulfoxide in experimental brain injury, with comparison to mannitol. J. Neurosurg. **53**: 58-62.

38. JAMES, H. E., P. E. CAMP, R. D. HARBAUGH, L. MARSHALL & R. WERNER. 1982. Comparison of the effects of DMSO and pentabarbitone on experimental brain oedema. Acta Neurochir. **60**: 245-255.

39. LAHA, R. K., M. DUJOVNY, P. J. BARRIONUEVO, S. C., DeCASTRO, H. R. HELLSTROM & J. C. MAROON. 1978. Protective effects of methyl prednisolone and dimethyl sulfoxide in experimental middle cerebral artery embolectomy. J. Neurosurg. **49**: 508-516.

40. McGRAW, C. P. 1977. The effect of dimethyl sulfoxide (DMSO) on cerebral infarction in the Mongolian gerbil. Acta Neurol. Scand. (suppl.) **64**: 160-161.

41. DUJOVNY, M., P. J. BARRIONUEVO, R. K. LAHA, S. DeCASTRO & J. C. MAROON. 1976. Experimental middle cerebral artery microsurgical embolectomy. Surg. Forum **37**: 495-496.

42. ALBIN, M. S., L. BUNEGIN, P. HELSEL, M. BABINSKI & R. D. BELL. 1980. DMSO protect brain against experimental pressure induced cerebral ischemia. Crit. Care Med. **8**: 251.

43. DE LA TORRE, J. C. & J. W. SURGEON. 1976. Dexamethasone and DMSO in cerebral infarction. Stroke **7**: 577-583.

44. MULLAN, S., J. JAFAR & F. D. BROWN. 1980. Dimethyl sulfoxide in the management of postoperative hemiplegia. In Cerebral Arterial Spasm. R. H. Wilkins, Ed.: 646-653. Williams & Wilkins. Baltimore, Md.

45. WALLER, F. T., C. T. TANABE, S. W. JACOB & H. D. PAXTON. 1979. Dimethyl sulfoxide for control of intracranial pressure. Neurosurgery **5**: 583.

46. NEELDEMAN, P., S. MONCADA, S. BUNTING, J. R. VANE, M. HAMBERGER & B. SAMUELSSON. 1976. Identification of an enzyme in platelet microsomes which generates thromboxane A$_2$ from prostaglandin endoperoxides. Nature **261**: 558-560.

47. LEFER, A. M. 1979. Role of the prostaglandin-thromboxane system in vascular homeostasis during shock. Circ. Shock **6**: 297-303.

48. DYERBERG, J., H. O. BANG, E. STOFFERSEN, S. MONCADA & R. VANE. 1978. Eicosapentaenoic acid: prevention of thrombosis and atherosclerosis? Lancet *ii*: 117-119.

49. RAICHLE, M. E., R. L. GRUBB & J. O. EICHLING. 1977. Neural and hormonal regulation of brain water permeability. In Neurogenic Control of the Brain Circulation. Ch. Owman & L. Edvinsson, Eds.: 465-470. Pergamon Press. Oxford.

50. DE LA TORRE, J. C. 1976. Evidence for central innervation of intracerebral blood vessels: Local cerebral blood flow measurements and histofluorescence by the SPG method. Neuroscience 1: 455-457.

51. BERGSTROM, S., L-O. FARNEBO & K. FUXE. 1973. Effect of prostaglandin E_2 on central and peripheral catecholamine neurons. Eur. J. Pharmacol. 21: 362-368.

52. BALDINI, M. G. & T. J. MYERS. 1980. One more variety of storage pool disease. J. Am. Med. Assoc. 244: 173-175.

53. SCHIFFER, C. A., C. L. WHITAKER, M. SCHMUKLER, J. AISNER & S. L. HILBERT. 1976. The effect of dimethyl sulfoxide on in vitro platelet function. Thrombos. Haesmostas. (Stuttg.) 36: 221-229.

54. WIESER, P. B., M. A. ZEIGER & J. N. FAIN. 1977. Effects of dimethyl sulfoxide on cyclic AMP accumulation, lipolysis and glucose metabolism of fat cells. Biochem. Pharmacol. 26: 775-778.

55. DUJOVNY, M., R. ROZARIO, N. KOSSOVSKY, F. G. DIAZ & R. SEGAL. 1983. Antiplatelet effect on dimethyl sulfoxide, barbiturates, and methyl prednisolone. Ann. N.Y. Acad. Sci. 411: 234-244.

56. HOLTZ, G. C. & R. B. DAVIS. 1974. Inhibition of human platelet aggregation by dimethyl sulfoxide, dimethyl acetamide and sodium glycerophosphate. Proc. Soc. Exp. Biol. Med. 141: 244-248.

57. MUNOZ, L. G., R. A. ROZARIO, M. DUJOVNY & D. STROTH. 1980. Antiplatelet properties of DMSO and barbiturates in microvessels with scanning electron microscopy. Am. Assoc. Neurol. Surg. Scien. Abstr. April 20-24, pp. 165-167.

58. ROSENBLUM, W. I. & F. EL-SABBAN. 1982. Dimethyl sulfoxide and glycerol, hydroxyl radical scavengers, impair platelet aggregation within and eliminate the accompanying vasodilation of injured mouse pial arterioles. Stroke 13: 35-39.

59. RUIGROK, T. J. C., D. DE MOES, A. M. SLADE & W. G. NAYLER. 1981. The effect of dimethyl sulfoxide on the calcium paradox. Am. J. Pathol. 103: 390-403.

60. CLARK, M. G., B. J. GANNON, N. BODKIN, G. S. PATTEN & M. N. BERRY. 1978. An improved procedure for high-yield preparation of intact beating heart cells from adult rat: biochemical and morphologic study. J. Mol. Cell Cardiol. 10: 1101-1121.

61. SCHERBEL, A. L., L. J. MCCORMACK & M. J. POPPO. 1965. Alterations of collagen in generalized scleroderma (progressive systemic sclerosis) after treatment with dimethyl sulfoxide. Cleveland Clinic Quart. 32: 47.

62. GRIES, G., G. BUBLITZ & J. LINDNER. 1967. The effect of dimethyl sulfoxide on the components of connective tissue. Ann. N.Y. Acad. Sci. 141: 630.

63. LEHANN, T. R. & A. HORITA. 1975. Effects of dimethyl sulfoxide (DMSO) on prostaglandin synthetase. Proc. West Pharmacol. Soc. 18: 81-82.

64. JOHNSON, M. & P. W. RAMWELL. 1974. Implications of protaglandins in hematology. In Prostaglandins and Cyclic AMP. R. H. Kahn & W. E. M. Lands, Eds.: 275-304. Academic Press. New York.

65. RAO, CH.V. 1977. Differential effects of detergents and dimethyl sulfoxide on membrane prostaglandin E_1 and F_2 receptors. Life Sci. 20: 2013-2022.

66. GREENWALD, J. E., K. E. WONG, M. ALEXANDER & J. R. BIANCHINE. 1980. In vivo inhibition of thromboxane biosynthesis by hydralazine. Adv. Prostaglandin Thromboxane Res. 6: 293-295.

67. GOLLAN, F. 1967. Effect of DMSO and THAM on ionizing radiation in mice. Ann. N.Y. Acad. Sci. 141: 63-64.

68. LIM, R. & S. MULLAN. 1975. Enhancement of resistance of glial cells by dimethyl sulfoxide against sonic disruption. Ann. N.Y. Acad. Sci. 243: 358-361.

69. SANDBORN, E. B., H. STEPHENS & M. BENDAYAN. 1975. The influence of dimethyl sulfoxide on cellular ultrastructure and cytochemistry. Ann. N.Y. Acad. Sci. 243: 122-138.

70. WEISSMAN, G., G. SESSA & V. BEVANS. 1967. Effect of DMSO on the stabilization of lysosomes by cortisone and chloroquine in vitro. Ann. N.Y. Acad. Sci. 141: 326-332.

71. DE LA TORRE, J. C. 1981. Spinal cord injury: review of basic and applied research. Spine 6: 315-335.

72. DEMOPOULOS, H. B., E. FLAMM, D. PIETRONIGRO & M. L. SELIGMAN. 1980. The free

radical pathology and the microcirculation in the major central nervous system disorders. Acta Physiol. Scand. Suppl. **492**: 91–119.

73. FLAMM, E. S., H. DEMOPOULOS, M. SELIGMANN & J. RANSOHOFF. 1978. Free radicals in cerebral ischemia. Stroke **9**: 445–447.

74. REHNCRONA, S., B. K. SIESJO & D. S. SMITH. 1980. Reversible ischemia of the brain: biochemical factors influencing restitution. Acta Physiol. Scand. Suppl. **492**: 135–140.

75. DEL MAESTRO, R., H. H. THAW, J. BJORK, M. PLANKER & K. E. ARFORS. 1980. Free radicals as mediators of tissue injury. Acta Physiol. Acand. Suppl. **492**: 43–57.

76. PANGANAMALA, R. V., H. M. SHARMA & R. E. HEIKKILA. 1976. Role of hydroxyl radical scavengers, dimethyl sulfoxide, alcohols and methional in the inhibition of prostaglandin synthesis. Prostaglandins **11**: 599–607.

77. ASHWOOD-SMITH, M. J. 1967. Radioprotective and cryoprotective properties of dimethyl sulfoxide in cellular systems. Ann. N.Y. Acad. Sci. **141**: 41–62.

78. SCHLAFER, M., P. F. KANE & M. KIRSH. 1982. Effects of dimethyl sulfoxide on the globally ischemic heart: possible general relevance to hypothermic organ preservation. Cryobiology **19**: 61–69.

79. CONOVER, T. E. 1975. Influence of nonionic organic solutes on various reactions of energy conservation and utilization. Ann. N.Y. Acad. Sci. **243**: 24–37.

80. GHOSH, A. K., T. ITO, S. GHOSH & H. A. SLOVITER. 1976. Effects of dimethyl sulfoxide on metabolism of isolated perfused rat brain. Biochem. Pharm. **25**: 1115–1117.

81. HOLLAND, C. E. & R. E. OLSON. 1975. Prevention by hypothermia of paradoxical calcium necrosis in cardiac muscle. J. Mol. Cell Cardiol. **7**: 917–928.

82. SPILKER, B. 1972. Pharmacological studies on dimethyl sulfoxide. Arch. Int. Pharm. Ther. **200**: 153–167.

83. FREEDMAN, B., R. F. DUNN, D. R. RICHMOND & D. T. KELLEY. 1979. Coronary artery spasm: treatment with verapimil. (abstr.) Circulation **60** (suppl. II): 11–249.

84. NAYLER, W. G. & J. SZETO. 1972. Effect of verapamil on contractility, oxygen utilization and calcium exchangeability in mammalian heart muscle. Carciovasc. Res. **6**: 120.

85. LITTLE, J., A. COOK & R. LESSER. 1981. Treatment of acute focal cerebral ischemia with dimethyl sulfoxide. Neurosurgery **9**: 34–49.

86. DISTEFANO, V. & J. J. KLAHN. 1965. Observations on the pharmacology and hemolytic activity of dimethyl sulfoxide. Tox. Appl. Pharm. **7**: 660–666.

87. RODRIGUEZ, L. P., M. ARMIJO, J. RODRIGUEZ, J. SAN ROMAN & A. VELASCO. 1966. Efectos del DMSO sobre presion y respiracion. Arch. Inst. Farm. Exp. **18**: 97–101.

88. FINNEY, J. W., H. C. URSCHEL, G. A. BALLA, G. RACE & B. E. JAY. 1967. Protection of the ischemic heart with DMSO alone or DMSO with hydrogen peroxide. Ann. N.Y. Acad. Sci. **141**: 231–241.

89. MATHENY, J. L., C. WEISMAN, A. M. KAROW & M. SCHLAFER. 1975. Myocardial function during hypoxia: protective effects of dimethyl sulfoxide. Res. Comm. Chem. Path. Pharm. **10**: 77–92.

90. LEON, A. S., C. M. BLOOR & B. PITT. 1970. The effects of dimethyl sulfoxide (DMSO) on the healing of experimental myocardial necrosis. Am. Heart J. **79**: 384–389.

91. HAMEROFF, S. R., C. W. OTTO, J. KANEL, P. WEINSTEIN & C. D. BLITT. 1981. Acute cardiovascular effects of dimethyl sulfoxide. Crit. Care Med. **9**: 855–857.

92. PACE, D. G., J. KOVACS & L. KLEVANS. 1982. Dimethyl sulfoxide inhibits platelet aggregation in partially obstructed canine coronary vessels. Fed. Proc. **41**: 1530.

93. KEDAR, I., J. COHEN, E. T. JACOB & M. RAVID. 1981. Alleviation of experimental ischemic acute renal failure by dimethyl sulfoxide. Nephron **29**: 55–58.

94. RAVID, M., D. VAN-DYK, J. BERNHEIM & I. KEDAR. 1983. The protective effect of dimethyl sulfoxide in experimental ischemia of the intestine. Ann. N.Y. Acad. Sci. **411**: 100–104.

CONTROL TRIALS OF DIMETHYL SULFOXIDE IN RHEUMATOID AND COLLAGEN DISEASES

A. P. Alyabyeva and Yu. V. Muravyev

Institute of Rheumatism
USSR Academy of Medical Sciences
AMN Moscow USSR

This is a report of control trials using DMSO in 199 patients. Seventy patients were diagnosed as suffering from rheumatoid arthritis (RA), and ranged in age from 17 to 75 years. Thirty-five children ages 5–13 were diagnosed with juvenile chronic arthritis (JCA). The diagnosis was made according to American Rheumatology Association (ARA) criteria. Sixty-five patients ranging in age from 18–65, had Sjögren's syndrome. The diagnosis was based on clinical and laboratory findings. Twenty-nine patients suffered from systemic scleroderma with pronounced and extensive skin involvement. In 6 patients, ulcerations of fingers were seen.

All 199 patients continued basic anti-inflammatory therapy: 60 received corticosteroids (20–30 mg by mouth), 40 received intra-articular hydrocortisone injections (due to resistant synovitis) which were, however, ineffective. The key selective principle was the absence or a slight effect in response to the basic therapy. Before DMSO application, all patients had undergone a tolerance test: 50% DMSO (always diluted with distilled water) was applied on the back of the hand and 30% solution over the parotid glands. The follow-up lasted for 24 hours. Dermatitis on the tested areas was seen in only two cases. These patients were excluded from the trial. Patients and physicians knew that they were receiving DMSO application but not the concentration or drug combinations. These details were known only to the chief of the experimental trial, Dr. A. P. Alyabyeva.

The course of treatment lasted for two weeks. Each patient received 200 ml of 50% DMSO.

I. Hand Joint Involvement.

Twenty-seven patients had hand joint involvement. Seventeen of these patients received 50% DMSO mixed with heparin (250 IU/ml topically) on the right hand and 50% DMSO in distilled water on the left hand. Ten patients received 50% DMSO with a subsequent ultrasonic therapy (0.4 Watts/cm^2) on the right hand and 50% DMSO combined with ultrasonic effect (zero wattage) on the left hand (TABLE 1).

The following evaluation of symptomatology was performed by one of us (Y.V.M.) before and after the treatment: pain, on a scale of 0 to 5 (as judged subjectively by the patient); articular index; grip strength (mm Hg); and circumference of proximal interphalangeal joints (TABLE 1).

All DMSO treatment combinations proved effective. However, increased antiexudative and analgesic effects were seen in response to combined application of DMSO with heparin or with ultrasound.

309

0077-8923/83/0411-0309 $01.75/0 © 1983, NYAS

TABLE 1

DMSO ALONE OR COMBINED IN PATIENTS WITH RHEUMATOID ARTHRITIS

Treatment	Pain Before	Pain After	Joint Index Before	Joint Index After	Change in the Circumference of Interphalangeal Joints*	Grip Strength† Before	Grip Strength† After
Applications of	1.7	0.81	9.37	6.75	3.40 (0.50)	116.50	171.80
DMSO +	(0.19)	(0.2)	(1.04)	(0.83)		(21.90)	(20.10)
heparin							
(N = 17)	‡p < 0.01		N.S.		‡p < 0.05	N.S.	
DMSO applica-	1.67	1.17	8.56	7.17	1.50 (0.8)	100.90	134.30
tions only	(0.22)	(0.22)	(1.0)	(0.91)		(19.80)	(19.30)
(N = 17)	‡p < 0.05		N.S.		N.S.	N.S.	
DMSO ointment	1.75	0.75	6.0	4.75	2.66 (1.0)	117.4	149.2
+ ultrasonics	(0.25)	(0.25)	(0.65)	(0.7)		(21.6)	(24.9)
(0.4 Wt/cm²)	p < 0.01		N.S.		N.S.	N.S.	
(N = 10)							
DMSO ointment	1.50	0.87	6.20	5.50	1.77 (0.74)	122.30	124.60
+ ultrasonics	(0.26)	(0.22)	(0.74)	(0.70)		(26.20)	(27.90)
(zero	N.S.		N.S.		N.S.	N.S.	
capacitance)							
(N = 10)							

N.S. = non-significant, ( ) = standard error of the mean (SEM), * = measured metrically,
† = mm Hg, and ‡ = significant change.

II. Flexion Contractures

Twenty patients with flexion contractures in various joints received combined application of concentrated DMSO and hydrocortisone ointment (125 g hydrocortisone and 100 g lanolyne). After 5 or 6 applications, the range of articular flexion increased by 15–20 degrees, and after 10 to 12 applications, 95% of patients increased their range of motion by 20–30 degrees. Thirty to 40 days of follow-up have shown no contractural relapses in these patients.

TABLE 2

COMPARATIVE EFFICACY OF TOPICAL APPLICATION OF DMSO-BUTADION GEL AND PERCLUSONE OINTMENT IN PATIENTS WITH RHEUMATOID ARTHRITIS

	Pain Before	Pain After	Joint Index Before	Joint Index After	Reduction of Circumference of Proximal Interphalangeal Joints
DMSO: butadion	1.11	0.39	10.75	6.87	
gel	(0.19)	(0.14)	(1.44)	(1.20)	42.36 (8.33) 5.44 (0.80)
N = 20	p < 0.01		p < 0.05		p < 0.05
1	2	2	4	5	6 7
Perclusone	0.82	0.29	6.90	4.2	32.10 (6.35) 2.66 (0.76)
ointment	(0.15)	(0.14)	(0.83)	(0.84)	
N = 20	p < 0.01		p < 0.05		p < 0.05

Numbers in parentheses are standard error of the mean (SEM).

III. Comparative Efficacy of DMSO-Butadion Gel Application and Perclusone Ointment

20 RA patients with affected proximal interphalangeal joints, II and III degrees of activity, X-ray changes of the II and III stages, received DMSO-butadion gel applications on the right hand and perclusone ointment on the left one. The efficacy evaluation was done in accordance with the above-mentioned criteria (TABLE 2).

As seen in TABLE 2, a good effect was obtained in both cases, however, DMSO-butadion gel produced a more pronounced anti-inflammatory, anti-exudative, and analgesic action.

TABLE 3

DMSO EFFECT ON THE FUNCTIONAL STATE OF KIDNEYS AND PROTEINURIA

Signs	1980	1981	1982
	4 5 6 7 8 9 10 11 12	1 2 3 4 5 6 7 8 9 10 11 12	1 2 3 4 5

Proteinuria (g/L)
5
10
15
20

Creatinine (mg%)
0.5
1.0
1.5
2.0
2.5
3.0

| Glomerular filtration | 62.61 | 94 | 56.61 | 66 |
| Renal blood flow* | 461 | 587 | 431 460 | 436 |

Open circle = before treatment, closed circle = after DMSO treatment, and *ml/100 g tissue/min.

IV. Secondary Amyloidosis

Three RA patients suffering from secondary amyloidosis received 5 g DMSO in distilled water by mouth combined with 50% DMSO applications on affected joints. A 7-month follow-up showed a good tolerance, general improvement, decrease in pain and in exudative phenomena of joints, plus a significant reduction of proteinuria. Edema of the legs disappeared. In one patient, the dose of prednisolone was decreased from 7.5 to 2.5 mg. The dynamic changes in proteinuria are given in TABLE 3.

TABLE 4

DYNAMIC CHANGES IN MAIN CLINICAL SIGNS OF RHEUMATOID ARTHRITIS
DUE TO TREATMENT

Criteria of Efficacy Evaluation	Basic Group		Control Group	
	Before	After	Before	After
Pain in joints	5.0 (2.1)	1.2 (0.8)	4.1 (1.6)	1.7 (1.3)
(0-5) scale)		$p < 0.1$		$p < 0.2$
Changes in circumference	30.5 (2.0)	25.6 (4.3)	26.6 (0.8)	25.0 (0.6)
of joints (cm)		$p > 0.5$		$p > 0.5$
Range of articular	86.0 (7.2)	133.0 (4.8)	86.8 (3.1)	97.4 (1.8)
motion (degrees)		$p < 0.01$		$p > 0.05$
Articular index	7.8 (0.6)	3.1 (0.2)	6.8 (0.3)	5.75 (1.8)
(points)		$p < 0.01$		$p > 0.05$

Numbers in parentheses are standard error of the mean (SEM)

V. Juvenile Chronic Arthritis

Thirty-five children with JCA, ranging in age from 5 to 13 years, received 40% or 30% DMSO depending on their tolerance. Twenty-six children received the first or the second solution + heparin (250 IU/ml) during 2 weeks, 9 children from the control group received only 40% DMSO concentration. The remaining children received standard anti-inflammatory therapy. The physician following up the patients did not know what percentage and which solution mixed with heparin were being given. Knee joints were treated. The results are summed up in TABLE 4. TABLE 3 shows that DMSO combined with heparin is the most effective treatment. A reduction of local inflammation and exudative manifestations was quickly evident. The difference in DMSO concentration (30% or 40%) mixed with heparin did not significantly alter the results. In the control group, the effect of 100% DMSO application was weaker. The efficacy evaluation was performed by one of us (Y.V.M.) and a pediatrician.

VI. Results of DMSO and Ascorbic Acid

Forty-one of 65 patients with Sjögren's syndrome received 30% DMSO. Ten patients received 30% DMSO with 5 ml of 5% ascorbic acid. Ten other patients

TABLE 5

EFFICACY OF DMSO APPLICATIONS ON PAROTID GLANDS IN PATIENTS
WITH SJÖGREN'S SYNDROME

Mode of Treatment	Total Number of Patients	Improvement			
		Significant N (%)	Moderate N (%)	Slight N (%)	Without Effect N (%)
DMSO Only	41	21 (51)	14 (34)	5 (12)	1 (2.5)
DMSO + ascorbic acid	10	6 (60)	3 (30)	2 (20)	
DMSO + heparin	10	5 (50)	2 (20)	2 (20)	1 (10)
DMSO + hydrocortisone	4	2 (50)	2 (50)		
Overall	65	34	20	9	2

received 30% DMSO combined with 125 IU heparin; 4 children received 125 mg hydrocortisone combined with 30% DMSO. Each patient received 10 applications (100 ml 30% DMSO). The results are given in TABLE 5. The efficacy evaluation was carried out by one of us (Y.V.M.) and a stomatologist.

A significant improvement consisted of reduction in salivary gland size (down to normal anatomic dimensions), moist mucosal membrane in the oral cavity, disappearance of inflammatory phenomena and epithelial desquamation, and presence of salivation in response to stimulation.

A moderate improvement refers to a decrease in the size of the salivary glands and the disappearance of discomfort in the oral cavity. Slight effect refers to salivary diminution of gland size and reduced discomfort in oral cavity. In 2 patients, the treatment proved ineffective.

VI. Systemic Scleroderma

Twenty-nine patients with systemic scleroderma were divided into three groups. 50% DMSO was applied to hands and forearms (200 ml/application). In Group 1, 10 patients received 50% DMSO; in Group 2, 10 patients received 50% DMSO (the same site of application combined with 5 mg No-spa [1-(3,4-diethoxybenzyl) 6,7diethoxy-1,2,3,4-tetraisoquinoline hydrochloride] and in Group 3, 9 patients received 50% DMSO in combination with 1% nicotinic acid (5 ml).

Tissue microcirculation was studied before and after therapy by radioimmunoindicator ^{133}Xe clearance (according to technique modified by Sejorsen for skin and by Lassen for muscles). The results were as follows. Before treatment, dermal and muscle blood flow was equally reduced in nearly all patients. After therapy, effective dermal and muscle blood flow in Group 1 was slightly (not significant) elevated. Group 2 showed a 1.2-fold increase. In Group 3, a sixfold increase in blood flow was seen.

It is evident that 50% DMSO combined with No-spa or 1% nicotinic acid, significantly improves microcirculation and oxygenation of tissues. Vasodilation by 50% DMSO with nicotinic acid was confirmed by the disappearance of Raynaud's syndrome, the reduction of gross edema and hyperpigmentation of skin. Moreover, the application of 50% DMSO combined with 5% synthomycin (D,L-threo-1-para-nitrophenyl-dichloroacetylamino-propanediol-1,3) emulsion completely healed ulcers on fingers in all 6 patients after one month of therapy.

In our judgement, the interest in DMSO as a drug exerting a measurable therapeutic action in various musculoskeletal and collagen disorders is quite justified.

The mechanism of its action is not yet clear. However, our own experience, as well as the data obtained by physicians not only in Moscow (DMSO in the USSR is employed in Svedrlovsk, Kazan, Saratov, Volgograd, Lyvov, Kiev, Tbilisi, etc.) but also by scientists all over the world, confirms that DMSO therapy is extremely useful in patients. In some cases it can be used as an alternative drug.

Non-control trial application of DMSO at our institute began to 1972. By now, the total number of patients at our institute who have received either short- or long-term DMSO therapy amounts to 2,500 patients.

Of these, 70% have shown good to excellent effects. The best treatment was observed when DMSO was combined with heparin, analgin, (1-phenyl-2,3-dimethyl-4-methylaminopiroxalon-5-N-methanesulfonate sodium), hydrocortisone, No-spa (drotazerine) or nicotinic acid. We have described elsewhere a

TABLE 6

INDICES OF EFFECTIVE DERMAL AND MUSCLE BLOOD FLOW IN PATIENTS WITH SCLERODERMA
(ml/100 g tissue/min)

Method of Treatment	Number of Patients	Dermal Blood Flow			Muscle Blood Flow		
		Before	After	Increase	Before	After	Increase
Group 1 DMSO only	10	17.25 (±2.19)	13.77 (±1.00)	0.98 (±0.28)	2.58 (±0.81)	3.69 (±0.90)	3.12 (±0.95)
Group 2 DMSO + No-spa	10	13.73 (± 2.21)	15.98 (±2.65)	1.27 (±0.20)	2.93 (±0.69)	3.63 (±1.65)	4.07 (±1.00)
Group 3 DMSO + nictotinic acid	9	17.35 (±3.20)	30.24 (±3.88)	2.50 (±0.66)	3.61 (±0.67)	4.79 (±0.84)	2.44 (±0.49)

Numbers in parentheses are standard error of the mean (SEM).

case where tissue necrosis following an erroneous intramuscular injection of 10% $CaCl_2$ solution in a patient was prevented by DMSO administration. We have succeeded in healing trophic ulcers on fingers and other sites in patients with scleroderma and varicose veins while treating them with the combination of 5% synthomycin emulsion and DMSO.

A wide variety of DMSO effects and the possibility of using it as a carrier for other drugs through biological membranes are of a particular importance to us. We are inclined to think that once DMSO penetrates into the blood, it enhances the effect not only of incorporated drugs but also of drugs that are received by patients orally or parenterally. In our experience, side effects are rare (1–2%) and include dermatitis and odor intolerance. The technique of DMSO application is extremely simple and useful since it permits out-patient and home treatment.

ACKNOWLEDGMENTS

The authors are greatful to Drs. M. V. Simonova, N. I. Melikhova, R. M. Balabanova, and E. S. Mutch, for clinical evaluation of patients. Prof. V. A. Nassonova is the director of our institute.

REFERENCES

1. ALYABIEVA, A. P., E. S. MUTCH & R. M. BALABANOVA. 1978. J. Therapevt. Archiv. N9:105–107.
2. BALABANOVA, R. M., A. P. ALYABIEVA, V. D. ACHNAZAROVA et al. 1977. J. Therapevt. Archiv. N11:99–102.
3. MURAVYEV, YU V. & A. P. ALYABIEVA. 1977. J. Therapevt. Archiv. N11:82–85.
4. ALYABIEVA, A. P. 1980. J. Therapevt. Archiv. N1:94–95.
5. ALYABIEVA, A. P., N. I. MELIKHOVA & YU. V. MURAVYEV. 1980. J. Pediatria N9:50–52.
6. ALYABIEVA, A. P., M. V. SIMONOVA & YU. V. MURAVYEV. 1981. J. Therapevt. Archiv. N1:87–89.
7. MURAVYEV, YU V. & A. P. ALYABIEVA. 1981. J. Therapevt. Archiv. N11:38–39.

SUMMARY

Arthur L. Scherbel

Cleveland Clinic Foundation
Cleveland, Ohio 44106

Most of the scientific reports presented at this conference have re-emphasized unique biological properties that characterize dimethyl sulfoxide (DMSO). In contrast to previous conferences where the number of experimental and clinical studies were equally divided, only 10% of the papers presented at this conference were clinical.

There were several interesting reports on the effect of DMSO in experimental ischemic lesions. A protective action was observed against acute ischemia of the intestines following appropriate arterial ligation and renal ischemic damage following experimentally induced renal failure. The protective action of DMSO in experimental cardiac damage was believed to result from a scavenging effect on hydroxyl radicals, which are suspected to play a role in organ damage. DMSO may also play a protective role in other diseases through a similar mechanism of action.

The analgesic effect of DMSO in an experimental study was reported to be comparable to the analgesic effect of morphine. The mechanism of action was unknown and not thought to be similar to the action of morphine. Other reports discussed the effect of DMSO on prostaglandins, platelet activity, blood cells, thrombus formation, and drug interactions.

A number of interesting and controversial experimental and clinical reports were presented that described the effect of DMSO on a variety of lesions involving the brain and spinal cord. These included cerebral edema, vascular occlusion, hemorrhage, and trauma. Studies have now progressed from experimental to clinical trials in several neurosurgical centers. It is likely that the greatest progress with DMSO in the next few years will be in the area of neurosurgery.

Unfortunately, the multiplicity of biological actions reported to occur with DMSO have hindered Food and Drug Administration (FDA) approval of the drug for human use. Despite extensive study of the compound in both experimental and clinical settings, it is very unlikely that it will be made available within the near future. An FDA official reported at this conference that the risk of ocular toxicity has not been resolved and no clinical studies submitted to the FDA have been acceptable. The only change in the FDA position on DMSO has been the recent removal of restrictions imposed in 1965 on clinical investigation of this drug. When the restrictions were imposed, the pharmaceutical industry lost interest and consequently research funds necessary for clinical trials disappeared. I believe this is one of the reasons why so few clinical papers were presented at this conference.

In the meantime, while the FDA resistance to DMSO approval for human use continues, millions of Americans have been able to purchase commercial grade DMSO for self-medication without adequate medical supervision. This, indeed, has become one of the great tragedies of American medicine in the twentieth century. The saga of DMSO has become further complicated because a number of states have now passed legislation that allows physicians to use medicinal DMSO by prescription.

During my closing comments at the Second Conference on Biological Actions of DMSO, I stated that it would be at least fifteen more years before DMSO would become available as a prescription drug, if it continued to be studied under a cloud of controversy. I am concerned that approximately one-half of this time has already elapsed without any real progress being made in the DMSO controversy.

DIMETHYL SULFOXIDE INHIBITION OF PROSTACYCLIN PRODUCTION IN CULTURED AORTIC ENDOTHELIAL CELLS

Syed S. Alam and Don L. Layman*

Department of Anatomy
Oregon Health Sciences University
Portland, Oregon 97201

INTRODUCTION

Prostaglandin metabolism is significantly altered in advanced atherosclerosis, resulting in an increased platelet aggregation and adhesiveness.[1] Inhibition of prostacyclin (PGI$_2$) biosynthesis by arterial endothelial cells and stimulation of thromboxane A$_2$(TxA$_2$) by platelets has been observed in experimentally induced atherosclerosis in animals.[2,3] Dimethyl sulfoxide (DMSO) has been reported to impair platelet aggregation[4] and to inhibit PGE and PGF synthesis in seminal vesicle microsomes *in vitro*.[5] Because of these reports we have investigated the effect of DMSO and its major metabolite, dimethyl sulfone (DMSO$_2$), on the synthesis of PGI$_2$ by cultured endothelial cells.

METHODS

Cultures of endothelial cells were established from intact bovine aortas by a modified method of Jaffe *et al.*[6] Cells were grown to confluency in McCoy's medium supplemented with 20% fetal calf serum and antibiotics. Only cultures between the third and sixth subculture and exhibiting the typical monolayer growth and morphology of endothelial cells were used. The amount of PGI$_2$ released into the culture medium was measured by radioimmunoassay of its stable product, 6-keto-PGF$_{1\alpha}$.[7] Radiolabeled ^{14}C-6-keto-PGF$_{1\alpha}$ and cellular ^{14}C-phospholipids were analyzed by thin layer radiochromatography using authentic prostaglandins and lipids as markers.[8] Cell protein was determined by the method of Lowry *et al.*[9]

RESULTS AND DISCUSSION

The production of PGI$_2$ by cultured aortic endothelial cells was inhibited approximately 70% by DMSO and 50% by DMSO$_2$ in the culture medium, as measured by radioimmunoassay of 6-keto-PGF$_{1\alpha}$ (TABLE 1). Total PGI$_2$ production for 24 h per 1×10^6 cells was 93.3 ng for controls, 26.5 ng for the DMSO-treated, and 46.5 ng for the DMSO$_2$-treated cells.

To determine whether DMSO or DMSO$_2$ suppressed PGI$_2$ production by interfering with the release of arachidonic acid from cellular phospholipids, endothelial cells were incubated with [^{14}C]arachidonic acid to prelabel endogenous arachidonic acid-containing cellular phospholipids prior to incubation with

---

*To whom all correspondence should be addressed.

INHIBITION OF PROSTACYCLIN PRODUCTION IN CULTURED AORTIC ENDOTHELIAL CELLS BY DIMETHYL SULFOXIDE OR DIMETHYL SULFONE

Incubation	Radioimmunassay of Medium 6-Keto-PGF$_{1\alpha}$ (ng/mg cell protein)	Percent Reduction
Control	18.7 ± 0.9	100
2% DMSO	5.3 ± 0.4	72*
2% DMSO$_2$	9.3 ± 0.6	50*

*Student's t test, $p < 0.001$.

nonlabeled medium containing 2% DMSO or DMSO$_2$. After a 24-h incubation the medium was analyzed for ^{14}C-6-keto-PGF$_{1\alpha}$ and the cells for ^{14}C-phospholipids by thin layer radiochromatography. As shown in TABLE 2, the conversion of endogenously labeled arachidonic to labeled 6-keto-PGF$_{1\alpha}$ was inhibited approximately 70% by DMSO and 50% by DMSO$_2$. The release of labeled arachidonic acid from phosphatidylcholine and phosphatidylethanolamine was inhibited correspondingly, further indicating that DMSO and DMSO$_2$ interfered with the release of arachidonic acid from cellular phospholipids.

To examine the effect of DMSO on the cyclooxygenase system, cultures of endothelial cells were incubated concurrently with exogenously added [^{14}C]arachidonic acid and 2% DMSO for 30 min. The medium was analyzed for labeled 6-keto-PGF$_{1\alpha}$ by thin layer radiochromatography. Results illustrated in TABLE 3 indicate that DMSO stimulated the generation of 6-keto-PGF$_{1\alpha}$ from exogenously added arachidonic acid by about 27%. Indomethacin, a known inhibitor of cyclooxygenase, almost completely inhibited PGI$_2$ production in the DMSO-treated cells. These results suggest that the cyclooxygenase system was not appreciably affected by DMSO because the generation of PGI$_2$ from exogenously added arachidonic acid was not inhibited. The apparent stimulation in the conversion of [^{14}C]arachidonic acid to ^{14}C-keto-PGF$_{1\alpha}$ may have been caused, in part, by the reduced availability of endogenous arachidonic acid, which would result in a higher relative specific activity of exogenously added [^{14}C]arachidonic acid in the DMSO-treated cells as compared to nontreated controls.

These studies indicate that DMSO significantly inhibits the production of PGI$_2$ by cultured aortic endothelial cells and that this inhibition is the result of an

TABLE 2

INHIBITION OF THE RELEASE OF ENDOGENOUS [^{14}C]ARACHIDONIC ACID FROM CELLULAR PHOSPHOLIPIDS IN CULTURED ENDOTHELIAL CELLS BY DIMETHYL SULFOXIDE AND DIMETHYL SULFONE

Incubation	6-Keto-PGF$_{1\alpha}$ (DPM/ml medium)	% Reduction 6-Keto-PGF$_{1\alpha}$	Phosphatidyl-ethanolamine	Phosphatidyl-choline (DPM/mg cell protein)
Control*	5893 ± 279	100	19013 ± 1250	17466 ± 383
2% DMSO*	1587 ± 139†	-73	23312 ± 1032¶	19136 ± 593¶
2% DMSO$_2$*	3025 ± 145†	-49	27680 ± 575‡	19978 ± 184¶

*Mean of two separate experiments done in triplicate.
P values: †$p < 0.001$; ‡$p < 0.01$; ¶$p < 0.05$.

TABLE 3

CONVERSION OF EXOGENOUS [^{14}C]ARACHIDONIC ACID TO 6-KETO-PGF$_{1\alpha}$ BY CULTURED ENDOTHELIAL CELLS EXPOSED TO DIMETHYL SULFOXIDE

Cell Treatment*		Medium 6-Keto-PGF$_{1\alpha}$ per mg Cell Protein (cpm mean ± S.E.)	% Change	
Experiment 1				
Control	(2)	50,341 ± 1838		
DMSO	(2)	67,513 ± 1733	+34%	
Experiment 2				
Control	(2)	31,689 ± 988		
DMSO	(2)	38,704 ± 668	+22%	+27%
Experiment 3				
Control	(2)	45,695 ± 3266		
DMSO	(2)	56,666 ± 4891	+24%	
Indomethacin	(2)	2,744 ± 126	−94%	

*Cells were pre-incubated for 24 h with medium containing 0 or 1.5% DMSO followed by a 30-min incubation with 10 μCi/ml of [^{14}C]arachidonic acid. Medium was analyzed for 6-keto-PGF$_{1\alpha}$ by thin layer radiochromatography. Some cells were preincubated for 30 min with 10 μg/ml of indomethacin before the addition of [^{14}C]arachidonic acid.

interference in the release or availability of arachidonic acid from cellular phospholipids.

REFERENCES

1. OLCOTT, C. & E. J. WYLIE. 1978. J. Surg. Res. **24:** 343–346.
2. GRYGLEWSKI, R. J., A. DEMBINSKA-KIEC, A. ZMUDA & T. GRYGLEWSKA. 1978. Atherosclerosis **31:** 385–389.
3. ZMUDA, A., A. DEMBINSKA-KIEC, A. CHYTOSKI & R. J. GRYGLEWSKI. 1977. Prostaglandins **14:** 1035–1039.
4. ROSENBLUM, W. I. & F. E SABBAN. 1982. Stroke **13:** 35–39.
5. PANGANAMALA, R. V., H. M. SHARMA, R. E. HEIKKILA, J. C. GEER & D. G. CORNWELL. 1976. Prostaglandins **11:** 599–607.
6. JAFFE, E. A., R. L. NACHMAN, C. G. BECKER & R. C. MINICK. 1973. J. Clin. Invest. **52:** 2745–2756.
7. SALMON, J. A. 1978. Prostaglandins **15:** 383–387.
8. SKIPSKI, V. P., R. F. PETERSON & M. BARCLAY. 1964. Biochem. J. **90:** 374–378.
9. LOWRY, O. H., N. J. ROSENBOROUGH, A. L. FARR & R. J. RANDALL. 1951. J. Biol. Chem. **193:** 265–275.

EFFECT OF DIMETHYL SULFOXIDE ON CHEMOTAXIS
OF PHAGOCYTIC CELLS*

Veena B. Antony,† Steven A. Sahn, and John E. Repine

Pleural Space Laboratory
Laboratory of Experimental Medicine
Webb-Waring Lung Institute
and
Department of Medicine
University of Colorado School of Medicine
Denver, Colorado 80262

Dimethyl sulfoxide (DMSO) has been highly publicized as an anti-inflammatory agent but its mechanism of action[1,2] remains unknown. We hypothesized that DMSO acts by inhibiting influx of phagocytic cells to sites of inflammation and tested this premise by examining the effect of DMSO on the locomotion of polymorphonuclear leukocytes (PMN) and monocytes (MN) in vivo and in vitro. In the present study, we found that DMSO inhibits influx of PMN and MN into infected pleural spaces and decreases locomotion of PMN and MN in vitro. Empyemas were induced by injecting 1×10^6 CFU of Staphylococcus aureus 502A into pleural spaces of New Zealand White rabbits that had sterile, nonhemorrhagic effusions induced by turpentine 120 hours earlier.[3] Pleural fluids were sampled before injection of S. aureus, 4 hours later, and then every 24 hours and analyzed for cell counts, S. aureus colonies, cytology, and chemotactic activity for PMN and MN. In some experiments, rabbits were pre-injected intravenously with DMSO 2–2.4 g/kg/day in four divided doses over 30–45 minutes. After 120 hours, rabbits were sacrificed and their pleural spaces examined for pleural thickening and fibrosis. For in vitro experiments, PMN and MN were purified by Ficoll Hypaque (Sigma Chemical Co., St. Louis, Mo.) separation from blood obtained from healthy donors.[4] Subsequently, unstimulated or stimulated locomotion of PMN or MN was evaluated using single-well Boyden chambers equipped with 5 μm Millipore filters.[5] For studies of stimulated locomotion, zymosan-activated serum (ZAS) was added to the bottom compartment in concentrations chosen to produce peak locomotion of PMN and MN. Experiments were also performed with different concentrations of DMSO added to the top and bottom chambers. Indices of locomotion were the numbers of PMN or MN migrating through filters in 10 random, high-power fields.

The numbers of PMN and MN that entered pleural spaces of DMSO-treated rabbits were significantly decreased compared to untreated rabbits (TABLE 1). The effects of DMSO were not due to decreased numbers of circulating PMN or MN or altered pleural fluid chemotactic activity for PMN and MN since they were the

*This work was supported in part by grants from the Council for Tobacco Research, Kroc, Hill, Swan, and Kleberg Foundations, National Institutes of Health (HL24248 and HL28182), Colorado and American Heart Associations, and Colorado and American Lung Associations. J. E. R. was an Established Investigator of the American Heart Association. V. B. A. is the recipient of a New Investigator Award from the National Institutes of Health (AI-19384-01).

†Address all correspondence to: V. B. A. Webb-Waring Lung Institute, C-322, University of Colorado, Health Sciences Center, 4200 East Ninth Avenue, Denver, Colorado 80262.

321

TABLE 1

NUMBERS OF POLYMORPHONUCLEAR LEUKOCYTES AND MONOCYTES IN PLEURAL FLUIDS OF
INFECTED RABBITS TREATED WITH DMSO

Test Conditions*	PMN†		MN†	
	Untreated	DMSO Treated	Untreated	DMSO Treated
4 hours	6.2 ± 2.4 (8)	1.0 ± 0.4 (8)‡	2.3 ± 0.4 (8)	0.7 ± 0.4 (8)‡
24 hours	61 ± 4.0 (8)	14.6 ± 7.2 (8)‡	0 (8)	2.5 ± 0.2 (8)‡
48 hours	30 ± 4.8 (8)	10 ± 7.0 (8)‡	2.8 ± 0.8 (8)	2.8 ± 0.6 (8)‡
72 hours	13 ± 4.4 (8)	6.0 ± 5.0 (8)‡	13 ± 0.8 (8)	4.6 ± 0.8 (8)‡
96 hours	5.4 ± 3.0 (8)	3.0 ± 1.4 (8)‡	11.5 ± 0.6 (8)	5.0 ± 1.2 (8)‡
120 hours	5.0 ± 3.0 (8)	1.5 ± 1.0 (8)‡	5.0 ± 0.4 (8)	1.8 ± 0.6 (8)‡

*Time following injection of S. aureus intrapleurally.
†Mean ± SEM (number of determinations). Absolute number of cells (× 1,000).
‡Significant difference from untreated.

same in DMSO-treated and untreated rabbits. In addition, S. aureus could be
cultured from pleural fluid of DMSO-treated rabbits for 72 hours while pleural
fluids from control rabbits were able to clear the bacteria from their pleural space
within 24 hours. Moreover, after 120 hours, at autopsy, DMSO-treated rabbits had
thickened, fibrosed pleural surfaces with numerous adhesions while control
rabbits had only rare adhesions between visceral and parietal pleura. In addition,
increasing concentrations of DMSO progressively and significantly ($p < 0.01$)
decreased ZAS-stimulated locomotion of PMN and MN in vitro (TABLES 2 and 3)
but did not alter unstimulated locomotion of PMN or MN. Furthermore, when
PMN or MN were pretreated with DMSO and washed, their locomotion returned
to normal indicating that the effects of DMSO were reversible. Finally, in
additional control studies following incubation in DMSO (280 mM), PMN and
MN showed no abnormalities in either release of cytoplasmic lactate dehydrogenase or ultrastructure as evaluated by electron microscopy suggesting that
DMSO did not cause cell damage.

The present study offers a possible explanation for the reported beneficial

TABLE 2

EFFECT OF DMSO ON ZAS-STIMULATED LOCOMOTION OF HUMAN POLYMORPHONUCLEAR
LEUKOCYTES AND MONOCYTES

Test Conditions*	Locomotion†	
	(PMN/10HPF)	(MN/10HPF)
No Additions	104.8 ± 12.6 (6)	63.4 ± 6.5 (6)
DMSO (0.14 mM)	101.8 ± 8.8 (6)	60.0 ± 7.1 (6)
DMSO (1.4 mM)	68.0 ± 4.6 (6)‡	36.0 ± 3.9 (6)‡
DMSO (14 mM)	18.9 ± 8.3 (6)‡	8.6 ± 2.2 (6)‡
DMSO (140 mM)	8.0 ± 3.1 (6)‡	3.2 ± 0.4 (6)‡
DMSO (280 mM)	6.8 ± 4.0 (6)‡	3.6 ± 2.1 (6)‡

*PMN or MN in HBSS in the top compartment, ZAS in the bottom with listed additions to
both compartments.
†Mean ± SEM (number of determinations). HPF = high power field.
‡Value significantly different ($p \leq 0.05$) from value with no DMSO added.

responses seen in certain individuals who use DMSO. Since inflammation is often mediated and perpetuated by continued influx of PMN and MN and release of their products, such as lysosomal enzymes or toxic oxygen radicals, DMSO-mediated decreases in numbers of PMN or MN present at the sites of inflammation could account for some of the purported therapeutic effects of DMSO. However, it should be noted that very high concentrations of DMSO approaching the maximum dose administered in rabbits were needed to achieve these effects. Whether lower concentrations of DMSO or the influence of a more prolonged exposure to DMSO *in vivo* would produce significant inhibitions of PMN or MN chemotaxis remains unknown. DMSO has also been found to decrease the killing of *S. aureus* by PMN and chemical systems that generate hydroxyl radicals.[6,7]

TABLE 3

EFFECT OF DMSO ON UNSTIMULATED LOCOMOTION OF HUMAN POLYMORPHONUCLEAR LEUKOCYTES AND MONOCYTES

	Locomotion†	
Test Conditions*	(PMN/10 HPF)	(MN/10 HPF)
No Additions	4.8 ± 0.3 (6)	2.3 ± 0.6 (6)
DMSO (0.14 mM)	4.7 ± 0.4 (6)‡	2.3 ± 0.3 (6)‡
DMSO (1.4 mM)	4.1 ± 0.0 (6)‡	1.9 ± 0.2 (6)‡
DMSO (14 mM)	5.9 ± 0.2 (6)‡	1.6 ± 0.6 (6)‡
DMSO (140 mM)	4.6 ± 0.3 (6)‡	3.1 ± 0.7 (6)‡
DMSO (280 mM)	4.8 ± 0.6 (6)‡	2.5 ± 0.4 (6)‡

*PMN or MN in HBSS in the top compartment and HBSS in the bottom compartment with the following additions to both compartments.
†Mean ± SEM (number of determinations). HPF = high power field.
‡Value not significantly different ($p \geq 0.05$) than value with no DMSO added.

REFERENCES

1. ROSENBAUM, E. E. & S. W. JACOB. 1964. Dimethyl sulfoxide (DMSO) in musculoskeletal injuries and inflammation. II. Dimethyl sulfoxide in rheumatoid arthritis, degenerative arthritis. Northwest Med. **63:** 277–229.

2. SHIRLEY, S. W., B. H. STEWART & S. MIRELMAN. 1978. Dimethyl sulfoxide in treatment of inflammatory genitourinary disorders. Urology **11:** 215–220.

3. SAHN, S. A. & D. E. POTTS. 1978. Turpentine pleurisy in rabbits: A model of pleural fluid acidosis and low pleural fluid glucose. Am. Rev. Respir. Dis. **118:** 893–901.

4. BOYUM, A. 1968. Isolation of mononuclear cells and granulocytes from human blood. Scand. J. Clin. Lab. Invest. **21** (Suppl. 97): 77.

5. REPINE, J. E. & C. C. CLAWSON. 1978. Influence of surface proteins and separation techniques on neutrophil unstimulated and stimulated locomotion *in vitro*. J. Reticuloendothel. Soc. **24:** 217–226.

6. REPINE, J. E., R. B. FOX & E. M. BERGER. 1981. Dimethyl sulfoxide inhibits killing of *Staphylococcus aureus* by polymorphonuclear leukocytes. Infect. & Immun. **31:** 510–513.

7. REPINE, J. E., R. B. FOX & E. M. BERGER. 1981. Hydrogen peroxide kills *Staphylococcus aureus* by reacting with staphylococcal iron to form hydroxyl radical. J. Biol. Chem. **256:** 7094–7096.

THE EFFECT OF DIMETHYL SULFOXIDE ON ENDOTOXIN-INDUCED PULMONARY DYSFUNCTION: A BIOCHEMICAL AND ELECTRON MICROSCOPE STUDY

Roy E. Breen, Reid S. Connell,* and Marvin W. Harrison

Departments of Surgery and Anatomy
School of Medicine
Oregon Health Sciences University
Portland, Oregon 97201

INTRODUCTION

The administration of endotoxin in experimental animals has been shown to cause alterations in pulmonary capillary endothelial cell (PCEC) metabolic activity and ultrastructure.[1,2,4,7] These changes occur in the presence of intravascular accumulations of platelets and leukocytes. It has been postulated that lysosomal enzymes and/or highly reactive O_2 metabolites released from blood elements may be responsible for these cytotoxic changes.[5,8] The present study was designed to evaluate dimethyl sulfoxide (DMSO), a known scavenger of free radicals, with regard to its protective effect on PCEC function and fine structure and on survival in endotoxin-treated rats.

MATERIALS AND METHODS

Fifty-four male Sprague Dawley rats weighing between 300 and 500 g were divided into three groups. The first group of 10 animals served as normal controls and were assayed for PCEC luminal adenosine triphosphatase (ATPase) activity. The second and third groups consisting of 22 animals each were given an intraperitoneal injection of 6 ml/kg of either saline or 70% DMSO 30 minutes prior to an intravenous injection of 20 mg/kg of E. coli endotoxin (Sigma-serotype 026:B6). Ten rats each from groups 2 and 3 were assayed for ATPase activity at 4 h and the survivors of the remaining 12 rats in each of the groups were assayed at 24 h. Lung biopsies were taken at 24 h from additional animals in groups 2 and 3 and prepared for an electron microscopic examination. At the time of assay the isolated heart and lungs were flushed with normal saline to remove the blood. Once the effluent was clear, the lungs were perfused with a modified Wachstein-Miesel solution for the demonstration of luminal ATPase activity.[9] The first 5-minute collection of effluent was discarded and the subsequent 5-minute collection was assayed for inorganic phosphorus (P_i) using the method of Fiske and Subbarow.[3] The lungs were removed and dry weights determined. The amount of P_i liberated was used as a marker for PCEC metabolic activity and expressed as mg P_i per ml effluent per gram of dry lung tissue (mg/ml/g).

---

*Send all correspondence to: R. S. C., Department of Anatomy, School of Medicine, Oregon Health Sciences University, 3181 S.W. Sam Jackson Park Rd., Portland, Oregon 97201.

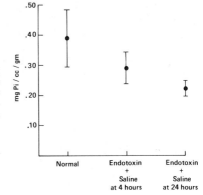

FIGURE 1. The mean P_i level was .390 ± .095 for normal rats. The amount of P_i assayed at 4 and 24 h was .288 ± .052 and .221 ± .024 for the rats given an intravenous injection of endotoxin (20 mg/kg) and an intraperitoneal injection of 6 ml/kg of saline.

RESULTS

The mean amount of P_i liberated after perfusion of isolated heart and lungs with the ATP-containing buffer in normal rats was .390 ± .095. In the saline/endotoxin-treated group the P_i levels were decreased at both 4 and 24 h (.288 ± .052 and .221 ± .024) compared to normal rats (p < .005). In the DMSO/endotoxin-treated group the P_i levels at 4 h were not significantly different from normal rats (.367 ± .057) but at 24 h were somewhat lower than normal (.315 ± .113, p < .1, FIGURES 1 and 2). At 24 h, the lungs of the saline/endotoxin-treated rats exhibited microvascular aggregations of leukocytes and degeneration of the capillary endothelium and overlying alveolar type I epithelium. These ultrastructural lesions were not observed in rats treated with DMSO. All 12 DMSO/endotoxin-treated rats survived 24 h (100%) compared to only 7 of the 12 saline/endotoxin-treated rats (58%, p < .025, FIGURE 3).

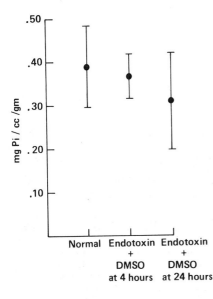

FIGURE 2. The mean P_i level was .390 ± .095 for normal rats. The amount of P_i assayed at 4 and 24 h was .367 ± .057 and .315 ± .113 for the rats given an intravenous injection of endotoxin (20 mg/kg) and an intraperitoneal injection of 6 ml/kg of 70% DMSO.

DISCUSSION

The results of this study indicate that DMSO has a significant effect in preserving PCEC luminal ATPase activity and fine structure and survival in endotoxin-treated rats. Although the exact mechanisms remain speculative, data from this study and others suggest that the effect may involve the inhibition of the release of lysosomal enzymes and the scavenging of O_2 metabolites, such as superoxide anion ($\cdot O_2^-$), hydrogen peroxide (H_2O_2), and hydroxyl radicals ($\cdot OH$), produced by endotoxin-stimulated phagocytes.[6] Most organisms have active enzymes for the catabolism of H_2O_2 and $\cdot O_2^-$ (precursors of $\cdot OH$). However, there are no direct enzymatic mechanisms for the clearance of the highly cytotoxic $\cdot OH$. Thus, the reaction of DMSO with $\cdot OH$ may be an explanation for the protective mechanism.

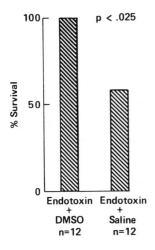

FIGURE 3. All 12 DMSO/endotoxin-treated rats survived 24 h (100%) compared to only 7 of the 12 rats (58%) treated with saline/endotoxin (p < .025).

REFERENCES

1. BISIO, J. M., R. E. BREEN, R. S. CONNELL et al. 1983. Pulmonary capillary endothelial dysfunction in hypoxia and endotoxemia. A biochemical and electron microscope study. J. Trauma. (In press.)
2. COALSON, J. J., L. B. HINSHAW & C. A. GUENTER. 1970. The pulmonary ultrastructure in septic shock. Exp. Molec. Pathol. **12:** 84–103.
3. FISKE, C. H. & Y. SUBBAROW. 1925. The colorimetric determination of phosphorous. J. Biol. Chem. **66:** 375–400.
4. HARRISON, L. H., L. B. HINSHAW, J. J. COALSON et al. 1971. Effects of E. coli sepsis in pulmonary hemodynamics and capillary permeability. J. Thorac. Cardiovasc. Surg. **61:** 795–803.
5. JANOFF, A., G. WEISSMANN, B. W. ZWEIFACH et al. 1962. Pathogenesis of experimental shock. Studies on lysosomes in normal and tolerant animals subjected to lethal trauma and endotoxemia. J. Exp. Med. **116:** 451–466.
6. REPINE, J. E., J. W. EATON, J. R. ANDERS et al. 1979. Generation of hydroxyl radical by enzymes, chemicals, and human phagocytes in vitro. J. Clin. Invest. **64:** 1642–1651.
7. ROBB, H. J., R. R. MARGOLIS & C. M. JABS. 1972. Role of pulmonary microembolism in the hemodynamics of endotoxin shock. Surg. Gynec. Obstet. **135:** 777–783.

8. SACKS, T., C. F. MOLDOW, P. R. CRADDOCK et al. 1978. Oxygen radicals mediate endothelial cell damage by complement-stimulated granulocytes: An in vitro model of immune vascular damage. J. Clin. Invest. **61:** 1161–1167.

9. WACHSTEIN, M. & E. MIESEL. 1957. Histochemistry of hepatic phosphatases at physiological pH with special reference to the demonstration of the bile canaliculi. Am. J. Clin. Pathol. **27:** 13–23.

COMPARISON OF DIMETHYL SULFOXIDE LEVELS IN WHOLE BLOOD AND SERUM USING AN AUTOSAMPLER-EQUIPPED GAS CHROMATOGRAPH

Susan E. Garretson

U.S. Army Reserves
Department of Clinical Pathology
School of Medicine
Oregon Health Sciences University
Portland, Oregon 97201

John P. Aitchison

Department of Clinical Pathology
School of Medicine
Oregon Health Sciences University
Portland, Oregon 97201

INTRODUCTION

Due to a lack of an established method for measurement of DMSO in biological fluids, we previously published a method for its determination in serum, urine, and CSF by means of protein precipitation and gas chromatography.[1] The use of DMSO in both human and animal research has been and continues to be extensive. In order to increase the method's range of applications, it was modified for application to whole blood and its linearity was extended down to 0.025 g/l. Simultaneously drawn whole blood and serum samples from patients receiving DMSO therapy were analyzed in order to establish the relationship between concentrations in the two matrices. Utilization of an autosampler greatly facilitates the analysis of large numbers of samples as would be encountered in research or therapeutic-drug monitoring situations. Modification of the autosampler was necessary to achieve satisfactory chromatography. This extension of our previous method increases its applicability to DMSO-related research, especially in situations where specimen volumes are limited.

MATERIALS AND METHODS

Sample preparation, reagents, instrument program parameters, and quantitation were similar to our previously published method for serum[1] with the following modifications for whole blood: (1) The amount of $HClO_4$ was increased to 400 μl for protein precipitation. (2) Initial vortex time was increased to 30 seconds. (3) Initial ice bath time was increased to 15 minutes. (4) Initial centrifugation time was increased to 10 minutes. (5) The correction factor to account for the difference in recovery between whole blood and the aqueous standard was 0.900. (6) The concentrations of the DMSO standard and internal standard, diethyl sulfone, used in this study were 2.368 and 5.0 g/l, respectively.

A Hewlett-Packard Model 7671A Automatic Sampler was attached to the Hewlett-Packard Model 5840A Gas Chromatograph previously used. The auto-

328

ORIGINAL CIRCUIT:

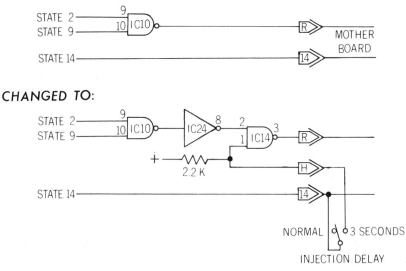

CHANGED TO:

FIGURE 1. Modification of A2 logic board of Hewlett-Packard Model 7671A Autosampler to provide an optional 3-second delay during injection. A switch was added to the back panel of the control box. This modification was designed by Mr. William Sheppard, Instrument and Safety Services, the Oregon Health Sciences University.

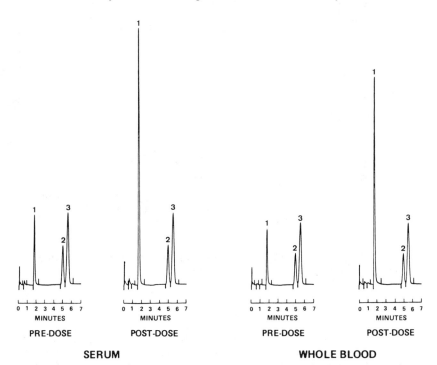

FIGURE 2. Chromatograms of a patient receiving intravenous DMSO therapy. Levels are as follows: pre-dose serum = 0.648 g/l; post-dose serum = 2.415 g/l; pre-dose whole blood = 0.548 g/l; post-dose whole blood = 2.045 g/l. Peak 1 = DMSO, Peak 2 = dimethyl sulfone, Peak 3 = diethyl sulfone (internal standard).

sampler was modified as in FIGURE 1 to include a 3-second pause before withdrawing the needle from the injection port.

Blood bank whole blood was supplemented with DMSO and dimethyl sulfone at levels of 0.025, 0.050, 0.100, 0.500, 1.000, 3.000, and 5.000 g/l. Peak area versus concentration was plotted and linear regression analysis was performed to establish linearity. Freshly drawn whole blood was supplemented with DMSO (2.00 g/l) and dimethyl sulfone (1.022 g/l) and analysis of 10 aliquots was performed on 2 different days. Coefficient of variation was then determined.

Simultaneous whole blood (sodium fluoride anticoagulant) and serum samples were collected from patients receiving DMSO either intramuscularly or

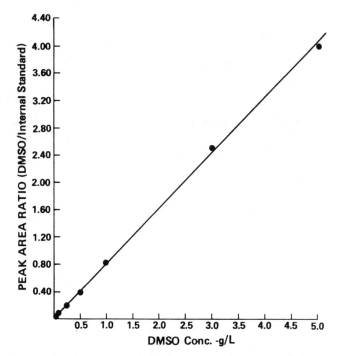

FIGURE 3. Linearity of DMSO in whole blood: Range 0.025–5.000 g/l. Linear regression analysis (x = peak area ratio, y = concentration) is as follows: Slope = 1.2274; intercept = −0.0038; standard error of estimate = 0.041 and R^2 = 0.9995.

intravenously. Levels in both whole blood and serum were quantitated and compared.

RESULTS

FIGURE 2 represents chromatograms of whole blood and serum (both pre- and post-dose) from a patient receiving intravenous DMSO therapy. FIGURE 3 demonstrates the linearity of the method applied to whole blood. The coefficient of variation (N = 20) was 1.13% at a concentration of 2.0 g/l. The concentrations measured in pre- and post-dose samples ranged from 0.050 to 2.32 g/l in whole blood, and 0.064 to 2.63 in serum. These were used to determine that whole blood averaged 14.5 ± 2.0% less than serum levels.

CONCLUSIONS

Statistical analysis of the data indicates that DMSO can be reliably quantitated with good precision in whole blood even at low concentrations. Whole blood levels averaged 14.5% lower than serum levels in patients, a finding similar to the difference between whole blood and serum levels for ethanol.[2] The autosampler greatly decreased the amount of time and effort required for injecting samples onto the gas chromatograph. Modification of the autosampler to provide a 3-second delay upon injection resulted in excellent chromatography. Although assay volume used with whole blood is the same as that used with serum, required sample volume is less. This is important where sample volume is limited or where multiple samples are needed from a small subject or test animal.

REFERENCES

1. GARRETSON, S. E. & J. P. AITCHISON. 1982. Determination of dimethyl sulfoxide in serum and other body fluids by gas chromatography. J. Anal. Toxicol. 6(March/April): 76–81.
2. BASELT, R. C. 1982. Disposition of toxic drugs and chemicals in man. 2nd edit. p. 300. Biomedical Publications. Davis, Calif.

CELL-CYCLE RELATED EVENTS IN THE DIMETHYL SULFOXIDE-INDUCED COMMITMENT OF HEPATIC TUMOR CELLS TO ENHANCED LIVER FUNCTION*

Paul J. Higgins

Laboratory of Investigative Cytology
Memorial Sloan-Kettering Cancer Center
New York, New York 10021

Certain melanoma and hepatoma cell lines respond to treatment with the polar solvent dimethyl sulfoxide (DMSO) with alterations in morphology, proliferative rate, and accumulation of specific gene products, such as melanin (in melanocytes)[1] and albumin or transferrin (in hepatocytes).[2,3] Since the synthesis of at least one hepatocyte-specific protein (albumin) is reported to be cell-cycle related,[4] changes in hepatic tumor cell proliferative kinetics as a consequence of *in vitro* exposure to differentiation-inducing agents may be reflected in the expression of particular cellular genes. It was of interest, therefore, to evaluate the effect of DMSO on albumin secretion and cell-cycle kinetics in established mouse hepatic tumor cells (BW77-1 and BW77-2 hepatoma cell lines) known to exhibit growth restriction in response to DMSO.[2,3]

Cultures of BW77-2 cells (at 50–60% confluency) were exposed to growth medium containing 1% DMSO for a period of 4 days. During the initial 24–48 h of culture (after medium replacement), the amount of secreted albumin in control and DMSO-treated populations was similar, although there was a trend toward lower cell density in DMSO cultures relative to control. Three and 4 days after the medium change, DMSO-treated hepatocyte cultures comprised fewer cells than the corresponding controls and had accumulated significantly greater quantities of albumin (TABLE 1). Additional experiments employing the BW77-1 cell line (which secretes approximately 50% less albumin/10^6 cells compared to BW77-2 cells) indicated that the amount of albumin that accumulated (within a 24-h period) in the extracellular compartment was dependent upon the concentration of DMSO in the culture medium (TABLE 2). This enhanced accumulation of albumin was linked to a marked change in overall cell culture morphology from a random monolayer-type of growth (0% DMSO) to one in which the hepatocytes were organized into individual colonies (3% DMSO).

DMSO-induced re-direction of hepatoma cell growth and albumin accumulation patterns were accompanied by alterations in population kinetics. Flow cytometric measurements of isolated, acridine orange-stained, hepatoma cell nuclei[5,6] revealed a gradual decline in the percentage of hepatocytes with 2C DNA content (diploid G_1 cells), as a function of DMSO concentration, and a corresponding increase in the percentage of 4C DNA content (G_2-like) hepatocytes after a 4-day exposure of hepatoma cell cultures to DMSO. Analysis of computer-generated DNA frequency histograms (FIGURE 1) fixed the percentage of 4C nuclei, in each hepatocyte population, at the following levels: 0% DMSO (38% 4C); 0.5% DMSO (42% 4C); 1% DMSO (46% 4C); and 3% DMSO (53% 4C).

*Supported by National Cancer Institute grant R23 CA25285.

Since control and DMSO-treated cultures primarily comprised mononucleate cells, the nuclear measurements described above accurately reflected the cellular composition of the cultures.

The present data indicate that DMSO perturbs the proliferative kinetics of mouse hepatoma cells *in vitro*. This reduced proliferative capacity and concomitant stimulation in albumin accumulation, as a consequence of exposure to

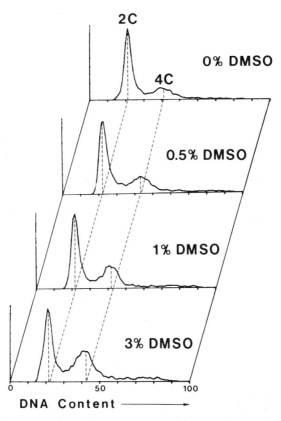

FIGURE 1. Computer-generated DNA frequency histograms obtained by flow cytometric analysis of nuclei from control and DMSO-stimulated BW77-1 hepatic tumor cells. Nuclei were isolated after a 4-day exposure of hepatoma cell cultures to control or DMSO-containing growth medium, stained with acridine orange and analyzed with an Ortho FC 200 Cytofluorograf. The position of nuclei with a 2C (diploid G_1 cells) or 4C DNA content in each population is indicated.

DMSO, are associated with an increase in the percentage of 4C, G_2-like, hepatocytes in the culture. This expanding 4C compartment may represent a subpopulation of hepatocytes arrested (or prolonged) in G_2. Tsukada and Hirai[4] have shown that albumin synthesis is restricted to the mid S to late G_2 phase of the hepatoma cell cycle. The marked increase in albumin accumulation, as a function of DMSO concentration, in the mouse hepatoma cells used in the present study is

TABLE 1

ALBUMIN ACCUMULATION IN CULTURES OF BW77-2 HEPATIC TUMOR CELLS*

Medium	Cells/Culture	Duration of Exposure (h)†	µg Albumin per ml × 10⁶ Cells‡	% of Control¶
Control	1.2×10^6	24	35.3 ± 4.6	
Control	1.7×10^6	48	43.5 ± 10.9	
Control	1.9×10^6	72	57.7 ± 4.8	
Control	2.2×10^6	96	97.3 ± 6.8	
1% DMSO	1.0×10^6	24	41.8 ± 9.6	118.4
1% DMSO	1.0×10^6	48	57.7 ± 13.3	132.6
1% DMSO	1.1×10^6	72	108.2 ± 13.6	187.5
1% DMSO	1.2×10^6	96	236.9 ± 23.1	243.5

*Cells were grown to a density of approximately 1×10^6 cells/60 mm Petri dish (late log phase) at which time the growth medium (Ham's F-12/15% FBS/10^{-6} M dexamethasone/5 µg per ml insulin) was removed and replaced with fresh control or 1% DMSO-containing medium.

†Total time of exposure to either fresh control or 1% DMSO-containing growth medium.

‡Total extracellular albumin accumulated during the exposure period; mean ± standard deviation of three separate determinations.

¶Relative to the corresponding exposure-period control; calculated using group mean.

consistent with this finding. DMSO-stimulated hepatic tumor cells, therefore, may provide a useful *in vitro* system for investigations into the control of gene expression during the hepatocyte cell cycle.

TABLE 2

SECRETION OF ALBUMIN BY
BW77-1 HEPATIC TUMOR CELLS IN A 24-HOUR PERIOD

Medium*	µg Albumin per ml × 10⁶ cells†‡	% of Control¶
0% DMSO	18.7 ± 2.8	100
1% DMSO	28.0 ± 1.8	149.7
2% DMSO	39.5 ± 1.5	211.2

*When cultures reached 25% confluency, the medium (Ham's F-12/15% FBS/10^{-6} M dexamethasone/5 µg per ml insulin) was changed to fresh control or DMSO-containing growth medium. After 72 h, the medium was again changed with either control or DMSO-containing medium; 24 h later the cells and culture fluids were harvested for analysis.

†Total albumin secreted into 1 ml of growth medium per 10^6 cells over a 24 h period; radial immunodiffusion assay.

‡Mean ± standard deviation of nine separate determinations for each DMSO concentration.

¶Calculated from group mean.

REFERENCES

1. HUBERMAN, E., C. HECKMAN & R. LANGENBACH. 1979. Cancer Res. **39:** 2618–2624.
2. HIGGINS, P. J. & E. BORENFREUND. 1980. Biochim. Biophys. Acta **610:** 174–180.

3. HIGGINS, P. J. 1982. Cell. Mol. Biol. **28:** 299–305.
4. TSUKADA, Y. & H. HIRAI. 1975. Ann. N.Y. Acad. Sci. **259:** 37–44.
5. DARZYNKIEWICZ, Z., F. TRAGANOS & M. R. MELAMED. 1980. Cytometry **1:** 98–108.
6. DARZYNKIEWICZ, Z., F. TRAGANOS, S. XUE, L. STAIANO-COICO & M. R. MELAMED. 1981. Cytometry **1:** 279–286.

SUPPRESSION OF ATHEROSCLEROSIS IN CHOLESTEROLEMIC RABBITS BY DIMETHYL SULFOXIDE

Don L. Layman, Syed S. Alam, and Kenneth C. Newcomb

Department of Anatomy
School of Medicine
Oregon Health Sciences University
Portland, Oregon 97201

INTRODUCTION

In 1968 Herzmann reported that 1% dimethyl sulfoxide (DMSO) in the drinking water of cockerels fed cholesterol reduced the accompanying hypercholesterolemia by 50%.[1] We reasoned that if DMSO is an agent that decreases lipid concentration, it may reduce hypercholesterolemia and artherosclerosis in rabbits fed cholesterol. While our studies were in progress Kedar and Sohar reported that DMSO slows cholesterol-induced atherosclerosis in rabbits without affecting plasma cholesterol levels.[2] Our studies support and extend those findings and suggest that DMSO retards the development of atherosclerosis by suppressing the uptake and accumulation of cholesterol by tissues and cells.

METHODS

Hypercholesterolemia and atherosclerosis were induced in 24 male, New Zealand white rabbits, weighing 2-3 kg, by feeding them 0.5% cholesterol in their diet. Half of the animals received 2% DMSO in their drinking water. At 2-week intervals plasma cholesterol and triglycerides were measured by standard autoanalyzer II techniques.[3] Tissue cholesterol was analyzed by the method of Abell et al.[4] Atherosclerosis in the thoracic aorta was scored by drawing images of the luminal surface on paper and calculating the area involved by planimetry. Cultures of dermal fibroblasts were derived from explants of newborn foreskin and grown to confluency in McCoy's medium supplemented with 20% human serum and antibiotics. Cells between the third and eighth subculture were used in these studies. Human low density lipoproteins (LDL) were iodinated with ^{125}I by the iodine monochloride technique of MacFarlane.[5]

RESULTS AND DISCUSSION

No significant differences were observed in the body weights of the control and DMSO-treated rabbits (4.2 ± 0.2 versus 4.1 ± 0.2, respectively). DMSO treatment did not delay the onset or reduce the severity of the dietary-induced hypercholesterolemia. The mean plasma cholesterol of all rabbits rose from less than 100 mg/dl about 1300 mg/dl after four weeks and remained elevated throughout the cholesterol feeding. Plasma triglycerides were not affected by the cholesterol feeding or by DMSO administration. Gross inspection of the thoracic aortas showed that DMSO treatment reduced the severity of the cholesterol-

336

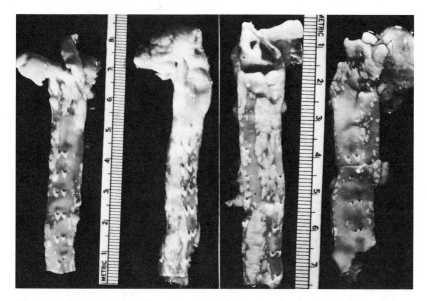

FIGURE 1. Representative thoracic aortas of New Zealand white rabbits fed 0.5% cholesterol and 2% dimethyl sulfoxide for 12 weeks.

induced atherosclerosis 30–40% (FIGURE 1 and TABLE 1). Because the DMSO-treated rabbits appeared to have accumulated less fatty material in thier visceral tissues, several tissues were analyzed for total cholesterol (TABLE 2). As expected, the control animals accumulated a considerable amount of cholesterol in their aorta, skin, and visceral tissues. By comparison, in the DMSO-treated rabbits the cholesterol content of six and the nine tissues analyzed was reduced. The cholesterol content of the thoracic and abdominal aorta was reduced significantly by 50% despite a plasma cholesterol of about 1500 mg/dl.

In order to determine the mechanism of action of DMSO in reducing the accumulation of plasma cholesterol by tissues *in vivo*, the uptake and accumulation of LDL-cholesterol by cultured dermal fibroblasts *in vitro* was investigated.

TABLE 1

INHIBITION OF GROSSLY VISIBLE ATHEROSCLEROTIC LESIONS
BY DIMETHYL SULFOXIDE IN RABBITS FED CHOLESTEROL

| | Atherosclerotic Involvement | | | | | |
| | 12 wks 0.5% Cholesterol | | | 12 wks 0.5% Cholesterol + 12 wks Normal Diet | | |
Treatment	Mild (<20%)	Moderate (20–50%)	Severe (>50%)	Mild (<20%)	Moderate (20–50%)	Severe (>50%)
Group I (Control)	+	+ +	+ + +	+	+ +	+ + +
Group II (DMSO)	+ +	+ + +	+	+ +	+ + +	+

Each + represents one animal.

TABLE 2

CHOLESTEROL CONTENT OF TISSUES FROM RABBITS
FED CHOLESTEROL AND DIMETHYL SULFOXIDE FOR 12 WEEKS

| | mg Cholesterol per g Dry Weight ± S.E.M. | | | |
Tissue	Untreated Controls	Group I 0.5% Cholesterol	Group II 0.5% Cholesterol + 2% DMSO	Percent Reduction
Thoracic aorta	2 ± 2	59 ± 11	28 ± 6	53*
Abdominal aorta	4 ± 1	28 ± 3	15 ± 1	45*
Heart	7 ± 1	16 ± 1	17 ± 1	–
Lung	20 ± 3	52 ± 6	41 ± 6	22
Liver	10 ± 1	128 ± 12	92 ± 5	28
Spleen	11 ± 2	104 ± 11	66 ± 10	37
Kidney	11 ± 1	40 ± 3	34 ± 4	15
Upper jejunum	13 ± 4	21 ± 3	23 ± 3	–
Skin	6 ± 1	30 ± 8	20 ± 5	33
Plasma cholesterol	60 ± 10	1570 ± 225	1490 ± 156	

Statistical analysis was by Student's t-test. Each value is the mean ± S.E.M.
*p < 0.04.

Confluent fibroblasts were preincubated for 48 h with lipoprotein-deficient serum (to maximize LDL receptors) and then incubated with [^{125}I]LDL (30 μg protein/ml) for 3 h at 37°C.[6] The medium was removed, the cells were dissociated with 0.05% trypsin-EDTA to release receptor-bound [^{125}I]LDL. Radioactivity in trichloroacetic acid (TCA)-soluble fraction of medium is assumed to represent degraded LDL, that in the TCA-precipitable portion of the cell trypsinate is taken as bound LDL and the radioactivity in the TCA-precipitable, nonlipid-extractable fraction of the cells represents internalized LDL. TABLE 3 shows that DMSO in the culture medium significantly reduced the binding of LDL to the cell surface receptors by about 35%. The amount of LDL that was subsequently internalized and degraded was also reduced by 38 and 26%, respectively.

The results of this study indicate that DMSO retards the development of dietary cholesterol-induced atherosclerosis in rabbits and suppresses the accumulation of cholesterol in tissues despite severe hypercholesterolemia. While the mechanism of action of DMSO in suppressing atherosclerosis is not known, our *in*

TABLE 3

EFFECT OF DMSO ON THE BINDING, INTERNALIZATION, AND DEGRADATION OF [^{125}I]LDL
BY HUMAN SKIN FIBROBLASTS

| | Nanogram [^{125}I]LDL/mg Cell Protein ± SEM | | |
	Binding	Internalization	Degradation
Control	188 ± 11	160 ± 4	584 ± 59
2% DMSO	122 ± 7	99 ± 9	432 ± 23
% Reduction	35	38	26

Cells were preincubated for 48 h with 10%, lipoprotein-deficient serum to maximize LDL receptors.
Cells were incubated for 3 h with [^{125}I]LDL equivalent to 30 μg LDL protein/ml medium.

vitro studies suggest that one of its antiatherogenic effects is related to its capacity to reduce the binding, uptake, and degradation of plasma LDL by tissues and cells.

REFERENCES

1. HERZMANN, E. 1968. Acta Biol. Med. Ger. **20:** 483–486.
2. KEDAR, I. & E. SOHAR. 1981. Isr. J. Med. Sci. **17:** 289–291.
3. LEON, L., R. L. RUSH & J. TURREL. 1952. *In* Advances in Automated Analysis. Technicon Intl. Congress. (Miami, Florida) **1:** 503–507. Thurman.
4. ABELL, L. L., B. B. LEVY, B. B. BRODIE & F. F. KENDALL. 1952. J. Biol. Chem. **195:** 366–372.
5. MACFARLANE, A. S. 1958. Nature **182:** 53–54.
6. ALAM, S. S. & D. L. LAYMAN. 1982. Biochim. Biophys. Acta **710:** 306–313.

THE EFFECT OF TOPICAL DIMETHYL SULFOXIDE ON CLOTTING ACTIVITY IN THE SPRAGUE-DAWLEY RAT

Charles D. Lox, Nora Frederick, and M. Wayne Heine

Department of Obstetrics and Gynecology
Texas Tech University Health Sciences Center
Lubbock, Texas 79430

In 1964 the first report describing the clinical use of dimethyl sulfoxide (DMSO) appeared,[1] soon followed by similar clinical studies.[2-7] Studies on toxicological effects of dimethyl sulfoxide soon appeared. But few evaluated potential hepatic toxicity. Dimethyl sulfoxide was reported to act as a possible carrier of hepatic carcinogens[8] and cause an occasional increase in liver enzymes,[9] and also acted as a very mild potentiator of hepatic lesions in the rat.[10] As some of the clotting proteins are synthesized in the hepatic cell, this study was undertaken to see what, if any, changes in coagulation parameters might result following topical dimethyl sulfoxide treatment of the Sprague-Dawley rat.

METHODS AND MATERIALS

Experimental Design

Twenty-six male Sprague-Dawley rats, 60 days of age, and 66 female Sprague-Dawley rats, 30 days of age, were used on this study (Sasco Animal Farms, Omaha, Nebraska). Twelve-hour circadian light patterns were maintained and water and Purina rat chow were available ad libitum throughout the experiment. The rats were prepared as follows. The hair on the back of each animal was clipped from a point just posterior to the forelimbs to slightly anterior to the hind limbs and approximately 2 cm on each side of the vertebral column. Dimethyl sulfoxide, commercially purchased and packed by PAT-Y-KEN Inc. (Albuquerque, N.M.) was used undiluted (99% pure). The dimethyl sulfoxide or water was applied to the skin of the back where the hair had been clipped utilizing an Eppendorf pipette delivering 250 microliters. The solutions were lightly finger-rubbed in the back area to assure dermal contact. All solutions were given once a day or twice a day between 0800 and 0900 and 2000 to 2100 hours for seven days. Body weights were obtained prior to initiation of the experiment and at its conclusion. The animals were sacrificed on the eighth day of the experiment under ether anesthesia and 4.5 ml of sodium citrated (3.8%) whole blood was collected from the aorta.

Analysis

The plasma hematocrit was determined using a Clay Adams Autocrit II. The clot formation times for the prothrombin time (PT), partial thromboplastin time (APTT), fibrinogen, and coagulation factors II, V, VII, VIII, X, and XII were determined on an Electra 750 coagulation timer (Medical Laboratories Automation, MLA, Inc.) utilizing Dade reagents supplied by Scientific Products Corpora-

TABLE 1

EFFECTS OF DMSO ON CLOTTING ACTIVITY*

	PT (sec)	APTT (sec)	FIB (sec)	II (sec)	V (sec)	VII (sec)	VIII (sec)	X (sec)	XII (sec)	HCT (%)
Male Control N = 13	14.0 ± 0.8	30.2 ± 3.1	11.2 ± 1.6	19.1 ± 1.9	15.9 ± 1.6	18.4 ± 0.9	57.5 ± 4.8	32.0 ± 2.3	42.1 ± 2.7	40.6 ± 2.0
Male DMSO N = 13	14.4 ± 0.2	29.1 ± 1.5	10.6 ± 0.3	18.8 ± 1.3	15.4 ± 0.8	19.3 ± 0.8†	49.6 ± 1.6†	31.6 ± 0.9	36.9 ± 1.8†	38.5 ± 1.5†
p<	N.S.	N.S.	N.S.	N.S.	N.S.	0.05	0.05	N.S.	0.05	0.05
Female Control N = 22	14.1 ± 0.7	34.3 ± 8.3	10.6 ± 1.6	17.8 ± 1.1	14.4 ± 0.8	16.2 ± 1.2	48.4 ± 4.5	28.7 ± 2.4	33.3 ± 3.0	36.7 ± 4.9
Female DMSO 1/day N = 22	13.2 ± 2.0	32.8 ± 6.1	11.3 ± 3.3	17.7 ± 1.5	14.0 ± 1.2	15.7 ± 2.1	46.9 ± 3.5	29.2 ± 2.2	31.0 ± 3.8†	37.0 ± 4.6
p<	N.S.	N.S.	N.S.	N.S.	N.S.	N.S.	N.S.	N.S.	0.05	N.S.
Female DMSO 2/day N = 22	13.2 ± 0.6†	27.9 ± 7.4†	11.2 ± 1.8	18.0 ± 0.9	14.3 ± 0.6	14.6 ± 0.6†	38.9 ± 6.0†	28.0 ± 1.8	31.0 ± 1.4†	37.4 ± 1.0
p<	0.001	0.02	N.S.	N.S.	N.S.	0.001	0.001	N.S.	0.01	N.S.

†S.D. N.S. = Not significant. $\bar{x}$ ± S.D.
*250 μl of DMSO were applied topically once (1/day) or twice (2/day) daily on male and female Sprague-Dawley rats.

tion. The values represent seconds required for a clot to be detected spectrophotometrically when the test plasma is added to specific factor-deficient substrate plasma. All data were analyzed for statistical significance utilizing the Student's t-test. All data were considered significant at the 95% confidence interval (p < 0.05) or greater.

RESULTS

There was no significant alterations in body weight in either male or female Sprague-Dawley rats following one week of topical DMSO. Clotting time following treatment can be seen in TABLE 1.

DISCUSSION

Heinz and Laudahn[2] and Brobyn[9] failed to detect any pathological changes in humans following exposure to DMSO. Dimethyl sulfoxide has been shown to have a toxic effect on hepatic tissue,[10] where fibrinogen and factors II, V, VII, IX, and X are synthesized.[11] A relationship between topical dimethyl sulfoxide and antithrombotic effects on the wall of the blood vessel was detected. De la Torre et al.[13] reported that in the rhesus monkey intravenous DMSO had no effect on the PT, while the APTT decreased immediately following the dimethyl sulfoxide treatment, and returned to normal following withdrawal. In these experiments, both male and female rats given topical DMSO once daily indicated no changes in either the PT or the APTT, yet female rats treated twice a day with DMSO had accelerated PTs and APTTs (TABLE 1). The hematocrit significantly decreased in the male rat treated once a day yet was not altered in either once a day or twice a day treatment of the female rat. With the exception of a slight reversal between sexes in clotting activity of factor VII, all other trends were similar. Factor VIII and factor XII were accelerated in the male rat treated once a day and in the female rat treated twice a day. Treatment of the female twice a day resulted in an accelerated PT and APTT. This suggests that the hepatic-synthesized factors, with the possible exception of factor VII, are not inhibited by topical DMSO.

The primary observations suggest that inhibition of hepatic-synthesized clotting factor activity by DMSO is minimal. The significant acceleration in clotting times of the intrinsic pathway factors (VIII and XII) plus the PT and APTT suggest that by some mechanism DMSO may lead to a more hypercoagulable state instead of one of hypocoagulability. These experiments now need to be expanded by changing the routes of administration and by extending periods of treatment. Experiments must be done with human subjects. This seems important given the widespread use of dimethyl sulfoxide as a "home remedy" for many forms of arthritic discomfort.

REFERENCES

1. JACOB, S., M. BISCHEL & R. HERSCHLER. 1964. Dimethyl sulfoxide (DMSO): A new concept in pharmacotherapy. Curr. Ther. Res. **6**: 134–135.
2. HEINZ, J. & G. LAUDAHN. 1967. Clinical experiences with the topical application of DMSO in orthopedic diseases: Evaluation of 4180 cases. Ann. N.Y. Acad. Sci. **141**: 506–516.

3. ROSENBAUM, E. & S. JACOB. 1964a. Dimethyl sulfoxide in acute musculoskeletal injuries and inflamations. I. DMSO in acute subdeltoid bursitis. Northwest Med. **64:** 167–168.

4. ROSENBAUM, E. & S. JACOB. 1964b. DMSO in rheumatoid arthritis degenerative arthritis and gouty arthritis. Northwest Med. **63:** 227–229.

5. ROSENBAUM, E., R. HERSCHLER & S. JACOB. 1964. Dimethyl sulfoxide in musculoskeletal disorders. J. Am. Med. Assoc. **192:** 309–313.

6. KLINMAN, A. 1965. Topical pharmacology and toxicology of dimethyl sulfoxide-I. J. Am. Med. Assoc. **193:** 796–804.

7. KLINMAN, A. 1965. Dimethyl sulfoxide-II. J. Am. Med. Assoc. **193:** 923–928.

8. LEVINE, W. 1975. Effect of dimethyl sulfoxide on the hepatic disposition of chemical carcinogens. Ann. N.Y. Acad. Sci. **243:** 185–193.

9. BROBYN, R. 1975. The human toxicity of dimethyl sulfoxide. Ann. N.Y. Acad. Sci. **243:** 497–506.

10. MATTHEWS, F., R. KARUNANITHY, M. YEE & P. NATARAJON. 1980. Hepatotoxicity of dimethylformanide and dimethylsulfoxide at and above the levels used some aflotoxin studies. Lab. Invest. **42:** 257–262.

11. RATNOFF, O. 1977. Blood clotting factors: an overview. In Haemostasis: Biochemistry, Physiology and Pathology. D. Ogston & B. Bennett, Eds.:1–24. John Wiley & Son. London.

12. GOROG, P. & I. KOVACS. 1975. Antiarthritic and antihrombotic effects of topically applied dimethyl sulfoxide. Ann. N.Y. Acad. Sci. **243:** 91–97.

13. DE LA TORRE, J., J. SURGEON, T. ERNEST & R. WOLIMANN. 1981. Subacute toxicity of intravenous dimethyl sulfoxide in Rhesus monkeys. J. Toxicol. Envir. Health. **7:** 49–57.

THE EFFECTS OF CHRONIC DMSO ADMINISTRATION ON THE SPONTANEOUS DEVELOPMENT OF AUTOIMMUNE DISEASE IN NZB, BXSB, AND MRL/LPR STRAIN MICE*

J. I. Morton, B. V. Siegel, W. J. Weaver, T. Bristol, and S. W. Jacob

Departments of Medicine, Pathology, and Surgery
Oregon Health Sciences University
Portland, Oregon 97201

Due to recent interest in the possible palliative role of dimethyl sulfoxide (DMSO) in the treatment of human rheumatic disorders, a study was undertaken to examine the effects of a chronic regimen of DMSO on lymphoproliferative disease development in several mouse models of systemic lupus erythematosus (SLE). Murine SLE is associated with immunologic hyperresponsiveness,[1,2] and immunosuppression is employed in human disease therapy. In this regard, Pestronk and Drachman[3] recently reported that DMSO reduced anti-receptor antibody titers in experimental rat myasthenia gravis and suggested that DMSO might be effective in depressing the humoral responses involved in the formation of other autoantibodies.

In the present study, autoimmune strain NZB, BXSB, and MRL/lpr mice, and Balb/c strain controls, were initiated on a thrice weekly injection schedule of 100% or 50% DMSO in saline (0.10 ml, i.p.) at ages prior to overt disease development; NZB females were 30 weeks old, BXSB males were 20 weeks old, and MRL/lpr male and female mice were 8 weeks old. Treatment was continued for 20 weeks. Indirect immunofluorescence assay for antinuclear antibodies (ANA), Coombs' tests for antibody against autologous erythrocytes, and radial immunodiffusion for serum IgG levels were performed periodically. Body and lymphoid organ weights and hematocrits were recorded.

Throughout the course of treatment there were no significant differences between DMSO groups and saline-injected controls in the development of ANA (FIGURE 1), positive Coombs' tests, anemia, splenomegaly, or lymph node enlargement. Body weights and hematocrits were not significantly different. No abnormalities were precipitated in DMSO-treated nonautoimmune strain Balb/c mice. Animals given 100% DMSO showed a statistically significant early decline in serum IgG followed by restoration to normal values (FIGURE 2), reminiscent of the changes described for DMSO-treated rats.[3] Chronic i.p. injections of 100% DMSO, however, were toxic and decreased long-term survivals, 50% of the deaths occurring by approximately 9 weeks of treatment. No effects on survival were observed using chronic injections of 50% DMSO.

In conclusion, chronic DMSO injections did not retard or accelerate the pathogenesis of autoimmune-lymphoproliferative disease in three genetically distinct mouse models of systemic lupus. This result is consistent with observations described in our accompanying study,[4] which showed no effect of DMSO injections on primary IgM or secondary IgM plus IgG antibody plaque-forming

*Supported by Grant CA-18149 from The National Cancer Institute, The Oregon Arthritis Foundation, and The John C. Higgins Foundation.

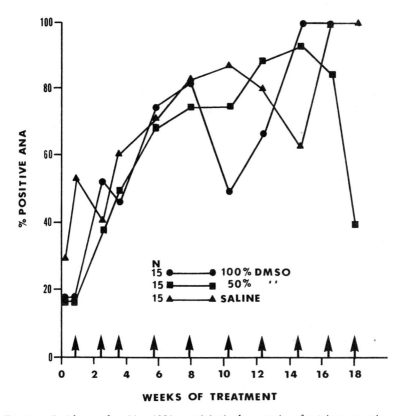

FIGURE 1. Incidence of positive ANA reactivity in three strains of autoimmune mice.

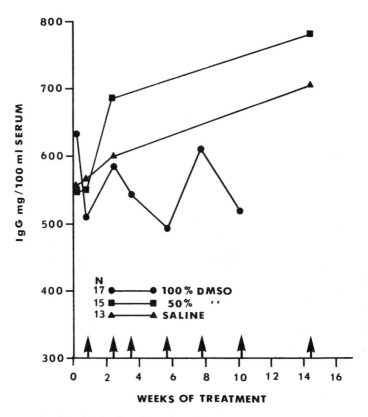

FIGURE 2.   Combined IgG values for each autoimmune treatment group.

cell responses after sheep erythrocyte immunization. Nor was any change in natural killer cell activity observed. It remains possible that other doses, routes, or regimens of DMSO treatment might influence disease pathogenesis.

REFERENCES

1. MORTON, J. I. & B. V. SIEGEL. 1969. Response of NZB mice to foreign antigen and development of autoimmune disease. J. Reticuloendothel. Soc. **6:** 78–93.
2. MORTON, J. I., P. A. JENSEN & B. V. SIEGEL. 1981. Secondary antibody formation as an index of autoimmune potential. J. Reticuloendothel. Soc. **30:** 10a.
3. PESTRONK, A. & D. B. DRACHMAN. 1980. Dimethyl sulphoxide reduces anti-receptor antibody titres in experimental myasthenia gravis. Nature **288:** 733–734.
4. SIEGEL, B. V., J. I. MORTON & S. W. JACOB. 1982. Immunologic defense mechanisms in DMSO-treated Balb/c mice: Immunologic memory and natural killer cell activity. Ann. N.Y. Acad. Sci. (This volume.)

DIMETHYL SULFOXIDE—A SAFE DRUG SOLVENT FOR *IN VITRO* SCREENING AGAINST CESTODE PARASITE

M. Ahmad and Wajih A. Nizami*

Section of Parasitology
Department of Zoology
Aligarh Muslim University
Aligarh 202001, India

INTRODUCTION

The selection of a suitable solvent for water-insoluble anthelminthic drugs is one of the major problems in the study of the mode of action of anthelminthic drugs. Generally a suitable solvent should have maximum solubility and least toxicity to the parasites and/or biological models.

Dimethyl sulfoxide (DMSO) is known to be a potent cryoprotective agent of cells[1-3] and does not have any specific nephrotoxicity at lower concentrations.[4] The higher concentrations are toxic to lower biological systems.[3,5] DMSO has also been used as a drug solvent, particularly for benzimidazole derivatives,[6] but the effect of DMSO on the metabolism of the parasites hitherto remains unstudied. Therefore, the present study was undertaken on a parasite model, *Avitellina lahorea*, and some aspects of the carbohydrate metabolism were studied in presence of DMSO, because mebendazole (a benzimidazole derivative) specifically affects the carbohydrate metabolism.

MATERIALS AND METHODS

A. lahorea were collected from the intestines of sheep and goats slaughtered at the local abattoir. The worms were rinsed thrice in Hank's medium without glucose before being blotted and weighed. DMSO was used in 0.1% concentration (final concentration) throughout in each of the studies. All *in vitro* experiments were performed at $37 \pm 2°C$ under aerobic conditions.

For the uptake studies, the worms were incubated in a known volume of Hank's medium containing glucose (10 mM) and DMSO, for 3, 6, and 9 h. After incubation, the incubate was centrifuged at 1000 g for 10 min, and the supernatant was used for the glucose assay.[7]

To study the effect of DMSO on the glycogen content of *A. lahorea*, the worms were incubated as mentioned for the uptake studies, except that the glucose concentrations in Hank's medium were 1.8, 3.6, and 5.4×10^{-2} M for 3, 6, and 9 h incubation periods, respectively, After incubation, the worms were used for their glycogen estimation.[8]

The effect of DMSO on various enzyme activities was determined by two ways: (1) direct addition of DMSO to the freshly prepared homogenates and (2) worms were preincubated for four hours in DMSO and then homogenized for enzyme assays.

*To whom all correspondence should be addressed.

347

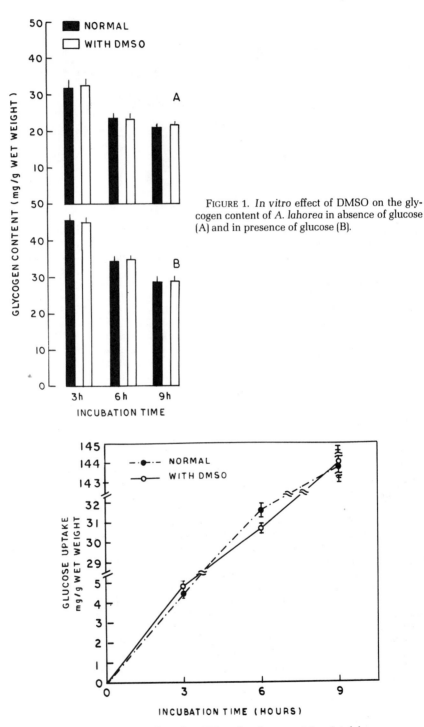

FIGURE 1. In vitro effect of DMSO on the glycogen content of A. lahorea in absence of glucose (A) and in presence of glucose (B).

FIGURE 2. In vitro effect of DMSO on the glucose uptake of A. lahorea.

Homogenates (10%, w/vol) were prepared in ice-cold 0.25 M sucrose solution, except for the hexokinases where ice-cold distilled water was used.

The enzyme activities were assayed according to the following methods: alkaline phosphatase (AlPase) and acid phosphatase (AcPase);[9] adenosine triphosphatase (ATPase);[10] hexokinase;[11] phosphorylase;[12] glucose-6-phosphatase (G-6-Pase);[13] phosphoglucomutase (PGM).[14] Phosphorus and protein were estimated by standard methods.[15,16]

All enzyme activities are expressed in μmols and nmols products liberated/mg protein/min at $37 \pm 2°C$. In all experiments, a control without DMSO was also run simultaneously.

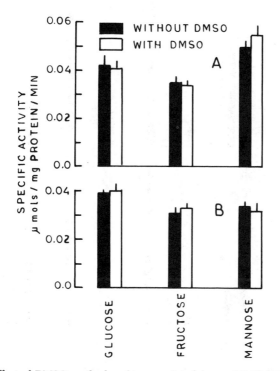

FIGURE 3. Effect of DMSO on the hexokinases of *A. lahorea*. (A) DMSO added in the homogenates. (B) Homogenates of the worms preincubated in DMSO.

RESULTS AND DISCUSSION

The results shown in FIGURES 1 and 2, indicate that DMSO has no effect on the glycogen content and glucose uptake of the parasite during *in vitro* incubations. The glucose uptake is not affected by DMSO, possibly because DMSO does not affect the activities of AlPase, AcPase, and ATPase in this parasite (FIGURE 4). These enzymes in helminth parasites have been reported to be associated with the tegumental uptake processes.[17] The hexokinase of *A. lahorea* is of nonspecific type that is capable of phosphorylating glucose, fructose, and mannose; DMSO has no effect on the levels of their activities (FIGURE 3). The other glycolytic enzymes studied also remain unaffected by DMSO as shown in FIGURE 4. This may be the reason for the ineffectiveness of DMSO on the glycogen content of *A. lahorea* during *in vitro* incubations.

The above results tempt one to infer that DMSO in low concentrations (0.1%) does not alter the normal physiological and biochemical activities related to the carbohydrate metabolism of the parasite under *in vitro* conditions. Hence, DMSO

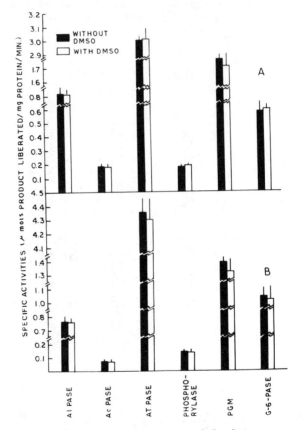

FIGURE 4. Effect of DMSO on some phosphatases and glycolytic enzymes of *A. lahorea*. (A) DMSO added in the homogenates. (B) Homogenates of the worms preincubated in DMSO.

can safely be used as a drug solvent for the *in vitro* screening of the benzimidazole compounds, like mebendazole, against cestode parasites.

REFERENCES

1. LOWENTHAL, R. M., D. S. PARK, J. M. GOLDMAN, K. H. THING, R. S. HILL & G. WHYTE. 1976. Br. J. Haematol. **34**(1): 105–117.

2. BALDINI, M. G., M. STEINER & B. K. KIM. 1976. Transfusion **16**(1): 17–19.
3. ALINK, G. M., J. ACTERBERG, A. W. HELDER & F. G. J. OFFERIJNS. 1976. Cryobiology **14**(3): 305–316.
4. SMALL, A. & R. S. IDE. 1976. Cryobiology **13**(3): 328–333.
5. KIRSCHNER, D. A. & D. L. D. CASPAR. 1975. Proc. Natl. Acad. Sci. USA **72**(9): 3513–3517.
6. VAN DEN BOSSCHE, H. 1972. Biochemical effect of anthelmintic drug mebendazole. *In* Comparative Biochemistry of Parasites. H. Van den Bossche, Ed.: 139–157. Academic Press. New York, N.Y.
7. Sigma Technical Bulletin. No. 510. 1976.
8. ROE, J. H. & R. E. DAILEY. 1966. Anal. Biochem. **15**: 245–250.
9. BERGMEYER, H. U., K. GAWEHN & M. GRASSL. 1974. Enzymes as biochemical reagents. *In* Methods of Enzymatic Analysis. 2nd edit. H. U. Bergmeyer, Ed. **1**: 495–497. Academic Press, New York.
10. KIELLEY, W. W. 1972. Mg-activated muscle ATPases. *In* Methods in Enzymology. S. P. Collowick & N. O. Kaplan, Eds. **2**: 588–591. Academic Press. New York.
11. CRANE, R. K. & A. SOLS. 1953. J. Biol. Chem. **203**: 273–292.
12. CAVIER, R. & J. SAVEL. 1952. C.R. Seanc. Soc. Biol. **234**: 2562–2564.
13. BAGINSKI, E. S., P. P. FOA & B. ZAK. 1974. Methods for determination of enzyme activities. *In* Methods of Enzymatic Analysis. 2nd edit. H. U. Bergmeyer, Ed. **2**: 876–880. Academic Press. New York.
14. SUTHERLAND, E. W. 1949. J. Biol. Chem. **180**: 1279–1284.
15. MARINETTI, G. V. 1962. J. Lipid. Res. **3**: 1–20.
16. LOWRY, O. H., N. J. ROSEBROUGH, A. L. FARR & R. J. RANDALL. 1951. J. Biol. Chem. **193**: 266–275.
17. LUMSDEN, R. D. 1975. Expt. Parasitol. **37**: 267–339.

DIMETHYL SULFOXIDE INHIBITS PLATELET
AGGREGATION IN PARTIALLY OBSTRUCTED
CANINE CORONARY VESSELS

Daniel G. Pace, John L. Kovacs, and Larry R. Klevans

Hoffmann-La Roche Inc.
Nutley, New Jersey 07110

Both clinical and experimental studies suggest that platelets play a major role in the development of several cardiovascular disorders, particularly those related to ischemic heart disease.[1-5]

The results from numerous reports indicate that dimethyl sulfoxide (DMSO) inhibits platelet aggregation *in vitro*,[6-9] but there are few studies on its action *in vivo*.[10,11] Since an agent that inhibits platelet aggregation should not be used as a diluent in experiments that test antiaggregatory activity of other agents, DMSO was tested in dogs with partially constricted coronary arteries to evaluate its effect on platelet aggregation *in vivo*.

Mongrel dogs (13.4-21.8 kg) of either sex were premedicated with morphine (3 mg/kg i.m.) and anesthetized 30 minutes later with sodium pentobarbital (25 mg/kg i.v.). The left femoral artery and vein were cannulated for blood pressure measurement and drug infusion, respectively. Each animal was intubated with a cuffed endotracheal tube and the chest was opened at the fifth intercostal space to expose the left ventricle. Each dog was respirated with a Harvard pump adjusted to maintain blood pH, pCO_2, and pO_2 within the normal range. The pericardium was incised approximately 1 cm above and parallel to the phrenic nerve. The left atrial appendage was tied back. The left circumflex branch of the left main coronary artery was isolated and a 2-centimeter length was exposed. All branches along this section were ligated. A flow probe (Carolina Medical Electronics) was placed on the proximal portion of the left circumflex branch, while a loose snare ligature (for total occlusion) was placed distally. A portion of the ascending aorta was isolated, and a flow probe (Gould-Statham) was applied for measurement of cardiac output. A Millar Mikro-Tip catheter pressure transducer was placed into the left ventricle via the left carotid artery to measure left intraventricular pressure.

After all surgical manipulations were completed, the animal was allowed to stabilize. A plastic constrictor was then placed around the circumflex artery between the flow probe and the snare to produce a "critical stenosis," i.e., that degree of stenosis which abolishes the reactive hyperemic response following release of a 20-second total occlusion of the artery. Final adjustment of the stenosis was accomplished by sliding a tapered monofilament nylon leader between the constrictor and the vessel. When the "critical stenosis" was established, cyclic reductions in coronary blood flow (CRCBF) would develop. This dog model was originally described by Folts *et al.* to study the effects of aspirin on platelet aggregation.[12] Each single CRCBF was defined as a gradual decrease in flow of at least 3 ml/min followed by a rapid increase of 3 ml/min or more toward baseline levels. In most cases, the cyclic reductions far exceeded the minimum criteria (FIGURE 1). Measurements were recorded continuously on a Grass Model 7 polygraph for one hour prior to and one hour following a 5-minute intravenous

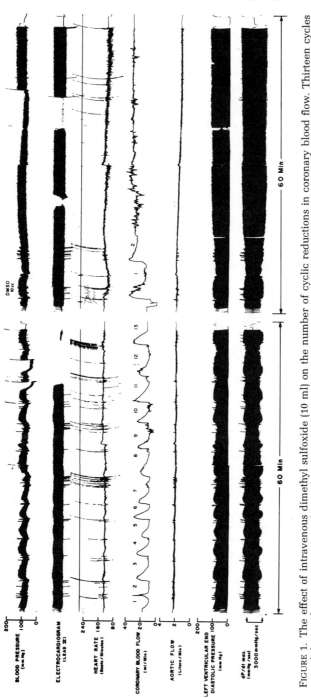

FIGURE 1. The effect of intravenous dimethyl sulfoxide (10 ml) on the number of cyclic reductions in coronary blood flow. Thirteen cycles occurred during the 60-minute control period and two cycles occurred in the 60 minutes following DMSO administration. DMSO did not alter blood pressure, heart rate, aortic flow, left intraventricular and diastolic pressure, and dP/dt max.

infusion of DMSO (Fisher Scientific; density = 1.096 g/ml). Five doses were tested, 0.5 (N = 3), 1 (N = 3), 2 (N = 3), 3 (N = 2), and 10 (N = 1) ml. Each dog received only one dose.

Blood pressure, heart rate, lead II ECG, cardiac output, and left intraventricular pressure were monitored directly (FIGURE 1). The left intraventricular pressure signal was amplified to show left ventricular end diastolic pressure, and differentiated to measure maximum rate of isovolemic pressure rise (dP/dt max). These measurements were used to calculate other hemodynamic indices such as cardiac index, stroke volume index, and total peripheral resistance index. The significance ($p < 0.05$) of differences between paired measurements was calculated by the Wilcoxon Signed-Ranks test.[13] All results are recorded as the mean ± the standard error of the mean.

Intravenous DMSO (1, 2, 3, and 10 ml) significantly reduced the number of CRCBF (TABLE 1) but did not change other hemodynamic measures in the nine

TABLE 1

ANALYSIS OF PAIRED OBSERVATIONS WITH DIMETHYL SULFOXIDE ON CYCLIC REDUCTIONS IN CORONARY BLOOD FLOW (CRCBF) USING THE WILCOXON SIGNED-RANKS TEST

Rank	DMSO (ml i.v.)	CRCBF/Hour		Δ
		Pre-DMSO	Post-DMSO	
1	1	18	17	−1
2	1	16	14	−2
3	2	7	4	−3
4	1	21	17	−4
5	2	17	12	−5
6	3	26	20	−6
7	3	18	9	−9
8	10	13	2	−11
9	2	19	4	−15

Positive Ranks = 0, Negative Ranks = 45, p < 0.01.

animals tested (TABLE 2). The response following 10 ml of intravenous DMSO is shown in FIGURE 1. Thirteen CRCBF occurred during the one-hour control period. Two CRCBF occurred during the one-hour period after DMSO. At the lowest dose of DMSO tested (0.5 ml) in three animals, the number of CRCBF per hour was 13 ± 1 in controls and 14 ± 1 post drug.

Although the mechanism by which DMSO inhibits platelet aggregation in vivo is undefined, mechanisms proposed from the results of in vitro experiments may play a role. Intravenous DMSO could: inhibit prostaglandin biosynthesis[14] and subsequent formation of the platelet aggregating substance thromboxane A_2,[8] scavenge hydroxyl radicals that may induce platelet aggregation,[10] alter cell membrane fluidity and indirectly increase intracellular cyclic AMP,[9] inhibit phosphodiesterase,[15] or bind sulfhydryl groups[16] that may play an important role in the normal aggregation of platelets.[17,18] Since these results suggest that DMSO affects platelet aggregation in vivo, it should not be used as a diluent in experiments to identify new antiaggregatory agents.

TABLE 2

HEMODYNAMIC RESPONSE TO INTRAVENOUS DIMETHYL SULFOXIDE IN PENTOBARBITAL ANESTHETIZED DOGS

DMSO (cc i.v.)	N	Time (min)	Mean Arterial Blood Pressure (mm Hg)	Heart Rate (bpm)	Left Ventricular End Diastolic Pressure (mm Hg)	dP/dt max (mm Hg/sec)	Cardiac Index (ml/min/m²)	Stroke Volume Index (ml/beat/m²)	Total Peripheral Resistance Index (dynes·sec·cm⁻⁵/m²)
0.5	3	Control	92 ± 5	139 ± 23	6†	1725†	2162 ± 536	17 ± 6	68 ± 24
		15	96 ± 3	129 ± 22*	6†	1913†	2049 ± 483	18 ± 5	73 ± 23
		30	93 ± 4	131 ± 21	7†	1950†	2079 ± 568	18 ± 6	76 ± 30
		60	95 ± 3	133 ± 23	5†	2025†	2106 ± 485	18 ± 6	71 ± 23
1.0	3	Control	93 ± 12	146 ± 9	1	2225 ± 478	3388 ± 756	23 ± 4	44 ± 17
		15	100 ± 13	134 ± 9	1	2100 ± 414	3290 ± 821	24 ± 5	51 ± 22
		30	98 ± 9	132 ± 4	3	2175 ± 434	3518 ± 735	26 ± 5	43 ± 14
		60	95 ± 15	134 ± 9	1	2150 ± 523	3640 ± 649	27 ± 4*	39 ± 13
2.0	3	Control	102 ± 6	108 ± 17	−4†	2325†	3270 ± 332	32 ± 5	43 ± 6
		15	108 ± 8	97 ± 19	−5†	2175†	3178 ± 165	35 ± 6	46 ± 6
		30	109 ± 8	107 ± 12	−6†	2288†	2965 ± 115	33 ± 5	49 ± 5
		60	110 ± 8*	107 ± 12	−8†	2400†	2922 ± 142	28 ± 5	51 ± 6*
3.0	2	Control	94	158	−5	2400	2392	16	56
		15	102	146	−7	2288	1939	14	73
		30	95	151	−6	2363	1609	11	82
		60	101	149	−4	2400	1611	12	84
10.0	1	Control	83	134	4	1575	2721	20	41
		15	88	138	3	1725	2794	20	42
		30	107	116	N.R.	2100	2426	21	59
		60	108	112	4	2250	2059	18	70
Saline	3	Control	99 ± 0	151 ± 8	3 ± 1	2250 ± 86	2596 ± 250	17 ± 1	52 ± 5
		60	114 ± 13	169 ± 13	4 ± 2	2500 ± 304	2377 ± 174	14 ± 1	65 ± 11

Mean ± S.E., N.R. = not read.
*p < 0.05.
†N = 2.

ACKNOWLEDGMENTS

We thank Mrs. J. Jusinski for typing this manuscript.

REFERENCES

1. BRAUNWALD, E., W. T. FRIEDEWALD & C. D. FURBERG. 1980. Circulation 62(part II, No. 6): V-1-V-135.
2. HAFT, J. I. 1979. Am. J. Card. 43: 1197–1206.
3. ROBERTSON, R. M., D. ROBERTSON, S. TIMMONS, G. C. FRIESINGER & J. HAWIGER. 1980. Lancet 829–831.
4. HAEREM, J. W. 1971. Atherosclerosis 14: 417–425.
5. LEVINE, P. H. 1973. Circulation 38: 619–626.
6. HOLTZ, G. C. & R. B. DAVIS. 1972. Proc. Soc. Exp. Biol. Med. 141: 244–248.
7. STREIFF, F., P. ALEXANDRE, J. F. STOLTZ & B. GENETET. 1970. Ann. Biol. Clin. (Paris) 28: 295–301.
8. PANGANAMALA, R. V., H. M. SHARMA, R. E. HEIKKILA, J. C. GEER & D. G. CORNWELL. 1976. Prostaglandins 11: 599–607.
9. HYNIE, S., F. LANEFELT & B. B. FREDHOLM. 1980. Acta Pharmacol. Toxicol. 47: 58–65.
10. ROSENBLUM, W. I. & F. EL-SABBAN. 1982. Stroke 13: 35–39.
11. GOROG, P. 1975. Ann. N.Y. Acad. Sci. 243: 91–97.
12. FOLTS, J. D., E. G. CROWELL & G. G. ROWE. 1976. Circulation 54: 365–372.
13. GOLDSTEIN, A. 1964. Biostatistics. pp. 62–63. MacMillan. New York.
14. LAHANN, T. R. & A. HORITA. 1975. Proc. West. Pharmacol. Soc. 18: 81–82.
15. WIESER, P. B., M. A. ZEIGER & J. N. FAIN. 1977. Biochem. Pharmac. 26: 775–778.
16. WOOD, D. C., D. SWEET, J. VAN DOLAH, J. C. SMITH II & I. CONTAXIS. 1967. Ann. N.Y. Acad. Sci. 141: 346–380.
17. ROBINSON, C. W., JR., R. G. MASON & R. H. WAGNER. 1963. Proc. Soc. Exp. Biol. Med. 113: 857–861.
18. HARRISON, M. J. G., P. R. EMMONS & J. F. A. MITCHELL. 1966. Thromb. Haemostasis 16: 122–133.

IMPROVEMENT IN SOMATOSENSORY EVOKED RESPONSE AMPLITUDE AND NEUROLOGIC FUNCTION FOLLOWING DMSO IN A CAT MODEL OF CHRONIC SPINAL CORD COMPRESSION

J. E. McCallum

Fort Worth Medical Center
Texas Tech University School of Medicine
Fort Worth, Texas 76104

INTRODUCTION

Dimethyl sulfoxide (DMSO) has been investigated as a possibly useful agent in several models of central nervous system dysfunction. It has been shown to lessen the effects of ischemia and trauma to brain.[1,5] Conflicting results have been obtained in acute spinal cord injury models.[4,9]

We have investigated the effect of DMSO on the somatosensory evoked responses (SSEPs) and function in cats subjected to chronic, progressive compression of the cervical spinal cord by an implanted extradural mass. Amplitude of some SSEP components increased transiently, and some functional improvement was seen following administration of DMSO to these animals.

MATERIAL AND METHODS

Casein plastic masses were implanted beneath the arch of C1 in eight cats. Casein is a hygroscopic plastic, which slowly absorbs water, and, eventually, doubles its dry weight and volume. Blocks of plastic that had been dessicated to a dry weight of 100–300 mg were used. Drying was carried out in a vacuum oven at 68°C and −1.5 atmospheres over 18 hours. After implantation, the animals were monitored daily until the SSEPs were absent or barely obtainable.

SSEP recording was carried out with the animals anesthetized with ketamine and pentobarbital and paralyzed with decamethonium. Ventilation and temperature were externally controlled. Stimulating electrodes were inserted directly into the median and sciatic nerves. A constant current stimulator with a rate of 3 Hz, a pulse width of 100 microseconds, and an amplitude 1–5 ma above motor threshold was employed. Recording was done with a Nicolet 1024 signal averager and Grass amplifiers. Averaging interval was either 100 or 200 msec, bandpass 1–300 Hz, and amplification was 5,000 times, 256 trials were used. Records were repeated at intervals over 90–220 minutes following intravenous administration of 2 g/kg of 40% solution of DMSO. Because control amplitudes varied, the records were adjusted to a common control level arithmetically.

The following day, a second 2 g/kg dose of DMSO was given intraperitoneally in unanesthetized animals. Neurologic function was monitored for six hours. The animals were then sacrificed.

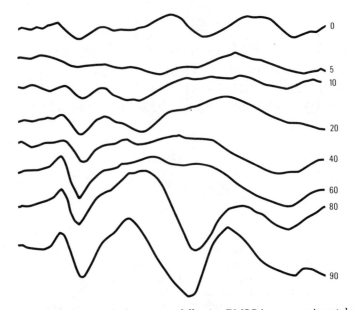

FIGURE 1. Median nerve evoked responses following DMSO in an experimental animal.

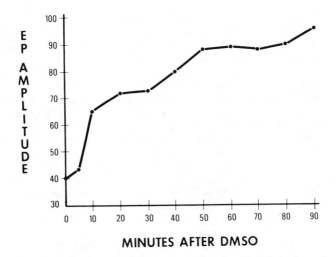

FIGURE 2. Summary of change in SSEP amplitude after DMSO in the entire group of animals.

RESULTS

Beginning at approximately five minutes after administration of intravenous DMSO, the evoked response amplitude increased rapidly (FIGURE 1). This increase was most striking in the second five minutes after administration, by which time the amplitude of the early components had increased by an average of 175%. A slow increase continued over the next 35 minutes, at which time the response seemed to plateau at about 225% of the control value (FIGURE 2).

When the animals were examined following intraperitoneal DMSO the next day, the results were mixed. All animals were unable to stand at this time. Three animals showed no improvement after DMSO. Three animals were able to stand but not walk. Two were able to ambulate unsteadily. The improvements in function lasted from five to six hours, following which the animals returned to their pre-DMSO state and were sacrificed.

DISCUSSION

Conflicting results have been published regarding attempts to improve spinal cord function by administering DMSO after trauma. De la Torre demonstrated functional improvement and improvement in SSEPs after impact injury in dogs treated with DMSO.[4] Goodnough and co-workers[6] failed to demonstrate change in the extent of post-traumatic necrosis or loss of cytochrome oxidase activity, and Parker and co-workers[9] could not demonstrate recovery of function after DMSO in a similar model.

In models of brain ischemia, thermal injury, impact injury, and chemical injury, DMSO has been shown to improve cerebral perfusion,[8] enhance oxidative metabolism,[1] and improve functional outlook.[5] Decreases in cerebral edema and intracranial pressure have also been demonstrated.[2,3] DMSO has also been shown to increase glycolysis in isolated, perfused rat brain.[6]

We have demonstrated an apparent increase in conduction through a chronically compressed segment of spinal cord, and a transient improvement in neurologic function following DMSO administration in cats. This effect is of rapid onset and appears to plateau in less than an hour. The duration of the functional improvement seems to be from five to six hours.

Whether this is a result of decreasing cord edema, improved cord circulation, a metabolic alteration at the area of cord compression, or some as yet unidentified mechanism, is not clear.

REFERENCES

1. BROWN, F. D., L. M. JOHNS & S. MULLAN. 1980. Dimethyl sulfoxide in experimental brain injury, with comparison to mannitol. J. Neurosurg. **53:** 58–62.
2. CAMP, P. E., H. E. JAMES & R. WERNER. 1981. Acute dimethyl sulfoxide therapy in experimental brain edema. Part 1. Effects on intracranial pressure, blood pressure, central venous pressure, and brain water and electrolyte content. Neurosurgery **9:** 28–33.
3. DEL BIGIO, M., H. E. JAMES, P. E. CAMP, R. WERNER, L. F. MARSHALL & H. TUNG. 1982. Acute dimethyl sulfoxide therapy in brain edema. Part 3. Effect of a 3-hour infusion. Neurosurgery **10:** 86–89.

4. DE LA TORRE, J. C., C. H. JOHNSON, D. J. GOODE & S. MULLAN. 1975. Pharmacologic treatment and evaluation of permanent experimental spinal cord trauma. Neurology (Minneap.) **25**: 508–514.
5. DE LA TORRE, J. C. & J. W. SURGEON. 1976. Dexamethasone and DMSO in experimental transorbital cerebral infarction. Stroke **7**: 577–583.
6. GHOSH, A. K., T. ITO, S. GHOSH & H. A. SLOVITER. 1976. Effects of dimethyl sulfoxide on metabolism of isolated perfused rat brain. Biochem. Pharmacol. **25**: 1115–1117.
7. GOODNOUGH, J., N. ALLEN, M. E. NESHAM & N. R. CLENDENON. 1980. The effect of dimethyl sulfoxide on gray matter in experimental spinal cord trauma. Surg. Neurol. **13**: 273–276.
8. LAHA, R. K., M. DUJOVNY, P. J. BARRIONUEVO, S. C. DE CASTRO, H. R. HELLSTRON & J. C. MAROON. 1978. Protective effects of methyl prednisolone and dimethyl sulfoxide in experimental middle cerebral artery embolectomy. J. Neurosurg. **49**: 508–516.
9. PARKER, A. J. & C. W. SMITH. 1979. Lack of functional improvement from spinal cord trauma following dimethylsulphoxide and epsilon amino caproic acid therapy in dogs. Res. Vet. Sci. **27**: 253–255.

EFFECT OF DIMETHYL SULFOXIDE
ON PRECIPITABILITY OF BENCE JONES PROTEINS
AND THEIR CONVERSION TO AMYLOID FIBRILS*

W. Pruzanski, A. Katz, D. Stark, and N. Lofchy

Immunology Diagnostic and Research Centre
Department of Medicine
The Wellesley Hospital
Department of Pathology
The Western Hospital
University of Toronto
Toronto, Canada

One hundred and twenty five Bence Jones proteins (BJP) were tested for heat-dependent precipitability. Seventy BJP (33 k and 37 λ), which gave typical precipitation reaction, were processed further by mixing with 1.5 M DMSO. DMSO completely abolished precipitation in 9 k (27%) and 11 λ (30%) BJP, and altered precipitation in further 21 k (69%) and 22 λ (59%) BJP (TABLE 1). Altered reaction consisted of change in the temperature and/or in the intensity of precipitation. The latter was especially prominent in 14/21 k and 18/22 λ BJP, changing arbitrary units of maximal precipitation from 1.6 to 0.6 and from 1.6 to 0.7 respectively.

Twelve BJP were tested in concentrations from 0.5 mg/ml to 5.0 mg/ml. Beginning of heat precipitation depended inversely on the concentration being $62 \pm 7.1°C$ at 0.5 mg/ml and $36.3 \pm 17.4°C$ at 5.0 mg/ml. DMSO inhibited precipitation in 11/12 BJP at 0.5 mg/ml, 7/12 at 2.0 mg/ml, and 0/12 at 5.0 mg/ml. The influence of DMSO on heat precipitation did not depend on pH, no differences being observed at the range of pH 5.0 to 7.0.

Sixteen BJP were tested with DMSO of various molarities. One molar DMSO abolished precipitation in 10 of 16 BJP tested. Two molar DMSO abolished precipitation of two additional BJP.

Seven BJP (6 λ and 1 k) were converted to amyloid fibrils by pepsin digestion, as proven by alkaline congo red stain, green birefringence in polarized light, and electron microscopy. Preincubation of the above BJP with 3.0 M DMSO prevented conversion to amyloid fibrils in 5 of 6 λ BJP, but not in one λ and the one k BJP (TABLE 2). Simultaneous addition of DMSO to BJP-pepsin mixture prevented from conversion to amyloid fibrils in 4 λ BJP. DMSO added to BJP before pepsin digestion may prevent conversion to amyloid fibrils by two alternative mechanisms: it may influence BJP and/or inhibit enzymatic activity of pepsin. To test the latter, BJP preincubated with 4.0 M DMSO was subsequently digested by pepsin in concentrations from 40 to 160 μg/ml and incubation times from 4 to 16 hours. When no DMSO was added, conversion into amyloid occurred at all concentrations and at all incubation times, with the largest amount of amyloid fibrils obtained when incubation time was 16 hours. When DMSO was

*Supported by the Medical Research Council of Canada.

361

TABLE 1

EFFECT OF DMSO ON HEAT PRECIPITATION (PPT) OF BENCE JONES PROTEINS*

Type	Number Tested	Atypical PPT Reaction	Negative PPT Reaction	Positive PPT Reaction Abolished/Altered/ Unchanged by DMSO		
k	64	22	9	9	21	3
				(27)†	(64)	(9)
λ	61	20	4	11	22	4
				(30)	(59)	(11)
Total	125	42	13	20	43	7
				(29)	(61)	(10)

*Bence Jones proteins–2 mg/ml. DMSO–1.5 M.
†(%)

added, no conversion of BJP into amyloid fibrils was observed at low concentrations of pepsin and at short incubation times. In specimens incubated for 16 hours and in those with high concentration of pepsin, DMSO was unable to block conversion. Therefore at least in part, DMSO is acting directly on pepsin, either weakening its enzymatic activity or changing the interaction between the enzyme and the substrate. None of the preformed amyloid fibrils incubated with 2–3 M DMSO for 36–72 h dissolved completely, but preliminary results using SDS gels and spectrophotometry have shown that DMSO is capable of partially dissolving or altering amyloid fibrils. Bence Jones protein was converted into amyloid fibrils by digestion with pepsin. Five molar DMSO was added to the washed precipitated fibrils and aliquots were incubated at 37°C for 12, 36, and 72 hours. At each time the samples were spun and the turbidity of the supernatant checked in spectrophotometer at OD = 280. Undigested BJP mixed with DMSO and amyloid fibrils without DMSO served as controls. There was marked change in the turbidity of the supernatant after 12 hours of incubation. Turbidity increased to a maximum at 48 hours and subsequently decreased at 72 hours. The latter could be

TABLE 2

EFFECT OF DMSO ON THE CONVERSION OF BENCE JONES PROTEINS TO AMYLOID FIBRILS*

#	Type of BJP	Standard Pepsin Digestion	Preincubation† with DMSO	Simultaneous Addition of DMSO	Incubation of Preformed Amyloid with DMSO‡
1	λ	+¶	−	+	+
2	λ	+	−	−	insufficient
3	λ	+	−	−	+
4	λ	+	−	−	+
5	λ	+	−	−	+
6	λ	+	+	+	+
7	k	+	+	+	+
Total	−/+	7/7 (100%)	5/7 (71%)	4/7 (57%)	0/6 (0%)

*DMSO–2 M; Proteolytic digestion (10 mg Protein/40 µg Pepsin, 4 h/37°C).
†BJP preincubated for 2 h with 2 M DMSO.
‡36 h/37°C.
¶− Absence, + presence of amyloid fibrils.

explained by either partial precipitation of altered fibrils or by further change in the fibrils leading to reduced turbidity.

The above observations indicate that DMSO can alter precipitability properties of Bence Jones proteins and their conversion to amyloid fibrils. It may be potentially useful in treatment of immunoglobulin-related amyloidosis and of Bence Jones protein-induced nephropathy.

DIMETHYL SULFOXIDE ALTERATION OF COLLAGEN*

Y. Erk,† D. J. Raskin, M. Mace, Jr., and M. Spira

Division of Plastic Surgery
Baylor College of Medicine
Houston, Texas 77030

INTRODUCTION

A minimally toxic collagenolytic compound was sought by the authors for the treatment of established scar tissue *in vitro*. Dimethyl sulfoxide (DMSO) is a highly polar hygroscopic solvent of minimal toxicity.[1] Animal studies have documented decreased tensile strength in tissues treated with DMSO.[2] Light microscopic investigation of DMSO-exposed tissues has revealed the presence of characteristic collagen fiber swelling. The suggested etiology of this phenomenon was that collagen fiber intra- and intermolecular cross-links are ruptured.[3,4] With these effects in mind, a study to further examine the effect of DMSO upon collagen fibers was designed.

MATERIAL AND METHODS

Fresh specimens of human collagen were obtained from the dense, undesirable scar that surround implanted foreign bodies (silicone breast prostheses). Different specimens were obtained from seven randomly selected patients for this laboratory study. The tissue specimens were divided into six uniform strips. Two prepared strips of collagen were incubated in 10 ml of balanced saline solution (BSS); two were incubated in 10 ml of 50% DMSO (diluted with BSS); and two collagen strips were incubated in 10 ml of 99% DMSO. Strips were tested for tensile strength after 12 and 24 hours of 37°C incubation. Collagen specimens were then sectioned for light microscopy and for electron microscopy.

RESULTS

The tensile strengths of saline or 50% DMSO-incubated tissue were identical. The seven collagen specimens incubated in 99% DMSO had a 40% decrease in tensile strength at 12 hours and a 23% decrease in tensile strength at 24 hours of incubation. The altered tensile strengths were not statistically significant ($p > 10$).

Light Microscopy

Light microscopic studies of human scar tissue samples revealed that BSS or 50% DMSO-induced tissues consistently appeared to have histologically normal

*Supported in part by U.S. Public Health Service Grant No. RR-05425.
†Address correspondence to: Yücel Erk, M.D., Division of Plastic Surgery, 1200 Moursund, Baylor College of Medicine, Houston, Texas 77030.

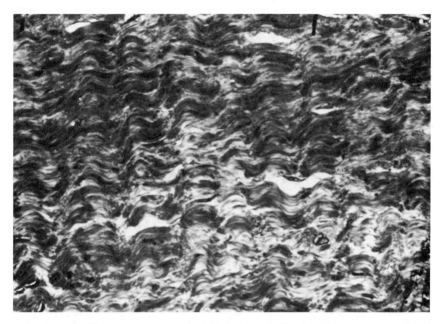

FIGURE 1. A collagen specimen incubated in balanced saline is seen here at × 625. Figure reduction of 70%.

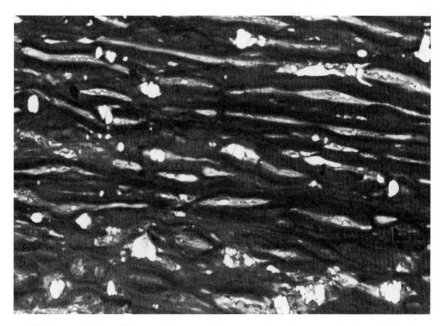

FIGURE 2. Collagen fiber swelling is seen at × 625 in those specimens incubated in dimethyl sulfoxide. Figure reduction of 70%.

FIGURE 3. Balanced saline solution incubated collagen appears structurally well defined at × 25,000. Figure reduction of 70%.

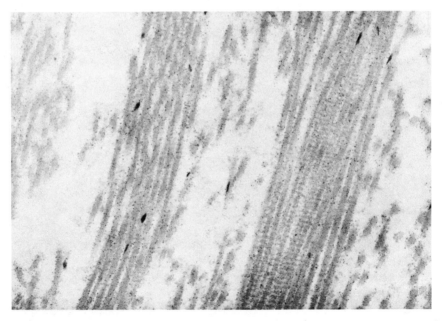

FIGURE 4. 50% dimethyl sulfoxide incubation resulted in some loss of fiber definition which was visualized at × 25,000. Figure reduction of 70%.

collagen fibers (FIGURE 1). The collagen incubated in 99% DMSO had marked alteration in the appearance of the collagen fibers. These collagen bundles appeared swollen with gross architectural distortion (FIGURE 2).

Electron Microscopy

Normal dense collagen was visualized by transmission microscopy in the tissues incubated in BSS (FIGURE 3). The appearance of periprosthetic collagen has been well studied.[5] Tissues incubated in 50% DMSO showed moderate loss of the periodic striations in the collagen fibers. There was minimal fiber fraying in

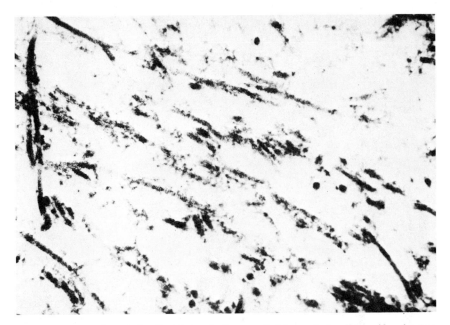

FIGURE 5. 99% dimethyl sulfoxide incubation resulted in marked collagen fiber fraying seen here at × 25,000. Figure reduction of 70%.

this group (FIGURE 4). The collagen specimens incubated in 99% DMSO had dramatic architectural changes. There was marked collagen fiber destruction with the loss of periodic cross-striations (FIGURE 5).

SUMMARY

In vitro incubation of human scar in our laboratory with 99% DMSO demonstrated, by electron microscopy, the disruption of the collagen fibers. This may prove to be a useful preparatory step for selective enzymatic assault upon exuberant or undesirable scar tissue in the clinical setting. Further study of this concept is planned.

REFERENCES

1. RUBIN, L. 1975. Toxicity of dimethyl sulfoxide alone and in combination. Ann. N.Y. Acad. Sci. **243**: 98–102.
2. SULZBERGER, M., T. CORTESE, L. FISHMAN, H. WILEY & P. PEYAKOVITCH. 1967. Ann. N.Y. Acad. Sci. **141**: 437–450.
3. GRIES, F., G. BUBLITZ & J. LINDNER. 1967. The effect of dimethyl sulfoxide on the components of connective tissue. Ann. N.Y. Acad. Sci. **141**: 630–637.
4. SCHERBEL, A., L. MCCORMICK & J. LAYLE 1967. Further observations on the effect of dimethyl sulfoxide in patients with generalized scleroderma. Ann. N.Y. Acad. Sci. **141**: 613–629.
5. GINSBACH, G., L. BUSCH & W. KUHNEL. The nature of the collagenous capsule around breast implants. Plastic Reconstr Surg. **64**(No. 4): 456–464.

DIMETHYL SULFOXIDE AND THE CALCIUM PARADOX

T. J. C. Ruigrok and D. de Moes

Department of Cardiology
University Hospital
Utrecht 3500CG, the Netherlands

A. M. Slade

Cardiothoracic Institute
University of London
London, England

W. G. Nayler

University of Melbourne
Department of Medicine
Austin Hospital
Heidelberg
Victoria, Australia

Reperfusion of isolated hearts with calcium-containing solution after a short period of calcium-free perfusion results in irreversible cell damage (calcium paradox).[1] It has been reported that dimethyl sulfoxide (DMSO) protects isolated heart cells against calcium-induced degeneration.[2] We therefore studied the effect of DMSO on the occurrence of the calcium paradox in the intact, isolated perfused rat heart.[3] Cell damage was quantitated in terms of creatine kinase release and ultrastructural changes.

METHOD

Isolated rat hearts were perfused at 37°C by the Langendorff technique at a constant pressure of 75 mm Hg. The standard perfusate had the following composition (mmol/l): NaCl, 124; KCl, 4.7; $CaCl_2$, 1.3; $MgCl_2$, 1.0; $NaHCO_3$, 24.0; Na_2HPO_4, 0.5; glucose, 11.0. During calcium-free perfusion, calcium chloride was omitted from the standard perfusate. When required, 1.4 mol/l (10%, vol/vol) DMSO was added to the calcium-free or standard perfusate. The perfusion fluids were equilibrated with 95% O_2–5% CO_2. Samples of the effluent perfusate were analyzed for creatine kinase (CK) activity. For electron microscopy, the hearts were perfusion-fixed with glutaraldehyde/sodium cacodylate buffer and post-fixed in OsO_4.

RESULTS

FIGURE 1a shows normal ultrastructure after control perfusion with standard perfusate. During control perfusion and subsequent calcium-free perfusion the hearts released negligible amounts of CK. Reperfusion with calcium-containing solution without DMSO after calcium-free perfusion with DMSO (see legend for

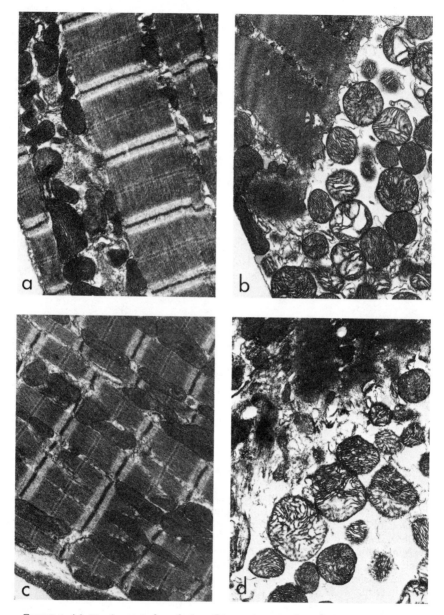

FIGURE 1. (a) 15 min control perfusion. (b) 20 min control perfusion (15 min without DMSO, 5 min with DMSO), 5 min Ca-free perfusion with DMSO, 10 min reperfusion with Ca. (c) 15 min control perfusion, 10 min Ca-free perfusion (5 min without DMSO, 5 min with DMSO), 5 min reperfusion with Ca with DMSO. (d) 15 min control perfusion, 10 min Ca-free perfusion (5 min without DMSO, 5 min with DMSO), 15 min reperfusion with Ca (5 min with DMSO, 10 min without DMSO). × 10,000.

perfusion time sequence) resulted in occurrence of the calcium paradox: contracture of myofibrils and swelling of mitochondria (FIGURE 1b), and massive release of CK.[3] Analysis of the micrographs revealed that almost 100% of the cells displayed the effects of calcium paradox. Upon reperfusion with calcium-containing solution with DMSO after calcium-free perfusion without DMSO, the myofibrils remained well organized and relaxed, and the mitochondria were undamaged (FIGURE 1c). Only 4% of the cells displayed effects of the calcium paradox, and there was a moderate release of CK. As soon as DMSO was omitted from the reperfusion medium, CK release was exacerbated and almost 100% of the cells displayed the calcium paradox: formation of empty cytoplasmic spaces and contraction bands, and swelling of mitochondria (FIGURE 1d).

DISCUSSION

The results indicate that DMSO does not protect rat hearts against the effects of calcium-free perfusion that predispose the myocardium to the calcium paradox. The calcium-paradox damage is reduced, however, when DMSO is present during the reperfusion phase. The reduction of the calcium paradox damage may be affected by the hyperosmolarity of the DMSO-containing reperfusion medium, reduction by DMSO of the energy-dependent accumulation of calcium by mitochondria, which can lead to severe cell damage, and enhancement of the calcium-accumulating ability of the sarcoplasmic reticulum, resulting in a decreased supply of calcium to the mitochondria during the reperfusion phase.

ACKNOWLEDGMENT

The authors thank Drs. F. L. Meijler and C. Borst for valuable discussions and reading the manuscript.

REFERENCES

1. ZIMMERMAN, A. N. E. & W. C. HULSMANN. 1966. Paradoxical influence of calcium ions on the permeability of the cell membranes of the isolated rat heart. Nature **211:** 646–647.
2. CLARK, M. G., B. J. GANNON, N. BODKIN, G. S. PATTEN & M. N. BERRY. 1978. An improved procedure for the high-yield preparation of intact beating heart cells from the adult rat. J. Mol. Cell. Cardiol. **10:** 1101–1121.
3. RUIGROK, T. J. C., D. DE MOES, A. M. SLADE & W. G. NAYLER. 1981. The effect of dimethylsulfoxide on the calcium paradox. Am. J. Pathol. **103:** 390–403.

DMSO-CYTOSTATIC COMPLEXES:
SELECTIVE CANCER CHEMOTHERAPY

Kai Setälä

Uimarinpolku 10 B 10,
SF-00330 Helsinki 33, Finland

Present cytostatics, agents that suppress growth and multiplication of cancer cells, are nonspecific and are generally administered in doses near the tolerated ones. This, however, violates even the normal rapidly proliferating cells and masks subtle differences between the specific modes of response of the normal and the cancer cells.

Our experimental studies on extensive materials and varying techniques have revealed among other things that (1) benign, rapidly proliferating cells and cancer cells, originating from the same normal homologous tissue, the mouse epidermis, behave in all respects in opposite ways.[1-4] (2) Only utilization of subthreshold doses of the same cytostatics unmasks the specificity of, and differences between, the modes of response. Normal and benign rapidly proliferating cells are highly susceptible to the effects of the cytostatics. In contrast, the cancer cells appear almost nonresponsive or indolent, showing a "cytoplasmic barrier" towards the drug effects.[5-10] (3) Utilization of DMSO-cytostatic complexes with the cytostatic in subthreshold (marginal) concentrations completely reverses the situation.[11-16] Now, the cancer cells respond vigorously while the viability of the normal and benign rapidly proliferating cells is spared. This phenomenon signifies a marked selectivity. (4) The specific target for the effects of the DMSO-cytostatic complexes is the three-dimensional cytoskeleton, the differentiation organelle,[4,14-16] first described by us.[17,18] The cytoskeleton of the cancer cells is deranged, dehydrated, shaggy, and the fiber lattices appear irregularly intertwined or cemented together (FIGURES 1 and 2).[14-18] (5) In cancer cells, the DMSO-cytostatic complexes cause a high-degree re-hydration, swelling and liberation of the fiber bundles of the cytoskeleton, and a morbid increase (by 20- to 100-fold) in the cell volume and edema of the cytoplasm resulting in collapse of the cytoskeleton and death of the cancer cells. These occurrences can be demonstrated by direct techniques down to the (sub)molecular level. (6) Application of the cytostatics in the form of DMSO complexes, allows reduction of the dose of the cytostatics to 1/30, possibly even to 1/100 or 1/1,000 of the conventional doses.[14-16]

The differences between relevant parameter-pairs are statistically highly significant (p < 0.001). All technical details have been presented (op. cit.). In all, eight different known cytotoxic agents have been tested. If indicated, it is even possible to use DMSO-cytostatic complexes comprising two or more cytostatics having different desired properties.

Except in animal experiments, preliminary trials on some patients with stomach cancer have been made using DMSO-vinblastin sulfate intravenously. The tumor masses necrotized rapidly (unpublished).

The observations described are easy to control. The simplest way to proceed is to use cutaneous cancer as the target and its surrounding skin as the reference tissue. If the trials are performed correctly, the first positive signs appear within three days.

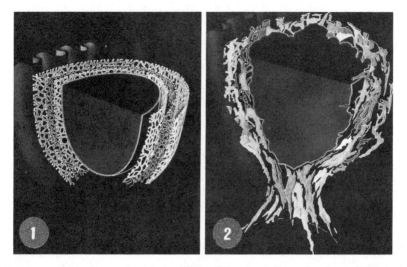

FIGURES 1 and 2. Images in polarized light of the three-dimensional cytoskeleton, the differentiation organelle, in the normal epidermal cell (FIGURE 1) and in epidermal cancer cell (FIGURE 2).

REFERENCES

1. SETÄLÄ, K. 1960. Progress in carcinogenesis, tumor-enhancing factors. A bioassay of skin tumor formation. Progr. Exp. Tumor Res. 1: 225–278.
2. SETÄLÄ, K. 1961. Nature and mechanism of tumour promotion in skin carcinogenesis in mice. (Symposium on Functional Components of Carcinogenesis, Rehovot 1959.) Acta Un. Int. Cancr. 17: 32–44.
3. SETÄLÄ, K. 1962. Relation of benign and malignant epidermal hyperplasia in mouse. In Proceedings of the International Conference. (University of Perugia, 1961). L. Severi, Ed.: 529–540. Perugia University Press, Perugia, Italy.
4. SETÄLÄ, K. 1964. Defective cell maturation, an alternative to accelerated cell division as target for cancer chemotherapy. Progr. Exp. Tumor Res. 5: 1–52.
5. SETÄLÄ, K. 1964. The essentially different pharmacodynamic response to colchicine of benign and of malignant epidermal hyperplasia in skin-tumor-resistant RA mice. Naturwissenschaften 51: 245–246.
6. SETÄLÄ, K., A. HUJANEN, B. LINDROOS & O. NYYSSÖNEN. 1965. Disparities in the modes of pharmacodynamic response to colchicine of malignant and of benign epidermal hyperplasia in skin-tumor-susceptible Swiss CF 1 mice. Naturwissenschaften 52: 519–520.
7. SETÄLÄ, K. 1965. Further evidence for the incompatible pharmacodynamic response to colchicine of benign and of malignant epidermal hyperplasia in mice of skin-tumor-resistant strain. Naturwissenschaften 52: 520.
8. SETÄLÄ, K. 1965. Konträre pharmakodynamische Antwortsweise der gutartigen and kanzerösen Epidermishyperplasie der RA Mäuse auf das onkolytische Alkaloid Vinca rosae Linn. Naturwissenschaften 52: 564–565.
9. SETÄLÄ, K. 1965. Differences in pharmacodynamic response to colchicine between benign and malignant epidermal hyperplasias. Acta Radiol. (Suppl.) 237: 1–89.
10. SCHRECK-PUROLA, I. 1969. Failure of malignant epidermal cells to respond to vinblastine sulfate. A study in skin-tumor-resistant mice. Acta Radiol. (Suppl.) 291: 1–99.
11. SETÄLÄ, K. & L. STJERNVALL. 1967. The solubilizing effect of dimethylsulfoxide (DMSO)

on keratins of malignant epidermal cells in the mouse back. Contrib. 1st Dept. Path. University of Helsinki: 1-3.

12. STJERNVALL, L. 1969. Penetration of cytostaticum in DMSO into malignant cells. Naturwissenschaften **56:** 465-466.

13. METSÄLÄ, P. 1971. Effect of dimethyl sulfoxide (DMSO) on cytoplasmic barrier of malignant epidermal cells. An investigation in skin-tumor-resistant mice. Acta Radiol. (Suppl.) **307:** 1-122.

14. SETÄLÄ, K. 1981. U.S. Patent application No. 293,973.

15. SETÄLÄ, K. 1981. A new suggestion for the design of rational anticancer therapy: Experimental studies in mice. IRCS Med. Sci. **9:** 1117-1118.

16. SETÄLÄ, K. 1982. A rational anti-cancer (anticarcinostatic) therapy: Experimental studies in mice. Medical Hypotheses **8:** 207-230.

17. SETÄLÄ, K., O. ÄYRÄPÄÄ & E. E. NISKANEN. 1961. Input of energy compelling carcinogen injured epidermal cells in mice to proceed with differentiation. Naturwissenschaften **48:** 226-227.

18. SETÄLÄ, K., O. ÄYRÄPÄÄ & E. E. NISKANEN. 1962. Mechanism of experimental tumorigenesis. 9. Sulphydryl groups, disulphide bonds, and birefringence in mouse epidermis after dipole-type tumor promoter and carcinogen. Acta Path. Microbiol. Scand. **54:** 39-58.

IMMUNOLOGIC DEFENSE MECHANISMS IN
DMSO-TREATED Balb/c MICE: IMMUNOLOGIC
MEMORY AND NATURAL KILLER CELL ACTIVITY*

B. V. Siegel, J. I. Morton, and S. W. Jacob

Departments of Pathology, Medicine, and Surgery
Oregon Health Sciences University
Portland, Oregon 97201

Immunologic memory plays an important role in resistance to infectious organisms. However, as we have recently demonstrated,[1] excessive memory capacity may be linked to autoantibody formation and the pathogenesis of immune complex renal disease. On the other hand, natural killer (NK) cells are a class of cytotoxic effector cells found in normal animals without prior immunization, and lack immunologic memory.[2] In this regard they may constitute an important first-line mechanism for antitumor surveillance.

The possible effects of chronic dimethyl sulfoxide (DMSO) administration were studied in young adult Balb/c mice receiving thrice weekly i.p. injections of 67% DMSO in saline (0.10 ml). To measure responses to a T-cell–dependent B-cell antigenic stimulus, mice were primed i.v. with 5×10^7 washed sheep red blood cells (SRBC) one day following a series of three alternate daily injections of DMSO. Animals continued to receive DMSO injections to the end of each experiment. One group was assayed for primary IgM plaque-forming cell (PFC) responses four days after priming. The remaining animals were challenged 3 weeks later with a second i.v. injection of 5×10^7 SRBC and secondary IgM and antiglobulin-facilitated IgM plus IgG responses measured 4 days later. In another study, of the autoimmune MRL/lpr strain, which had been injected with 50% DMSO for 16 weeks starting at two months of age, were immunized i.p. with 5×10^8 SRBC and primary IgM PFC assayed. Sera were also collected from all animals for IgG determinations, and hematocrits and body, spleen, and thymus weights measured. As shown in TABLE 1, there were no significant differences brought about by DMSO treatment in primary IgM responses in either the normal Balb/c strain or the autoimmune MRL/lpr strain. Balb/c mice showed normal immune responsiveness, organ weights, and IgG and hematocrit values. All MRL/lpr mice evidenced the profound primary immunosuppression characteristic of animals with advanced lymphoproliferative diseases.[3] The extended schedule of DMSO treatment, starting before overt disease development, also exerted no significant effect on the spontaneous development of splenomegaly, thymoma formation, anemia, and serum IgG elevation in this disease-prone strain.

Balb/c mice, receiving a second SRBC injection three weeks after priming, responded with vigorous IgM and total (IgM + IgG) PFC formation (TABLE 1). These memory responses, along with serum IgG levels and lymphoid organ weights were not significantly altered by chronic DMSO treatment.

Natural killer cell activity was measured by chromium-51 release from YAC-1 tumor cells following a four-hour incubation at 37°C with spleen cells from Balb/c mice that had received five alternate daily injections of 67% DMSO (0.10

*Supported by Grant CA-18149 from The National Cancer Institute, The Oregon Arthritis Foundation, and The John C. Higgins Foundation.

TABLE 1

PRIMARY AND SECONDARY PLAQUE-FORMING CELL RESPONSES, SERUM IgG, AND LYMPHOID ORGAN WEIGHTS FOR CONTROL AND AUTOIMMUNE STRAIN MICE WITH AND WITHOUT DMSO TREATMENT

Mice and Treatment	Body Wt. (g)	Spleen Wt. (mg)	Thymus Wt. (mg)	Serum IgG (mg %)	PFC/spleen ($\times 10^{-3}$)	
					IgM	IgM + IgG
Primary Response						
Balb/c females 8–12 wk old saline control	not done	198 ± 12	56 ± 4	331 ± 50	52.3 ± 16	not done
Balb/c females 8–12 wk old DMSO-treated	not done	181 ± 14	54 ± 4	346 ± 65	112 ± 37	not done
MRL/1 pr male and female 5.5 mo old saline control	37 ± 1*	466 ± 69	417 ± 250	780 ± 102	1.7 ± 0.6	not done
MRL/1 pr male and female 5.5 mo old DMSO-treated	32 ± 3	320 ± 63	311 ± 110	964 ± 80	0.9 ± 0.4	not done
Secondary Response						
Balb/c females 11–15 wk old saline control	25 ± 0.3	161 ± 7	56 ± 8	402 ± 26	102 ± 22	872 ± 175
Balb/c females 11–15 wk old DMSO-treated	26 ± 1	165 ± 8	45 ± 7	353 ± 41	112.4 ± 21	985 ± 194

*Mean ± S.E.M. No significant differences (p > 0.05) in any of the groups between DMSO and saline-injected mice.

TABLE 2

NATURAL KILLER CELL ACTIVITY OF SPLEEN CELLS DERIVED FROM MALE Balb/c MICE
WITH AND WITHOUT DMSO TREATMENT

Treatment	Percent Specific Cytolysis*	
	100:1	50:1
DMSO	23.3	5.8
	39.2	24.2
	47.5	15.0
	36.7 ± 7.11†	15.0 ± 5.32
Saline	25.8	10.0
Control	27.5	23.3
	64.2	20.0
	39.2 ± 12.50	17.8 ± 4.00

*One to two spleens for 6-week-old mice were pooled and assayed at two effector:target cell ratios in the same experiment against the YAC-1 tumor cell line. Each value represents one assay.
†Mean ± S.E.M.

ml). NK activity was assessed two days after the final injection when mice were six weeks of age. Cytotoxicity, measured at two different effector:target cell ratios, was not notably different from that of saline-injected controls, indicating that NK activity was unimpaired by DMSO treatment (TABLE 2).

REFERENCES

1. MORTON, J. I., P. A. JENSEN & B. V. SIEGEL. 1981. Secondary antibody formation as an index of autoimmune potential. J. Reticuloendothel. Soc. **30:** 10a.
2. KIESSLING, R., E. KLEIN & H. WIGZELL. 1975. Natural killer cells in the mouse. 1. Cytotoxic cells with specificity for mouse Moloney leukemia cells. Specificity and distribution according to genotype. Eur. J. Immunol. **5:** 112–117.
3. SIEGEL, B. V., R. E. BROOKS & J. I. MORTON. 1970. Ultrastructural aspects of antibody plaque-forming cells from clinically normal and overtly autoimmune NZB mice. Blood **35:** 386–394.

AUTOLOGOUS BONE MARROW TRANSPLANTATION USING UNFRACTIONATED CELLS WITHOUT RATE-CONTROLLED FREEZING IN HYDROXYETHYL STARCH AND DIMETHYL SULFOXIDE

Patrick J. Stiff,* Michael F. DeRisi,† Adrian Langleben,†
Subhash Gulati,† Alan Koester,* Victor Lanzotti,*
and Bayard D. Clarkson†

*Division of Hematology-Oncology
Department of Medicine
Southern Illinois University School of Medicine
Springfield, Illinois 62708

†Hematology-Lymphoma Service
Department of Medicine
Memorial Sloan-Kettering Cancer Center
New York, New York 10021

Autologous bone marrow (BM) transplantation has become an innovative approach allowing the use of supralethal doses of chemotherapy and/or radiation for patients with malignant diseases.[1] Cryopreservation of BM for this purpose has been accomplished using dimethyl sulfoxide (DMSO) as the cryoprotective agent.[1-3] Lysis and clumping of mature granulocytes occurs when unfractionated samples of BM are cryopreserved in DMSO alone and this has been a major problem in the clinical application of this technique. This has led some investigators to physically remove these cells prior to freezing, a technically difficult and time-consuming process.[2,3] Others have added foreign proteins such as animal serum[2,4] or DNase[4] to minimize this problem.

We have previously shown that unfractionated BM cells including stem cells, as measured by the CFU-C assay (Colony Forming Unit-Culture), cryopreserved in 5% DMSO, 6% hydroxyethyl starch (HES), and 4% human albumin in small aliquots, survive in greater numbers and without clumping in comparison to cells cryopreserved in 10% DMSO alone.[5] We present here our initial clinical experience and in vitro cell recovery data using this combination to cryopreserve large aliquots of unfractionated BM cells in bags (300 ml), using as in our initial study, a non-rate-controlled freezing technique.

To make the cryoprotectant, 138 ml of Normosol-R in 5% dextrose (Abbott Labs) and 42 grams of HES powder (mol. wt. of 150,000; American Critical Care) were placed in a sterile 500 ml bottle. The mixture was autoclaved for 15 minutes and after cooling to room temperature, 100 ml of salt-poor albumin (25%) and 70 ml of 50% DMSO (Rimso-50; Research Industries Corp.) were added. The mixture was kept in sterile glass bottles at 4°C until use.

BM collected under general anesthesia for use in autologous transplantation was transferred after filtering to a 2,000 ml transfer bag. The red blood cells (RBC) were sedimented from the BM by adding one part 6% HES solution to eight parts BM and allowing the mixture to stand at room temperature for one hour. The RBC were removed to a sterile bag and these and the cell-rich supernatant cells were

378

centrifuged at 400 × g for 10 minutes at room temperature. The buffy coat cells from the sedimented RBC were added to those obtained from the supernatant cell-rich plasma, and this mixture was brought to a final volume of 300 ml with RPMI-1640. An equal volume of the DMSO/HES cryoprotectant was added to the cells, and they were frozen in polyolefin bags without rate-controlled freezing by simple placement horizontally into a −80°C freezer. The mean cell recovery during the initial processing was 90.1 + 7.4% (N = 17).

To transplant, the bags were thawed at 37°C and infused, unfiltered. The *in vitro* recovery data are shown in TABLE 1. No clumping or clinical toxicity resulted from the reinfused BM, except for a patient whose bag had a tear in it. These cells had to be transferred to a different bag, and clumping did occur after the transfer. Conditioning regimens prior to transplantation were high dose cyclophosphamide and total body irradiation (2), or high dose melphalan (3), or BCNU (13), in combinations with other drugs. Of the 18 transplanted patients there were four early deaths resulting from non-hematologic toxicity (3) or progression of disease (1). Of the remaining 14, all had WBC recovery (defined as a count greater than 1,000 cell/mm^3), with a median time of 14 days, and 12 had platelet recovery (defined as a count greater than 20,000 cells/mm^3), with a median time of 13 days. The remaining two died of infections at 28 and 34 days.

TABLE 1

MEAN TRYPAN BLUE VIABILITY AND CELL RECOVERIES AFTER THAWING OF LARGE ALIQUOTS OF BM CRYOPRESERVED IN 5% DMSO AND 6% HES

Trypan blue viability	69 ± 14% (N = 16)
Cell recovery	96.0 ± 8.0% (N = 17)
CFU-C recovery	72.1 ± 16.0% (N = 14)

These findings expand on our small aliquot data demonstrating a lack of clumping when unfractionated BM cells are cryopreserved in the DMSO/HES mixture. The very high viable cell recovery after thawing is attributed to the successful preservation of terminally differentiated granulocytes. That granulocytes could be cryopreserved by DMSO and HES was first demonstrated by Lionetti,[6] and later confirmed by others.[7,8] Included in our excellent viable cell recovery are stem cells, which are preserved in sufficient numbers to successfully reconstitute the majority of our patients.

Although many groups have stressed the necessity of rate-controlled freezing set at a constant 1°C per minute,[2-4] this procedure has not been necessary to successfully cryopreserve either platelets[9] or granulocytes.[7,8] As shown by our high viable-cell yield after thawing, including CFU-Cs, and the prompt hematopoietic reconstitution the majority of our patients had, we do not feel that rate-controlled freezing is necessary when large aliquots of unfractionated BM cells are cryopreserved in the DMSO/HES mixture.

In short, we have developed a successful and non-toxic yet simple, rapid, and inexpensive method of BM cryopreservation that should allow for a wider application of autologous BM transplantation as a therapeutic alternative for patients with malignant diseases.

ACKNOWLEDGMENT

The authors wish to thank the American Critical Care Company, McGaw Park, Illinois for the gift of the hydroxyethyl starch powder.

REFERENCES

1. DEISSEROTH, A. & R. A. ABRAMS. 1979. The role of autologous stem cell reconstruction in intensive therapy for resistant neoplasms. Cancer Treat. Rep. **63:** 461–471.
2. WELLS, J. R., A. SULLIVAN & M. J. CLINE. 1979. A technique for the separation and cryopreservation of myeloid stem cells from human bone marrow. Cryobiology **16:** 201–210.
3. WEINER, R. S., C. M. RICHMAN & R. A. YANKEE. 1979. Dilution techniques for optimum recovery of cryopreserved bone marrow cells. Exp. Hem. **7**(Supp 5): 1–11.
4. SPITZER, G., K. A. DICKE, J. LITMAN, D. S. VERMAN, A. ZANDER, V. LANZOTTI, M. VALDIVIESO, K. B. MCCREDIE & M. L. SAMUELS. 1980. High-dose combination chemotherapy with autologous bone marrow transplantation in adult solid tumors. Cancer **45:** 3075–3085.
5. STIFF, P. J., A. J. MURGO, C. G. ZAROULIS, M. F. DERISI & B. D. CLARKSON. 1983. Unfractionated human marrow cell cyropreservation using dimethylsulfoxide and hydroxyethylstarch. Cryobiology. (In press.)
6. LIONETTI, F. J., S. M. HUNT, R. J. MATTALIANO & C. R. VALERI. 1978. In vitro studies of cryopreserved baboon granulocytes. Transfusion **18:** 685–692.
7. ZAROULIS, C. G. & I. LIEDERMAN. 1980. Successful freeze-preservation of human granulocytes. Cryobiology **17:** 311–317.
8. LIONETTI, F. J., F. W. LUSCINSKAS, S. M. HUNT, C. R. VALERI & A. B. CALLAHAN. 1980. Factors affecting the stability of cryogenically preserved granulocytes. Cryobiology **17:** 297–310.
9. SCHIFFER, C. A., J. AISNER & P. H. WIERNIK. 1978. Frozen autologous platelet transfusions for patients with leukemia. N. Eng. J. Med. **299:** 7–12.

DIMETHYL SULFOXIDE INHIBITS METABOLIC
ACTIVATION OF SULINDAC

B. N. Swanson, P. Mojaverian, V. K. Boppana, P. H. Vlasses, and
R. K. Ferguson

Division of Clinical Pharmacology
Department of Medicine
Jefferson Medical College
Philadelphia, Pennsylvania 19107

Sulindac, a nonsteroidal anti-inflammatory agent, is now widely prescribed for the treatment of arthritis. In humans and experimental animals, the sulfoxide moiety of sulindac is metabolized reversibly to a sulfide and irreversibly to a sulfone.[1] Sulindac is considered to be a prodrug in that the sulfide metabolite (IDE) is several-fold more potent than the parent drug in animal models of inflammation.[2] Therefore, factors that alter the equilibrium between sulindac and IDE *in vivo* can potentially affect the therapeutic efficacy of sulindac.

Dimethyl sulfoxide (DMSO), now used experimentally and covertly as an antiarthritic agent, also undergoes sulfoxide reduction and oxidation *in vivo*.[3] It is readily apparent that DMSO and sulindac may compete for the same drug-metabolizing enzymes. To investigate this possibility, we administered sulindac to rats and men, either as a single agent or in combination with DMSO. Plasma and urine samples were assayed for sulindac and its metabolites by high-performance liquid chromatography with UV detection.[4] As indicated in TABLE 1, IDE accumulation in plasma after sulindac administration was markedly suppressed by pretreatment with DMSO.[5-7] In a randomized, crossover study in healthy men, sulindac (400 mg) was given orally either alone or 60 min after an oral dose of DMSO (30 ml, 70% solution). The mean area under the plasma IDE concentration-time curve (0–12 h) was 30% lower (range 7–56%) after DMSO treatment. DMSO did not affect oral absorption of sulindac, as mean plasma concentrations of sulindac and mean urinary recoveries of sulindac and its metabolites were not

TABLE 1

EFFECT OF DMSO ON IDE FORMATION *IN VIVO*

Species	Treatments DMSO	Sulindac	Maximal IDE Concentration in Plasma $\bar{x}$, μg/ml	% of Control
Human	None	400 mg, p.o.	3.94	100
	30 ml (70%), p.o.	400 mg, p.o.	2.85	72
Rat	None	5 mg/kg, i.v.	4.70	100
	0.34 ml/kg, i.p.	5 mg/kg, i.v.	1.85	39
	1.7 ml/kg, i.p.	5 mg/kg, i.v.	0.63	13
	3.4 ml/kg, i.p.	5 mg/kg, i.v.	0.43	9
	5 ml (75%), dermally	5 mg/kg, i.v.	0.60	13
	None	5 mg/kg, i.p.	3.11	100
	1.5 ml/kg, p.o.	5 mg/kg, i.p.	0.76	24

TABLE 2

EFFECT OF DMSO AND DIMETHYL SULFIDE (DMS) ON SULINDAC METABOLISM BY RAT
HEPATIC ENZYMES (10,000 g SUPERNATANT)

Initial Concentration		Sulindac Reductase Activity % Control	Initial Concentration		IDE Oxidase Activity % Control
Sulindac (mM)	DMSO (mM)		IDE (mM)	Inhibitor (mM)	
0.28	0	100	0.29	0	100
0.28	1.4	47	0.29	DMSO, 14	74
0.28	14	12	0.29	DMSO, 141	58
0.28	141	0	0.29	DMS, 0.14	68
			0.29	DMS, 1.4	55
			0.29	DMS, 14	8

significantly altered by DMSO. Similar results were observed in the rat, but with even greater suppression of IDE formation. The rate of sulindac elimination and rate of sulfone metabolite formation were significantly diminished only at the highest parenteral dose (3.4 ml/kg, i.p.) of DMSO. Constant, intravenous infusions of sulindac (1 mg/kg/h) alone and with DMSO (0.34 ml/kg/h) resulted in sulindac:IDE plasma concentration ratios of 1.75 and 8.04, respectively, at steady-state. This shift in equilibrium between sulindac and IDE *in vivo* was apparently due to selective inhibition of sulindac reductase, since DMSO was shown *in vitro* to be a potent inhibitor of this enzyme and only a weak inhibitor of IDE and sulindac oxidases.[5,6,8] Dimethyl sulfide, a metabolite of DMSO, was a potent inhibitor of IDE oxidase (TABLE 2).

These studies indicate that DMSO can inhibit metabolism of other sulfoxide drugs and may antagonize the therapeutic efficacy of sulindac.

REFERENCES

1. DUGGAN, D. E., K. F. HOOKE, R. M. NOLL, H. B. HUCKER & C. G. VANARMAN. 1978. Comparative disposition of sulindac metabolites in five species. Biochem. Pharmacol. **27:** 2311.
2. DUGGAN, D. E., K. F. HOOKE, E. A. RISLEY, T. Y. SHEN & C. G. VANARMAN. 1977. Identification of the biologically active form of sulindac. J. Pharmacol. Exp. Ther. **201:** 8.
3. HUCKER, H. B., J. K. MILLER, A. HOCHBERG, R. D. BROBYN, F. H. RIORDAN & B. CALESNICK. 1967. Studies on the absorption, excretion and metabolism of dimethyl sulfoxide (DMSO) in man. J. Pharmacol. Exp. Ther. **155:** 309.
4. SWANSON, B. N. & V. K. BOPPANA. 1981. Measurement of sulindac and its metabolites in human plasma and urine by high-performance liquid chromatography. J. Chromatogr. **225:** 123.
5. SWANSON, B. N., P. MOJAVERIAN, V. K. BOPPANA & M. R. DUDASH. 1981. Effect of dimethyl sulfoxide on sulindac disposition in rats. Drug Metab. Dispos. **9:** 499.
6. SWANSON, B. N., P. MOJAVERIAN & V. K. BOPPANA. 1983. Inhibition of sulindac metabolism by dimethyl sulfoxide in the rat. J. Toxicol. Environ. Health. (In press.)
7. SWANSON, B. N., V. K. BOPPANA, P. H. VLASSES, H. H. ROTMENSCH & R. K. FERGUSON. 1983. Dimethyl sulfoxide inhibits bioactivation of sulindac. J. Lab. Clin. Med. (In press.)
8. RATNAYAKE, J. H., P. E. HANNA, M. W. ANDERS & D. E. DUGGAN. 1981. Sulfoxide reduction: *in vitro* reduction of sulindac by rat hepatic cytosolic enzymes. Drug Metab. Dispos. **9:** 85.

THE EFFECT OF DIMETHYL SULFOXIDE ON THE MEMBRANE DYNAMICS AND THE PHOSPHOLIPID COMPOSITION OF TWO DIFFERENT CELL LINES*

H. Tapiero,[†] G. Zwingelstein,[‡] A. Fourcade,[†] and
J. Portoukalian[¶]

[†]Département de Pharmacologie Cellulaire et Moléculaire
et de Pharmacocinétique Unité Simone et Cino Del Duca de
Pharmacologie Humaine des Cancers de l'Institut de
Cancérologie et d'Immunogénétique
INSERM U-50, CNRS LA-149
Hôpital Paul-Brousse
94804-Villejuif, France

[‡]Groupe CNRS 33
69371-Lyon Cédex, France

[¶]INSERM FRA 24
69-Lyon, France

INTRODUCTION

The differentiation of a wide variety of cells, such as Friend leukemia,[1] neuroblastoma,[2] quail embryonic yolk sac,[3] and human promyelocytic leukemia cells[4] can be induced by the addition of dimethyl sulfoxide (DMSO) to grow cells. The expression of globin genes during Friend leukemia cell (FLC) differentiation can be suppressed by various unrelated compounds such as 5-bromo-2'-deoxyuridine (BUdR),[5] interferon,[6] corticosteroids,[7] and tumor promoter phorbol myristate acetate (PMA).[8] Although the events that occur in induced FLC suggest that the cell membrane is the primary site of DMSO induction,[9-12] the mechanism whereby inducers and inhibitors operate is still unclear.[13,14] In appropriate clones of myeloid leukemia cells, differentiation can also be induced by chemical inhibitors (corticosteroids, BUdR, PMA) and the inducer (DMSO) of differentiation in FLC.[15] However, lymphocyte proliferation and the expression of Epstein-Barr virus (EBV) early antigen (EA) in Raji cells are induced by PMA and IUdR but inhibited by DMSO.[16,17] We therefore assumed that the action of DMSO might not be specific and that specificity of expression reflected an intrinsic property of the target cells. In this report, this assumption was investigated in two different cell lines in which the membrane dynamics and the lipid composition were analyzed.

MATERIAL AND METHODS

Cells

Friend leukemia cells (FLC) were derived from a clone of Friend virus-transformed cells 745 A. They were grown in static suspension culture in a

*Supported by INSERM CRL 822034 and by ARDC (Association pour le développement de la Recherche sur le Cancer).

modified Eagle's medium lacking calcium and containing 10 mM sodium phosphate and nonessential amino acids (Gibco, Grand Island, N.Y.). Lymphoblastoid Raji cells were cultivated in RPMI 1640 medium. Media were supplemented with 10% fetal calf serum.

Determination of Fluorescence Polarization

Cells were labeled in PBS containing 0.10% dispersion of a stock solution of 1.6 diphenyl 1,3,5-hexatriene (DPH) 2×10^{-3} M in tetrahydrofuran for 20 min at 37°C. The degree of fluorescence polarization (P) was determined with a MV-1 microviscosimeter (Elscint, Israel) as previously described.[18,19]

Lipid Analysis

Lipids were obtained from cells by several extractions with a chloroform-methanol mixture (1:1, vol/vol) and purified as previously described.[19] Neutral lipids and phospholipids were separated by thin layer chromatography as previously described.[20]

TABLE 1

THE EFFECT OF DMSO ON THE FLUORESCENCE POLARIZATION OF
DPH LABELED FLC AND RAJI CELLS

		Fluorescence Polarization (P) at 37°C	
		48 Hours	96 Hours
FLC	Untreated	0.243	0.203
	DMSO (280 mM)	0.230	0.245
Raji	Untreated	0.122	0.181
	DMSO (280 mM)	0.120	0.167

Friend leukemia cells and Raji cells were cultivated in state suspension culture in medium containing or not 280 mM DMSO. At the indicated times, which corresponded to growing and resting state, the cells were labeled with diphenyl hexatriene (DPH) and the fluorescence polarization (P) was determined at 37°C.

RESULTS AND DISCUSSION

Studies in a variety of biological systems have led to the general hypothesis that cells regulate their membrane lipid composition to maintain a level of membrane fluidity that is constant for a given cell type in a given physiological state. To examine this hypothesis, the relationship between membrane dynamics and cellular growth of Friend leukemia cells (FLC) and Raji cells were studied by fluorescence polarization (P) using diphenyl hexatriene (DPH). In these cells, the P value changes as a function of the state of the cells. In FLC, maximum and minimum P values are related respectively to growing and resting state, whereas in Raji cells minimum P values were observed in the growing state (TABLE 1). When both cell lines were grown in presence of 2% DMSO, further changes in P values were observed in FLC but not in Raji cells (TABLE 1). We therefore assumed that the membrane action of DMSO is related to the structure and/or to

TABLE 2

THE EFFECT OF DMSO ON THE LIPID CONTENT OF FRIEND LEUKEMIA AND RAJI CELLS

	FLC		Raji Cells	
	Untreated	DMSO (280 mM)	Untreated	DMSO (280 mM)
Total Lipids	27.1	25.7	14.4 ± 0.4	15.4 ± 0.3
Phospholipids	9.0 ± 0.1	11.5 ± 0.2	8.1 ± 0.1	9.4 ± 0.1
Total cholesterol	2.6 ± 0.2	2.8	1.8 ± 0.1	2.3 ± 0.1
Other neutral lipids	15.4	11.5	4.5 ± 0.3	3.7 ± 0.3

Two separate experiments are done on cells and values reported are means of two different determinations of each experiment with range of variations of 7–10%.

Values of lipid fractions are expressed as percent (w/w) of proteins.

TABLE 3

THE EFFECT OF DMSO ON PHOSPHOLIPID COMPOSITION OF FRIEND LEUKEMIA AND RAJI CELLS

	FLC		Raji Cells	
	Untreated	DMSO (280 mM)	Untreated	DMSO (280 mM)
Lysophosphatidylcholine (LPC)			1.1 ± 0.1	0.6 ± 0.1
Sphingomyelin (SPH)	4.6 ± 0.2	2.8 ± 0.1*	3.3 ± 0.2	3.6 ± 0.1
Phosphatidylcholine (PC)	50.9 ± 0.8	61.7 ± 1.2*	60.1 ± 0.3	58.9 ± 1.1
Phosphatidylserine (PS)	3.0 ± 0.1	4.5 ± 0.3†	4.1 ± 0.1	4.2 ± 0.1
Phosphatidylinositol (PI)	8.2 ± 0.2	6.5 ± 0.4*	6.2 ± 0.2†	6.9 ± 0.6
Phosphatidylethanolamine (PE)	25.2 ± 0.9	17.5 ± 0.5*	17.9 ± 0.5	17.3 ± 1.5
Diphosphatidylglycerol (DPG)	8.1 ± 0.2	7.0 ± 0.3	5.9 ± 0.2	6.7 ± 0.7
Phosphatidylglycerol (PG)			1.5 ± 0.1	0.9 ± 0.05
Molar Ratios				
PC:PE	2.02 ± 0.2	3.5 ± 0.2	3.4 ± 0.1	3.5 ± 0.4
PC:SPH	10.3 ± 1.4	22.1 ± 0.9	18.5 ± 1.1	16.2 ± 1.3
PI:PS	2.7 ± 0.2	1.4 ± 0.2	1.5 ± 0.2*	1.6 ± 0.1

Friend leukemia cells (FLC) and a human lymphoid cells (Raji) were cultured for five days in medium supplemented or not with 280 mM DMSO. The phospholipid composition was determined in triplicate from two separate experiments. The values are expressed as percent of total lipid phosphorous.
Statistical significance: *p = 0.01 †p = 0.05.

the composition of the cell membrane. To support this assumption, the lipid analysis was carried out. Among the total lipid extracted, the relative amount of the neutral lipid fraction differs between FLC and Raji, being 15.4 and 4.5%, respectively (TABLE 2). Moreover, the phospholipid composition showed that the molar ratios of phosphatidylcholine (PC) to phosphatidylethanolamine (PE) and PC to sphingomyelin (SPH) were higher in Raji than in FLC (TABLE 3). Since membrane P values increased by raising either the ratio of cholesterol to phospholipids or the ratio of SPH to lecithin,[18] it is not excluded therefore that the lower P value observed in Raji cells is the consequence of lipid and phospholipid composition of the cell membrane. If the DMSO effect is related to cell membrane, one might expect changes according to the cell type. The data in TABLE 3 confirm this expectation. When cells were exposed to 2% DMSO the phospholipid composition of FLC but not of Raji cells was altered. We conclude therefore that the effect of DMSO is related to the composition and the organization of the cell membrane components that are different in the various cell types.

ACKNOWLEDGMENTS

We are indebted to Dr. J. Huppert, Pr. G. Mathé, and Nicole Vriz for helpful discussions and encouragements.

REFERENCES

1. FRIEND, C., W. SCHER, T. G. HOLLAND & T. SATO. 1971. Hemoglobin synthesis in murine virus-induced leukemic cells in vitro: stimulation of erythroid differentiation in dimethyl sulfoxide. Proc. Natl. Acad. Sci. USA **68:** 378–382.
2. KIMHI, Y., C. PALFREY, I. SPECTOR, Y. BURAH & U. Z. LETTAUER. 1976. Maturation of neuroblastoma cells in the presence of dimethyl sulfoxide. Proc. Natl. Acad. Sci. USA **73:** 462–466.
3. MIURA, Y., T. TERASAWA & S. SAWATANI. 1976. Dimethylsulfoxide stimulated heme synthesis in quail embryonic yolk sac cells. Exp. Cell Res. **99:** 197–199.
4. COLLINS, S. J., F. W. RUSCETTI, R. E. GALLAGHER & R. C. GALLO. 1978. Terminal differentiation of human promyelocytic leukemia cells induced by dimethyl sulfoxide and other polar compounds. Proc. Natl. Acad. Sci. USA **75:** 2458–2462.
5. PREISLER, H. D., D. HOUSMAN, W. SCHER & C. FRIEND. 1973. Effects of 5-bromo-2′-deoxyuridine on production of globin messenger RNA in dimethyl sulfoxide stimulated Friend leukemia cells. Proc. Natl. Acad. Sci. USA **70:** 2956–2959.
6. ROSSI, G. B., A. DOLEI, L. CIOE, A. BENEDETTO, G. P. MATARESE & F. BELARDELL. 1977. Inhibition of transcription and translation of globin in RNA in DMSO stimulated Friend leukemic cells treated with interferon. Proc. Natl. Acad. Sci. USA **74:** 2036–2040.
7. SCHER, W., D. TSUEI, S. SASSA, B. PRICE, N. GABELMAN & C. FRIEND. 1978. Inhibition of dimethyl sulfoxide stimulated Friend cell erythrodifferentiation by hydrocortisone and other steroids. Proc. Natl. Acad. Sci USA **75:** 3851–3855.
8. YAMASAKI, H., E. FIBACH, V. NUDEL, I. B. WEINSTEIN, R. A. RIFKIND & P. A. MARKS. 1977. Tumor promoters inhibits spontaneous and induced differentiation of murine erythroleukemia cells in culture. Proc. Natl. Acad. Sci. USA **74:** 3451–3455.
9. EISEN, H., S. NAGI, C. P. GEORGOPOULOS, D. ARNDT-JOVIN & W. OSTERTAG. 1977. Surface changes in differentiation Friend erythroleukemia cells in culture. Cell **10:** 685–689.
10. GAZITT, Y. 1979. Early decrease of 2-deoxyglucose and α-amino isobutyric acid transport are among the first events in differentiating synchronized immune erythroleukemia cells. J. Cell. Physiol. **99:** 407–416.

11. TAPIERO, H., A. FOURCADE & C. BILLARD. 1980. Membrane dynamics of Friend leukemic cells. II. Changes associated with cell differentiation. Cell Differ. **9:** 211–218.

12. HAREL, L., F. LACOUR, C. FRIEND, P. DURBIN & M. SEMMEL. 1979. Early inhibition of phospholipid synthesis in dimethyl sylfoxide treated Friend erythroleukemia cells. J. Cell. Physiol. **101:** 25–32.

13. MISHAL, Z., F. TUY, C. BILLARD & H. TAPIERO. 1981. Effect of pH on fluorescence polarization of DMSO induced Friend leukemic cells. Cancer Biochem. Biophys. **5:** 147–152.

14. MISHAL, Z., A. FOURCADE & H. TAPIERO. 1981. The effect of HMBA on multiparameter analysis of Friend leukemia cells. Cytometry **2:** 165–169.

15. SACHS, L. 1978. Control of normal cell differentiation and the phenotypic reversion of malignancy in myeloid leukemia. Nature **274:** 535–539.

16. STENZEL, R. H., R. SCHWARTZ, A. L. RUBIN & A. NOVOGRODSKY. 1980. Chemical inducers of differentiation in Friend leukemia cells inhibit lymphocyte mitogenesis. Nature **285:** 106–108.

17. TOVEY, M. G., G. LENOIR, J. BEGON-LOURS, H. TAPIERO & C. ROCHETTE-EGLY. 1979. The effect of mitogens on the expression of Epstein-Barr birus antigen in human lymphoid cell lines. J. Immunol. **123:** 138–142.

18. SHINITZSKI, M. & M. INBAR. 1974. Difference in microviscosity induced by different cholesterol levels in the surface membrane lipid layer of normal lymphocytes and malignant lymphoma cells. J. Mol. Biol. **85:** 603–615.

19. FOURCADE, A., C. BILLARD & H. TAPIERO. 1980. Membrane dynamics of Friend leukemia cells. I. Changes associated with cell growth. Cell Differ. **9:** 203–210.

20. ZWINGELSTEIN, G., H. TAPIERO, J. PORTOUKALIAN & A. FOURCADE. 1981. Changes in phospholipid and fatty acid composition in differentiated Friend leukemia cells. Biochem. Biophys. Res. Commun. **98:** 349–358.

DIMETHYL SULFOXIDE IN ADULT RESPIRATORY DISTRESS SYNDROME: ABSTRACT OF PRELIMINARY REPORT

Harvey A. Klein,* Sushilkumar Samant, Burton L. Herz, and Hubert S. Pearlman

Maimonides Medical Center
Brooklyn, New York 11203

End-stage adult respiratory distress syndrome (ARDS)[1] is a devastating illness whose outcome is often fatal. This disease is characterized by alveolar infiltrates, interstitial edema, low paO_2 despite high FiO_2, rising $paCO_2$, and complete opacification of both lung fields on chest x-ray.[3] Current modes of therapy are most often unsuccessful.[3,5,6,8] Based on the properties of DMSO as a powerful osmotic agent, a mucolytic agent, and its ability to lower tissue oxygen requirements,[2,4,7,9,10] we used DMSO intravenously for three patients on whom conventional therapy had failed. In all three patients we saw a rise in paO_2 from the 50s or 60s to the high 80s or 90s, with O_2 saturation rising to 95% within eight hours of initiation of therapy (TABLE 1). One patient was also given the drug by nebuliza-

TABLE 1

Patient		pH	$paCO_2$	paO_2	HCO_3^-	% O_2 Sat.
1	pre-DMSO	7.37	50	60	29	89.0
	1 h post-DMSO	7.35	43*	91*	26	95.0*
2	pre-DMSO	7.36	51	58	29	87.6
	8-h post-DMSO	7.33	52	86*	27	94.5*
	5 days into therapy	7.37	34*	84*	19	94.5*
3	pre-DMSO	7.32	48	66	24	89.9
	8-h post-DMSO	7.27	45	95*	20	94.9*

*Asterisks used for emphasis.

tion and showed the above improvements within one hour. Another patient showed dramatic improvement both on chest x-ray and by clinical auscultation over a period of a week, so much so, that her chest x-rays showed a reversal of the process (ARDS). A concentration of 10% or less was used in all cases.

All three patients were near death to begin with, and all three patients eventually succumbed to what may be termed multi-system failure. However, our experience with the drug strongly suggests that DMSO is worthy of further investigation in the treatment of what was thought until now to be an essentially untreatable syndrome.

*Address all correspondence to H.A.K., 1000 E. 19 St., Brooklyn, N.Y. 11230.

REFERENCES

1. Acute respiratory distress syndrome. 1978. The Merck Manual of Diagnosis and Therapy. 13th edit. pp. 571–573 Merck and Co., Inc., Rahway, N.J.
2. ARTURSON, G. & B. PONTÉN. 1973. Effects of DMSO on edema formation in experimental thermal trauma. Scand. J. Plast. Reconstr. Surg. 7: 74.
3. BROBYN, R. D. 1975. The human toxicology of dimethyl sulfoxide. Ann. N.Y. Acad. Sci. 243: 497–506.
4. CONDON, R. E. & L. M. NYHUS. 1975. Manual of Surgical Therapeutics. 4th edit. p. 275. Little, Brown and Co.
5. GRIES, G., G. BUBLITZ & J. LINDNER. 1967. The effect of DMSO on the components of connective tissue. Ann. N.Y. Acad. Sci. 141: 630.
6. HUREWITZ, A. & E. H. BERGOFSKY. 1981. Adult respiratory distress syndrome—Physiologic basis of treatment. Medical Clinic of N.A. 65(1).
7. INGRAM, R. H., JR. 1977. Adult Respiratory Distress Syndrome. Harrison's Principles of Internal Medicine, 8th edit. chapter 268, pp. 1412–1413. McGraw-Hill, Inc.
8. PETERSON, C. G. & R. D. ROBERTSON. 1967. A pharmacodynamic study of dimethyl sulfoxide. Ann. N.Y. Acad. Sci. 141: 273–276.
9. ROBINS, S. L. 1974. Morphology of shock, fluid and hemodynamic derangements. In Pathologic Basis of Disease. chapter 9, pp. 349. W.B. Saunders Co.
10. RUNCKEL, D. N. & J. R. SWANSON. 1980. Effect of dimethyl sulfoxide on serum osmolality. Clin. Chem. 26(12): 1745–1747.
11. WALLER, F. T., C. T. TANABE & H. D. PAXTON. 1983. Treatment of elevated intracranial pressure with dimethyl sulfoxide. Ann. N.Y. Acad. Sci. (This volume.)

STRUCTURAL BASIS FOR BIOLOGICAL ACTIVITIES OF DIMETHYL SULFOXIDE*

Norman Kharascht

Department of Anesthesiology
School of Medicine
and
Biomedicinal Chemistry Department
School of Pharmacy
University of Southern California
Los Angeles, California 90033

B. S. Thyagarajan

Department of Earth and Physical Sciences
University of Texas
San Antonio, Texas 75095

INTRODUCTION

The subject we address is a fascinating and difficult one, besides being very pertinent to the theme of this volume. Happily, the overall task is made more feasible by appreciation of the broad scope and values of the studies presented in these proceedings and in recent studies related to it.

It is quite clear that the topic of DMSO, from a broad variety of aspects, has matured markedly. It is receiving very serious attention from many qualified investigators and is now making a strong bid to take its place as a highly valued substance for clinical studies and as a trusted and approved medicinal agent for specific purposes. Questions about how DMSO exerts its biological effects obviously are of prime importance because answers to them are essential for guiding its further development. DMSO also has much to teach us about how a substance so constituted can interact with body components and exert its particular effects. New knowledge about the chemical and physical properties of DMSO[1,2] must go hand-in-hand with increased understanding of its biological effects and medical applications. Earlier considerations of these topics were made in papers at two previous New York Academy of Sciences conferences on DMSO, published in 1967 and 1975.[3,4]

As organic chemists, we are versed in the concept that DMSO is a dipolar aprotic substance, endowed with unique physical, chemical, and solvent properties that provide singular opportunities for chemical and biological applications as the research base develops. FIGURE 1 shows the dipolar nature of DMSO, with the

---

*This paper is dedicated with special affection and admiration to the memory of our friend and colleague, Alan James Parker (1933–1982), in recognition of his deep insights and pioneering research concerning aprotic solvents, particularly DMSO. For a brief account of his many contributions, see *Chemistry in Australia*, **407** (1982).

†Mailing address: Louis Pasteur Foundation, P.O. Box 30109, Terminal Annex, Los Angeles, Calif. 90030.

0077–8923/83/0411–0391 $01.75/0 © 1983, NYAS

negative end of the dipole centered on the electronegative oxygen of the sulfoxide bond:

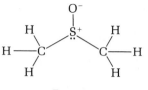

FIGURE 1.

The unshared pair of electrons on sulfur is directed to the fourth corner of a regular tetrahedron and plays important roles in contributing to the properties of DMSO.

The term aprotic suggests that the acidity of DMSO in water is not sufficient to allow it to act as a proton donor to water; indeed, DMSO acts rather as the acceptor of hydrogen bonds from water. The hydrogen bonds between DMSO and water are stronger than those between water molecules *per se*. Formamide, dimethylformamide, acetronitrile, etc., likewise are aprotic, polar solvents of great interest, but none of these has quite the powerful dipolar character that DMSO possesses. Thus, for our assigned purposes, we may first take into account those special properties of DMSO that make it uniquely adapted for its roles in chemical and biological systems.

SPECIAL PROPERTIES OF DMSO

Physical Properties; Hydrogen Bonding Abilities

DMSO is a stable, nonvolatile, hygroscopic, highly associated liquid that crystallizes at 18°C, boils at 189°C, and is completely miscible with water, as well as with many organic solvents. The separation of charge at the sulfur-oxygen bond leads to a dipole moment of 4.17 debye units and a high dielectric constant, reflecting the ability of DMSO molecules to orient themselves in a magnetic field as dipoles.

Oxidant-Reductant Properties

DMSO can act both as an oxidant—whereby it is reduced to its metabolite, DMS (dimethyl sulfide); or as a reducing agent—accepting oxygen at sulfur, for example, to yield another metabolite, dimethyl sulfone. The redox reactions can be carried out *in vitro*, and such conversions are also known to occur *in vivo*.

Complexing/Associating Properties

Dimethyl sulfoxide can associate (complex) with a multitude of compounds. This includes nearly every type of molecular species that occurs in the mammalian body, including metal cations (Na^+, K^+, Ca^{2+}, Mg^{2+}, Zn^{2+}, Ni^{2+}, etc.), and the components of tissues, blood, plasma, spinal fluid, etc. This capability also extends to proteins, nucleic acids, carbohydrates, fats, as well as various drugs, and especially to water, with which DMSO associates through dipole-dipole interaction and through hydrogen bonding. Indeed, DMSO forms stronger hydrogen bonds with hydrogen of water than does water itself. Thus, association and hydrogen bonding can occur at the cell membrane, at the skin surface, at the "pores" of cells, as well as with hormones (such as steroids), enzyme systems, and the various classes of eicosanoids (prostaglandins, etc.). Associations can also occur between DMSO and unshared electron pairs of amines, of oxygen in alcohols, ethers, esters, acids, as well as anions such as acetate, olefinic unsaturated systems, and many others. TABLE 1 summarizes other key physical properties of DMSO, which can serve as reference points for discussion or for experimental considerations in designing experiments.

Diversity of Biological Effects of DMSO

TABLE 2 provides a brief list of physiological and pharmacological/clinical properties and potential medical uses of DMSO. This list is only suggestive and can be greatly extended; indeed, because of its special properties and because DMSO can spread throughout the biological system into which it is introduced, it necessarily has marked influences on important biological processes. The Table suggests some features of the biological activities that offer possibilities for

TABLE 1

PHYSICAL PROPERTIES OF DIMETHYL SULFOXIDE

Calculated molecular weight	$C—H = 1.08$Å	78.13
Bond lengths for DMSO	$C—S = 1.82$A	
Boiling point at 760 mm	$S—O = 1.47$A	189°C
Melting Point		18.45°C
Coefficient of expansion		8.8×10^{-4}
Specific heat, at m.p. (solid)		0.5 cal/g
Specific heat, at m.p. (liquid)		0.7 cal/g
Heat of solution (20°C)		60 cal/g
Heat of formation (from rhombic sulfur and		
beta graphite, at 18°C.)		cal/mole
Heat of vaporization at 189° (boiling point)		132 cal/g
Molar heat of vaporization at 25°C		12.6 Kcal
Heat of fusion at melting point		20 cal/g
Molar freezing point depression		4.36°C
Dipole moment		4.3 debye units
Index of refraction, N_D^{20}		1.783
Viscosity (cp)	at 20°C, 2.14	
	at 25°C, 1.99	
	at 35°C, 1.65	
	at 45°C, 1.39	
Heat of combustion		6.05 kcal/g
Calculated molecular refraction at 21.2°C		20.13
Polarity (Z values)		71.10
Flash point (open cup)°C		95°C
Vapor pressure, 25°C		0.60 mm

After Kharasch, N. & B. S. Thyagarajan. 1966. Q. Repts. Sulfur Chem. **1:** 1–91.

TABLE 2

PHARMACOLOGICAL ACTIONS OF DMSO

Analgesic	Relieves pain and swelling. Very widely studied. Can be administered by various routes.
CNS effect	Causes sedation. Has antipsychotic and antianxiety effects.
Anti-inflammation	Such effect has been shown on edema, leukocyte movement, dermatitis, and others.
Collagen	Decrease in collagen components and the metabolites.
Diuresis	Causes diuresis.
Vasodilation	Causes vasodilation and increases the absorption of other drugs.
Nervous system	Increases the stimulatory effect on vagal nerve.
Smooth muscle	Increases contraction through its effects on muscle fiber metabolism or membranes.
Bacteriostatic effect	Has such effect on various bacteria by causing RNA and protein changes.
Drug interaction	Interacts little with common drugs.
A vehicle for topical drugs	Increases skin penetration of antiviral agents.
Hormone production	Stimulates synthesis of growth hormone and prolactin *in vitro* and inhibits it *in vivo*.
Nephrotoxicity	Produces hemoglobinuria. Has no short-term nephrotoxicity.
Retinitis pigmentosa	Has no effect yet lacks side effects and may be used as a vehicle to increase penetration of eye agents.
Familial amyloidosis	Increases excretion of an immunoactive protein of molecular weight of 30,000 in urine.
AA-amyloidosis	Dissolves amyloid fibrils, reduces inflammation.
Acute cardiovascular effect	May be useful for tissue protection against ischemia with no adverse acute hemodynamic effects.
Ischemic acute renal failure	Provides protection against ischemic damage by stabilizing biological membranes, dilating arterial vessels, increasing blood level of PGI_2, inducing the incorporation of oxygen into tissues, and avoiding thrombocyte aggregation.

modifying normal or pathological conditions in body tissues through the actions of DMSO.

DMSO is well-tolerated in the mammalian body, without reported deleterious, toxicological effects in reasonable dose limits. The mammalian metabolism of DMSO has been extensively studied and is fairly well understood in broad outline.

DMSO in Free Radical Reactions

In the past 10 to 15 years, it has been well-established that biological free radicals, (such as hydroxyl, hydroperoxy, superoxide, peroxy, and sulfhydryl) are fundamentally involved in processes of great physiological importance.[5] The reactions that may occur, especially with peroxy radicals, may be damaging. Hence, actions that induce formations of such damaging radicals *in vivo* (e.g., ionizing radiation, X-rays, or ultraviolet light) may be partially protected against by agents that can trap such damaging radical species *in vivo*. DMSO, with its dipolar aprotic character, the unsaturated nature of the sulfur atom, and its ability to transfer H· atoms readily from its methyl groups to a radical species, R·, which needs a H· atom complement, can serve as an effective "radical trap" or radical-transfer intermediate. This opens new significant areas of study for DMSO, which are particularly considered by Professor Thyagarajan in the second half of this paper. Again, it is the penetrant properties of DMSO, coupled with a special proclivity to interact with free radicals such as the above, that appear to promote such actions, although the exact mechanisms for such actions still require much detailed study.

The Sandborn Theory and DMSO Actions

At the second conference on biological actions of DMSO of the Academy,[4] E. T. Sandborn and co-workers brought forward a revolutionary concept for DMSO penetration of cells and tissues. They envisioned, based on electron microscopic examination evidence, the entry of DMSO into cells through a "pore" system in the cell membrane; and, further, that passage within a cell takes place via a microcirculatory tubule system, and therefore that such processes are directed and are not a matter of random distribution in the cytoplasm. This insight provides a rationale to explain many actions of DMSO. It is here emphasized that such understanding may indeed be a key factor in clarifying DMSO action whereby DMSO replaces water in the pores of cells, or at the cell surface, and may thus readily gain access to the interior of cells, dermal layers, microcapillaries, and other areas of the physiological system. The presence of physiologically active dipolar DMSO molecules at strategic action sites for biochemical reactions is a consideration of basic importance for clarifying its actions at the molecular level.

Dr. Sandborn has communicated to us further developments of his work and that of Bendayan on the concepts of microcirculatory systems in cells, based on further electron microscopic studies and related considerations, and these tend to confirm the earlier conclusions. The pores are opened by the action of contractile filaments, whose nature has been shown to be actin-stimulated, using the gold-protein A immunocytochemical technique of Bendayan.[6] These extensions serve to affirm the present considerations that the Sandborn findings, coupled with more detailed analysis of the physical, chemical, and biochemical consequences of the interactions of DMSO with cells and in the interior of cells, will lead to valuable deductions about its mode of action and possible clinical potentials.

Specifically, the proposals of Sandborn and co-workers for how DMSO enters cells and circulates therein allows rationalization for observations on the biological actions of DMSO (e.g., its effects in maintaining circulation in injured tissues).

Thus, together with a realistic evaluation of the unique physical and chemical properties of DMSO, the Sandborn hypothesis may be especially valuable for guiding experimental studies and protocols for the therapeutic effects of DMSO in diverse conditions, such as stroke, prevention of paralysis, reduction of swelling and pain, the more effective delivery of drugs to desired action sites, and the report in this volume that DMSO prevented irreversible kidney damage in animals with acute kidney failure.

The key to many of the above considerations may possibly be in the demonstrated ability of DMSO to inhibit platelet aggregation, thus keeping circulation channels open and preventing ischemia in tissues that are at high risk because of strokes, spinal injuries, or biochemical imbalances incurred because of impaired circulation.

*Possible Relations of DMSO Actions to Those
Displayed by Certain Prostaglandins*

Certain actions of DMSO and physiological effects in inhibition of platelet aggregation, reduction of swelling and inflammation, possible modifications of scar tissue and plaque formations, and also in the reported inhibition of tumor growth and cell differentiation indicate some parallel to the pervasive nature and actions of the prostaglandins.[8]

The suggestions of Sandborn et al. on the manner in which DMSO interacts with cell membranes and enters into cells also allow speculation as to how prostaglandins of the type $PGF_{2\alpha}$, for example, may enter cells, as well; and how DMSO may affect actions of prostaglandins, through interaction with them, as de la Torre[8] indicated recently. His considerations are pertinent to the suggestion that the effect of DMSO in reducing ischemic injury in the brain is predominantly involved with its interaction with the prostaglandin-thromboxane systems, since "these appear to be the most important candidates implicated in vessel occlusion and spasm."[8] While the precise basis for the effects and the possible causative relations are not at all clear, the indications from the studies of de la Torre are sufficient to indicate that this is an important area to explore. Both DMSO and certain prostaglandins have actions in cardiovascular disease, for example, which warrant much further study. Specific *in vitro* and *in vivo* studies to test these relations can be an important way to begin.

FURTHER CONSIDERATIONS OF THE CHEMISTRY OF DMSO IN ITS INTERACTIONS
WITH FREE RADICALS, PARTICULARLY HYDROXYL RADICALS
AND HYDROGEN ATOMS

In conclusion, we present a discussion extending the role of DMSO in free-radical reactions and how such reactions may relate to carcinogenesis.

One of the significant events in the carcinogenic behavior of many organic compounds is the formation of free radical intermediates of one sort or another. Hydrogen atoms and hydroxyl radicals play a very important role in such reactions. Their role cannot be emphasized any better than the summarizing statements by Robert A. Floyd in a recent article in Radiation Research.[10] To quote Floyd:

... if cancer is viewed as the end process of a series of sequential steps, some of which are included in the free radical domain, then one could expect free radical processes to govern cancer development only if the progression through the free radical domain is a necessary event and only then if these steps become rate-limiting. There may be several routes to the final state, and trying to impose a narrow viewpoint on the whole process may be only acting out again and again one blind man's concept of an elephant. But certainly this caveat should not be taken to limit the activity in trying to define the free radical domain in the overall cancer development process.

In view of the numerous references in the literature to the ability of DMSO to act as a scavenger for free radicals, specifically hydroxyl radicals and hydrogen atoms, the role of DMSO in cancer control assumes considerable importance. In addition, radiolysis of aqueous media also readily forms hydroxyl radicals. Inhibition of such hydroxyl radicals becomes important in radioprotection, or protection against radiation damage of tissues and cells. Attention has been devoted to the helpful role of DMSO in offering protection against radiation damage by acting as a hydroxyl radical scavenger. Our discussion centers mainly on these two aspects, although the literature on the biological implications of the use of DMSO abounds in citations to every conceivable aspect of biological activity.

Hozumi et al. assigned a significant tumor-inhibitory role to DMSO in two-stage skin carcinogenesis experiments.[11]

Similarly, Belman and Troll[12] found that DMSO caused a significant inhibition of promotion, with reduction of both tumor rate and yield. Therefore, it was inferred that in some respects the effects of DMSO are analogous to those of retinoids, which have been proposed as possible anticancer agents.

What exactly is the nature of the role played by DMSO in tumors? In one study, by Scher et al.[13] it was observed that mouse erythroleukemia cells (MEL cells), when cultured in the presence of very small amounts of DMSO (1.8%) over a period of 3 to 4 days, produced a significant drop in DNA ligase activity. In comparison with untreated cells, the DMSO-treated cells showed only 12% of the normal ligase activity. Additionally, it was also found that DNA formed after the addition of DMSO was hypomethylated. Such reduction in DNA ligase activity (if it truly signifies similar reduction in vivo) could indicate that the loss of proliferative activity seen in tumor cells could be attributed to the effect of DMSO. But this is not absolutely clear and requires further study.

Christman et al.,[14] who reported that DMSO interferes with the methylation of DNA observed that during a period of rapid growth Freund leukemia cells produce DNA that is hypomethylated. However, the tRNA isolated from the DMSO-treated cells did not reveal such hypomethylation! (Methylation is usually postulated to occur at N-6 of adenine or C-5 of cytosine.) Based on this observation, they inferred that some metabolite of DMSO is an inhibitor of DNA methyl transferase. But, because tRNA isolated from these cells is not hypomethylated, Christman et al. concluded, "... it appears that the mechanism by which methylation is regulated may be quite subtle."

Available data, thus far in the literature, appear to warrant a more extensive and thorough study of this aspect of the influence of DMSO on tumor cells. Indeed, this was also the conclusion of Kim et al.,[15] who stated, "To assess adequately the long-term potential of butyrate, DMSO or other 'differentiating' agents as chemotherapeutic drugs for treating cancer, further experimentation is required."

The uncertainty of the role of DMSO in inhibition of carcinogenesis is further adumbrated in the study of Iversen, Throud, and Golden.[16] This publication refers to several aspects of the role of DMSO in tumor control. (1) Tumor inhibition could be accomplished by the "oxygen scavenging action of DMSO." This was reported by Troll[17] who observed 100% blocking of tumor promotion by DMSO. (2) DMSO may enhance the metabolism of hydrocarbon carcinogens and DNA binding in mouse epidermal cultures as reported by Yuspah et al.[18] (3) DMSO may affect the metabolism of target cells or it may affect the delivery of carcinogens to the target cells. This inference is based on the fact that DMSO tends to labilize cellular membranes, which may make it easier for materials to get in or get out. One may expect that carcinogenic agents may enter the nucleus more readily than otherwise. Alternatively (or additionally) DMSO may also facilitate the transport of toxic metabolites out of the cell! Only more thorough study into the transport of metabolites in and out of cells under the aegis of DMSO will clarify this question. (4) DMSO, functioning only as a solvent, may reduce the general vigor of the experimental animal because it transports the carcinogen more efficiently to other internal organs. The Iversen study showed that the group of animals that received MCA (methylcholanthrene) in acetone/DMSO had a significantly higher death rate than the group that received MCA in acetone alone. This might account for the decrease in concentration of MCA in the skin and increased distribution of MCA to the internal organs, causing death. (5) Another factor could be that DMSO itself is cytotoxic to the epidermal cells in the Iversen study.[16] Iversen et al. believe that "DMSO reduced the MCA-induced initiation of epidermal cells, caused deterioration of the general health of the animals, and increased the epidermal cell loss."

The multiple channels available for DMSO to act in cell bodies, therefore, make the problem of pinpointing its role in tumor inhibition extremely complex. Even the reaction with oxygen or oxygenated species by DMSO is not simple.

For example, Klein et al.[19] showed that formaldehyde is formed from DMSO when it reacts with hydroxyl radicals. The exact mechanism for the formation of formaldehyde was not discussed by the authors, but a possible pathway can be pictured as shown FIGURE 2.

Preliminary evidence suggests that other systems that produce hydroxyl radicals also produce formaldehyde from DMSO. Indeed, it is reported that considerably greater amounts of formaldehyde than methane are obtained from

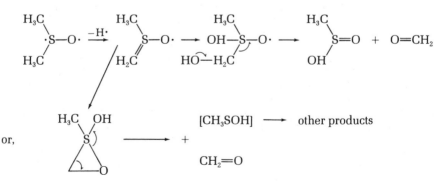

FIGURE 2.

DMSO under these conditions. Formaldehyde by itself may be responsible for several of the actions attributed to DMSO under conditions where hydroxyl radicals are generated. If formaldehyde is a significant and major metabolite of DMSO, it would imply that DMSO cannot be considered a simple inert solvent system for biological matrices.

The question therefore centers around what are the reactions or likely reactions of DMSO with hydroxyl radicals? What are the products of such reactions? How does the latter affect the cellular components?

There are a few excellent studies devoted to this aspect of DMSO. That DMSO is a potent hydroxyl radical scavenger has been reported and confirmed repeatedly by several investigators.[20-24]

The reaction has been repeatedly studied and found to generate methane as a major product. The method was considered sufficiently accurate that it has been used to detect the generation of hydroxyl radicals by several biological systems.[25]

There are, however, pitfalls in wide generalizations regarding the quantitative reliability of the methane generation. The Klein et al. study[19] does refer to greater amounts of formaldehyde than methane being formed from the reaction of hydroxyl radicals with DMSO. Other papers also refer to the fact that the production of methane from DMSO is at least one order of magnitude less than from other hydroxyl radical scavengers like 3-thiomethylpropanal or 2-keto-4-thiomethylbutyric acid. In a study devoted to the radiation protecting ability of DMSO, Koulkes-Pujo et al.[26] demonstrate that in acidic media, DMSO gives only a low yield of methane. They suggest that the reaction with hydroxyl radicals does not lead quantitatively to methane. Approximately 23% of the radicals lead to formation of methane. The rest may indeed be involved in the formation of formaldehyde as suggested by Klein et al.[19] If this observation is encountered consistently in all biological systems studied to date, then the yield of methane is not a reliable quantitative measure of the hydroxyl radicals available in the system. This can be illustrated by the following scheme of reactions (FIGURE 3), which accommodates the production of methane as well as formaldehyde from the interaction of DMSO and hydroxyl radicals.

There are other circumstances also where the interaction of DMSO with

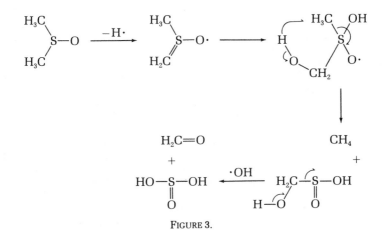

FIGURE 3.

hydroxyl radicals has been implicated. Repine et al.[27] report an interesting behavior of polymorphonuclear leukocytes (PMN) in the presence and absence of DMSO. PMN kills bacteria, such as Staphylococcus aureus. However, when DMSO is added to medium, it inhibits the bactericidal activity of PMN. PMN normally generates a variety of oxidizing intermediates like the O_2^-, the superoxide ion, hydrogen peroxide, singlet oxygen, and hydroxy radicals. The authors suggest that these oxidizing species may participate in the bactericidal action of PMN. DMSO by itself did not seem to cause any damage to the ultrastructure of PMN. But as the concentration of DMSO was raised, the killing of S. aureus by normal PMN decreased. Methane was also generated in the process. Combination of these two observations led the authors to postulate that it is possible that the inhibition of the bactericidal action reflects the scavenging of hydroxyl radicals by DMSO.

While each one of these studies suggests a strong role for DMSO in the scavenging of hydroxyl radicals, there is to date no clear-cut mechanistic information as to how exactly this event occurs other than by the isolation of methane or formaldehyde as products of such reactions. This is indeed a matter of concern for further in-depth inquiry into the chemistry of DMSO and hydroxyl radicals (and other radicals, too) over a wide range of pH conditions.

As if to underscore the preceding comment, the work by Raleigh et al.[28] presents further interesting evidence. They report that DMSO does not protect against hydroxyl radical-induced peroxidation of model membranes. Radiation protection is usually attributed to hydroxyl radicals scavenging. When DMSO reacts with hydroxyl radicals, it can produce methyl radicals, which can then further react with oxygen to give methyl peroxide radicals ($CH_3OO\cdot$). The methyl radicals and the peroxymethyl radicals are generally ignored in the protective effects of DMSO. When one studies radiation-induced peroxidation of linoleate micelles, the hydroxyl scavenger HCOONa was found to inhibit peroxidation. But DMSO, which is considered a good scavenger for hydroxyl radicals, did not inhibit peroxidation!

At intermediate concentrations, it promotes peroxidation! The ability to sustain such oxidation can be attributed to the role of methyl and peroxymethyl radicals in being as effective as hydroxyl radicals in lipid peroxidation. It is easy to see that they may affect the hydrogen abstraction just as effectively.

Under conditions where the reaction with methyl radicals or peroxymethyl radicals is slow, DMSO can offer some radiation protection. However, as long as hydroxyl radicals are more reactive, then DMSO cannot offer adequate protection. The other intriguing feature of promotion of peroxidation by DMSO is not completely understood, according to Raleigh and Kraemers.[28]

There is one more feature to the free radical reactions with DMSO. This was unfolded in the study by McCord et al.[29] Their report on the aerobic oxidation of sulfite by DMSO revealed that the mechanism of this oxidation changes with changes in the relative concentrations of DMSO. When the ratio of sulfite to DMSO was high, sulfite oxidation was inhibited by superoxide dismutase. But when the ratio was low, dismutase stimulated the oxidation of sulfite. McCord et al. suggest that the lag seen when sulfite oxidation was initiated by DMSO is caused by a small impurity in DMSO. The nature of this impurity is such that it is not removed by careful vacuum distillation or by adsorption onto charcoal. According to McCord et al.[29] "This impurity appears to act as an efficient scavenger of chain propagating radicals. Sulfite oxidation does not escape from its inhibitory effects until the impurity has been consumed by its reaction with the chain propagating radicals." The chemical identity of this impurity is unknown.

And yet, as estimated by titration with hydrogen peroxide, it is present to the extent of only 0.2% in DMSO. Further comments of McCord et al.[29] are even more intriguing: "It is likely that this impurity has been universally present in preparations of DMSO which have been used by many workers interested in the biological effects of DMSO. One wonders how many of the reported effects of DMSO in biological and biochemical systems may actually have been due to this small impurity which so effectively scavenges reactive radicals."

In summary, the role of DMSO in reacting with free radicals has been repeatedly emphasized in numerous publications dealing with tumor-inhibition as well as protection against radiation damage to cellular materials. Its ability to react with hydroxyl radicals has also been demonstrated adequately. However, what has not been demonstrated is whether all of such reactions lead to the formation of methane or formaldehyde or methyl radicals or peroxymethyl radicals under all circumstances. It is also not quite clear whether DMSO annihilates hydroxyl radicals by a radical-quenching pathway, or by its reaction with hydroxyl radicals, it produces other free radicals which can multiply the number of ways the original free radical species can interact with cellular components. There appears to be a clear and immediate need for characterizing the products of the reaction of DMSO with hydroxyl radicals. What happens to the sulfur-containing moiety after the oxidation is still not well understood. Has it become dimethyl sulfide, dimethyl disulfide, methanesulfinic acid, or any other such similar product? Also, is the impurity pointed out by McCord et al.[29] real and does it indeed affect all free radical reactions of DMSO? If it does affect the reactions so much, when it is present only to the extent of 0.2%, perhaps it would be worthwhile to characterize such an impurity. These are some of the possible directions of inquiry that await future studies into the reactions of DMSO with hydroxyl radicals.

REFERENCES

1. JACOB, S., E. E. ROSENBAUM & D. C. WOOD. 1971. Dimethyl Sulfoxide. Vol. 1. Marcel Dekker, Inc. New York.
2. MARTIN, D. & H. G. HAUTHAL. 1976. Dimethyl Sulphoxide. Halsted Press. New York.
3. JACOB, S. & E. E. ROSENBAUM. 1967. Biological Actions of DMSO. Ann. N.Y. Acad. Sci. **141:** 1–671.
4. JACOB, S. W. & R. HERSCHLER, Eds. 1975. Biological Actions of Dimethyl Sulfoxide. Ann. N.Y. Acad. Sci. Vol. 243.
5. PRYOR, W. A. 1976–1982. Free Radicals in Biology. Vols. 1–5. Academic Press. New York.
6. BENDAYAN, M., E. B. SANDBORN & E. RASIO. 1976. The intracellular tubular system in capillary endothelium. In Microcirculation. J. Grayson & W. Zingg, Ed. **1:** 149–152. Plenum Publishing Corp. New York. (cf. Bendayan, M., N. Marceau, A. R. Beaudoin & J. M. Trifaro. 1983. Histochem. J. **15:** 39–58.)
7. NELSON, N. A., R. C. KELLY & R. A. JOHNSON. 1982. Prostaglandins and the arachidonic acid cascade. Chem. Eng. News: 30–44.
8. DE LA TORRE, J. C. 1983. Role of DMSO in prostaglandin-thromboxane and platelet systems after cerebral ischemia. Ann. N.Y. Acad. Sci.
9. HAMEROFF, S. R., C. W. OTTO, J. KANEL, P. R. WEINSTEIN & C. D. BLITT. 1983. Acute cardiovascular effects of dimethyl sulfoxide. Ann. N.Y. Acad. Sci.
10. FLOYD, ROBERT A. 1981. Radiation Res **86:** 243–263.
11. HOZUMI, M., M. OGAWA, T. SUGIMURA, T. TAKEUCHI & H. UMEZAWA. 1972. Cancer Res. **32:** 1725–1728.
12. BELMAN, S. & W. TROLL. 1974. Cancer Res. **34:** 3446–3455.

13. SCHER, B. M., W. SHER, A. ROBINSON & S. WAXMAN. 1982. Cancer Res. **42:** 1300–1306.
14. CHRISTMAN, J. K., P. PRICE, L. PEDRINAN & G. ACS. 1977. Eur. J. Biochem. **81:** 53–61.
15. KIM, Y. S. 1980. Cancer **45:** 1185–1192.
16. IVERSEN, O. H., E. THROUD & V. GOLDEN. 1981. Carcinogenesis **2:** 1129–1133.
17. TROLL, W. 1980. Blocking of tumor promotion by protease inhibitors. *In* Cancer, Achievements, Challenges, and Prospects for the 1980's. J. H. Burchenal & H. F. Oettgen, Eds. **1:** 549–555. Grune & Stratton. New York.
18. YUSPAH, S. H., H. HENNINGS, P. DERMER & D. MICHAEL. 1976. Cancer Res. **36:** 947–951.
19. KLEIN, S. M., G. COHEN & A. I. CEDERBAUM. 1980. Fed. Exp. Biol. Soc. Lett. **116:** 220–222.
20. ANBAR, M. & P. NETA. 1967. Int. J. Appl Radiat. Isotopes **18:** 493–523.
21. DORFMAN, L. M. & G. E. ADAMS. 1973. NSRDS, Nat. Bur. Standards Vol. 46.
22. LAGERCRANTZ, C. & S. FORSHULT. 1969. Acta. Chem. Scand. **23:** 811–817.
23. DIXON, W. T., R. O. C. NORMAN & A. L. BULEY. 1964. J. Chem. Soc. 3625–3634.
24. SMITH, N. J. ASHWOOD. 1975. Ann. N.Y. Acad. Sci. **243:** 246–256.
25. BROWNLEE, N. R., J. J. HUTTNER, R. N. PANGANAMALA & D. G. CORNWELL. 1977. J. Lipid Res. **18:** 635–644. G. COHEN & A. I. CEDERBAUM. 1979. Science **204:** 66–68. G. COHEN & A. I. CEDERBAUM. Arch. Biochem. Biophys. 1980. **199:** 438–447. J. E. REPINE, J. W. EATON, N. W. ANDERS, J. R. HOIDAL & R. B. FOX. 1979. J. Clin. Invest. **64:** 1642–1651.
26. KOULKES-PUJO, A. M., M. MOREAU & J. SUTTON. 1981. Fed. Exp. Biol. Soc. Lett. **129:** 52–54.
27. REPINE, J. E., R. B. FOX & E. M. BERGER. 1981. Infection and Immunity **31:** 510–513.
28. RALEIGH, J. A. & W. KREMERS. 1981. Int. J. Radiat. Biol. **39:** 441–444.
29. MCCORD, J. M. & I. FRIDOVICH. 1969. J. Biol. Chem. **244:** 6056–6063.

Index of Contributors

403